Europe

SECOND EDITION BY

SAMUEL VAN VALKENBURG

Clark University

AND

COLBERT C. HELD

University of Nebraska

JOHN WILEY & SONS, INC., NEW YORK
CHAPMAN & HALL, LIMITED, LONDON

To

The memory of

ELLSWORTH HUNTINGTON

Friend and Scholar

Preface

In this volume on the geography of Europe, we have attempted to describe the patterns of distribution of phenomena—physical, human, and economic—in Europe and to analyze the significance of such patterns, especially by relating one to another. We examine factors and elements in the many and varied geographical environments both as things of interest in themselves and as influences on one another and on man and his activities. Forthrightly eschewing the philosophy of geographical determinism, we nevertheless can only conclude that geographical factors exert both obvious and subtle influences on many aspects of European life. We have, therefore, attempted to analyze the fundamental bases of the remarkable role that Europe and Europeans have played and are playing in the fascinating drama of mankind.

There is so much that is new and different in this second edition that it might almost be considered a new book. The momentous events and great changes that have taken place in Europe since the first edition appeared in 1935 have required an almost complete rewriting of the original material. Only Chapters 2 through 5 and Chapter 14 emerged with no more than limited emendations. The chapters on Germany, the Soviet Union, and Poland have naturally been entirely rewritten, since these three countries have experienced the most remarkable vicissitudes. The mounting significance of the Soviet Union demanded that especially full treatment be given European Russia. The growing role of Scandinavia is recognized in expanded chapters on the five Fennoscandian countries, including Iceland. France, Italy, Yugoslavia, and Czechoslovakia have also been given new treatment. The changed and changing economic and political situations in Europe are fully considered, and the forces—especially Soviet influence—at work at mid-century are given the attention they merit.

Not only are various aspects of Europe as a whole and of the respective countries exhaustively presented in maps, but 48 maps are either new or redrawn from the first edition; 53 additional maps are retained from the earlier edition, and there are also numerous cross sections and graphs. As a special convenience for the reader, each map is referred to by the number of the page on which it appears. The 34 halftones are completely new and have been selected for their geographic relevancy or their suggestiveness of regional "personality"; all are placed in the regional section in intimate association with their textual reference.

The "systematic" or topical treatment of Europe as a whole in the first third of the book and the modified "regional" treatment of the various countries—a feature that recommended the first edition—is retained in this second edition. Thus, the reader can gain a general perspective of the various aspects of the continent as a unit as well as a close view of each country. No particular attempt has been made to group the countries of Europe into a few broad regions (such as the Mediterranean area, central Europe, western Europe), since any definite grouping can justifiably be criticized as to composition. Certain groupings, deliberately kept loose, are referred to as a matter of orientation and convenience; Fennoscandia is even discussed as a unit. Otherwise, simply the arrangement of chapters is intended to suggest relationships.

No attempt has been made to follow a standard or uniform presentation of material under the countries. The significance of the various factors differs in different areas. Virtually all countries are divided into "natural" or "geographical" regions, but each country is given individual treatment according to its unique character. The methodology of handling some countries is one of the distinctive features of this text. Greece, for example, is compared with Norway; Rumania is compared with Nebraska and Iowa; northern Italy is compared with southern Italy.

The comprehensive coverage given both the topics and the countries is intended to appeal to a wide range of general readers and students. The more advanced material or especially detailed material is set in smaller type at the end of certain chapters. The selected bibliography at the end of the volume includes many helpful references, both books and articles, in English and in foreign languages. All European cities with more than 100,000 population and some selected cities with fewer inhabitants are listed by countries in the Appendix, which also gives country populations and areas. Therefore, with some exceptions, populations of countries and cities are not given in the text but may be found in the Appendix.

The spelling of European place names—especially those of eastern and southeastern Europe that either have numerous diacritical marks or are transliterated from a non-Roman alphabet—has long been a major problem. In recent years, however, the United States Board on Geographical Names has given a reliable listing of standard spellings, and decisions of the Board have been generally followed in this book. The Board's decisions on Russian place names are especially helpful, since in the past there has been such variable spelling of Russian geographical names. The names of large European cities that are familiar to American and British readers in a form other than the native version are usually employed in this book, although the native form is given in parentheses in the main discussion (Roma for Rome, Wien for Vienna, Warszawa for Warsaw, etc.). As a point of interest, the local names of countries are given in the respective chapter titles; variant forms in bilingual and multilingual countries (Belgium, Luxembourg, and Switzerland) are included.

The regrettable death of Dr. Ellsworth Huntington, co-author of the first edition, required that the senior author seek a new collaborator. The new partnership proved to be a happy one, with the senior author bringing a "European" viewpoint tempered by years of experience in America, and the junior author bringing an "American" viewpoint tempered by residence and study in Europe. Both authors, especially the senior one, have done both intensive and extensive field work in postwar Europe.

We are indebted to many people for invaluable assistance or helpful suggestions: Professor Charles B. Fawcett of the University of London, who read critically the chapters on Britain; Mr. Johannes K. Reumert, supervisor of geography in the schools of Denmark, who made detailed suggestions regarding the chapters on Scandinavia; Professor James Thorp, formerly Principal Soil Correlator for the Great Plains and Lecturer in Geography at the University of Nebraska and now at Earlham College, who read critically the chapter on soils and vegetation; Mr. Daniel F. Pawlikowski, graduate student at Clark University, who drew most of the maps for the new edition; Miss Marion Henderson of the Clark University Library and Miss Ruby Wilder and Miss Ruth Hadley, both of the University of Nebraska Library, all of whom were very helpful in collecting source material; and Miss Mary A. Moore, secretary in the Clark University Graduate School of Geography, who typed much of the rough draft.

We are especially grateful to Mrs. Mildred Held, wife of the junior author, who typed the entire final manuscript, gave invaluable editorial suggestions, and aided in the reading of all proof.

SAMUEL VAN VALKENBURG
COLBERT C. HELD

June, 1952

A Note to the Teacher

As a text in college and university classes in the geography of Europe, this book is suitable for courses of either one or two semesters. For a one-semester course, either the systematic or regional section may be used, with the other employed as supplementary material. The authors suggest that one good method for the instructor to follow is to present a thorough study of the continent as a whole during the class meetings and to assign the country studies as additional reading. Or, each student might select certain countries in which to specialize while reading others less intensively.

Although the latest available information is used in maps and tables, and although the political alignments and situations as discussed are correct as of the date of publication, the instructor and other readers are cautioned always to utilize latest figures from such reliable sources as the excellent United Nations yearbooks (see Bibliography) or the handy *Statesman's Year-Book*. Constant reference to a recent, reliable atlas is indispensable for the greatest benefit from reading the text. Naturally, more detailed maps of European countries are available in European atlases; especially good are the *American Oxford Atlas* and the Bartholomew's *Advanced Atlas. Goode's School Atlas* is a useful American atlas. National Geographic Society maps of Europe are excellent.

A Note to the Reader

Contents

·1·
Europe
as a Continent

The Concept of Europe

From one viewpoint, Europe is the fountainhead of western civilization, where the landmarks of cultural development are the monuments, museums, cathedrals, and ruins. From another viewpoint, it is a land of relatively small groups of people occupying relatively small states that often war among themselves. It is the focus of political control of much of the world, and it is, still, a center of concentration of much of the world's capital. It is frequently referred to as "the continent of Europe," yet it is a relatively small appendage of the great landmass of Asia. No man can say with any finality that the eastern boundary of Europe should be drawn along the Ural Mountains, although that is the usually accepted border of Europe in the east; nor can one say that the southern boundary of Europe is along the northern shore of the Mediterranean Sea, since northern Africa has many geographical, cultural, and historical ties with Europe. Finally, wherever Europeans have migrated—and they have gone in large numbers to many lands—they have carried something of Europe with them. Such are the fascinating connotations of Europe.

Actually, of course, Europe is like any other combination of land and people in having its different facets. However, Europe is especially interesting because of the astonishing diversity that it presents in so many of its qualities and because of the influence that it has exerted and still exerts on the rest of the world. No other area of comparable size in the world displays such variable man-and-land relationships.

The geographer examines Europe in order to determine what tangible qualities are present, where they are located, and in what quantity. He is concerned with the distributional aspect of things, whether they be people, mineral deposits, soils, cities, steel plants,

1

types of agriculture, canals, types of climate, or other such phenomena. He observes differences from place to place and attempts to
map them in order to arrive at significant patterns. By relating
and explaining the patterns as best he can, the geographer thus attempts to interpret Europe as a geographical area. From such an
interpretation, Europe emerges as a complex combination of highly
diverse peoples, cultures, and natural and cultural landscapes, with
the landscapes molded by many different peoples and adapted to their
respective modes of occupance through long periods of time. Therefore, Europe must be conceived as a complex geographical whole to
be understood only after careful study of its aspects in both their
time and space relationships.

Europe after Two Wars

Europe as a whole has changed a great deal in a lifetime. The
senior author of this book received his formal education on the continent when Europe was apparently still at its economic and cultural peak. During that time, there were, indeed, such forewarn-
ings of impending disasters as economic tensions followed by political stresses. Other parts of the world had already begun to rival
Europe's economic supremacy, and there came to be too many
Europeans for the work to be done. But overshadowing such fore-
warnings was the feeling of pride—perhaps complacent—that Europe
was the center of world progress and civilization. A feeling of unity
of "Europeanism" existed in spite of political complexity and cultural diversity. It was possible to travel without passports, and
money could be exchanged easily—indeed among the Latin countries
there was common acceptance of coins. There was free exchange of
ideas, scientific as well as cultural. Among the university students,
the coming generation of leadership, there was a feeling of responsi-
bility to improve the old and create the new. Thus, despite possible
decadence in some circles, Europe in the first decade of the twentieth
century was not senile; it was alive and eager.

Nevertheless, the disasters came. World War I brought Europe
four years of destruction and virtual isolation from the rest of the
world. Even so, Europe hoped that after the war the old days would
return and that time would heal the wounds. But the human and
cultural seeds planted by Europeans in other lands had germinated,
and the rest of the world had learned to look after itself. It was
impossible for Europe to return to its former pinnacle. Human and
physical resources had been severely taxed or exhausted. Many

markets on which Europe had relied to take its goods and whose purchasing power had helped swell European industrial capacity were gone; and the center of financial power, formerly in Europe, had shifted to the United States. Many raw materials that had long flowed automatically to Europe were consumed by the producing countries or were shipped to other and new producing regions. Peace treaties that seemed at the time to have many laudable points created political-geographical units that were not viable in the tense years after the war, and economic dislocations were too severe to be withstood. In the east, Russia was lost behind political, economic, and cultural clouds—far away and of little interest and no danger.

During the 1920's there emerged a sentiment of hope that the political units could be brought closer together so that united they might put Europe back on its feet. Statesmen such as the Frenchman Briand, the German Stresemann, and the Englishman Churchill spoke in other than national terms and envisioned a Europe united with little regard for political boundaries.

Even that brave effort was broken by the great depression of the 1930's, during which misery and discontent created an atmosphere in which strong measures were necessary and totalitarianism prospered. In such an atmosphere Hitler came to power as the self-styled deliverer of Germany from the miseries that plagued it. Unlike Stresemann, he was not "Europe-minded" but was entirely German and saw his country as the base for his ambitions. Even earlier, Mussolini had promised Italy deliverance under his dictation, and still other strong men attracted followings when they announced panaceas for national woes. Europe could not readjust to the rearranged world patterns and was plunged into World War II by a Hitler leading Germany to a solution of its difficulties through conquest.

Even the obvious, direct consequences of the war, not to mention its subtle ramifications, are incalculable. A new political map of Europe has emerged, with all that such an alteration entails, albeit the changes themselves are not so numerous and radical as those that followed World War I. Even more significant than the map of actual political boundaries is the less concrete but still terribly real dividing line that, as the "Iron Curtain," symbolizes the great schism in mid-century Europe (A19). Because of the East-West conflict, peace treaties with Germany and Austria had not even been signed by early 1952, and many other aspects of European recovery are perforce held in abeyance because of the "Cold War." Such is the tragic consequence of failure to provide properly during the war for European reorganization after its conclusion, especially in the direction of greater intra-European co-operation. On the strictly human level, the war brought enormous psychological forces into play: disillusionment, distrust, terror, and other subjective feelings that have actual influences in the new geography of Europe.

And last but far from least is the physical destruction to the cities and land of the continent. The economic loss must be figured not only in the cost of the original structures but also in the cost of replacing them in this much more expensive age. The magnitude of the loss must be conceived not only in terms of how much time will be required to replace the structures but also of how many centuries of building they represented. And no value can be set on the cultural loss sustained in the destruction of cathedrals, museums, palaces, and other monuments, great and small, of the rich past that only Europe possesses in western civilization. Strictly on the practical level, destruction of industries, power plants, and transportation lines was staggering to the European economy. But the Europe that emerged from the war immediately started to build anew, despite the magnitude of the destruction and the darkness of the future. Partly because of assistance from the United States, much of Europe has largely recovered; and as early as 1949 and 1950 many western European countries actually had a greater industrial production—to take one significant yardstick—than they had in the index years 1937–38. Of course, a very great deal remains to be done, but it is just such persistence and display of energy as that made by Europe after World War II that contribute to its being the significant area of the world that it is.

The difficulty of writing a balanced account of contemporary European geography should be made clear at the outset. So far as conditions in eastern Europe are concerned, only a somewhat sketchy picture may be drawn of those geographical aspects that change rapidly, since no regular release of reliable information is made by the Soviet satellite countries, and no field work has been possible. However, despite the handicap under which geographers must operate in such conditions, in other respects geography has especial value in the same situation, since there are certain relatively unchanging factors that are of fundamental significance in a country, such as its climate, relief, and soils. No five-year plan can alter the dependence of Poland's textile industry on outside sources of cotton or Hungary's deficiency of iron ore. Intelligent planning can, of course, accomplish a great deal, and deficiencies can be compensated to a large extent; but many geographical factors tend to remain persistent.

Looking at eastern Europe in another way, some argument could be presented for limiting a study of Europe to that part west of the Iron Curtain. From the point of view of western civilization, Russia is not European; the contemporary Russian is no longer even as "European-minded" as he was during the time of the tsars. However, the western Soviet Union is of supreme significance in contemporary European geography and is in intimate geographical relationship with the rest of Europe.

From the American point of view, a thorough knowledge and understanding of Europe is more necessary than ever before. American aid to western Europe in two world wars and in recovery from them, especially from World War II, has bound the United States to the countries of western Europe even more closely than cultural and trade relationships could have done. The assistance given by the United States to most of the European countries west of the Iron Curtain is based not only on the sentiment of community of culture but also on the fundamental geographic fact that the countries aided by the European Recovery Program comprise the first line of cultural, economic, political, and military defense against the danger of expansion of Soviet communist domination. Therefore, this book has been written to present not only the salient aspects of the enduring geographical factors in Europe but also the complex contemporary forces arising from geographical patterns that make Europe the focus of world attention at mid-century.

The Importance of Europe

The world's civilization is essentially still largely European. The people of the United States, Canada, and Australia all rightly claim to be European in blood and culture. Those of Latin America make the same claim, but that is true for only part of the population. Other parts of the world have introduced certain elements of European culture or have at least followed the modified European culture of America. Europe is still justly proud of her art and science, her universities and art galleries, her architecture, her rich past; and every summer millions of tourists travel around to inhale the atmosphere of European culture. Nor is the contribution of Europe to the culture, in the broadest sense, of the world merely a thing of the past. In the practical and fine arts, Europe remains a fountainhead of ideas: a good example is found in modern architecture, which combines new applications of engineering and artistic arrangements. To select only a few examples of precision manufactured goods, European watches, cameras, and even sewing machines are the finest available—especially at the price. Indeed, in such a special American sphere as motion pictures, postwar European productions have won acclaim in cinemas in the United States.

Economically and politically Europe has declined. Among the five great powers of the world, two (excluding the Soviet Union) are still European, but they no longer have top ranking. Europe's colonial possessions have greatly declined in size, but Africa is still essentially a European-controlled continent, although for how long no one can tell. In population, Europe has about one-fourth that of the world (0.6 billion out of 2.3 billion), which is almost equally divided between Russia and its satellites on the one hand and the rest of Europe on the other. Some idea of its economic significance can be obtained from Table A7, which compares the production of Europe west and east of the Iron Curtain with that of the United States. In the table and throughout the book, figures for the Soviet Union refer to Asiatic and European Russia combined. The list is incomplete because of the great difficulty of obtaining statistical information from countries beyond the Iron Curtain.

Despite the missing statistics for grains, the general situation in the production of grains is interesting. Of course, they represent only one class of food; but it is the most important one, especially in eastern Europe, where most of the diet is based on cereals. Generally speaking, Europe east of the Iron Curtain is self-supporting and in normal times has a surplus. The United States has an appreciable surplus, but a great part of the corn production goes into livestock feeding. Western Europe has a great deficit in grains; of all the countries involved, only France is, in years of good yields, self-supporting, whereas all the others have to import. This grain deficiency is one of the greatest weaknesses in the European economy.

In coal production, western Europe equals the United States, with the Russian sphere producing only slightly more than half as much. In petroleum, the United States is far ahead, and the production of western Europe is almost negligible. Both areas east and west of the Curtain are fairly well off in metals; in iron ore production, the two areas combined exceed that of the United States. However, in other metals—copper, lead, zinc—the total European-Soviet production is less than that in the United States; for copper especially the difference is large. In bauxite, Europe, particularly the west, ranks high,

TABLE A

PRODUCTION OF SELECTED ITEMS, 1949

	West of the Iron Curtain	East of the Iron Curtain	United States
Area (millions of square kilometers)	3,948	23,288	7,829
Population (millions)	300	290	152
Wheat (millions of metric tons)	32	?	34
Rye (millions of metric tons)	7	?	6
Oats (millions of metric tons)	15	?	20
Barley (millions of metric tons)	11	124	6
Corn (millions of metric tons)	8	?	90
Rice (millions of metric tons)	1	?	2
Potatoes (millions of metric tons)	70	65	11
Coal (millions of metric tons)	440	236	428
Oil (millions of metric tons)	2	40	252
Iron ore (metal content—millions of metric tons)	28	22	43
Copper ore (thousands of metric tons)	100	233	719
Bauxite (thousands of metric tons)	1,439	800	1,167
Lead ore (metal content—thousands of metric tons)	203	161	372
Zinc ore (metal content—thousands of metric tons)	290	228	538
Steel (millions of metric tons)	47	30	71
Aluminum (thousands of metric tons)	332	180	712

but in the production of aluminum the United States is far ahead. Finally, the two areas east and west of the Curtain together produced in 1949–50 more steel than did the United States. Chapter 8 considers other aspects of the production of power and minerals in Europe.

There is another lesson to be learned from Table A7. From these figures it becomes clear that, in case of an East-West conflict, a combination under Soviet control of the two parts of Europe would be a great threat to the United States. It was such reasoning that led the United States to help Western Europe protect itself in the years after 1945 against possible Russian aggression.

Location

One of the most widely recognized reasons for the importance of Europe is its location. Just as every human being, by reason of his egoistic nature, is disposed to think of himself as the center of

the sphere in which he moves, so every country and continent tends
to see itself as the center, with the rest of the world grouped around
it. Old maps of the time of Ptolemy are centered around Egypt;
Rome in its ancient glory looked upon itself as the heart of the uni-
verse. For outstanding countries like these, this view was essentially
sound, because at the time in question they were really dominant.
This dominance was partly a matter of favorable location in respect
to other active people and partly a matter of the geographic conditions that at the time were most conducive to the progress of civilization. Thus Egypt was located near the line of contact between the
parts of Africa and Asia where progress was then most rapid. At a
later date Rome was for centuries the geographical center of the
Mediterranean world around which civilization had then spread.
In the same way, during the nineteenth century, Europe, surrounded
by its political and economic vassals, looked upon itself as the center
of the world. This is the natural result of historical development,
but from the earliest times this development has been influenced
by Europe's peculiar location. The importance of this location depends partly on the accessibility of the continent to other continents
and to the oceans. Even more important is the combined climatic
effect of the continent's position in respect to latitude, ocean currents, winds, and storms.

Location in Respect to Asia and Africa. The early population of
Europe came mainly from Asia and Africa, and the proximity of
these continents has always been highly important. After the Ice
Age, when the climate became sufficiently mild to melt the glaciers
that had covered northern Europe, an almost empty continent was
ready for human occupation. Asia was the chief source of immigrants, although the anthropological relics discovered in Europe also
display marked African traces. In later times, when the continent
was well populated, and when the main lines of present ethnic divisions had been established, the connection with Asia and Africa
saved Europe from the disadvantages of isolation that hampered the
Americas and especially Australia. New migrations brought vigorous, fresh inhabitants from among whom the weaklings had been
eliminated. Even more important, perhaps, is the fact that the cultural and intellectual contributions of these two great continents
spread into Europe, thus stimulating its civilization.

The association with Asia and Africa, however, is not so close as to
prevent the individual development of Europe. The long zone
where Europe joins Asia north of the Caspian Sea is partly a desert

and partly a mountainous country bordered by dense forests and the cold Arctic tundra. Hence constant or intimate relations were long precluded except under the impetus of world migrations. Only in later centuries did Russia extend its influence eastward beyond this border as far as the Pacific Ocean. Farther south the high Caucasus Mountains offer only a few passes, and direct connection between the Balkan Peninsula and Asia Minor is interrupted by the open straits between the Black Sea and the Aegean. The famous Bosporus, in spite of frequent crossing from the time of the Persians to that of the Turks, remains a barrier, made greater by the dry basin of Asia Minor and the difficult relief of the Balkan Peninsula. Nevertheless, the mutual influence of each continent upon the other has been extensive; the eastern Roman Empire was partly European and partly Asiatic; the Greeks populated the coast of Asia Minor until they were forced out only in the 1920's; the Turks still occupy the European shores of the Bosporus—relics of an empire that might have made Europe subservient to Asia if communication had been easier. However, Europe is so separated from Asia that cultural influences have spread more easily than people. "Ideas," as Ellen C. Semple well said, "are light baggage."

A similar situation prevails even more strongly in respect to Africa. The straits at Gibraltar and south of Sicily have never been great impediments to mutual influence. Sicily was often under African rulers from the great days of Carthage to the period of the Saracens. The Carthaginians conquered Spain, and Hannibal marched from there to Italy by way of France and the Maritime Alps. In later days the Moors inhabited the Iberian Peninsula for centuries, but the wall of the Pyrenees set a limit to their successful expansion. Outward from Europe, on the other hand, Rome extended her sway into northern Africa, and in recent times the French, Italians, and Spaniards have taken this same region under control. But in Africa the great Sahara Desert prevented the southward advance of Europeans overland until the development of such modern means of transport as caterpillar motorcars and airplanes.

Even today the advantages of Europe's position in relation to Asia and Africa are distinct. The two great continents have served as an outlet for European energy by providing territory for colonial expansion, a market for European products, and a source of raw materials and food. The opening of the Suez Canal made southern and eastern Asia more accessible to Europe. Especially after 1945, Asia awakened nationally and showed anti-European attitudes, but

Africa is still composed largely of European possessions, as was mentioned previously. The commercial and political expansion of western Europe was due in part to Asia and Africa. The difficulties of modern Europe arise partly because it must now share its export markets in both continents with non-European countries.

Location in Respect to America. Europe is also advantageously located in relation to the Americas. Western Europe faces the economic heart of the United States. The value of this situation has been enhanced by the shortening of the time of transit between Europe and America to four or five days by water and a few hours by air. Yet the distance is such that it has permitted independent development of the lands overseas. The breakdown of Spain's former colonial empire, the total loss of what is now the United States by Great Britain, and the establishment of only very loose political connections between Great Britain and Canada indicate that the economic and political leadership of Europe in North America has passed. But this does not lessen the value of the location of western Europe opposite the most active part of North America.

In relation to South America the location of western Europe is. as good as that of any other highly advanced region. The distance to Argentina and Brazil from western Europe is not much longer than from New York. Hence the commercial interests of Europe and the United States meet there on an equal footing. Airlines from the United States southward over the West Indies, and from Europe to Brazil by way of northwest Africa, now bring both regions nearer to South America. They intensify the rivalry in the South American market but do not give either of the northern continents any new advantage of location. In earlier times the distance of South America from the colonizing countries of Europe was a fundamental factor in the loss of colonial control.

Today Europe retains all the advantages of its world location and is ready to use them in the battle for self-preservation. Some authorities hold, however, that the location of the United States, facing Europe on one side and the most productive part of Asia on the other, is even better. The true value of Europe's location can be judged only at a later stage of this study when the effect of climate is also considered.

Size and Shape

The size and shape of Europe also contribute to its significance. In comparison with gigantic Asia, Europe is almost too small to be accounted a separate continent. We call it a continent only because the idea of Europe and Asia as separate landmasses became fixed long ago among people who knew only of the separation caused by the Aegean and Black seas and had no idea of the plain that joins the two north of the Caspian Sea. Nevertheless, Europe is so divided from Asia by deserts and mountains and its character and history have been so different that it is very convenient to call it a continent.

Size. The small size of Europe presents decided advantages. In conjunction with the relatively slight breadth from north to south it gives Europe a high degree of compactness. In Asia the different centers of civilization have been too far apart to become closely connected; they influenced one another but remained separate. In Africa the same conditions prevailed. Deserts cut off the center of the continent from the extreme north and south. In the center, dense equatorial forests interpose an almost impassable barrier except by way of the Nile and the eastern upland. Hence North and South Africa have always been greatly separated, and the south remained isolated until Europeans reached it by sea.

In Europe, on the contrary, the small size, as well as the relief and climate, is favorable to unity through the interchange of people and ideas. Despite the great variety of its political and economic units, as well as of its peoples and cultures, most of Europe has a certain quality that is recognized as European. The much-discussed tendency toward a United States of Europe, or at least toward an economic union, is opposed by no unfortunate geographical factor and is favored by the small size of the continent.

Shape. In shape, as well as size, Europe finds an advantage over the other continents. Nowhere else do interior seas, having open connections with the ocean, invade the land so deeply without dissecting it into disconnected islands. Not only do the arms of the sea enter the continent, but nearly everywhere the coastline is bordered by small islands that favor the establishment of settlements and the development of shipping. All around the continent the sea penetrates the land, creating the irregular coastline that offers so many economic advantages.

The Baltic Sea and the North Sea, for example, provide seacoast advantages for all of northern Europe. The medieval Hanseatic League, the beginning of modern commercial Europe, found its reason for existence in these seas. It included seaports near the Baltic and North seas and cities as far inland as Cologne. Its later growth was due largely to the possibilities of sharing directly in world trade by way of these arms of the sea.

England, separated from Europe only by the English Channel, reaps all the advantages of these waterways. It has still other advantages, because it not only faces the most productive European countries but also has an advanced position in Europe in the direction of North America, and the sea has largely protected it during periods of continental disorders. The Strait of Dover, although crossed by boat in a few hours and by airplane in a few minutes, is still a real factor in Great Britain's isolation. A tunnel might be dug under it if England did not fear so direct a contact. Modern technology has, however, finally gone far to nullify the strategic advantages of the Channel, as was shown by the German use of air power and "V" weapons in World War II. Ireland seems to have many of these same advantages, but its isolation is too great, and its importance has declined. This decline, however, is due more to political circumstances and lack of natural resources than to the location and shape of the country.

The climatic effect of the shape of western Europe is even greater than its effect on transportation. The long northeasterly trend of the coast from Portugal to northern Norway enables the westerly winds to send a constant flow of warm water along this coast. Thus the winters of western Europe are kept mild, and frequent storms are produced, giving rain at all seasons. All this will be explained more fully later. Here the point is that the shape of Europe gives to the northwest even greater advantages than to the south. These advantages are increased by the fact that the North Sea and the Baltic, like the Mediterranean and Black seas, carry the oceanic conditions far inland.

The Mediterranean and Black seas, which originally caused Europe to be counted as a continent, bring coastal advantages to all of southern Europe. By way of the Suez Canal they also lead to southern and eastern Asia. Without these seas Europe would have no identity, for it would be a mere fraction of a combined Asia and Africa. Their warm waters were the basis of the ancient Mediterranean civilizations expressed in the rise of Phoenicia, Greece, Carthage, and Rome. Today they provide the background of the Mediterranean development of France and Italy. They do this not only by affording easy means of transportation, but still more by their effect on climate. Without the Mediterranean and Black seas the whole region from Spain to southern Russia would be desert or steppe. As it is, the so-called Mediterranean type of climate, with its rainy winters and dry summers, penetrates far eastward, even to western Iran and the southern coast of the Crimean Peninsula. The densely populated and fertile Mediterranean coastal plains, with their subtropical vegetation, their thousands of coastal settlements, their great modern harbors exporting products of the hinterland, and their numerous islands with fishing settlements—all these are the result of a great downfold in the earth's crust that led the Atlantic Ocean so far inland as nearly to connect it with the Indian Ocean. To Europe the Mediterranean is a gift of the gods. This intimate penetration of the sea both north and south of Europe prevents any part of the continent except Russia from being far from oceanic influences. It tends strongly to produce unity by reducing the contrasts of climate. The nature of the climate in turn has much to do with that of the soil. Thus climate, soil, transportation, and many other conditions are all greatly influenced by the shape of the continent and the intrusion of arms of the sea.

The Diversity of Europe

The preceding discussion of the relationship between Europe's importance and its location, size, and shape has been based on the way the continent appears in outline. Inside the continent, relatively small as it is, the various regions display a kaleidoscopic diversity. Within the frontiers of tiny Switzerland the inhabitants speak four distinct languages and scores of dialects. The railway from Paris to Metz traverses a dozen markedly different landscapes. Nestled in a scenic forest by a quiet lake in Sweden is a large, bustling steel mill. In one day's railway journey a traveler may pass through six or seven different countries, each with its characteristic landscapes and individual language. Trade flows through the Varder-Morava corridor of Yugoslavia, passing valleys whose inhabitants have never been out of sight of their home villages. Combined with Europe's diversity across space is its diversity through time. Within sight of a limestone cave with walls painted by Stone Age man is a Roman building close by a medieval cathedral over which an airliner is flying. Such are the diversities of Europe.

On the other hand, the cultured European who lives outside Europe and views his continent with a far perspective discovers that national differences, at least, lose much of their significance: the continent stands out in many ways as a unit, although composed of various political divisions. In Europe he may be French, German, or Scandinavian; away from Europe he is above all European.

But, if he analyzes his European concept more carefully, he discovers that his idea of Europe and the Europe of the map are not identical. His Europe is the Europe of high intellectual and cultural standards; the Europe of economic efficiency, with well-tilled fields and modern factories; the Europe of big cities, full of vitality, and with harbors teeming with world trade. But there is another, contrasting Europe that he may not know, or, if he knows, may prefer to ignore because he is not proud of it.

The Economic-Cultural Map

The French economist Delaisi presented the contrast mentioned above most vividly in his book *Les Deux Europes,* published in 1929, which depicted the whole European scene in bare facts not very attractive to the critical eyes of his continental contemporaries. The map of economic-cultural zones (A15) follows Delaisi's general idea but deviates widely in detail, since it introduces a transitional B zone between economically-culturally high Europe A and economically-culturally low Europe C. The terms "economics" and "culture" are employed here in a very broad sense, and numerous factors of great variety have been combined as criteria for determining the final outlines of the zones: agricultural practices and production, industrial activity, education, public health, government, transportation, trade, man-food ratios, and others.

A Sample Comparison. The differences between Europe A and Europe C are well demonstrated by comparing Belgium and Bulgaria. Bulgaria is not one of the lowest nations in Europe C, and the contrast would be more pronounced if Rumania were selected. However, Bulgaria has a population numerically comparable with that of Belgium, whereas Rumania's is much larger.

Belgium is a small country (11,783 square miles), with a population of 8.6 million and a density of 731 per square mile (Map A199). It has a low death rate but also a low birth rate: the annual increase is 4.3 per 1,000 people (Table A192). Infant mortality is low (Map A188). One third of the population is engaged in manufacturing (Map A127); and the export is mainly in manufactured products amounting in value to $190 per capita (Table A145). More than 60 per cent of Belgium is under cultivation, and the yields are among the world's highest (Map A102); yet only 17 per cent of the population is occupied with agriculture, forestry, and fishing. The national income is $582 per capita, one of the highest in Europe (Map B16). Transportation is based on a very dense railroad system (Map A159), an excellent road system, and many canals connecting navigable

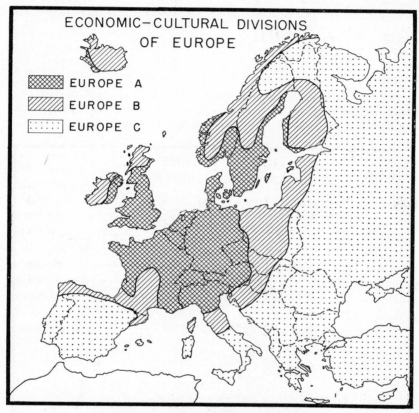

A. Economic-Cultural Zones of Europe.

rivers. Antwerp is one of the chief ports of Europe. On the cultural side, illiteracy is practically absent (Table A16). There are only 38 people per passenger car (Map A163), which is low for Europe. The average Belgian writes 20 domestic letters a year, and there are 7 telephones per 1,000 people. Politically, Belgium is a democracy; and although at times political sentiments run high, there have been no revolutions or persecutions, and there is absolute freedom of speech and worship.

TABLE A

Illiteracy in Europe

(Population above 10 years of age)

Belgium	(1930)	5.6	Italy	(1931)	21.6
Bulgaria	(1934)	31.4	Poland	(1931)	23.1
Czechoslovakia	(1930)	4.1	Portugal	(1940)	48.7
Finland	(1930)	0.9	Rumania	(1948)	23.1
France	(1936)	3.8	Spain	(1940)	23.2
Greece	(1928)	40.8	Sweden	(1930)	0.1
Hungary	(1941)	6.0	Yugoslavia	(1931)	45.2

No comparative figures are available. In the missing countries (Netherlands, United Kingdom, Norway, and Denmark) illiteracy is practically nonexistent. In some of the others, illiteracy has dropped substantially since the 1930's.

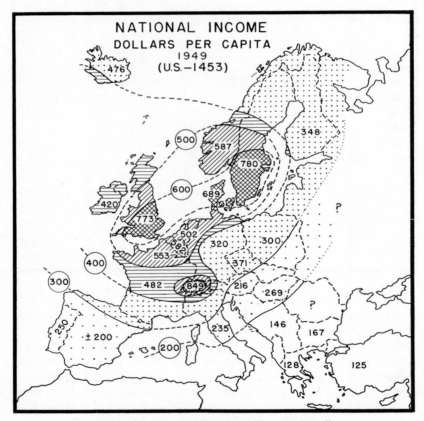

B. National Income per Capita, 1949, in U. S. Dollars.

Bulgaria is much larger (42,796 square miles) than Belgium, although its population (7.1 million) is somewhat smaller than that of Belgium. Accordingly density of population is lower, 167 per square mile (Map A199). The birth rate is much higher than Belgium's, and, because the death rate is rather low, the annual increase is 10.6 per 1,000 people (Table A192). However, infant mortality is more than twice as high, although still rather low if compared with other C nations (Map A188). Roughly two fifths of Bulgaria is under cultivation, and yields are relatively low (Map A103), although agriculture occupies 80 per cent of the population and the density of agrarian population is much higher than that of Belgium. Only 8 per cent of the population is engaged in manufacturing (Map A127), and the use of electric energy per person is only one-fourteenth that of Belgium. The value of exports, chiefly agricultural products, is only $12 per capita (Table A145), and the national income is only $167 per person (Map B16). There are not many railroads, most of the roads are rather poor, and there are very few passenger cars. On the cultural side, illiteracy is fairly high (Table A16), although much lower than that of the neighboring countries. The average Bulgarian writes 9 letters a year, which is high for the C nations, and there are few telephones. Politically, Bulgaria is a "people's republic" but is in reality a communist dictatorship with all the tragedies of intolerance and bloody persecution.

The Map in General. The preceding comparison between Belgium and Bulgaria employed many of the criteria used as a basis for Map A15 and referred to maps that depict the pattern of some of the individual criteria employed in determining the economic-cultural zones. In all of them, to varying degrees, the nations around the North Sea stand out as being more highly developed than those to the south and to the east. Generally the decrease in development is a gradual one, with the exception that Switzerland always ranks among the highest. Whereas it is fairly easy to rank the countries, it is rather difficult to draw the exact boundaries between zones A and B and between B and C within nations; the changes rarely coincide with political boundaries. For some individual factors, detailed maps, such as that of wheat yield in central Europe, were available for individual countries. In another approach, the senior author had made a detailed study of Italy, showing the difference between the northern and southern parts of that country. In some instances the location of the zonal borders is based on personal knowledge, which of course introduces a subjective element over

which debate is always possible. On the whole, however, the map
has a solid factual foundation. Naturally, small areas of Europe A
exist as islands in Europe B and even in Europe C and conversely;
but these are minor and must be ignored on a map of this scale.

Changes since the War. Important changes in the political, economic, and cultural structure of Europe as a result of World War II
brought up the question whether the original map as published in
the first edition of this text should be modified. For example, in
prewar Poland there was a clear gradation from west to east, which
revealed itself in such maps as the yield of grain, the number of
brick houses, and the number of persons per room; accordingly, the
border of Europe A could be drawn through western Poland (in
general it included former German territory), and the zone of Europe B included the central section. After 1945 a new Poland was
created, the old Poland having lost its eastern territory to the Soviet
Union and having gained in the west up to the Oder River at Germany's expense. This western gain was part of Europe A on the
original map, and the new eastern boundary follows approximately
the line separating B and C on the original map. But what about
the new Poland? The people who lived in the formerly German
part and who had made it a part of Europe A have been forced to
emigrate. What have the Poles done with the area? In a communist state there is a tendency to destroy the effort of the individual and to equalize conditions all over the state. Where should
the zonal boundaries be drawn now? What should be done with
the three former Baltic states, now to a large extent Russianized, and
with Czechoslovakia, once a nation of high liberal cultural traditions? In view of these unanswerable questions, the map is presented as a compromise and may have to be redrawn when conditions become more stable and more factual information becomes
available.

The Iron Curtain (A19)

After World War II, a line of economic, cultural, and political
separation was drawn from the Arctic almost to the Mediterranean—
the tragic Iron Curtain. How the lowering of the Curtain might
have been avoided is now an academic question; it is there and must
be reckoned with. Even before 1939, there had been an Iron Curtain along the western boundary of the Soviet Union, but it had
left the rest of Europe in the free zone. In any case, the Curtain is

one of the most significant realities in the geography of contemporary Europe.

The new Curtain did not come overnight. Whereas the Baltic states, eastern Poland, and eastern Rumania had become parts of

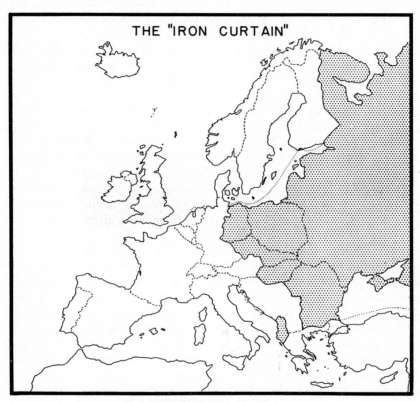

A. The Iron Curtain in 1952.

the Soviet Union before Russia was attacked by Germany, Russian control over the other nations in its sphere of influence increased only gradually, leaving, at least in the beginning and on paper, a token of democratic freedom and interparty co-operation. The *coup d'état* in Czechoslovakia in 1948 and the creation of the German Democratic Republic in the Soviet zone of occupation in 1949 were the last steps toward complete Russian control of eastern Europe. Czechoslovakians and eastern Germans were the most resistant to Soviet control because they belonged in Europe A and had known better days. Neither would have voted in a free election for Soviet control.

The Curtain starts at the Norwegian boundary in the Arctic and follows the eastern boundary of Finland, leaving that nation, surprisingly, outside. The line enters Germany east of Lübeck, crosses the Elbe and makes a prong into Thuringia before turning eastward toward the northwestern corner of Czechoslovakia. The Curtain follows the western boundaries of Czechoslovakia, Hungary, Rumania, and Bulgaria and turns eastward north of Greece and Turkey to the Black Sea. Eastern Austria, although occupied by the Soviets, is not included, and its administration by the nationwide Austrian government is based on free elections. Since the break between Yugoslavia and the Cominform, Albania has been a communist exclave. Both Berlin and Vienna, although in the respective Soviet zones of occupation, have Allied-occupied sectors. In Vienna, a joint control has been retained, but in Berlin there is a sharp line between the Russian and Allied sectors, and connections between Berlin and the west have at times been interfered with by the Russians.

The Iron Curtain is an ideological dividing line, but it is much more than that. It is an effective barrier in the realm of most human activities, with barbed wire and police patrols along strategic stretches of the line. For example, few trains cross it, and other traffic is stringently restricted. It has forced a virtual economic reorientation on both sides: the former flow of manufactured products from the west in exchange for agricultural products from the east has diminished to a trickle. With certain exceptions, it would seem that the east would suffer more than the west as a result of the near-stoppage of trade, since the west can trade with the rest of the world. In the autumn of 1951 the Soviet bloc was making vigorous efforts to reopen trade in items that it desired and that had been held up by an embargo on strategic goods destined for the east.

Like the effects of World War II, consequences of the lowering of the Iron Curtain cannot be put into words. It suffices to say that it is one of the greatest tragedies ever to come to Europe, and the implications behind the existence of the Curtain are even more tragic. At mid-century there were two Europes, separated by the most formidable human barrier of modern times of "peace." When or how the Iron Curtain might be raised can only be a matter of speculation and hope.

The Plan of This Book

The geographic story of Europe can be told in various ways, each of which presents both advantages and drawbacks. According to the method here followed, the continent as a whole is first reviewed in its essential physical, economic, and human aspects. The physical aspects comprise the location of Europe on the globe, the continent's size and shape, climate, and relief and scenery and their relation to geological origin, soil, and natural vegetation. The chapter on soils and vegetation leads logically to an analysis of European agriculture. Since minerals and sources of power are of vital importance to modern industry, the chapter describing them logically introduces chapters on the development of manufacturing and the evolution of transportation and trade. The next chapter describes the human stock of Europe in terms of ethnographic history as well as of political divisions. Thus a picture is drawn not only of present-day Europe, but also of the background for some of the serious problems of overpopulation, international rivalry, and political and social tendencies. The first part of the book ends with a chapter on the northwestward march of civilization and man's changing geographic adaptations during Europe's historic period.

The second portion of the book gives an account of the various countries, classifying them according to the geographic regions into which they naturally fall. It points out the specific application of the generalizations of the first section. For each country some of the most pressing economic, social, and political problems are analyzed, especially from the viewpoint of the way in which they are related to the geographic background. Thus, Europe at mid-century will be presented in its general and regional geographical aspects.

·2·
Climate

Geographic Factors in Relation to Zones of Culture

The zonal distribution of economic and cultural development in Europe is strongly influenced by geographic factors. Among these factors relief appears to be of lesser importance, for mountainous Switzerland as well as the lowlands of Holland belong to Zone A. Neither can the soils be a dominant factor in determining the pattern of the zones, for the soils are generally poor and leached in Zone A, whereas Zone C, especially in Russia, has large areas of the most fertile soil in the world. Neither can sources of power and mineral resources be held responsible. In most cases their development came long after the general outlines of the zones had been established, and was primarily a response to the energy of the population. The long coastline, the many arms of the sea, and the many inland waterways are certainly an asset, but they appear to be as favorable along the Mediterranean and Black Sea coasts as along that of the Atlantic.

Thus relief, soil, minerals, sources of power, and waterways are all eliminated as major factors in shaping the geographic forms of the zones. The only other possible physical factor is climate. That this is really the main factor is indicated by the way in which the map of zones of economic and cultural development agrees with a map of climatic efficiency (A23). This map indicates the degree of energy or efficiency that people of the European type would have in different parts of the continent if their efficiency depended solely on climate. It is based on studies of the amount and quality of work, both mental and physical, that is done under various conditions of weather. Therefore, the resemblance between the map of climatic efficiency and the map of economic-cultural zones either must be accidental or must mean that climate is a major factor in the location and shape of the zones.

That this is the case is also indicated by the fact that people have good health in the places where the climate is of the kind that also goes with efficiency. Such an agreement between climate and living beings is not confined to man, but is also found in animals and plants. This appears in A103, which shows the yield of wheat per acre. Thus the maps of human health, yield of crops, and zones of culture are all essentially alike, but none of them pays much attention to the distribution of relief, soils, minerals, sources of power,

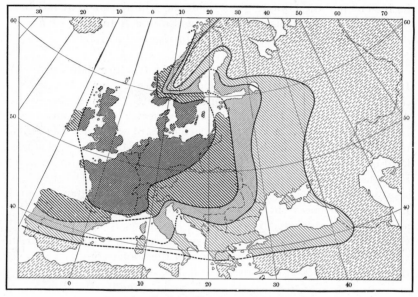

A. Climatic Efficiency in Europe.

or location in respect to waterways. All of them, however, are almost duplicates of the map showing the degree to which climate promotes efficiency. The inference is that this agreement is not accidental but indicates that climate is a leading factor in the geographical distribution of economic-cultural development.

The Climatic Advantages of Zone A. The climate of northwestern Europe—that is, of Zone A—combines many factors that are highly favorable to human health and activity. These include (1) comparatively mild winters and cool summers, (2) a sufficient rainfall distributed fairly evenly at all seasons and with little variability from year to year, and (3) a constant sequence of cyclonic storms that prevent climatic monotony and provide the constant changes of weather that are so valuable as stimulants of human energy. No one would select this climate because of its pleasantness; its strong winds, prolonged cloudiness, and dreary rainy days are often a despair to the American visitor. But such a climate is by no means bad for agriculture. In fact, the abundance of moisture at all seasons and the lack of extreme cold in winter or heat in summer make it very favorable. Far more important is the fact that now that the inhabitants have solved the problem of protecting themselves from its inclemency the climate gives them the stimulation that has been one of the main factors in permitting Europe A to have such a remarkable historic development, and to rise so far above the rest of Europe and above most other regions.

Europe C is more complex in its climatic structure than Europe A. It combines the delightful climate of southern Europe with the continental climate of eastern Europe and the coldness of the Arctic. All of these have in common a relatively weak cyclonic control, and hence a comparative lack of regular changes of weather. But this is not the only disadvantage, for each part of Zone C has its own special kind of climatic extremes. The north, being too remote to be much influenced by the warm waters of the North Atlantic Drift, has too short a growing season and too long and dark a winter. Eastern Europe experiences the grave disadvantages of continentality that are greatly accentuated in Siberia. The long, severe winter with very little precipitation and yet a great deal of cloudiness is disadvantageous for both crops and man. In the cooler countries all over the world the highest death rates and lowest ebb of human efficiency are found in cold, dry weather such as is strongly characteristic of the continental interior that forms a large part of Zone C. Then, too, the summer rain is scarcely sufficient in view of the comparatively high continental temperature at that season. Since the amount of rain also varies a great deal from year to year, and there is much danger of drought, agriculture suffers as well as man. In southern Europe the main disadvantage is the summer. There a rainy and productive winter is combined with a long, hot, dry summer in which man's energy is diminished, and much of the economic activity languishes until the fall rains start again.

The Main Climatic Factors

The favorable climate of Europe A and the decline in desirable characteristics elsewhere depend on a few main factors. (1) Europe possesses the decided climatic advantage of being located between 35° and 70° N on the west side of a continental mass. (2) Therefore,

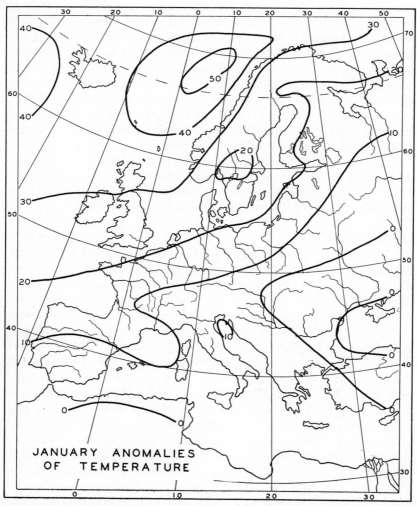

JANUARY ANOMALIES
OF TEMPERATURE

A. Anomalies of Temperature in Winter in Degrees Fahrenheit. Note that the positive anomalies reach a maximum (50° F) between Iceland and northern Norway. Only in southeastern Russia and in Africa do isonomalous lines of zero indicate that the winter temperature is as high as the average for any given latitude.

it is in the zone of prevailing westerly winds and in the part of the
continent where such winds are most effective. The dominating
westerly winds, characteristic of this latitude, bring marine influences
far inland, softening the severity of the winter and diminishing the
summer heat. The North Atlantic Drift, a gift from the tropical
parts of the North Atlantic, increases the beneficial influences of the
ocean, bringing heat from equatorial regions far into the Arctic
Ocean. Thereby it causes a winter anomaly of as much as 50° F;
that is, it makes the temperature of northeast Iceland 50° warmer
than the average of all regions in the same latitude (A25). (3) Another influence also comes from the west, namely, a sequence of
cyclonic storms. Born of the contact between cold Arctic and warm
subtropical air in the main zone of cyclonic activity, these storms
whirl over the Atlantic and bring a climatic instability that is of
outstanding value to human energy and consequently to progress.

Climatic Regions

Europe may be divided into climatic provinces on the basis of the
degree to which each of these three factors is favorable to man and
his activities. A27 shows three basic types of climate. One is the
Western European, or "west coast marine" type, prevailing along
the Atlantic shores from Spain to northern Norway and including
the British Isles. The second is the *Mediterranean* type, which is
also more or less marine and extends from the Atlantic Coast of
Portugal through the entire Mediterranean area to the Crimean
Peninsula. Third comes the *Eastern European,* or continental type,
with which, for the sake of simplicity, may be placed the climate of
the main European mountains. Between these three types are two
zones of transition. One is the *Central European* type between the
Western and Eastern types. The other is the *Southern Transition*
type farther south, representing the transition from the climates
farther north to the Mediterranean. To these five regions must be
added not only the dry *Steppe* climate of the Iberian Peninsula,
southeastern Russia, and bits of Turkey and Greece, but also the
Tundra climate of far northern Europe, and of some of the highest
mountains.

Western Europe. The climate of western Europe is typically
marine. Mild winters, in which freezing periods are rare, are followed by cool summers. The differences between the average temperatures of summer and winter are small, ranging from 15° F on
the western border to 30° on the eastern. The average temperatures

approach those most favorable for human health, and regular cyclonic storms add the variety that stimulates productivity. The growing season is scarcely interrupted by winter in the more marine

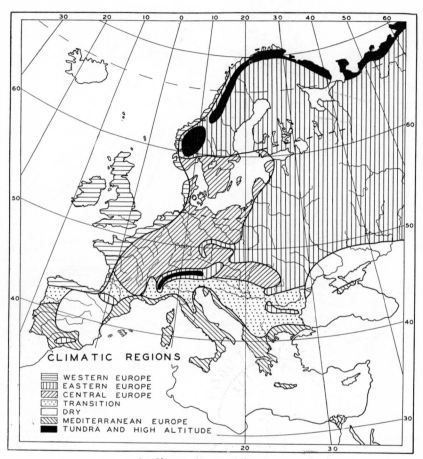

A. Climatic Regions of Europe.

coastal sections, and even inside the Arctic Circle the frost period is scarcely longer than 100 days. The precipitation is regular and well distributed, with a tendency toward a late fall or winter maximum. It is heavy on some mountain slopes and moderate in the lowland sections, but everywhere sufficient. One unpleasant factor in the weather is the generally strong winds, often reaching the force of

gales during the winter months. Others are high humidity and a
high amount of cloudiness and fog with a consequently low percentage of sunshine, especially around the North Sea and the Eng-

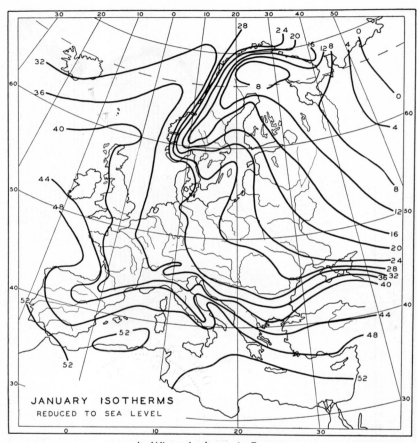

JANUARY ISOTHERMS
REDUCED TO SEA LEVEL

A. Winter Isotherms in Europe.

lish Channel. Although the latitudinal factor is not of major importance, the disadvantages of an Arctic location are evident in the
depressingly dark winters and long, exhausting summer days of the
extreme northern part. On the other hand, in the south, especially
on the northern coast of Spain, subtropical influences show themselves in relatively high temperatures and much sun.

As a whole, this marine west coast climate stands out as one of the world's most favorable types. Western Europe's high rank in health, energy, productivity, and culture is certainly not a passing whim of history, but is based on a sound climatic foundation.

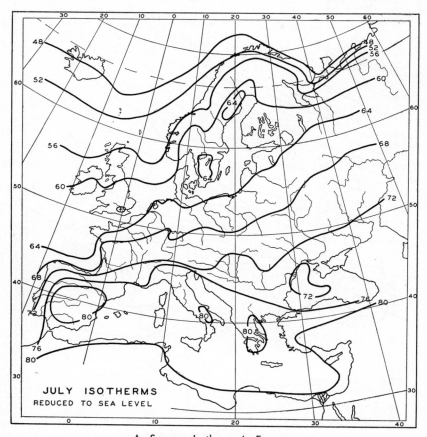

A. Summer Isotherms in Europe.

Eastern Europe. The main feature of the climate of eastern Europe is its continentality, although even here marine influences are easily recognizable in contrast to the more continental Asiatic regions farther east. This continentality shows itself in long, cold, dry winters and short, warm summers during which the inblowing monsoonal winds bring humidity and rainfall in the form of convectional

showers.   In winter the influence of the Atlantic shows itself in high
cloudiness, the region northeast of Moscow being cloudy more than
80 per cent of the time.   The oceanic influence is also evident in an

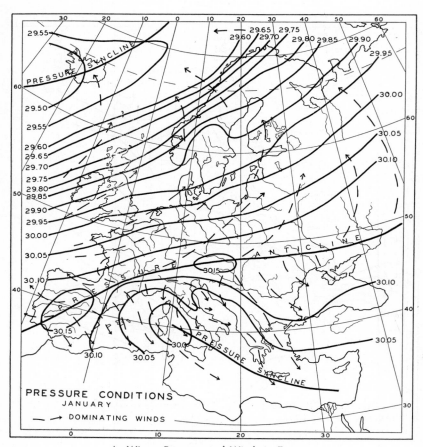

A. Winter Pressure and Winds in Europe.

occasional invading storm's causing a light snowfall—which, nevertheless, remains on the surface for a long time.   Rivers, lakes, bays,
and gulfs are frozen in winter, and the frost period nearly everywhere exceeds 150 days.   If the Eastern European climatic region is
subdivided, the northern section shows not only the effects of latitude in producing low temperature, but also those of position on the

leeward side of the Scandinavian uplands, giving rise to low rainfall. The dividing line between the northern and southern sections is determined partly by vegetation, for it separates the coniferous

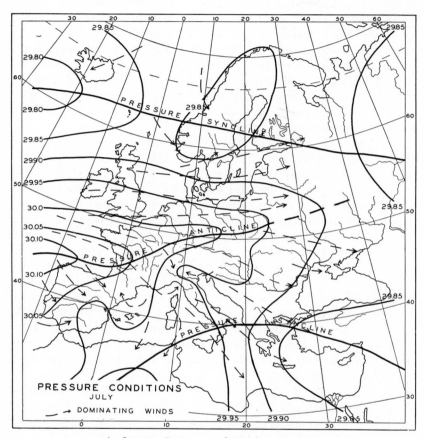

A. Summer Pressure and Winds in Europe.

forests, or taiga, from the region farther south where utilization of the land for agriculture is widely possible.

The western boundary of the southern and main section of the Eastern climatic province is the January isotherm of 27°, which swings nearly north and reaches the Baltic Sea near Riga (A28). This isotherm has been used by Köppen, the great authority on climatic regions, to separate his warm temperate climate from the boreal climate with its intemperate winters. This same isotherm surrounds the more important central European mountains, the climate of which otherwise approaches that of the general region in which they are located. It does not show on A28 because there the isotherms are reduced to sea level; that is, they show what the temperature would be at sea level. Among the mountains the Alps stand out not only because of their abundant precipitation with a summer maximum, but also because of winter conditions that are rather unusual for central Europe. At that time, as is shown below, the high-pressure axis of Europe is responsible for clear, sunny, comfortably mild weather on the upper mountain slopes, while the lower parts feel the raw unpleasantness of thick fog.

Coming back to eastern Europe, the climate has a very good feature in the warm summers when the precipitation is at a maximum. Unfortunately the rainfall is so low as to be close to the danger line for agriculture, and its unreliability often causes distress. Moreover, the long, dreary, unproductive winter causes the unfavorable features of the climate to prevail over the good ones. From the climatic point of view this makes eastern Europe decidedly inferior to the regions farther west.

Central Europe. The climatic region marked as Central Europe is primarily a transition area between the thoroughly marine climate of western Europe and the thoroughly continental climate of eastern Europe. Therefore, at the two extremes it includes climates as diverse as those of central France and the Hungarian Plain. Different as these are, their general characteristics show enough similarity to make them parts of a climatic region that can easily be recognized. Owing to Atlantic winds, the winters are relatively mild even in the east. This is true in spite of the fact that cyclonic storms passing through the northwest of this region cause an inflow of more continental air so that spells of cold, clear winter weather interrupt the cloudy, mild, marine conditions. The summers are much more continental than on the coast, and the range of average monthly temperature from the warmest to the coldest month varies from 30° to 50° F. Precipitation is heavy on the mountain slopes and moderate elsewhere, but always adequate. It is rather well distributed through the year, but with a pronounced summer maximum showing the influences of monsoonal continental conditions. Snow may cover the ground for a considerable period, especially in the eastern part of the region, and the frost period varies between 70 days per year in the west and 150 in the east. The marine influence of the

Baltic and the greater frequency of cyclonic storms in that region make it necessary to distinguish a Baltic subtype of climate. This Baltic littoral climatic region extends northward to a latitude where the Scandinavian Highlands prevent the westerlies from having much influence, but includes southern Finland (A27).

In most respects mankind finds in this Central European climate another favorable region. Weakened cyclonic variations are balanced by greater seasonal differences, although these go too far in the eastern portions. The temperature is rarely extreme, and the precipitation is usually adequate. The main unfavorable point is the increasing length of the frost season toward the east and north, but this interrupts the sequence of work only a little, since preparation for the spring season requires most of the farmers' free time in winter. Here, as in western Europe, the climatic conditions are excellent for human progress, and it is not surprising that high cultural standards prevail. Nevertheless, the decline toward the east must not be overlooked. Western Poland and Hungary, for instance, do not have the advantageous climatic foundation that the more western sections of this region enjoy.

The Mediterranean Region. The climate of the Mediterranean part of Europe is decidedly different from those thus far described. The main difference is the shift of the unproductive period from winter by reason of low temperatures in the north to summer by reason of drought around the Mediterranean. The winters are delightful, with mild temperatures and sunny weather, occasionally interrupted by cloudy days and rain. The rainfall in general is fairly abundant and increases on the western slope of the mountains, attaining the European maximum on the Dinaric Alps. The winds from the European continental axis of high pressure are comparatively cold, and cold waves with snow may invade the Mediterranean region as far south as Rome and Athens. Nevertheless, in most places the growing season is continuous throughout the winter. These favorable conditions are even more pronounced during the spring and fall when increased insolation and at least moderate precipitation provide unusually good conditions for crops. The summers, however, spoil the chances of this region for honors as perfect in climate all the year round. The regular northerly etesian winds bring no moisture; from the cloudless sky the high sun scorches the land, and except where water is available for irrigation nature can no longer be productive. The length of the dry summer period increases from north to south, as does the unreliability of the rain. Both factors strongly limit the climatic possibilities.

From the human point of view the Mediterranean climate is certainly attractive, especially where the summer drought is not severe. Protected by mountain walls from the cold winters of more northern Europe and with winter temperatures close to those of maximum human energy, the sunny Mediterranean shores were once the cradle of world civilization. This was before man had conquered the more severe northern climate and learned unconsciously to gain the benefit of its great variability. The population of the Mediterranean lands is still dense and the general culture not inferior to that of the times of world supremacy, but the dry, hot summers are too great a handicap. So the Mediterranean as a region of human efficiency is surpassed by the north and suffers consequently by comparison, in spite of its many advantages.

The Southern Transitional Region. On the southern edge of the Central Plateau of France, a transitional zone separates the Mediterranean climatic region from the climates of western and central Europe. This zone is not continuous. It is interrupted by the dry region of Spain and by a projection of the Central European climate in the Cévennes. It is also reduced to a width of only a few miles where the French Alps approach the sea in the Riviera.

The main part of the transitional zone separates the Mediterranean climate with its winter rain from the Central European climate with its summer maximum. The result is rather favorable. Precipitation occurs throughout the year with a tendency toward a double maximum in the spring and fall. The temperature combines the winter mildness of the south with the milder summer heat of the north. A gradual shift, however, takes place from west to east. In the west the Po Basin is the best example. Cold air flowing from the Alpine high-pressure area makes the winters fairly cool, but the frost period ranges from only 30 days on the Adriatic shore to 75 at Turin. The rest of the year has warm to mild temperatures and an abundance of rain. These balance the disadvantage of a relatively high variability of the rainfall from year to year. The addition of greater activity of cyclonic storms than prevails in the Mediterranean type makes this an excellent climate for human occupation. It has shown its excellence from the times of Roman occupancy through the Renaissance up to the present period, when the Po Valley stands in the forefront of modern Italy.

Farther east the Southern Transitional Zone shows the disadvantages of continentality like that of the regions to the north. The winters in the Hungarian Plain and in Walachia are severe, with a frost period of more than 100 days. The summers are hot, and the rainfall, still showing a tendency toward a double maximum in spring and fall, declines in quantity. This fact, together with the unreliability of the rain, introduces a seriously dangerous factor in human activity. This danger becomes more pronounced toward the east, until finally the dry region of southern Russia is reached. For man this climate has the promise of a productive summer with sufficient rain, but it also brings the danger of drought and starvation. Lacking the cyclonic stimulus because of its continental position, it belongs to the more unfavorable climatic zone of Europe, although ranking above the eastern part of the continent.

The Portuguese section of this transition zone is different from the rest. It is the only place where there is a direct transition from the Western type of climate to the Mediterranean. The rainfall is abundant like that of the regions north of it. There is only a very short dry summer season, and the temperatures in winter as well as in summer are fairly high. This makes a rather ideal combination, although the cyclonic control is considerably weaker than farther south. Theoretically, the climate is rather favorable for human activity, but, although it represents the best part of Portugal, the development of the people is rather disappointing and not what might be expected from the climate.

The Dry Regions of Europe. Insufficient precipitation occurs mainly in three parts of Europe: first, in inland basins that open upon the eastern coast of Spain south of Barcelona; second, in the eastern Attic portions of Greece, a very small area; and third, in southern Russia. In both Spain and Greece, mountains shut out the rain-bearing winds from the Atlantic or Mediterranean. Moreover, on the Mediterranean coast of Spain the winds in winter are mainly from the west, whereas in summer the onshore winds become warm when they blow over the heated land and bring moisture only to the higher mountains. This Spanish dry region is irregular in shape, since the many mountains receive more precipitation than the lowlands, but their influence is omitted in A36 in order not to make the map too complex. Southeastern Russia owes its low rainfall—less than 10 inches per year—to its distance from the Atlantic. The effect of the Black Sea is very limited, as the winds are mainly from the land; and on the north side of the sea only the southern slopes of the Crimean Peninsula have the benefit of a Mediterranean climate. The Iberian Plateau, as well as southern Russia, shows strong continental characteristics in the form of cold winters and hot summers with low precipitation that is highly unreliable. The east coast

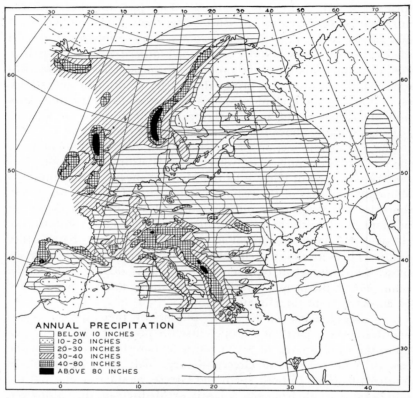

A. Annual Precipitation in Europe. Absence of shading has no significance outside of Europe.

of Spain, in contrast, has the mild Mediterranean climate, and its influence is more African than European, for it fosters the oasis type of land utilization. In all sections of the dry climate, insufficient rain greatly limits economic activity and makes the density of population low. A36 shows that large sections of northeastern Russia have a rainfall of less than 20 inches, but in such high, cool latitudes this does not lead to real aridity.

The Tundra and High Mountains. Long, cold winters and very short summers with the warmest month averaging below 50° F make the tundra a region of ever-frozen subsoil. Only during the short summer is vegetation able to grow, and only then does a little economic activity in the form of grazing temporarily break the complete unproductivity. The high Scandinavian uplands, partly covered by snow and ice at all times, and the narrow Arctic tundra belt, broken by the White Sea, make up the main tundra sections of Europe; but minor sections are found in the high parts of the Alps and in some other mountain areas, too small to be shown. The relatively small size of both the tundra and the dry types of climate, as well as the absence of tropical types, goes far toward explaining Europe's dominance.

The Seasons in Europe

Winter. Although Europe is so large and its relief so complex that the climatic regions described above are very distinct, the march of the seasons is sufficiently uniform so that a general discussion for the whole continent is better than special discussions for each region. In winter as well as in summer the regular subtropical high-pressure area over the Atlantic, the so-called Azores High, is well developed. In winter, however, it is not isolated, as in summer, but forms part of a continuous belt extending completely around the earth and is visible as the "pressure anticline" of A30. A bridge of high pressure extends across northern Africa and southern Europe and connects the Azores High with a much more intense Asiatic High, which extends over a vast area from Tibet to the Arctic Ocean. This intense high-pressure area, due to extreme cold, is balanced on the northwest by an equally extreme low-pressure area, the Icelandic Low. This "pressure syncline," as it is called in A30, owes its origin to the relatively very high temperature, the positive anomaly of 40° to 50° F, which is caused there by the warm North Atlantic Drift (A25).

The combined effect of the Azores-Asiatic High and the Icelandic Low, plus the deflection toward the right of the winds by the earth's rotation, causes a strong inflow of air from the southwest in the part of western Europe from France northward, as appears in the arrows of A30. Farther east, however, even when the winds come from a southerly quarter, as often happens in Germany, Finland, and northwestern Russia, they blow across continental areas that tend to grow very cool during the long winter nights of such high latitudes. This means that, in winter, northwestern Europe, in spite of its long nights and small amount of insolation, is kept relatively warm by winds from the ocean, while the area farther east, dominated more by continental winds, misses this benefit and shows the characteristics of its latitude in the form of low temperature. Consequently, since the source of heat is in the west, there exists the unique condition of winter isotherms that run north and south for nearly 2,000 miles and even bend back almost into loops at the far north (A28). The warm oceanic winds also lead to heavy precipitation on the Atlantic border (A36). This heavy precipitation decreases rapidly eastward, however, and Leningrad in western Russia, for example, has only one tenth as much January precipitation as has Florö in nearly the same latitude on the Atlantic Coast. In the west the precipitation is mainly in the form of rain, and when snow does fall it never stays long on the ground. In the east the precipitation is almost wholly snow, and even a small amount lasts so long that the ground is covered for a considerable period.

These general conditions are greatly modified by cyclonic storms from the Atlantic. In winter these storms approach the European coasts with great intensity and frequency. Following a course between the centers of high and low pressure, but nearer to the latter, they proceed in a northeasterly direction along the coasts of Ireland, Scotland, and Scandinavia toward the Arctic, or else swing inland in an easterly direction. If they do this, however, the continental high pressure soon blocks their progress, and they die out. This explains the monotony and slight rainfall of the winter climate in the far interior. When the storms move toward the north-northeast along the Scandinavian coast, the mild marine weather is limited to the narrow coastal belt. On the rarer occasions when they proceed inland, the Atlantic air may be carried into the interior, thus breaking the domination of the continental winds. The passing of such a depression means many changes. Mild ocean winds set in; the clear frosty weather comes to an end, the snow cover melts, and rain falls. Because of such conditions one might say that the Central European winter consists of a series of small winters separated by thaws, whereas eastern Russia has a long, steady winter with only very rare milder spells.

Farther south along the axis of the high-pressure belt from the Alps to northeastern Siberia, the winter conditions are generally stable, with descending outflowing air and clear, crisp weather. The Swiss mountains owe to this their reputation as a resort for sports and health in winter, for the higher parts bask in the sun even though the valleys and basins are filled with cold fogs. Vienna and Budapest get only half as much rain in winter as in summer. But, when cyclonic storms pass near-by, as may happen on either side of the Alps, the wall of high pressure that separates the great Icelandic Low from the minor Mediterranean Low may break down. This causes the well-known föhn winds, like the chinook winds of America. These descend from the mountains, especially on the north side, and cause a sudden rise of temperature.

During the winter the relatively warm Mediterranean Sea gives rise to a low-pressure zone between the continental high-pressure axis and the regular subtropical high of north Africa (A30). As a result, the air flows in general from the colder land toward the warmer sea. Hence clear weather prevails much of the time, and, if a place is protected against the cold land winds, as on the Riviera coast of southern France and northern Italy, the climate in winter is mild and pleasant. But here cyclonic storms are common in winter although rare in summer. Sometimes they come from the Atlantic, breaking through the axis of the high-pressure belt by way of the Gap of Carcassonne between the Central Plateau of France and the Pyrenees. Often, however, they are a product of the Mediterranean itself, arising perhaps in the stormy Gulf of Lions. In either case they cause changeable winds, cloudiness, and rain that is especially heavy on the westward side of the mountains (A36).

Spring. In spring the factors that control the winter climate become weak. The Azores High, to be sure, merely moves northward without losing its strength, but its eastern extension along the continental axis becomes faint, while in Asia the Siberian High is waning, and a summer low is developing in Iran and Arabia. Moreover, the Icelandic Low loses part of its intensity, and hence the winds are generally less strong than in winter. A rapid increase of insolation diminishes the contrast between land and sea, in both temperature and pressure, and cyclonic storms become less frequent and of less severity. Nevertheless, the equality of temperature between sea and land opens the inland road for some of the storms without diminishing their force, thus causing inland winds of high velocity.

Southern Europe and the interior warm up so much more rapidly than the north and the west coast that the isotherms shift toward their summer position, running from southwest to northeast. Meanwhile, in spring, southern Europe is getting many thundershowers. The more northern regions, on the contrary, remain relatively cool. This is partly because the snow and frozen ground of winter melt slowly, partly because of the frozen Baltic, and partly because cooling winds blow out from the snow- and ice-covered Scandinavian uplands. Such conditions do not favor much precipitation.

Summer. In summer a new system of barometric pressure greatly changes the winds and the rainfall (A31). The subtropical Atlantic High now has its center west or northwest of the Iberian Peninsula, while the heating of the great continents causes a pronounced low that covers all central Asia and extends into India, Arabia, and the eastern Sahara of Africa. At the same time the Icelandic Low becomes of minor importance. Because of all this, Europe experiences a monsoon-like flow of air from the Atlantic. This air moves eastward into the continent, but over the Mediterranean changes its direction toward the southeast. The northwest winds thus produced blow regularly toward the Iranian-Arabian Low and are called etesian winds. The cyclonic control of atmospheric circulation loses much of its force because differences in temperature between high and low latitudes are slight. Since insolation is more effective than radiation, the temperature rises. Along the Atlantic border, because of the comparatively slow warming of the water, the westerly winds have a cooling influence; the maximum temperature does not come until late July or August, and a negative anomaly exists; that is, the temperature is a little lower than the average for all places in the same latitude. On the other hand, inland temperatures are much higher than those on the coast and show a plus anomaly where the marine control dies out. That is why the isotherms in A29 trend from southwest to northeast. Part of the rainfall at this time in western and central Europe is still due to cyclonic storms, but part is due to convection with resulting thundershowers, and part to the relief. Thus, summer is the main rainy season for central and eastern Europe, whereas in western Europe the precipitation is less in summer than in winter. Over the Mediterranean regular northwest winds prevail. As they blow from colder to warmer regions, they do not cause precipitation, and the Mediterranean summers are clear, hot, and dry. Only on some coasts, like those of eastern Spain and the Po Basin, do onshore winds prevail because of the difference in temperature between land and sea. These bring increased cloudiness and orographic precipitation where they rise over mountains.

Fall. In the fall the climatic conditions shift again. As the altitude of the midday sun declines, insolation decreases rapidly, the sea is again warmer than the land, and as a result the isotherms shift back to a north and south direction. The Atlantic High moves southward, the Icelandic Low gains in intensity, and cyclonic activity increases rapidly. At the same time the Iranian Low disappears, and the continental high pressure of winter gradually develops. Atlantic coastal conditions of high precipitation, high cloudiness, and strong winds contrast with the rather clear, dry weather of the more interior sections. Here the combination of incipient high pressure and of insolation, which is still fairly strong, causes frequent periods of stable, beautiful weather—a kind of Indian summer. In the Mediterranean the northwesterly etesian winds now bring heavy rain, especially in the northern part, because the lands have now become cool enough to cause precipitation.

·3·
The Northwestern Uplands

Relief

Climate and the relief or form of the earth's surface constitute the background for human activity. Together they strongly influence man's mode of life and the kind of crops he can raise. More than this, they greatly influence his philosophy and cultural outlook. When climate and relief are compared, the climatic influence is undoubtedly the stronger, but the two are so intimately interwoven that it is often difficult to say which is the deciding factor. The geological origin of this complexity is described in the note at the end of this chapter.

The relief of Europe shows great complexity. Except on the lowland plain of Poland and Russia, one can scarcely drive a hundred miles without observing rapid changes in scenery and corresponding changes in the life of the inhabitants. The changes may be due to the contrast between life on plains and in mountains, or on coasts and inland, but even within the limits of any one major type of relief there is often high variability—a quality that is one of the characteristic features of Europe.

Because of this variability the geography of Europe is the geography of many small units, or natural regions, of which there are so many that it is impossible to show them all on a general map. Hence in A42 an attempt has been made to bring some simplification into this physiographic chaos. Four major divisions are recognized, each composed of numerous small units, but nevertheless uniform enough so that there are good grounds for calling it a distinct type. These four divisions are as follows:

I. The *Northwestern Uplands,* extending along Europe's northwestern border from western France, Great Britain, and Ireland to Scandinavia and Finland. With these higher regions, for practical reasons and also because of geological structure, may be placed the lowlands of Ireland and Scotland.

II. The *Central Lowlands,* stretching from the basin of the Garonne at the foot of the Pyrenees through the Paris Basin to Belgium,
Holland, and onward.   Southern England, although separated from
the rest by water, is part of the same lowland.   Eastward the plain

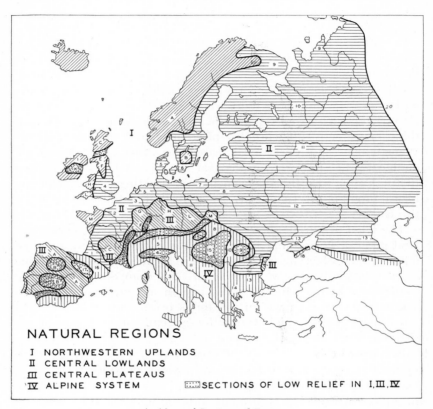

NATURAL REGIONS
I NORTHWESTERN UPLANDS
II CENTRAL LOWLANDS
III CENTRAL PLATEAUS
IV ALPINE SYSTEM   SECTIONS OF LOW RELIEF IN I,III,IV

A. Natural Regions of Europe.

includes Denmark and northern Germany and then expands in Poland, the Baltic lands, and Russia, so that it occupies all of eastern
Europe from the Baltic and the White Sea to the Black Sea and
the Caspian.

III. The *Central Plateaus,* or *Uplands:* the Spanish Meseta, the
Central Plateau of France, the many uplands of central Germany,
and the Bohemian Basin.

IV. The *Alpine System,* a complex combination of young mountains and their forelands with intermontane basins and plains.   This

division includes not only the Alps, but also the Pyrenees and Sierra Nevada in Spain, the Carpathians and Balkans with the enclosed plains of Hungary and Yugoslavia, the Balkan Peninsula, and the mountains of Crimea and the Caucasus.

Relation of Physiographic and Climatic Provinces

Some of the physiographic divisions correspond fairly well with the climatic divisions of the preceding chapter. Thus the *Northwestern Uplands* show a strong concordance with the climatic region of Western Europe. It extends farther east in Scandinavia so that it includes the alpine climate of the Scandinavian Highland, but this section is of little importance from the human standpoint. On the other hand, the Northwestern Uplands do not extend so far east as does the Western European type of climate in the regions around the North Sea. England and northern France, together with Belgium, Holland, and western Denmark, belong to the Central Lowlands, although they have the Western European climate. Hence, for descriptive purposes the Northwestern Uplands form a much better unit than the Western European climatic region. A strongly marine character gives considerable climatic unity even to regions as widely separated as Brittany and northwestern Norway.

The *Central Lowlands* display far less climatic unity than the Northwestern Uplands. They extend from the Western European type of climate in England across the Central European type. Then they expand to cover the whole of the Eastern European climatic region as well as the dry region of southeastern Russia and the tundra region of the north. Nevertheless, the unity arising from the widespread gentle relief and the gradual nature of the transitions from one climatic type to another make it easier to give a good general description on a physiographic rather than on a climatic basis.

The main portion of the third physiographic division, the *Central Uplands,* extends from southern France to Poland and lies mainly south of the Central European Lowlands. The contrast in landscape and in human activities between the plateaus and the lowland to the north makes it advisable to present the main description of this region in terms of physiographic regions rather than of climatic types. The other main part of the Central Plateaus—that is, the Iberian Meseta, is characterized by three types of climate, among which the dry type is predominant. It has a physiographic unity that justifies a general description in spite of the climatic diversity.

The fourth physiographic division, the *Alpine System,* combines the Mediterranean and Southern Transition types of climate with the Central European type.   Here the Mediterranean type of climate gives a very pronounced character to certain regions, but in its more typical forms the real Mediterranean influence is largely coast-wise, whereas the numerous mountains back from the coast have a climate much more like that of central Europe.   Hence, here too, in order to picture the country as a whole, it is well to use the physiographic divisions.

In conclusion, then, it may be said that the four great physiographic zones give the least confusing picture of a very complex continent, and in describing the picture there will be ample opportunity to bring out the climatic element.

The Northwestern Uplands

Facing the Atlantic and washed by the warm waters of the North Atlantic Drift, the uplands of Brittany, Wales, Ireland, Scotland, and Scandinavia show all the characteristics of a marine location. The westerly winds, loaded with moisture and forced to rise over the uplands, cause heavy precipitation, and the wind-swept, rain-drenched surface is often swampy and not suitable for intensive utilization.   As a result the density of population is low, except in a few especially favorable spots.   Limited possibilities and mountain isolation have here caused small groups of strong people to preserve ancient traits and customs.   The Bretons in western Brittany still talk a Celtic dialect; the Welsh and Scottish mountaineers are proud of their Celtic speech and defend their ancient folklore.   The Irish, who are like the Welsh and west Scots in being racially of Mediterranean origin, are an especially good example.   They owe their present political freedom partly to their adherence to a Celtic background, and the Irish language, long limited to the isolated mountains in the west, has had a mild literary revival.

The Coasts.   In most parts of the Northwestern Uplands the sea plays a major role, for it offers greater attractions than does the often inhospitable land.   Hence a description of coastal conditions will precede that of the land itself.   Most of the coast is extremely irregular because of an invasion of the land by the sea after the Ice Age. The invasion was due partly to an actual rise of sea level through the addition of water set free by the melting of the ice sheet, and partly to a sinking of the land under the weight of the ice and subsequent failure to rise again to the old level.   Thus the sea has transformed the lower portions of the land into bays and gulfs, leaving the higher parts as islands and peninsulas.

It is hard to find a more beautiful type of coast. In Brittany and Cornwall rocky promontories shelter peaceful bays from which green meadows lead gently to the upland surface; in Scotland narrow lochs extend far inland, bordered by the bare rounded slopes of the highlands. But in the Norwegian fjords nature reaches its peak of beauty. Former valleys, once deepened by glaciers and now invaded by the sea, reach far inland. Protected from the stormy ocean by rows of rocky islands, the calm waters of the fjords are often enclosed by almost perpendicular walls of rock, the bareness of which is broken by little patches of grass and flowers wherever the slope is less steep, and by roaring waterfalls where streams plunge down from the ice-covered *fjeld,* or plateau, high above. Coastal steamers glide for hours through these mountain streets, stopping frequently where a little space is left between the water and the mountain wall, and a few houses surrounded by vegetable gardens show the struggle of man to exist.

On these coasts it is not the land but the sea that supplies the economic basis of life. Here is one of the world's greatest fishing regions. The warm North Atlantic Drift, keeping the coastal water free from ice even beyond the Arctic Circle, and the large amount of food brought by the continental rivers, especially in the English Channel and the North Sea, provide excellent living conditions for fish. Fishing fleets pursue the cod in the coastal waters even to the Lofoten and Finnmark in far northern Norway where temporary fishing settlements disturb the silence of the long, dark winter nights. Herring are caught near the Shetland and Faeroes in winter and in the southern part of the North Sea in summer, and the sardine is seined in the coastal waters of France and Portugal. The fishermen often sail long distances. From the quaint Breton fishing towns, for example, where lace-capped women sit embroidering in front of their homes, the fishing boats sail to the Mediterranean for tuna and to Newfoundland and Iceland for cod.

Fishing dominates life; it means the money to pay for all sorts of necessities. It also means the everlasting danger of storms when the family waits in vain for the return of the husband and father. In Scotland the fishing population is especially concentrated along the sheltered northeast coast from which express trains bring the catch to the city markets for the English breakfast table. But it is in Norway that the sea's importance in human life reaches its greatest development. The relative abundance of the fish, and the varying oily content of their livers, mean comfort or poverty to the coastal settlements. Constant contact with the sea, whereas the land only with great difficulty provides a supplementary income, has made the Norwegians some of the best sailors of the world from the ancient time of the Vikings until now. These Norsemen colonized Iceland, knew Greenland and the Acadian Coast of Nova Scotia; they extended their trips southward along the western coast of Europe into the Mediterranean, often leaving smoking ruins in their path. The modern Norwegian inherits the love of the sea. Norwegian freighters can be found in the world's most isolated harbors looking for cargo.

Only along the Irish coasts and in western Scotland is fishing of less importance. This may be because the open Atlantic with its fogs and gales offers too great a handicap, or because the barren land does not provide the timber so necessary in building boats. Nevertheless, in the Northwestern Uplands as a whole, a productive sea opposes an inhospitable land, and a narrow fringe of denser coastal population surrounds the deserted uplands.

The Land. Latitude and elevation combine to make the high plateau of Scandinavia practically worthless. It is merely a starting point for the many rivers that, when they tumble down the slopes, can be used for the power so important in these countries without coal. The broad Norwegian fjeld (I-A in A42), an old surface of erosion, now far uplifted and cut to pieces along its flanks by rivers, is for the greater part covered with ice. Its high summits appear only as insignificant hills on the rolling white surface. From the fjords on clear days the tourists can see the glistening icy tongues of glaciers hanging over the border of the fjeld. Even when lower elevation causes ice to be absent, the flat, stone-covered surface, snowy most of the year, offers very scanty food for the cattle and goats of the peasant who brings his stock along steep trails up to the plateau in search of pasture.

The drop from the plateau toward the west coast is abrupt. Dark, treeless, barren slopes face strong westerly winds that often cause clouds to hang low over the mountains, while the beauty of the fjords is hidden under a falling rain. In contrast, the eastern slopes are more gradual, and their leeward location shows itself in less precipitation, more sun, and more extreme temperatures in summer and winter. Here the forest of conifers is dominant—from Oslo along the Swedish uplands to beyond the Arctic Circle. Locally some sum-

mits rise above the forest zone and are covered with grass and colorful flowers, but the general impression is of a dark green mantle of
trees, interrupted here and there by the glistening of innumerable
lakes and by the courses of rivers that follow the general incline
toward the Baltic.

In these forests on the eastern slope of the Scandinavian Highlands settlement is sparse. Although there is some farming, man is
chiefly engaged in mining or the exploitation of timber. Felled in
winter and transported by truck to a neighboring river, millions of
trees are floated down the river courses after the ice melts in spring.
In the valleys and in extensions of the Baltic coastal plain, fertile
soils and long summer days combine to make it possible to raise
crops of barley, oats, and hay. On the fjeld, especially in the far
north, the reindeer-herding Lapps represent almost the last European remnant of nomadic life, a true adjustment to an unfavorable
environment; however, many Lapps have taken up sedentary farming.

Disconnected from the other uplands by the central Swedish lowlands, the Småland Plateau (I-B in A42) in southern Sweden is similar
to the region just discussed except that the light green of deciduous
forest breaks the monotony of the dark green conifers and reflects
the influence of a more southerly latitude.

Taken as a whole, the Scandinavian uplands present a picture
of mountain and forest isolation, and human settlements are limited
to the coastal waters and fjords or to certain favorable valleys. The
few railroads follow the lines of lowest relief except for the connection between Oslo and Bergen, where the railroad, with great expense, had to be built over the fjeld to reach the west coast.

The uplands of the British Isles and western France do not differ
greatly from those of Scandinavia except that the elevation and
latitude decrease toward the south, thus causing less extreme conditions. The Scottish Highlands (I-C) are undoubtedly attractive on
a clear day when the summits, sculptured by the glaciers of the Ice
Age, show the purple color of blossoming heather, and many lakes
break the monotony of this stern but rather uniform landscape.
Nevertheless when clouds lay a dense fog over the hills and rain falls
for days and days, as frequently happens, the life of the Scottish
highlander caring for his flock of sheep approaches the limit of human endurance, and it requires the ardor of the English deerstalker
to wade through the spongy moor without complete disgust. But
the broad valleys opening toward the drier east offer better living
conditions; woodlands give color to the landscape; hedge-bordered

meadows and cultivated fields occupy the fertile valley bottoms; farmhouses reflect the general prosperity; and ancient castles add to the attractiveness of the environment. Here graze the cattle, here fatten the sheep, here the roads and railroads penetrate into the core of the upland.

How different are the Central Scottish Lowlands (I-D) that occupy the great rift between the Scottish Highlands and the Southern Uplands! Long belts of low hills, owing their existence to the outcrop of hard rocks, border fertile stretchers of level land. A mild climate with heavy precipitation favors the grassland that prevails in the west; and, in the drier east, fields of wheat and oats and many orchards, together with grassy meadows, give an impression of agricultural abundance surprising for so northern a latitude—a product of favorable conditions of climate and soil but also of the energy of the inhabitants. Great banks of smoke hanging over the Clyde River show that another factor here enters into human activity. Based on layers of coal and iron ore, large industries have developed, and the dirty factory cities in the west contrast strongly with the beautiful urban seats of learning and culture in the east.

The Southern Scottish Uplands (I-E) lack the severity of the Northern Highlands, the mountains are less high, and the relief is more gentle. Great herds of sheep wander over the rolling hills on which the heath still reigns, and cattle graze on the lower grasslands. Along the wide, fertile valleys with their park-like vegetation, intensive agriculture penetrates far inland; and the great north to south railroad lines connecting England with the Scottish Lowlands run through them, bringing modern life into once isolated vales.

To the south, the Pennine Chain (I-F) is no more than a great arch separating two of the greatest industrial developments of the world. Coal layers outcropping on the lower flanks of the arch have greatly stimulated this development. Industrial plants have invaded the Pennine valleys in search of water. Trains roar through the mountain gaps connecting Lancashire on the west with Yorkshire on the east, but the uplands are still covered with moors, a haven of peace surrounded by the buzzing of modern manufacturing.

Cumberland and Wales (I-H) are reminiscent of Scotland. The lakes of Cumberland, the land of the lake poets, are like beautiful jewels in their steep mountain frame; but most of the valleys are narrow and stony, and the moor-covered slopes are soaked by the many rains. From Snowdon, the highest point of Wales, the view is very similar to that from Ben Nevis in Scotland—an endless sea of summits, the highest gray, rocky, and glacially sculptured, with little lakes at the bottoms of cirques once occupied by glaciers, but the greater part brown in color because of moorland vegetation. Here, too, the people live on the borders of the highland; there lie the towns and villages, the cropped fields, and the orchards. Summer resorts abound along the coast of Wales; and in the south near the Bristol Channel, mining, with its noise of railroads, trolleys, and engines, has invaded the narrow valleys in search of coal. The main mass of the upland, however, is left in the majestic silence of mountain beauty; the shepherd with his flock is the only human element.

In the highlands of Ireland (I-I) the traditional green, a product of a marine climate, is broken by the somberness of the bog-covered uplands. Steep peaks of quartzite and granite rise abruptly from the marshy upland level devoid of any sign of human life. Enormous volcanic eruptions, such as those of the famous Scottish island of Staffa, have formed an extensive lava plateau in the northwest, in which Lough Neagh occupies a structural depression. Massifs of red sandstone enclose basins occupied by glistening lakes. But also there is many a charming valley where a tree-bordered river winds its way between green meadows and yellow fields of grain. This is especially true in the east where abundant fields are a token of climatic clemency wherever the relief and soil permit.

In the center of Ireland a great lowland (I-K) is completely surrounded by uplands except on the east. The underlying rock is limestone, so that karst topography with frequent undrained hollows prevails. Peat extends over the more humid western parts of this central lowland. Stagnant pools cover large areas, and slow-flowing rivers drain toward the Atlantic. Peat here assumes great importance, and the acrid smoke of burned turf hangs over the rural cottages, which are picturesque rather than hygienic. In the east where the rainfall diminishes and glacial deposits cover most of the limestone, grass and woodland replace the peat and make this section the economic heart of the Irish Republic. Here graze the cattle for which Ireland is famous. Here are found the fields of oats, barley, wheat, and potatoes. Nevertheless, here, only a little less than in the west, the marine influence dominates, giving Ireland its year-round verdure —green Erin, the Emerald Isle.

Cornwall (I-L), in southwestern England, and Brittany and Normandy (I-M) in western France, although separated by the English Channel, are very similar. Both are uplands of minor elevation in which the wind-swept open land is covered with moors, fit for little except sheep. On more sheltered spots woodland is found, and the farmer raises crops of rye and buckwheat, or grazes his cattle. But the soil is infertile, the yields are low, and the farmer's life is still primitive and backward. The monotony of these deserted uplands is broken by basins in which fertile alluvial soils and milder climate combine to increase productivity. Here cattle are fattened and famous cheeses are made; here fields of wheat and oats replace rye and buckwheat; and apple trees are so common that cider is the regional drink. The basins, however, are rather small; and open, rolling uplands, with only a limited use on the part of man, are dominant.

This ends the picture of the Northwestern Uplands, an area full of charm and beauty, but also one where man leads a life of struggle against many unfavorable elements, and where the sea plays a large part as a source of production.

NOTE TO CHAPTER 3

The Origin of Europe's Four Physiographic Regions (A42) *

From the geological point of view, all the continents may be thought of as the result of the interplay of two old blocks, southern and northern. According to the theory that now seems most probable, these blocks are masses of gneiss and granite that have persisted throughout geological times because of their rigidity, and have therefore become the nuclei of the present continents. The northern block is represented in Europe by some of the old rocks of Scotland and Scandinavia; it probably lies buried below the later deposits of the Russian lowlands, but its greatest extension is found in the Laurentian uplands of North America and the Siberian Plateau of Asia. The other block forms the core of the continents of the southern hemisphere. It is now broken into several sections between which lie the Indian and South Atlantic oceans. Throughout much of geological history the two main blocks—northern and southern—have been separated by a central depression, the so-called Tethys Sea, which in past ages more or less girdled the earth in semi-equatorial regions.

According to the ideas of many geologists, these blocks consist of material a little lighter than the main mass of the earth's outer layers. Therefore they float on the upper layers of the earth's crust and if subjected to constant and sufficient pressure can be moved in any direction. A52 shows an ideal cross section of such a block. The rigid block A is in equilibrium in respect to the upper layers of the earth's crust (B), which are less rigid but

---

* This section, as well as others in small type, is especially intended for more advanced students and may be omitted without injury to the general plan of the book.

heavier. In other words, it acts much like a piece of ice in water. The emergent part of *A* (labeled *a*) represents the continent, while the ocean (*c*) covers *B* completely. If *A* moves, the movement takes place only very slowly and in the face of great resistance. The result is that folding, involving both *A* and *B*, takes place in front of the moving block. The fold-

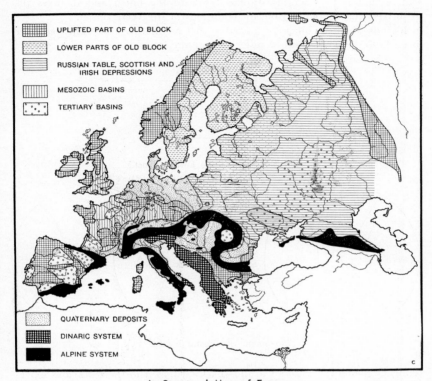

UPLIFTED PART OF OLD BLOCK

LOWER PARTS OF OLD BLOCK

RUSSIAN TABLE, SCOTTISH AND IRISH DEPRESSIONS

MESOZOIC BASINS

TERTIARY BASINS

QUATERNARY DEPOSITS

DINARIC SYSTEM

ALPINE SYSTEM

A. Structural Map of Europe.

ing shows itself at the earth's surface in the form of mountain ranges. According to the Swiss geologist, Staub, who may be considered the main exponent of this hypothesis of earth structure, a third block of extreme rigidity is completely submerged under the Pacific Ocean.

The present structure of the continents is supposed to be the result of movements of the northern and southern blocks in the gap between the two sides of the vast Pacific mass, as shown in B52.

Throughout the geological history of the world, blocks *N* and *S* have shown a tendency to move equatorward, probably as a result of the earth's rotation. During such movements mountain ranges are thrust up not only on the equatorial sides of the northern and southern blocks, thus narrowing or temporarily eliminating the Tethys Sea, but also along the edges of the Pacific block (*A* in C52).

In this way the world's mountains show a double aspect: a circum-Pacific system including the Sierra, Rocky, and Andes mountains, as well as the ranges in the islands and coastlands east of the Pacific, and an equatorial system that is considerably displaced toward the north and includes the Alps, Himalayas, and Caribbean mountains of the West Indies.

Periods when the blocks advanced so that mountains were upheaved have been followed by periods of rest. During the latter there has even been a

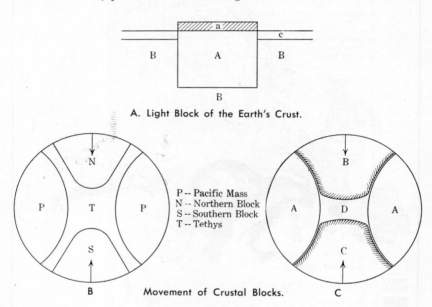

A. Light Block of the Earth's Crust.

P -- Pacific Mass
N -- Northern Block
S -- Southern Block
T -- Tethys

Movement of Crustal Blocks.

tendency for blocks *N* and *S* to slide backward, as if in their previous movement they had gone beyond the limits of equilibrium and had to fall back. It is impossible here to go into details of this process, or to mention its many complications, but the theory paves the way for a general understanding of Europe's relief.

The fourth or Alpine division of Europe, as shown in A42, represents the zone of contact between the northern and southern blocks during the last, or Alpine, period of movement. The way in which the mountains were formed is illustrated in A53. There the lower diagram shows the condition in ancient Permian times when the African part of the southern block was separated from the European part of the northern block by the Tethys Sea. In this sea thick sediments derived from both blocks were laid down. Later on, during the Jurassic Period, the movement of Africa northward diminished the width of the Tethys and caused the sedimentary layers to be folded in such a way that the upper parts of the folds, the anticlines, appeared as rows of islands in the Tethys Sea (A53). Finally, in the Tertiary Period, the old African and European blocks approached one another so closely that the Alpine mountain system was formed (A51). This consists mainly of Tethys material shoved up over the two blocks, and leaving only small remnants of the former Tethys. Thus the young Alpine mountains with their complex structure seem to be folded parts of both blocks as well as of the floor beneath the Tethys Sea. The Alps in the more limited sense,

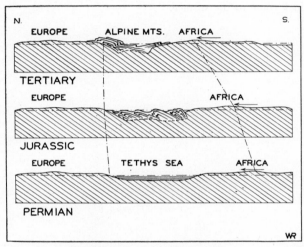

A. Cross Section Showing Origin of Alps.

as shown on the map of structure (A51), contain mainly northern material, whereas the Dinaric System in Yugoslavia represents the southern block. The Mediterranean is all that is now left of the Tethys. It was formed after the cessation of the last great movement and is the result of the recession of the southern block, which had gone far beyond the limits of equilibrium and therefore slid backward.

The Northwestern Uplands and the Central Plateaus of Europe, divisions I and III (page 41) are remnants of pre-Alpine periods of mountain building. They stood on the border of the Tethys, and were once high mountains like the Alps. During a long period when mountain building had come to an end they were attacked by erosion and leveled to the gently rolling condition known as a peneplain. The great stress of the ensuing Alpine period, however, exerted such pressure on the northern block that these old mountains, the most vulnerable parts of the block, were uplifted again as plateaus. Nevertheless, geologically they are old, and in many cases still show the peneplain, now uplifted and again under the influence of erosion.

During the Alpine uplift, the Central Lowlands (division II), which form a depression between the Northwestern Uplands and the Central Plateaus, remained low, and are now partly submerged to form the North and Baltic seas. Elsewhere also this great central lowland was once a shallow sea. In the west its sedimentary layers are slightly uplifted so that in England and France escarpments have been developed representing the outcrop of more resistant layers of rock, whereas in the east young glacial deposits bury the broken substrata entirely (A51). Around the Baltic Sea in Sweden and Finland the glacial cover is so thin that the rocks of the ancient block come to the surface.

· 4 ·

Central Lowlands
and Uplands

The Central Lowlands (II in A42)

Comparative levelness is the dominant feature of the Central
European Lowlands. These extend funnel-shaped from the Pyrenees
toward the northeast through France, Germany, Poland, and Russia
until finally the Urals separate them from their Siberian continuation. In the lowlands the rough topography and high elevation that
limit human occupancy of the highlands are eliminated, and differences in relief have little effect on human activity. One result of the
levelness is ease of transportation. Broad, slow-moving rivers provide in most cases an excellent means of transportation. Interconnected by many canals, they form the base for a system of waterways
that are unequaled in the world and that supplement a dense railroad net that is undisturbed by obstructions due to relief. Another
effect of the levelness, wherever the climate is favorable, is the density
of population. Here dwell most of Europe's inhabitants. Here, or
along the edges of the lowland, are found the great centers of manufacturing. Here are the great harbors. Here, too, are the great
European nations—all except Italy—that control the major part of
the world.

In spite of the levelness, it would be wrong to suppose that these
lowlands are uniform and monotonous. In the north the ancient
ice sheet left the rocks bare, although elsewhere a universal mantle
of loose soil makes it easy to use the soil for agriculture. In small
but very important sections the presence of coal, iron, and other minerals has greatly altered the scenery by stimulating industry. Nevertheless, on the whole, the climate with its effect on native vegetation,
agriculture, architecture, and transportation is the chief cause of the
difference between one section of the lowland and another. Only in
the east does uniformity prevail. A regional description starting in

the southwest and following the general trend toward the east will bring out the different geographical aspects.

The Aquitaine Basin (II-1 in A42). Between the limestone uplands of the Central Plateau and the huge and much-dissected cones of debris that border the northern slopes of the Pyrenees lies the Garonne Basin, forming the center of the Basin of Aquitaine. From a narrow but low gap opening easily toward the Mediterranean coastal plain it widens northwestward and includes the coastal lowlands from the Pyrenees to the Vendée Uplands south of Nantes. In the higher portions one drives for miles on a flat plain only to descend at intervals down a steep but cultivated hillside into a valley. Elsewhere the land is flat except that the rivers flow in terraced valleys. Hedges or houses rarely break the broad green expanses between village and village, but there are plenty of trees, and in the south the snowy peaks of the Pyrenees can be seen in the distance. The general impression is one of agricultural variety and abundance. Cattle fatten on the grass-covered river floodplains, and waddling lines of geese recall the fame of the goose liver (*pâté de foie gras*).

Open to the rain-bearing winds of the Bay of Biscay, heated by the summer sun of middle latitudes, and warmed in winter by winds from the ocean, the fertile alluvial soils are highly fruitful. On the higher terraces market gardening prevails, and the artichokes, asparagus, tomatoes, and cucumbers, along with the plum and walnut trees, reflect the relatively warm climate. Fields of wheat and corn ripen in the sun, but the most typical crop of the Garonne Basin is the vine. Grapes grow everywhere and dominate the landscape entirely in many places. Little villages and medieval castles bear names that are carried all over the world on the labels of bottles of dark red Bordeaux wines or of gold-colored brandy. Here the wine reaches its highest perfection, a product of sun-kissed fertile soils.

Whereas the east and south of the Aquitaine Basin present in general a rolling aspect, the western part along the Bay of Biscay is very flat. This is the broad zone called Les Landes. On its western edge, sand dunes border a straight coastline at the inner base of which shallow lagoons with no outlet to the sea form an almost continuous chain of lakes. The region inland from the lagoons was once an almost unproductive marsh where people used stilts as a means of traversing the swampy surface. In late years, however, the whole region has been drained and planted with the maritime pine. As a result malarial mosquitoes have disappeared, conditions of health have greatly improved, and the resin from the pines provides the naval stores of France.

The Paris Basin (II-2 in A42). North of Les Landes the Gate of Poitou between the Central Plateau of France and the Vendée off-shoot of the uplands in Brittany connects the Garonne Basin with that of Paris. Geologically the Paris Basin is a beautiful example of concentric escarpments with their steep sides outward, that is, away from Paris. The escarpments are due to outcrops of relatively resistant layers that dip toward the interior where Paris is the geographical as well as geological center. On the eastern side of the basin the escarpments facing the Vosges stand out most clearly. Their individual names were made immortal during the First World War when they formed obstacles in the German march toward Paris. The upper Loire and Seine rivers (A42), with their main tributaries, follow the slope of the rocks toward the center of the basin, but, instead of combining, break their way separately through the western rim toward the Atlantic. On the other hand, the eastern rivers, for example the Meuse and the Moselle, follow the escarpments and flow around the basin instead of inward.

Although differences in relief and soil give individuality to the various regions of the Paris Basin, they do not prevent a certain uniformity. In most parts the dominating impression is that of a gently rolling plain—in summer a waving sea of grain in which red poppies and blue cornflowers stand out amid the yellow straw, in winter a gray mass of sticky mud. The chimney of a sugar factory located among fields of sugar beets, villages rebuilt with red brick in the north after the devastating world wars, or made of stone as gray as the winter landscape in the south—these are the chief things that one sees in many places for mile after mile in winter. The gentle valleys of the rivers break the monotony of such a scene and give charm to rural France in summer. A wide, level valley with rather steep, wooded slopes, terraced for grapes where it faces the south; a slowly flowing shallow river bordered by poplars and often paralleled by a canal on which a boat moves slowly, pulled by a horse on a tow path; a fertile, alluvial valley bottom intensively cultivated with garden crops; little gray farmhouses overgrown with vines and surrounded by fruit trees; picturesque old stone chateaux, or country houses, standing in parks of magnificent old trees; walled cities of a medieval appearance standing out above the plain and protected at prominent points by medieval castles representing the outwardly glorious but inwardly wretched period of the French kings and bearing names that recall the dukes and counts of the Middle Ages—all these represent France in its most typical form. This is not the France of Paris with the luxuries and noisy life of a great capital, but the France of the industrious farmers and other thrifty villagers who are still their country's backbone. Only in the east do the escarpments of the Paris Basin present really prominent features of relief. There they stand out boldly as steep forested walls flanking the broad cultivated river valleys.

The Lowland of Brabant (II-3 in A42). Farther north the low plateau of Brabant in central Belgium resembles the Paris Basin. Only in the south, however, do a few traces of the escarpment type of scenery appear, and the general appearance is open and cheerful. Fertile loess, as in France, makes rich crops possible. Instead of being all crowded together in compact villages as in France, however, the small homes of the Belgian farmers, who often work in a near-by town, are surrounded by fruit and vegetable gardens that break up the great fields of grain most pleasantly. Towns are numerous—some being compact with the belfries of the churches rising above a sea of steep-gabled houses, others spreading through suburbs out over the surrounding hills. Here Latin and Germanic cultures meet on the great road from France to Germany, where all through history battles have been fought to decide political supremacy. Here, too, is the world's region of highest agricultural yield, a result not only of soil and climate, but also of the character of the farmers.

The Lowlands of England (II-4). The lowland of France and Belgium reappears in England. The shallow English Channel and North Sea are merely drowned portions of it. Beyond them in England the lowlands, which extend as far as the Pennine Chain and the uplands of Wales and Devon, are in many ways similar to the Paris Basin, showing the same geological structure. But how different the aspect! The long escarpments of limestone and chalk, with their treeless, rolling surface, approach the English uplands in appearance. Along the southern coast they break off in high, steep, white cliffs, almost dazzling in the sunshine. Across the narrow Strait of Dover these cliffs face the similar "Falaise" of northern France. But the broad, open vales between the escarpments and back from the coast give the real picture of rural England. There grassland dominates the scene, especially in the more humid west, although fields of grain are abundant in the drier east. One of the most characteristic features is that the meadows and cropped fields are almost everywhere enclosed by hedges. Tree-bordered lanes lead to villages where cottages with roofs of tile or even straw often stand in gardens full of colorful sweet peas. Trees abound everywhere. They may form little spots of woodland, remnants of the former widespread forest, or they may stand as individual trees, giving the typical park-like vistas amid which great castles raise their ancient towers. Here also one finds huge industrial developments connected with the underlying coal layers, which give rise to ugly, smoke-colored cities where even the suburbs consist of long and monotonous rows of two-story brick houses with only the tiniest gardens. These, however, are only minor features of the landscape. Nothing is more pleasant than to drive leisurely through these English lowlands visiting not only the villages with their beautiful gardens, but also the superb cathedrals in their setting of ancient trees, and stopping at some quaint inn beside a tree-bordered river that winds its way between green meadows. This is rural England.

The Low Country Type (II-5). Back on the continental side of the North Sea the lowlands northeast of the Brabant Plateau show a distinct zonal arrangement somewhat like that of Les Landes several hundred miles to the south. Along the coast, especially in Holland, lies a band of sand dunes. Behind this, and corresponding to the lagoon lakes of the Bay of Biscay, is a low district occupied partly by "polders," or old lake beds reclaimed by building dikes and pumping out the water, partly by drained swamps that also lie a little below the level of high tide, and partly by waters like the Zuider Zee, most of which now forms Lake IJssel, and the channel inside the Frisian Islands where the sea has broken through the dunes. Still farther inland a third zone takes the form of a sandy plain. In an attenuated form all three of these extend clear to the northern coast of Denmark.

The richest and most populous part of this region is a narrow belt of rather sandy soil between the inner margin of the sand dunes and the main polders. Here in Holland one finds dignified cities with suburbs full of flowery charm; stately country homes, which in their beautiful parks reflect the wealth brought from a colonial empire; and prosperous villages surrounded by vegetables and fruit, while in huge greenhouses tomatoes and grapes ripen in an artificial climate. All this shows the quiet cultural life of a contented nation. The great moment here is in early spring, when immense fields of brilliant tulips, hyacinths, and narcissuses attract innumerable visitors, both Dutch and foreign.

Color is also the main theme in the adjacent "polderland," once a coastal lagoon or marsh, but now reclaimed. Nowhere are the colors more impressive. Green meadows, in which graze many cattle— brown, or black and white; numerous canals and lakes reflecting the everlasting interplay of the clouds; large red-roofed farmhouses hidden amid dark green foliage; and finally villages and towns with bright red brick houses, carefully scrubbed: all this is Holland as the great Dutch painters have immortalized it.

Not everywhere has man been the winner. In many places the sea, breaking through the dunes, still occupies large parts of the polder zone. Especially in northwestern Germany, as far as the Jutland Peninsula of Denmark, the reclaimed polderland is separated from the dunes by broad mudflats in which the river estuaries form deep channels suitable for ocean transportation.

The inner zone of the North Sea lowlands, bordering the polders on one side and the uplands on the other, is generally a flat, sandy plain broken only by local sandy hills. From Flanders this type of land extends through southern and eastern Holland into Germany, where it widens considerably and sends out broad lowland bays into the southern upland. The sand of the plain was mainly deposited by streams from the great ice sheet, but rivers from the German highlands also contributed their part. The hills, on the other hand, are mainly glacial, being either moraines or places where the ice pushed up masses of earth and rock. Once a great forest of pine, oak, and beech covered this sandy stronghold of the old Germanic tribes, but these people learned gradually to cultivate the light soils and clear the forest. Even now agricultural value is often low, and meager crops of rye, buckwheat, and potatoes scarcely provide a living for the inhabitants of the straw-thatched farmhouses. Large sections remain waste land, and in the summer the warm air rises trembling above a carpet of purple heath against a background of dark green pines.

In some places, especially in Holland, new life has come into this sandy zone through the improvement of agricultural methods and the increasing demand for food in western Europe. When fertilizers are added, the sand becomes productive, and the yield of crops increases rapidly. Canals have been made to lower the water level and transport the peat, which in many places covers the sand. Factories have been built on this cheaper but firmer land, and industrial regions have developed where once sheep grazed and bees sucked the honey from the heather. This former waste land has also attracted many people for recreation and for summer homes. Bicycle paths cross the rolling heath, and attractive cottages, standing amid a wealth of flowers, show the great desirability of having free, open land in a country where in most sections all the land is used for production. Beyond the Elbe in Schleswig, and especially along the western side of the Jutland Peninsula in Denmark, a narrow strip of this same sandy plain has been the scene of a recent colonization that is curiously suggestive of the settlement of new lands in western America. Here, as in Frisia, land that seemed perfectly worthless—fit only for heather—has been made to support a profitable dairy industry.

Along the inner borders of the sand-plain near the upland, another definite change takes place. Coal layers near the surface have become the base for the continent's greatest industrial development. An almost continuous zone of factories and industrial towns extends from northern France through Belgium far into Germany. At night blast furnaces throw fantastic colors over the land where cinder piles look like volcanic cones rising out of the plains.

The Ground Moraines of Southern Scandinavia (II-6 in A42). Beyond the Elbe four main types of lowland landscape can be recognized. Beginning in the north, they are ground moraines, terminal moraines, alluvial river valleys, and the southern zone of loess. The ground moraine landscape is characteristic of the Baltic shores, but it is also found inland between the terminal moraines. The Danish islands east of the sandy peninsula are a typical example. The relief is gentle and rolling. Many lakes fill small hollows, and similar depressions on the coast are occupied by bays and gulfs giving a very complex coastline. Of the beech forests that once covered the loamy hills, all but a few scattered remnants are now replaced by fertile fields of hay, grain, sugar beets, and other root crops. It is chiefly around the old castles, such as that of Shakespeare's Hamlet, that were prominent at the time when this was the political key to the Baltic, that this forest is still kept as dark green islands amid the arable land. Prosperous-looking farmhouses reflect the high standard of agriculture. But the factor that makes this land especially attractive is the omnipresence of water—little lakes shaded by trees, but especially the sea, which is visible from most of the higher points. Summer cottages border the beach. The eastern coast of Jutland, the Baltic zone of Schleswig, and the most southern part of Sweden show similar features.

Central Sweden, in spite of its thin mantle of soil, its meadows, and its fields of oats, presents a picture more like that of the Swedish uplands with their dominant forest of conifers. In central Sweden this forest covers the slopes between which swift rivers run toward large lakes that are very attractive in their forest frame. The rocky islands along the coast are similar to those of western Norway and serve here also as a habitat for the fishermen. The large cities, where the power of the rapids and falls is used for manufacturing industries, suggest those of southern New England. Here, more than elsewhere in Europe, the cities are surrounded by true suburbs of the American type. At Stockholm and elsewhere attractive suburban homes, hidden under the pines, face narrow waterways between the islands where little steamers take care of transportation.

The North German Terminal Moraine (II-7). The second section of the lowland of central Europe, the terminal moraine, forms a long zone of sandy hills that sometimes attain an elevation of 900 feet. In the Jutland Peninsula it forms a very narrow strip. Then it bends eastward in Germany and extends northeastward into the lands east of the Baltic, broadening as it goes. This Baltic Moraine, as it is called, shows a profusion of pine-covered sand ridges surrounding thousands of ponds and lakes where summer cottages stand beside sandy beaches. In some places fields of rye and potatoes replace the forest, but without disturbing the general impression of sandy forested ridges and sparkling lakes. Farther east, the population of the moraine becomes more sparse, and for mile after mile one may see nothing but low, pine-clad hills, lakes, swamps, and sandy plains. Yet even here all tracts of good soil are used, and the population is dense in proportion to the resources. This has traditionally been a region of large estates.

North German Alluvial Plains (II-8). While the ice sheet was laying down the Baltic Moraine, its waters poured off to the south and joined those from the uplands of southern Germany and Czechoslovakia. Together these waters flowed westward to the North Sea. On their way they built a broad alluvial plain extending clear across northern Germany. In postglacial times new sections have been added to this plain by rivers that have once more resumed their former courses to the Baltic Sea. Thus from Hamburg, Bremen, and Hannover eastward past Berlin to Warsaw and beyond there extends one of the flattest parts of the great central lowland. Much of this alluvial plain is swampy and forested, but in large areas meadows prevail and are used for grazing. Near the cities the vegetable gardens and orchards in a marsh-like environment with narrow canals and broad pools remind one of Holland. Along the postglacial valleys that run from south to north, wheat, sugar beets, and potatoes reflect the fertile soil and form an interesting contrast to the rye and buckwheat of the sandy lands on the sides.

The Loess Zone. On the southern border of the Central Lowland the conditions for farming become very favorable. This is due

A. Maximum Extent of Glaciation in Europe during the Ice Age.

to a fertile loess of dark color, brought by dry winds that blew across the loose material laid down by the great floods that poured out of the melting ice sheet. Because of this fertile soil, fields of grain, sugar beets, and potatoes surround a great number of prosperous-looking villages and towns. Moreover, here, as in the west, coal, lignite, and potash have encouraged the growth of modern industries, of which those of Saxony and Silesia are examples. The industries of the latter region are only a recent development, but Saxony is a long-established center of art and culture.

The Eastern Plain

Toward the east, the Central Lowlands widen and finally extend from the shores of the Arctic Ocean to the Black Sea and the Caucasus, and only the range of the Urals prevents a direct continuation into the West Siberian Plain. Between the southern end of the Urals and the Caspian Sea, the lowland continues into Asia without a break. In the southwestern Ukraine, it swings around in the other direction into Walachia, as the Rumanian plain is called. In this vast lowland, differences of relief become of minor significance. Nevertheless the landscape varies a great deal, for the climatic factor exerts a strong influence.

Along the shores of the Arctic the snow cover melts in early summer and for a short time the tundra (II-9) attracts herds of reindeer that feed on its short mosses and grasses. Here the treeless scenery presents little except an unending monotony of tussocks of grass, beds of gray lichens, miry swamps, pale gray soil, and rocks. In winter the frozen White Sea contrasts strongly with the open harbors on the north coast of the Kola Peninsula that are influenced by the North Atlantic Drift so strongly that the Russian fishermen join the Norwegians in the search for cod. Everywhere, however, the tundra scenery is bleak, bare, monotonous, wet, and uninteresting to ordinary people.

Eastern Coniferous Forest (II-10). South of the tundra comes a great belt of coniferous forests in which multitudes of small pines, firs, spruces, and similar trees stand amid a tangle of fallen logs. The trees rise from a soft, deep bed of gray lichens. Where the forest is crossed by the terminal moraines of the Ice Age, it is sprinkled with lakes and swamps. Broad rivers flow slowly through it, bordered by a dark green army of trees. In Finland the thousands of lakes are bordered by bare granite rocks scraped smooth by the glaciers. Man's influence is still rather insignificant—clearings for timber along the rivers, some scanty fields—that is all. Here is the domain of the fur hunter, the home of the lumberman.

The Mixed Forest (II-11). Farther south, in the Leningrad and Moscow section, a mixed forest was the dominant feature of the landscape before man replaced it by crops. Nevertheless, in some of the wilder parts the aurochs roamed in virgin forests until recently. In most parts trees are still so abundant that the peasants live in log houses. Long rows of sandy moraines, finding their greatest development in the Valdai Hills, give to some sections a mild relief with charming lakes bordered by pine forests. Most of the land is flat, however, often even marshy, and the rivers wander in circuitous courses. East of the Polish frontier of Russia, the Pripet Marshes are so huge that they form a real barrier between the two countries. Here the zones of European agriculture continue eastward—the fields of barley, flax, and oats, followed southward by rye and potatoes. There are also some meadows for hay, but, although cattle are found everywhere, they are scarce in comparison with the numbers of cattle in western Europe and do not form a characteristic feature of the landscape as they do in Holland, Denmark, and Ireland.

The Black Soil Belt (II-12). More southerly latitudes, a longer summer, and less effective rain characterize the famous Russian black soil belt with Kiev as its representative city. Most of the land is softly rolling, but steep escarpments border the west side of the large southward-flowing rivers. West of the Dnieper the rivers have eroded rather deep valleys in the Podolian Plateau. But this does not destroy the general impression of immense level fields of wheat, which in late summer mantle vast areas with a golden cover, interrupted only here and there by large plots of sugar beets, blue flax, and sunflowers. The dark soils are themselves the product of limited rainfall and of the grass that replaces trees. This grassy cover, where the herds of Asiatic invaders once roamed, has now been replaced by grain fields where Soviet farms mow down the golden heads on which the life of millions of farmers depends. Here whitewashed adobe houses stand in compact groups, replacing the log houses farther north.

The Southern Steppe (II-13). Once more the picture changes, for increasing dryness causes the next strip of Russia to be the dry southern steppe, which lies south and east of the black soil region near the north shores of the Black and Caspian seas. Here also fields have replaced most of the former steppe. Nevertheless, a part of the steppe is still left, and large herds of cattle graze on the flat, grassy plains, which during the hot summer look parched and brown. Small salt lakes, surrounded by saline vegetation, show how dry the country is. The driest part of this southern steppe on the shore of the Caspian is one of Europe's few unproductive regions. Toward the Caucasus, however, the rainfall increases once more. Wheat fields reappear, but corn now enters as the main crop, and the high range of the Caucasus with its snow-capped summits and forested slopes forms a worthy European frontier.

The Central Uplands (III in A42)

South of the Central Lowlands and far less extensive but much more varied, the Central Uplands form an almost continuous zone of basins, plateaus, and mountain ranges from the Atlantic shores of the Iberian Peninsula to Poland. The Spanish portion of these is cut off from the rest by the Pyrenees, which belong to the Alpine section of Europe. Intermediate between the Central Lowlands and the Alpine mountain system, the Central Uplands resemble the Northwestern Uplands in that generally they provide an environment unfriendly to human occupancy. Nevertheless, the fertility and industrial development of the valleys and basins that separate the various subdivisions make up for the inhospitality and sparse population of the higher sections. Here as in the Northwestern Uplands a peneplained surface, referred to as the Hercynian, has been uplifted. It has also been broken, thus supplying many easy routes across it and in this way diminishing its barrier qualities. Beginning at the southeast, the Spanish Meseta is separated from the next section of the Central Uplands—the Central Plateau of France—by the Ebro Valley, the high Pyrenees, and the low Aquitaine Basin. East of the Central Plateau of France the Rhône-Saône Valley, approaching the headwaters of the Seine, cuts across the Central Uplands. Then come the Vosges, Eifel, Ardennes, and other uplands west of the Rhine in France, Germany, and Belgium. The Rhine, with its great "graben" or depressed block of the earth's crust in the south and its famous gorge in the north, provides another route across the Uplands. Next, the Central German Uplands and the Bohemian Plateau present a highly irregular mass of hills and low mountains. The Oder Valley, where it approaches that of the Morava, separates them from the small plateau basin of Łyso Góry in Poland. Far away on the coast of the Black Sea, the most easterly bit of the Central Uplands is found in the low plateau of the Dobruja in Rumania.

The Spanish Meseta (A and B in III, A42). In the Spanish portion of the Central Uplands, mountain ranges enclose an interior basin, the Plateau of Castile. Because of a dividing range, the Sierra de Guadarrama, this has a double character, with the basin of Old Castile in the north and that of New Castile in the south. It would have been allowable to include with these certain other basins of a lowland character, namely those of the Ebro in the north and of Andalusia in the south, but these will be treated with the Alpine system to which they are structurally related. The plateau quality of the Meseta is very evident in the north, east, and south, where steep escarpments rise abruptly from narrow coastal plains or even directly from the sea, as in the north, or else from interior lowlands like the basins just mentioned. In the west there is no such perfect physiographic boundary. The transition from the plateau to the Portuguese coastal plains is more gradual. Nevertheless, broken, rough topography separates the plateau and the plains as well as any mountain range could do, and it has for centuries influenced the location of the boundary between Portugal and Spain.

The Spanish Border Ranges (III-A). When seen from the Bay of Biscay, the Cantabrian Mountains in northwestern Spain rise as a great mountain wall. Because of the marine Western European climate—mild winters, cool summers, and plenty of rain—the scenery is very different from that generally associated with Spain. Densely forested mountain slopes, grassy meadows where cattle graze, fields of corn and rye, individual farmhouses with apple orchards, and coastal towns full of the bustle and noise of an industrial development resulting from coal and the mineral wealth of the hinterland— these things taken together give a picture that is typical of western Europe but supposedly not of Spain. The scarcity of level land and the shortness of the narrow river valleys limit the possibilities of human occupancy, and the straight, wave-beaten coast with its frequent rocky bluffs does not favor seafaring.

In the extreme west, in Galicia, conditions are more favorable, although isolation from the rest of Spain is a handicap. Here the ranges run out into the Atlantic, causing the "rias" type of coast along which long bays invade the land and are protected from winter storms by rocky promontories and coastal islands. At the heads of the bays, broad valleys run inland, causing the general level of the land to be lower than in the Cantabrian Mountains. Hence much more can be cultivated, and prosperous towns and villages line the valleys. Nevertheless, the favorable coastline and the abundance of fish attract the inhabitants to the sea, and here, as on the coasts of the Northwestern Uplands, fishing and navigation are important.

The other border escarpments of Spain, which often take the form of mountain ranges, reflect the summer dryness of the Mediterranean climate. In the west, to be sure, the ranges along the Portuguese frontier are fairly well forested, but along the edge of the Ebro Basin and on the east coast the lower slopes are almost bare. The vegetation has changed completely: gone are the dense forests of the northern mountains; the vegetation is of an open, grassy type with scattered oak trees, or else the trees are replaced by the Mediterranean scrub or maquis, a garden of blossoms during the rainy season but scorched and tawny during the hot, dry summer. Olive oil replaces butter as fat; wine replaces cider as the regional drink. The irrigated fields of wheat and various kinds of tropical fruit in the valleys and coastal plains contrast with the non-irrigated crops in the northern mountains. On the high slopes pines dominate, while the open grassland, or *páramo,* snow-covered in winter, attracts the herds of sheep in summer when the inland steppe is parched by the summer sun.

The Spanish Basins (III-B). Within the frame of mountains that stand on top of the escarpments, the basins or plateaus of Old and New Castile take the form of elevated interior plains. The relief, although generally gentle, changes in quality from the flat eastern parts, where young rocks lie horizontally, to the more rolling west, where older and more varied rocks come to the surface, and the rivers, following the general incline toward the west, have eroded deep canyons. Aridity prevails everywhere except at the highest altitudes, such as the forested hills of the Sierra de Guadarrama, which provide the inhabitants of Madrid with ski grounds in winter and cool shade in summer. Elsewhere marine influences are almost excluded by the mountains. The dryness increases toward the south (in the southern III-B of A42), where "La Mancha," made famous by Cervantes, is almost unproductive and serves only as a feeding ground for sheep in winter. In many parts of the plateau one can often drive full speed for hours over smooth, hard, and almost deserted trunk highways built under the auspices of the dethroned king, but the minor roads are very poor. Here and there, steep, rocky slopes rise precipitously for a few hundred feet to a *mesa,* or table, whose top in turn affords another level surface extending for many miles. In winter the plain is green with young wheat, or red where the soil has been freshly plowed. In rainy weather the villages of stone or untinted adobe look pitifully poor and wretched. But, when the sun shines in the bluest of skies, there is marvelous charm in the distant view of a little town of whitewashed houses, or of an ancient city built around a cathedral or castle which stands out against the clear sky amid an immense plain green with grain or grass and dotted perhaps with grazing flocks of sheep. In summer the plain is brown, the whitewashed houses glare painfully, a cloud of dust hangs over the land, and the air rises quivering from a hot surface whence signs of life have almost disappeared.

The Central Plateau of France (III-C). Between the Garonne Basin and the Rhône Valley lies an upland of a generally rounded shape except for a northward extension west of the Saône Valley. This upland is most impressive when approached from the south. Here above the flat Mediterranean coastal plain, where long sandy bars enclose shallow lagoons, and above the rolling foothills famous for their vineyards, rises the steep wall of the Cévennes. Narrow valleys, the lower slopes planted with olive trees and the upper covered with chestnuts, lead to the top of this high escarpment. From the crest the general level drops very gently toward the north and west as indicated by the river courses, but the general aspect is that of an old surface of erosion studded with gently rounded hills. In the southwest the limestone of Les Causses, the region described by Robert Louis Stevenson in *Travels with a Donkey,* serves only as a dry, bare pasture land for sheep, and only the red soils around the sinkholes can be used for meager crops. Sometimes the plateau is suddenly interrupted by an almost perpendicular drop into a deeply eroded, steep-sided canyon like that of the Tarn River, where a warmer climate permits a sort of narrow oasis with fruit and vegetable gardens between the blindingly white limestone walls.

The old erosion surface mentioned above is also broken by genuine rift valleys forming depressions below the general level, and by frequent volcanoes that have left lava flows and cones. The rifts are illustrated by the fertile croplands of the Limagne, a structural valley through which the Allier flows northward past Clermont-Ferrand until it combines with the Loire. The volcanoes are illustrated by the symmetrical cones (*puys*) of the Auvergne close by on the west, where large herds of cattle graze at high levels. In many places volcanic dikes protrude above the general relief, forming little plateaus bordered by perpendicular walls, such as the famous ancient stronghold of the inhabitants of Gallia against the invading army of Caesar. Elsewhere bizarre volcanic needles stand out sharply. Springs of high mineral content, like the famous one at Vichy, have become resorts where recovery from illness is sought.

Taken as a whole, this complex picture of fertile plains, grassy uplands, and forested ridges may be attractive, but the elevation gives it a raw winter climate, and the relief limits its economic value. Therefore, whereas the sunny valleys were centers of early occupancy, as shown by the prehistoric caves along many streams, the uplands themselves have only a sparse population, one of the most backward of France. From a racial standpoint these uplands stand out because they were used as a refuge in times of migration from the surrounding lowlands. Traces of the ancient Cro-Magnon people, who lived in Europe with the reindeer and buffalo during the Ice Age, can be recognized among the present inhabitants.

The escarpments of the Côte d'Or and of the Plateau of Langres (III-E) project northward and northeastward from the Central Plateau of France, connecting it with the Vosges. Both are part of the outer rim of the Paris Basin, and take the form of a rather steep escarpment facing east or southeast with a gentle slope on the Paris side. On the steeper, sunnier slope the dark grapes of Burgundy bask in the summer sun, while down below in the flat, fertile Saône Valley rich crops are raised and cattle graze on the poplar-bordered river floodplains.

The German Uplands. The French Vosges (III-F) in the south and the Belgian Ardennes (III-G) in the north form the western wing of the upland complex that is combined here with the main part of the German Uplands (III-H). The eastern wing borders the Bohemian Plateau (III-L), although still father east the wooded hills of the Łyso Góry (III-M) show upland conditions and break the monotony of the Polish plains with their wooded slopes.

The German Uplands taken as a whole are many-sided in their topography. Granite massifs have been rounded by ancient glaciers; clear glacial lakes are surrounded by a mantle of conifers; rolling plateaus with moorland vegetation resemble the Northwestern Upland; old volcanoes are still recognizable because of their conical shape; and long, forested ridges enclose fertile lowland depressions.

It is difficult to give an impression of such a region without going into detail, but some generalizations are possible. Perhaps the forests are the most impressive feature. They consist principally of conifers, giving a dark green color to the landscape, but also partly of oak and beech, forming an extension of the former great lowland forest. Narrow valleys, followed by roads and railroads and punctuated by picturesque little villages built along the river courses, wind their way between the forested slopes. Where the valleys widen, the villages grow larger; meadows border the stream, and crops of rye and potatoes are raised on the cleared lower slopes. Often inns and hotels reflect the importance of tourists in summer, when pleasant walks can be taken along shaded paths, and in winter, when there is skiing over upland trails. Wide, open basins, such as that of Thuringia, show a dense population. Small but attractive towns amid fields of golden grain and orchards of richly colored fruit reflect the quiet beauty of the land. Water power, derived first from old-fashioned water wheels and later from large plants fed from lakes held by dams, has fostered manufacturing. First came home industries, producing not only such things as cuckoo clocks and toys, but also tools of great precision such as technical instruments; later came big industries that with their smoke and noise disturb the clear silence of the forests, and ugly blocks of brick houses replaced the old homesteads with their frame architecture. This is especially true along the northern margin, where Europe's main manufacturing region borders the uplands and in many places extends into them, based everywhere on the thick coal layers laid down in ancient geologic times along the old continental border. Along the edge of the Ardennes in France and Belgium; in Westphalia, where the Ruhr, a small branch of the Rhine near Essen, has given its name to one of the world's greatest aggregations of industry; and, farther east in Saxony, huge manufacturing plants and urban developments everywhere invade the upland hills and valleys. They make this upland border a region of modern scientific production, but ruin the former vistas of rural beauty.

Central Europe's most important rivers are associated with this central section of the uplands. The Meuse and Oder border it to the west and east; the Weser is entirely an upland product; and the Elbe from Bohemia breaks through the surrounding mountain wall by way of a beautiful gorge bordered by almost perpendicular walls of sandstone. But the most important of all is the Rhine. From Switzerland it follows the Rhine graben (east of III-F), the wide rift between the Vosges and Black Forest. Protected by higher elevations on every side, this rift valley is central Europe's most favored spot, and many famous cities border the plain. Its carefully cropped lowlands contrast strongly with the forested mountains round about. Out of this graben the Rhine breaks its way in a narrow gorge through the northern part of the Upland until it reaches the North Sea lowlands. The Rhine gorge is Germany's most popular tourist valley. It is so narrow that rocky slopes sometimes rise directly from the swift-flowing river, and rapids have had to be tamed in order to facilitate navigation. Nevertheless, it has had a remarkable influence on human life and activity. The almost continuous procession of steamers and long barges pulled by tugs, the numerous villages and towns built along the banks, the railroads and roads on both sides that often have to be carried through rocky cuttings or even tunnels, the steeply terraced slopes covered thickly with vineyards producing the famous Rhine wine, the ruins of ancient castles that were once strongholds on one of Europe's most famous trade routes, and at the top of the slopes on both sides the gently rolling upland with its fields of grain—all these combine to make the Rhine a subject for song and folklore, an object of national pride and reverence.

The Bohemian Basin (between III and L in A42). This last main section of the Central Uplands does not differ greatly from the preceding one. Like the Iberian Peninsula, it is enclosed within a mountain frame, open only at the south where the ancient rocks of the Bohemian massif border the young deposits of the Alpine piedmont. These densely forested mountain walls make the climate of the interior basin somewhat continental, but they are not high enough to hamper the utilization of the land. On the contrary, agriculture is highly developed, for the black soils are of great fertility, and the fields of grain and sugar beets show that man has taken advantage of such favorable conditions.

The basin is not a flat product of sedimentation like part of the Meseta, but shows the rolling relief of an ancient surface that is largely intact but partly warped and broken, as is evident from many signs of volcanic action. The result is a pleasant picture of forested ridges and beautiful valleys, of rolling hills cultivated with fields of grain and sugar beets, of cities whose ancient towers border the river courses and which are surrounded by vegetable gardens and orchards. In some of the valleys, just as in the French Central Plateau, world-renowned spas have developed; their existence is based on mineral springs. Here, as in Germany, manufacturing, using the power of coal and lignite, has entered the rural picture, but it is based principally upon the former home industries. So the Central Uplands, in spite of their variety of relief and scenery, represent a unit, contrasting strongly with the flat or rolling lowlands north of them, whereas lesser elevation and smoother forms differentiate them from the Alpine System to the south.

· 5 ·

The Alpine Division

Complexity of the Alpine Division (IV in A42)

Because of the great complexity of relief and consequently of human activities, the southern division of Europe, the Alpine region, is difficult to treat as a unit. In many ways it is more a geological than a geographic division, but one great fact combines geology and geography—the fact that the relief of the mountains dominates human activities. Mountains enter everywhere into the explanation of man's activities. They may be high ranges or isolated blocks, they may be greatly dissected or show an almost undisturbed plateau character, they may enclose wide fertile valleys, frame intermontane basins, or border coastal plains, but they are always there and put their mark on man's occupance.

In contrast to the sparsely populated uplands of northwestern and even central Europe, or to the crowded Central Lowlands, the distribution of population here is very uneven. Europe's highest non-industrial densities are found in some of the coastal lowlands, and well-populated intermontane plains and valleys are often surrounded by high mountains almost completely devoid of human settlement. In this way, contrasts in man's distribution and mode of life are the characteristic anthropogeographic feature of the vast Alpine region, and it is these contrasts that justify the treatment of this zone as a unit. In this treatment the description will proceed from west to east, starting with the Sierra Nevada in southern Spain, following the Italian Apennines from south to north, curving around with the great arc of the Alps, and then proceeding along each of the two Alpine wings (the Carpathian-Balkan and the Dinaric-Pindus ranges) that surround the Danube Basin and give rise to the complex topography of the Balkan Peninsula. Finally the description will take up two isolated portions of the Alpine region: the Pyrenees, which are thrust like a wedge between two parts of the older Central Uplands, and the Crimea and the Caucasus, which represent the more northerly of the two lines along which the mountains of Europe merge into those of Asia.

Southern Spain. The Spanish Sierra Nevada (IV-1 in A42) stands out best when seen from the Mediterranean. In summer, above the parched coastal hills rises a great mountain range, partly hidden from the eye by the omnipresent haze. Snow covers the higher parts. As one climbs toward the mountains, the green color of grass and forests on the slopes contrasts strongly with the bare brownness of the hills lower down and is very different from the dull sage green of the neighboring olive orchards. In the valleys and on the narrow coastal plains, mountain rivers, fed by melting snow, bring water that can be used for irrigation. In this way oases of almost subtropical character nestle at the mouths of valleys and extend along the valleys far into the mountains. These Spanish oases, with their abundant citrus fruits, are almost the only part of Europe where dates ripen and sugar cane profitably replaces the beets of more temperate regions. Wheat makes the Andalusian lowland—the depression (dotted in A42) between the Sierra Nevada and the Meseta—a sea of waving golden grain in spring, for it ripens early, helped by the winter rains. On the hills and lower slopes, grapevines form bright green patches at that season. Olive groves, stretching almost continuously for miles and interrupted only by the whitewashed homes of country proprietors, retain the same color all the year. On the driest slopes, almond groves form lovely spots of pink while winter is still in full force farther north.

The Sierra Nevada contains the last strongholds of the Moors. Everywhere the utilization of the land still reflects the influence of these African invaders who brought prosperity and culture because in their desert home they had learned how to use a limited supply of water.

Mediterranean Islands. The Sierra Nevada breaks off in the east against the waters of the Mediterranean, but remnants of its former continuation appear in the form of islands. First among these are the mountainous little Balearic Isles fringed with coastal palm gardens in the blue setting of the sea. Sardinia and Corsica are similar remnants of an old land connection, but of a much larger size. Geologically most parts of them are similar to the Central Uplands, with mountain blocks and, especially in Sardinia, intervening lowlands. Nevertheless, in eastern Corsica the steep Alpine ranges reappear, and almost perpendicular rock walls border the coast. The isolation of these islands is the result partly of the mountain environment and partly of the malaria that infests the unhealthy plains. This makes them very backward, but the swamps are being drained, roads are opening the mountain uplands, and modern progress is invading regions until recently ruled by banditry and family feuds.

The most eastern and largest of these islands is Sicily. Along the northern coast the mountains rise abruptly, forcing the dense population to cluster in the valley bottoms or else cling to slopes so steep that a vast amount of terracing is needed. Nevertheless, luxuriant groves of oranges, lemons, and other fruits, as well as vegetable gardens and fields of wheat, make the mountain slopes appear very fertile and beautiful. The culminating point of Sicily is the volcano of Etna. It is a low, blue cone, perhaps with a wisp of smoke, when seen from the sea to the north. Near at hand, from the rich Catanian plain or the Strait of Messina, its densely populated but tree-clad lower slopes present a wonderful picture of fertility. South of the northern backbone of mountains, Sicily consists mainly of treeless hills and plains where wheat is the main crop except where vineyards and irrigated orchards surround mud-walled villages.

Italy. The next Alpine region is the Italian Peninsula, of which the Apennines (IV-3), a continuation of the African Atlas, are the mountain backbone. Interrupted only by the narrow Strait of Messina separating Sicily from the mainland, they form a great arc around the deep depression of the Tyrrhenian Sea and terminate as the southern part of the horseshoe-shaped mountain frame of the Po Basin.

The Apennines themselves are not very impressive, since in only a few places do they really attain a mountainous character. For the greater part a gradual slope leads to a rolling upland that, because of its raw climate, is not attractive to man. Shepherds guarding large flocks of sheep, and lumbermen exploiting the last remnants of a formerly widespread forest, are often the sole signs of human activity. Only the valleys show a dense population. Easy passes facilitate traffic between the two sides, so that the Apennines are not a complete barrier. Nevertheless, they serve not only to isolate the east coast, but also to make it drier and less habitable than the west. Although the mountains usually lack impressiveness, the bordering hills and lowlands make up for this. On the Adriatic side human occupancy is limited where bare limestone tablelands decrease the arable land; nevertheless, some broad lowlands with large fields of grain and vast olive orchards make Apulia, near the heel of Italy, a densely populated region.

Along the western border of the Apennines, Italy reaches its full beauty. Rocky peninsulas and islands, narrow coastal plains, broad river valleys, and softly sloping hills give a picture full of variety. Three examples will illustrate the variety: (1) the region around Naples, (2) the lower Tiber plain, and (3) Tuscany.

(1) Many people think that Naples has the most perfect setting of any European city. The bay of Naples is semicircular and is bordered by two wings of rocky uplands that break up finally into islands. The bare rock in its natural color rises steeply from the deep blue sea. Steep trails climb to the rolling upland where the white houses of the villages are surrounded by gardens full of fruit and vegetables, and grapes and olives grow on the terraced rocky slopes. The Roman emperors had pleasure gardens here; artist colonies still testify to the rich color and beauty of the scenery. The inner side of the bay is closed by the perfect cone of Vesuvius, from the crater of which smoke rises frequently. Numerous eruptions have played havoc in the neighborhood; lava flows have destroyed towns and villages, volcanic ash has sometimes covered them completely, but the addition of young soil gives the lower slope and coastal plain an almost inexhaustible fertility. Hence Europe's densest agricultural population is found here; and an almost continuous sequence of towns encircles the mountains. The inhabitants combine the grain and fruit of the soil with *frutti del mare* (fruit of the sea). And finally the city of Naples, a curious mixture of modernity on a picturesque, almost oriental, background, extends along the bay shore, and suburbs climb up the slopes of the neighboring hills.

(2) How different is the setting of Rome! The Tiber at this point has already entered the wide open plain of the Campagna Romana, which borders the sea. In its frame of fertile hills and volcanic cones, the plain presents a picture of emptiness and desolation. The straight, flat coastline offers no attraction to fishing or trade. And amid this, where little hills protect the plain against floods from the river and facilitate its crossing, rises Rome, the Eternal City. But the picture of the Campagna Romana is changing—before and after World War II government and modern science were reclaiming its marshes and changing the grasslands into fields of grain. The malarial mosquito has been virtually eradicated through drainage of the marshes in which it bred and through use of insecticides such as DDT. New towns have arisen, and modern harbor facilities are bringing new life to the coast.

(3) The last example is Tuscany, the Florentine country of sunny hills and fertile valleys, of dark blue crater lakes and rocky volcanic cones. Elevation and a more northern location temper the summer

dryness. Grain fields and green meadows fill the valleys and depressions; olives and grapes are cultivated on the slopes. But the most typical part of the picture is the numerous towns. Their location on the crests of ridges or of steep lava dikes, and their medieval walls, show how protection against attack dominated their historical development.

Although the lowlands of Italy are usually of very limited size, the large Po Basin (IV-4) in the north is of outstanding significance. In its mountain frame this plain, which was once a gulf of the Adriatic and is still growing in size, represents Italy's major region of production. Its rivers in their lower courses flow between natural levees and above the general level, and are still pushing the Po Delta out into the Adriatic. The scenery is rather monotonous, with fields of rice, wheat, and corn bordered by mulberry trees and green meadows where cattle graze near the rivers. But on clear days the surrounding mountains are visible, and the Alpine glaciers, the providers of the power on which Italy's manufacturing is based, sparkle white in the sunlight while the towers of medieval castles and cathedrals stand out against the blue sky as reminders of the time when this was the center of European culture.

The True Alpine Region

Rounding the Ligurian coast north of Genoa, the Apennines merge into the Alps (IV-5). From the sheltered coast of the Riviera these famous mountains sweep in a huge curve through southeastern France and Switzerland and diverge in Austria into two branches, the Carpathians and the Dinaric System. The Jura, detached from the Alps in northwestern Switzerland, and the wide foreland bordering the Alps on the north in Switzerland and Germany, are genetically part of the Alpine System. The Alps constitute Europe's greatest mountain range. Throughout most of their length, from the south-facing slopes of the Riviera up to the place where the Danube valley separates the Alps and the Carpathians, the main divide is above the perennial line of snow, and the highest parts are clad in an eternal mantle of glacial ice.

The Jura (IV-6 in A42). In the limited space available in this book it is impossible to give a complete description of the Alps. Therefore, a rather typical cross section, from Basel in the north to Milan in the south, is chosen as a sample of Alpine scenery and human responses. Basel is located at one of the important foci in the relief of Europe. Toward the north opens the wide, flat Rhine graben, bordered by the wooded slopes of the Black Forest and the Vosges. A gap toward the west, the Gate of Burgundy, connects the Rhine Valley with that of the Saône. South of Basel the long ridges of the Jura present the first sign of Alpine action, but around their eastern end there is an easy route to the Alpine foreland where most of the Swiss have their homes.

The Jura Mountains resemble the Folded Appalachian System in the United States. Synclinal valleys are separated by anticlinal ridges but are united by narrow gorges, the outlets of the drainage of the interior basins. Here, too, as in the United States, the folded ranges are bordered on the west by a plateau where the layers are still horizontal and in which the main rivers on their way toward the Saône have cut deep gorges.

The Swiss Jura may lack the majestic splendor of the Alps, but it has many scenic attractions. The wide basins between the ridges are mainly grassland, a result of a moist, raw climate. Towns and villages have used the power of the streams for home industries in order to provide work during the long winter, and here was born the Swiss watch industry, which finally outgrew its local origin and became a world factor. Rocky trails lead up the wooded limestone slopes of the ridges toward the broad, rolling upper surface where cattle graze on flower-covered meadows. The highest ridges are located farthest south. Seen from the Swiss Plateau still farther south, the Jura looks like a great mountain wall hemming in the plateau as far as the eye can see. On the high summits the view southward toward the Alps is beautiful. On clear winter days, when the plateau below is covered by fog, a sea of clouds reaches from the Jura to the Alps, whose white peaks with blue shadows stand out in full beauty against the sky.

In spite of the easy route around its eastern end, the Jura is a real barrier to transportation, for its continuous sequence of anticlinal ridges offers no direct passages. Tunnels have been made to overcome this handicap, for the Jura lies athwart the main road of commerce between northwestern Europe and Italy.

The Swiss Plateau (7 in A42). The low plateau where most of the Swiss have their homes was once a deep water-filled depression between the Alps and Jura, a narrow offshoot of the ocean reaching far eastward. But the rivers and glaciers laid down their deposits, and uplift finally left the region as a part of the Alpine Foreland with an elevation of 2,000 to 3,000 feet.

The Swiss Plateau may appear rather flat and uniform when seen from a bordering mountain summit, but in reality it shows a very pleasant variety. Broad valleys widened by the Ice Age glaciers, which once descended from the Alps, are flanked by softly sloping divides. Most of the land has been made productive. Fields of rye, oats, potatoes, root crops, and hay checker most of the country aside from the divides, which are still forested. Apple trees border the roads and surround large farmhouses, which stand apart by themselves. The neighboring barns shelter well-fed cattle that provide the well-known dairy products. But most of the Swiss live in the villages and towns where factories use the power of the Alpine rivers.

The main attraction of the Swiss Plateau is its lakes, drowned parts of river valleys often extending into the real Alps. Around the outer or northern end of a typical lake, rounded, but rather steep, slopes reach down to the blue-green waters on which white steamers, locally called "swallows," glide gracefully from one landing to the next. Villages border the shore; chalets stand in orchards that in blossoming time offer an eldorado of color. The slopes themselves are mainly in grass, whereas the deep-cut valleys are wooded. Higher up, conifers prevail, and their dark green color sharply accentuates the line of the ridge against the sky. If the lake runs east and west, the warm north side, facing the sun, is covered with terraced vineyards and orchards or is used for vegetables and flowers, whereas the cool south side, facing away from the sun, is left to grass and forest.

Toward the mountains the picture of a typical lake changes. The slopes beside the lake become steeper and higher; perpendicular walls of rock often rise directly from the lake, forcing the roads and railroads to betake themselves to tunnels. Villages are now restricted to the deltas or alluvial cones at river outlets. To find other habitations one must climb far up to the Alpine meadows that cover the terraces at the tops of the rocky slopes. Still higher up, white snow and glaciers sparkle in the sunlight. Once more, as in Holland, there is a paradise of color—the blue-green of the lake, the dark green of the conifers broken by bare black rocks, the light green meadows, the white snow, and the blue sky above.

But this picture of the Swiss lakes is typical only of ideal conditions. Many days are rainy, and strong west winds sweep the waves against the drenched shores. In winter, unpleasant fogs often hang over the plateau, and only the higher slopes rise above this cloudy mantle.

The Alps Themselves. South of the plateau are the real Alps. The lower front ranges are rounded by glaciers, but they are rockier and much higher than the hills of the plateau. The slopes are still mostly forested, but grassy terraces interrupt the pines, and, above the tree line, flowers form a colorful carpet on the dark background of green grass. The valleys are still wide and open because they were scoured into a U-shape by glaciers. Some crops can still be raised, but grass prevails in most places. The valley roads follow the fast-flowing rivers from village to village, where weather-stained wooden farmhouses with overhanging roofs and balconies on all sides surround the churches.

Nearer the heart of the mountains the signs of human influence become less. The valleys become narrower and stonier, the slopes steeper, and glaciers form a part of the picture. Man comes in only temporarily, following his cattle along the grassy terraces up to the snow line, or walking up a winding mountain trail to a cabin whence the next day's ascent of an important peak will be made. In winter the man on skis draws his long zigzag trail across the snow. Here the lover of the Alps finds his haven. Sitting before the little cabin in the evening, tired after a day of climbing, he looks over the sea of ice-capped summits glowing in the sunset while dark shadows hide the valleys. The mountain silence is interrupted only by the occasional noise of a falling rock or a snow avalanche, or by the whistling of the marmots who sit upright before their rocky holes. The Alps may have been partly spoiled because "tourism" exerts such a charm upon all sorts of people; modern hotels may look strange in the mountain environment, and some summits can be reached while sitting comfortably in the well-cushioned seat of a modern railroad; but the Alps are still beautiful, and many sections are remote and peaceful enough to satisfy the most exacting lover of nature.

The High Alps in Switzerland take the form of a double range separated by the longitudinal valley of the Rhône-Rhine. The French Alps show this same double tendency, whereas in Austria two longitudinal valleys separate the mountains into three high ranges. The longitudinal valleys, a product probably of warping, but re-modeled by rivers and glaciers, form a distinct unit in the Alpine region. Even amid the higher peaks, they are comparatively wide with flat bottoms that can be used for crops, or at higher elevations for hay. Mountain walls to the north and south give a dry touch to the climate, so that the sun-facing northern slopes are among the best regions for grapes. Apricots also ripen, and on the high terraces the larger amount of sun favors the location of health resorts. Power plants are located where the mountain streams leave the side valleys that lead far into the mountain core and tumble down the sharp drop toward the over-deepened main valley. Railroads use these major valleys as convenient places from which to cut through the Alps by means of tunnels. Numerous villages and little towns show that the density of population is relatively high in the valleys although very low outside them.

In Switzerland the second or southern high range is the most prominent. Great peaks sculptured by glaciers rise steeply out of a rather high and relatively flat ice-clad surface. Far below this surface the deep river valleys form ribbons of green trees and grass, and glacial tongues extend into the zone of human occupancy.

The southern slope of the Alps is rather abrupt, and the low plain of the Po is only 50 miles in a straight line from the crest of this second high Alpine range. The steep inclination, together with the heavy precipitation, has resulted in a much-dissected relief. Deeply eroded valleys with steep, terraced slopes lead down toward the blue lakes that, as in the north, occupy the portions of the valleys adjacent to the plain. But the picture here is different. Favored by the protection of the northern mountains and by the greater amount of sunshine of a climate that has here become partly Mediterranean, the Alpine piedmont is almost subtropical. The shores of the lakes display gardens of almost luxuriant vegetation where oranges and lemons can actually be raised in the latitude of St. Paul and Minneapolis. Corn ripens on the valley bottoms, and grapevines climb high up the slopes where majestic chestnut trees are typical. Early spring, when the mountains are still snow covered and the light green foliage and pink blossoms of the fruit trees are reflected in the deep blue lakes, is most beautiful here. But fall almost rivals spring, for brilliant autumn colors merge into the new snow on the high slopes while the gray-green color of the evergreen borders the waterfront.

Although the picture of the Alps varies according to local conditions, their influence on human life and activity is everywhere much the same. Man in this mountain environment has to face many hardships. Arable land is scarce and, except on some valley bottoms, infertile. Because the Alpine meadows where the cattle graze in summer are far away from the regular villages, the use of temporary dwellings is necessary. Often the villages are a long distance from the main roads of commerce and from the markets where the farmer has to sell his surplus and buy what he needs. Moreover, the summers are short, and the long winter greatly limits human activity. The result is a group of hardy people fond of their mountains and eager to defend their freedom. Out of these mountains came the spirit of democracy on which the Swiss Republic is based; from them came such men as Andreas Hofer, the Tirolese hero of Napoleonic days, who gave his life for the freedom of his land.

The isolation arising from the rugged relief of the Alps is evident in many diverse ways. Thus in eastern Switzerland the Rhaeto-Romans, a remnant of an ancient ethnographic group, still preserve most of their linguistic and cultural characteristics. In a similar way, in one of the highest villages of the French Alps there is a small group of Protestants whose ancestors escaped the furor of the French St. Bartholemew period and continued to follow their own creed.

In spite of all this the Alps have been remarkably unimpressive as a means of separating northern Europe from the Mediterranean. All through history, people have faced the danger of crossing the high Alps when it was necessary. Armies, for example, have frequently crossed them, from the time when Hannibal traversed them with his elephants until World War II, when large German forces with heavy equipment fought in Italy. Furthermore, political boundaries have not been located on the crest line of the Alps but have been pushed beyond it at different times and places. The Po Basin was for centuries under Austrian rule, and only as recently as 1920 were the frontiers of Italy carried up to the Alpine summits. This leaves only the Swiss canton of Ticino as a southern offshoot of northern rule.

Modern means of transportation prevail in the Alps in spite of high expenses; tunnels connect low valleys on opposite sides of the ranges, leaving only a comparatively small incline up to the tunnel entrance; modern motor roads wind up to the passes known long ago to ancient merchants, and cars sweep swiftly past the summit hospices where once the weary traveler found a welcome refuge. At the Simplon Tunnel, for example, one ascends very gently and easily to a height of 2,313 feet and then travels 12 miles on a level through the tunnel instead of toiling up to a height of 6,592 feet at the top of the pass.

The Carpathian Curve (8 in A42). The Vienna Basin, a structural depression through which the Danube breaks its way on its eastward course, marks the transition from the Alps to the Carpathians. Beyond it to the east, sandstone ranges of soft rounded forms, completely forested except for some high elevations, curve in a large half-circle from Vienna far around Hungary to the Iron Gate. The Carpathians lack the beauty and splendor of the Alps, and only the High Tatra in the west-central part is lofty enough so that glacial forms once more prevail and steep, ice-polished walls of cirques enclose mountain lakes surrounded by stately conifers.

Inside the eastern bulge of the Carpathians, where the mountains start their horseshoe curve around the Rumanian plain of Walachia, is located the Transylvanian Basin (9), which is separated from the Hungarian lowlands (15) by the Bihor Plateau (10). The rolling topography of this Rumanian Basin, with its alternating woodland and fields, contrasts sharply with the dark green slopes of the surrounding mountains. Narrow passes and gorges open through the mountains toward the south where the steeply dissected forested mountain slope gives way abruptly to the flat plains of Walachia, which in summer present a sea of ripening wheat and corn.

The northern foot of the Carpathians is bordered by a wide foreland. It begins beyond the Moravian Gate, which lies a hundred miles north of Vienna, and connects the fertile valley of the Morava with the northern lowland plains. Then it circles around through the Plateau of Podolia. This part of Russia is dissected by northward-flowing rivers and is forested on the higher divides. Most of it is cultivated, and the rich, dark soils produce crops of wheat, corn, and tobacco. The many agricultural settlements are surrounded by orchards and vegetable gardens. The little whitewashed, mudwalled, thatched cottages of the villages are very picturesque; but one feels that as one goes eastward the prosperous, progressive part of Europe is fast being left behind.

Taken as a whole, the Carpathians, in spite of a number of rather easy crossings used by roads and railroads, constitute a barrier separating two densely populated lowlands. The barrier is a narrow, almost empty zone, in which only the ax of the lumberman and the barking of the shepherd dog break the silence of the forest. During the First World War this forest barrier stopped the advance of the Russian armies that threatened to invade the fertile croplands of the Danube Basin.

The Balkan Mountains (13 in A42). The Carpathian Mountains are separated from the Balkans by the Iron Gate, where the Danube breaks through the mountain wall by way of a winding gorge. This gorge is often mentioned as Europe's historical entrance from the east, but the narrow valley is even now a handicap, and the railroads have to use another break in the mountains just north of it. The

Balkan range, the end of the northern Alpine wing, is much like the
Carpathians. Passes are few, and the relief is rugged for some distance on each side of them. Thus the mountains with their forests
and grasslands make a pronounced separation between the grain fields
on the north and the more southern valleys where vineyards and rose
gardens show a response to a more protected location and a milder
climate.

The Dinaric Wing of the Alpine System (11 in A42). At the eastern end of the Alps proper, there is a region of a totally different aspect. The eastern coast of the Adriatic Sea shows a distinctly Mediterranean character. Rows of islands running parallel to the coast
are remnants of partly drowned border ranges. The rocky coast,
where towns of ancient fame are surrounded by gardens of subtropical luxuriance, rivals the Norwegian coast in scenic beauty. But a
white limestone wall of mountains rises almost immediately from
the shore, and a dry, inhospitable karst plateau replaces the coastal
oasis. Here the bare limestone gives rise to one of the most unproductive parts of Europe. It is often so white that the country is
almost as dazzling in summer as when deep snows cover it in winter.
Only in the lower limestone depressions can *terra rossa,* or red soil,
be found for wheat and corn. Only there do little villages break
the otherwise almost total emptiness of the plateau. Undrained hollows of the typical karst formation are common. Some streams
plunge into deep holes dissolved in the limestone, and in many
places the water that flows into the cultivated depressions disappears
underground. It emerges in great springs after flowing many miles
in underground channels. Some such springs burst out under the
sea along the coast and provide sweet water in the midst of the ocean
brine.

Southward in Albania the limestone ceases to exercise so dominant
a control over the relief. Here the Dinaric System reaches its highest
elevations, and peaks that were once glaciated rise high above the
upper limit of the forest. Lower border ranges separate the main
chain from a swampy coastal plain, and fertile valley basins closed
by deep gorges offer advantageous living conditions although mountain isolation has caused cultural backwardness.

Greek Mountains and Basins. The southern continuation of the
Dinaric System, the Pindus ranges (12), passes through Greece, bends
toward Asia Minor, and strikes out across the Aegean Sea in lines
of islands. Faults have broken the curved mountain frame, and the
resulting relief is very complex. The whole region is divided into in-

dividual blocks separated by depressions. Some of the depressions form the typical Greek basins in which little city-states grew up of old. Long slopes of alluvial material spread out from the base of the mountains and merge into a plain. The upper, gravelly part of such a slope and the adjacent mountain slopes are green with grass and gay with flowers for a short time in spring, but during most of the year they are brown and bare—fit only for the pasturage of sheep and goats. Higher up, the mountains are scantily forested in some places, but the former forests and even the soil that supported them are now largely gone. Nevertheless, wherever springs supply water, the mountain sides are terraced for wheat, grapes, and figs. Olives and some grain are raised without irrigation, and flat-roofed villages of mud or stone appear. Down in the plains where the soil does not become dry so quickly, larger fields and larger villages support the main population. Some depressions have been drowned by the sea and give rise to the sequence of bays and gulfs that is so characteristic of Greece. Indented coasts where a colorful mountain wall rises steeply out of the sea, rocky promontories of fantastic shapes, high mountain blocks where goats look for food on the once forested but now often bare slopes, and also fertile valleys and basins with fields of wheat supplemented by vineyards and olive trees on the bordering hills—all these together make Greece.

Because of the many indentations, the coast is generally near at hand, and from the mountain tops the blue sea forms a background for the local panorama. Islands border the land. The beautiful Ionian Islands, where once the German emperor sought relaxation, flank the coast on the west. In the Aegean the numerous islands, some large and some mere whitish rocks with patches of green in the blue setting of the sea, represent what is left of the former link connecting the Pindus with the mountains of Asia Minor. It is easy to see why here, as in the Northwestern Uplands, the limitations of human activity imposed by hostile relief of the land impel man to look toward the sea for his main field of interest. The ancient Greek culture was marine in character and spread out along the coast of the eastern Mediterranean. Today Greek fishing boats, like those of old, still sail out to catch the fish so valuable to the Greeks as a food. Greek vessels still interconnect the many coastal settlements isolated in their mountain frame, or sail to the surrounding islands and coasts where Greek influence prevails. Greece and Norway have followed similar paths of development because the sea gave what the land missed—a unifying element.

The Hungarian Basin (15 in A42).   Between the two Alpine wings discussed above, and enclosed entirely by them, lies the Danube Basin or Alföld.   Once a great inland water body, it was filled by alluvial river deposits and drained by way of the Iron Gate.   Now only a few shallow lakes can be considered remnants of the former large body of water.   An offshoot of the Alps, a long range of hills, separates the Little Hungarian Plain between Vienna and Budapest from the Great Hungarian Plain south and east of Budapest.   Above Budapest the Danube River breaks through these hills in a beautiful narrow valley bordered by forested slopes.   Otherwise, the relief is very flat; and the rivers, bordered by wide floodplains, wind slowly over the level surface.   Signs of a dry continental climate appear: sand dunes and open steppes, which once attracted the Hungarian invaders with their herds of stock.   But the days of extensive utilization of the land for wandering herds and flocks are over.   Only here and there is a small part of the steppe, or "puszta," still left for such use. The fertile soil is now largely cultivated, and the plain in early summer presents a pleasant picture of immense fields of wheat and corn while vineyards cover the sandy hills.   The population is concentrated in large rural settlements; castles of the Hungarian nobility reflect the former feudal system.   One of the most typical features is long villages built along a single shady street, where ditches border the roadway, and the little whitewashed houses are surrounded by a few fruit trees and flowers.

The Balkan Peninsula.   Compressed between the Dinaric System in the west and the Balkan range in the east, the mountains of Serbia and Macedonia show the effects of pressure.   South of the Danube the relief is still gentle, with only here and there volcanic extrusions forming isolated mountains.   Prosperous-looking villages surrounded by gardens of plum trees lie between gently rising slopes on which cornfields take most of the available space.

Southward the elevation increases.   Steep mountain blocks, snow-covered in winter but in summer the feeding ground of sheep and goats, border deep depressions that were once lakes but are now filled with alluvial soils providing rich crops for the inhabitants of the many towns and villages.   But these basins have only limited possibilities for production.   Mountain massifs, of which Rhodope (14) is the chief, surround most of them completely, permitting an outlet for the drainage only by way of narrow gorges.   Thus here, as in Albania, isolation is the major factor.   This region is the meeting place of Serbs, Bulgarians, Albanians, and Greeks; Turks and Jews live in the cities, and Macedonians come into conflict with all the other peoples. Hence this region is an ethnographic as well as a physiographic puzzle and is still a great danger point of Europe. From quarrels among these isolated groups, always ready to fight, war has spread over Europe and may spread again.

The Isolated Pyrenees (16 in A42). Outside the main Alpine System there are a few ranges that are like it in their relief and origin, and hence should be described at this point. One of these, the Pyrenees, lies in the far west and forms a continuous mountain wall separating the Iberian Peninsula from the rest of Europe. Scarcely interrupted by accessible passes and pierced in only two places by railroad tunnels, the Pyrenees are an ideal "natural" boundary. In the west the Basques, a remnant people of ancient times, have survived as a group in the forested mountain environment, protected against French and Spanish cultural advance. Farther east the small state of Andorra has survived in an inaccessible upper valley set in a frame of mountains. A rough, mountainous region, in which aridity still further diminishes the productivity, borders the Pyrenees on the Spanish side in Catalonia. There a dry steppe vegetation covers the Ebro Basin (17), and crops can be raised only under irrigation. But the Catalonian coastal ranges, shutting off this Ebro Basin from the sea, present a typical Mediterranean climate with cork oaks and olive trees on the slopes and grain fields, vineyards, and orchards surrounding the many industrial towns and villages.

The Isolated Caucasus and Urals. Like the Pyrenees in the west, the Caucasus (19 in A42) with its extension in the Crimean Peninsula lies outside the Alpine ranges and is not an integral part of them. The Yaila Mountains or Crimean Alps (18) are not of great elevation, and their major significance is climatic. The protection that they render in winter against the cold winds from the interior gives the lovely mountain coast a climate somewhat comparable with that of the Riviera. The tremendous wall of the Caucasus shuts Europe off from the adjacent Near East. As a barrier it is almost perfect. No railway crosses it, although both ends are skirted by rail lines. The high mountain scenery resembles that of the Alps, but the peoples are highly diverse.

Finally, the low, rounded, forested Urals (20 in A42), with many easy gaps through which the railroads connect the two parts—Asiatic and European—of the Soviet Union, set a limit to Europe in the east. The inclusion of these hills in this grouping is simply a matter of convenience, since they actually are Hercynian in origin, like the

Central Uplands shown in Group III in A42, whereas the true Alpine folds were formed much later in geological time—the Tertiary. However, like the true Alpine ranges, the Urals are a long, rather continuous range, extending from the Arctic island of Novaya Zemlya well toward the Caspian Sea. Their barrier function—for either man or climatic influences—is slight, but they are a rich storehouse of minerals and are generally heavily forested; however, in the north the tundra dominates, and in the south dryness causes forest to give way to steppe.

· 6 ·
Soils and Vegetation

Factors Influencing Soils and Vegetation

The complexity of the geology and relief of Europe has been shown in the preceding three chapters. In view of the effects of complicated landforms on climate, and the effects of climate, in turn, on soils and vegetation, it is only to be expected that complexity should characterize European soils and vegetation.

Five major natural factors largely determine the character of soils: climate, relief (or slope), plants and animals, parent material, and time. Man and his activities have also influenced the character of most soils. If the quality or quantity of any one of the factors differs from one place to another, the nature of the respective soils likewise differs. The difference might be in the amount of precipitation, in the kind of vegetation growing on the soil, or in the number of micro-organisms present in the soil itself. Whatever the difference might be, it is reflected in the soil. Obviously then, in an area such as Europe, where many differences appear in small horizontal distances, a great variety of soils results. An American plainsman, accustomed to relative uniformity of soils over vast sections of the Great Plains, for example, might be unprepared for the diversity of European soils.

Because Europe has been occupied by man for so many thousands of years and because man has cleared forests, plowed and fertilized the soil, planted a variety of crops in a variety of combinations, dammed rivers, and otherwise altered the land and the soil-forming environment over such a long period of time, it is almost impossible to determine the original nature of certain soils. In the Low Countries, some soils that were originally infertile and acid have been managed so skillfully that they now produce some of the highest yields per acre in the world. In some parts of the Mediterranean, on the other hand, much land that produced well two thousand years ago has been ruined by soil erosion. In some of the best French vineyards the soil has actually been compounded according to a formula worked out over centuries of trial and error, until just the right combination has been reached to produce exactly the desired quality of grape. In the Netherlands, almost useless land and reclaimed sea bottom have been turned into productive farms by extensive mixing of lower layers with surface layers and by subsequent chemical treatment. Thus, the influence of man on the soils of this long-occupied continent is great. Starvation would have stalked Europe years ago had there not been the ingenious management of soils that is typical of many countries.

Some of the same factors that influence soils also influence vegetation: climate, relief, animals, time, and man. In addition, the character of vegetation is influenced by soils and plant species present. Again, then, complexity is to be expected, and again the long human occupation of the land has had profound effects. Whereas by far the greater part of the continent was forested by the time the human population reached any considerable numbers—that is, after disappearance of the last ice sheet—vast expanses of former forest land are now cleared and devoted to crops. Pressure of population has forced the forest off most soils that are capable of growing crops, until now, with minor exceptions, only the higher elevations, very poor soils, or higher latitudes support extensive woodlands. In central Europe, economic necessity has encouraged man to replace slow-growing deciduous trees with faster-growing conifers. Use of the forests is more fully discussed in the next chapter. The grasslands, which reach their greatest development in the western Soviet Union, have likewise been greatly altered, as have the prairies of the United States. Vast expanses of steppe have been put under the plow, until virtually none of the more humid steppe remains in its virgin state.

Since, broadly speaking, many environmental influences are the same for both soils and vegetation, and since they influence each other, it is convenient and geographically sound to consider them together. Certain general zonal groups of soil correspond well with certain general plant associations, although there are, of course, discrepancies.

Soils and Vegetation in Relation to Economic-Cultural Zones

Curiously enough, the areas of naturally most fertile soil are not found in the zone of highest economic-cultural development as shown in A15. The discussion in this chapter reveals that the most fertile soils—that is, those with the richest natural supply of plant nutrients—are actually found in the B and C zones, and that Europe A has had to devote enormous amounts of energy to management of soils because their natural fertility was low.

In addition, such factors as transportation, distance to markets, and scale of world prices, to say nothing of the increasing use of fertilizers, have deprived the soil of much of its determinative influence, especially in progressive western Europe. In the eastern countries, however, the soils have been drawn upon for generations with little return in fertilizers, and there the density of population, but not the degree of economic-cultural development, is a fair index of the natural soil fertility. In the 1930's, the Soviet government undertook a vigorous program of soil improvement; and after Soviet control was extended to the eastern European satellite countries, similar programs were announced for some of them. The results cannot be reliably determined, however, because of Soviet restrictions on such information as crop yields. The value of "sample" figures occasionally mentioned is, of course, doubtful.

There is an interesting correlation between the areas of mixed forest and advanced economic-cultural development, indicating that the general mixed forest environment is sufficiently varied to be conducive to human advancement. Despite exceptions, the correlation in Europe, at least, is interestingly close. In Russia, for example, where virtually the full gamut of vegetation zones exists between the Arctic and the Caucasus, the center of political power and of greatest development has been in the mixed forest belt, where Moscow is located.

The Soil and Vegetation Maps

It must be understood that maps A94 and A95 are small-scale, simplified presentations of highly varied and complex realities. Furthermore, the soils map especially must be considered a grouping of soils on a zonal basis that is deceptively simple and masks the diversity of European soils, despite the scientific soundness of the grouping. It is revealing that the Russians, with vast expanses of relatively uniform soils to study on the vast eastern European plains, should have seen the significance of soil genesis on soil morphology and pioneered in soil study and classification.

Within any one soil or vegetation zone there are small areas that differ in character from the general nature of the zone as a whole. Thus, within the Gray-Brown Podzolic soil zone, there are areas of true Podzols, some Degraded Chernozems, and many Intrazonal soils (as distinguished from the more widely spread Zonal soils), such as Rendzina, Planosols, Humic Glei, and others. In vegetation zones also, mention is made only of the principal, large-size species. Within the mixed forest there are, in addition to the principal trees, numerous species of trees that are represented by only a few individuals; and there are also hundreds of shrubs, grasses, and other smaller forms that are not mentioned at all because they are dominated by the larger trees. Finally, zones of transition exist between main belts. Rarely does the forest stop abruptly and grassland begin, nor does the coniferous forest abruptly turn to deciduous forest. On the map, however, definite lines must be drawn as if such sharp changes exist—or existed originally.

The analytical approach of this chapter and its emphasis on diversified details of soils and vegetation should not obscure the fact that other factors in the landscape frequently give striking unity to the individual regions of Europe. The Lowland of Scotland or the Schwarzwald (Black Forest) of Germany has a variety of soils and vegetation, yet the over-all impression of each is that of a distinctive region. Each has its characteristic relief, economic activity, climate, and people. Therefore, in the sections that follow—as well as in all analytical parts of this text—the broad outlines should not be lost in the detailed descriptions. Indeed, it is toward a better understanding of the whole that a discussion of the parts is pointed.

Zones of Vegetation and Soils

Tundra and High Mountain Zone (I in A94). In the far north and on the higher mountains the tundra and alpine types of vegetation correspond rather closely to the climatic zone in which the mean temperature of the warmest month is below 50° F. This temperature sets a limit to tree growth. Extending along the Arctic coast and reaching a much greater development farther east in the Soviet Union, the tundra varies somewhat in aspect from north to south. Typically, it is treeless, except in protected valleys toward the south, where spruces, larches, and birches struggle for existence; and the word "tundra," taken from the Finnish, indicates a barren area. The vegetation is made up almost entirely of perennials, since annuals have little chance in such a short, cool growing season. Typical in the tundra are lichens (symbiotically related fungi and algae) such as "reindeer 'moss'" (*Cladonia rangiferina*), which furnishes good fodder to the many reindeer grazing in the tundra; mosses such as sphagnum, which forms peat bogs especially toward the southern part of the tundra; sedges, commonly forming lowland bogs; hardy grasses; and dwarf bushes and dwarf "trees" such as the dwarf birch (*Betula nana*), which trails low on the ground as protection against cold, drying winds. The general aspect of the tundra, then, is that of a barren area.

Tundra soils are poorly developed because chemical and biological activity are retarded by the low temperature. The "profile," or vertical cross section, shows dark brown peaty layers over grayish horizons mottled with rust, the grayish horizon resulting from formation of ferrous oxide instead of ferric oxide because of retarded oxidation. The subsoil is permanently frozen, and there is much mechanical mixing of the upper horizons as a result of frost heaving resulting from alternate freezing and thawing. The coldness and wetness of the soils and the coldness of the climate make the soils of the tundra virtually useless for agriculture.

Similar conditions prevail on the European mountains above the forest limit, as the maps indicate. In the Alps, the classic example of this type, the Alpine meadows form a belt between the coniferous forests and the eternal snow and ice. After the long, snowy winter, the short summer brings an outburst of vegetative life of unique coloring. The bright green of the grassy meadows is mingled with the gay hues of brilliant flowers. Plants that lack prominence in the lowlands seem here to have rare beauty and, often, delightful odors. The many Arctic species, remnants of the Ice Age, make the Alpine equivalent of the northern tundra a botanical paradise. But in September snow comes once more, and for eight months a thick white mantle remains unbroken until the late spring, when the first crocus pushes its way through the snow and heralds the approaching summer.

Similar conditions are also found lower down in the meadows where the forests have been cut, although grass is far more abundant than higher up the mountains or in the true Arctic tundra. Furthermore, the typical Alpine meadows are covered with nutritious grasses of great value in the Alpine grazing economy. The cool upland moors of England, Scotland, and Scandinavia may be considered in this same zone, although they have less snow and a different type of vegetation. Shrouded by cool mist and rain, the peaty moors do not support trees in their acid soil; and mosses, lichens, hard grasses, and low bushes cover the earth with a soggy mantle.

Taiga (II). "Taiga" is a word used among Siberian peoples for a forested area and has been adopted as the name for the great belt

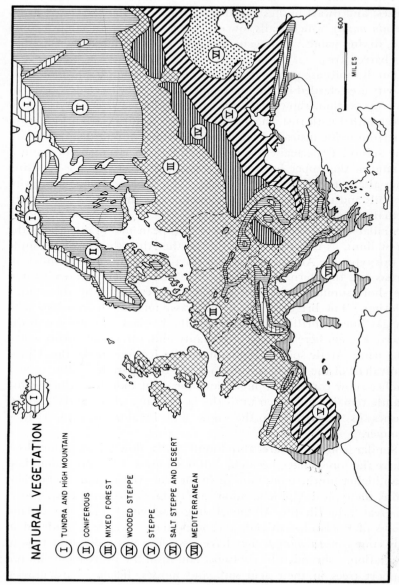

A. Generalized Map of Natural Vegetation of Europe.

NATURAL VEGETATION

Ⓘ TUNDRA AND HIGH MOUNTAIN

Ⓘ CONIFEROUS

Ⓘ MIXED FOREST

Ⓘ WOODED STEPPE

Ⓘ STEPPE

Ⓘ SALT STEPPE AND DESERT

Ⓘ MEDITERRANEAN

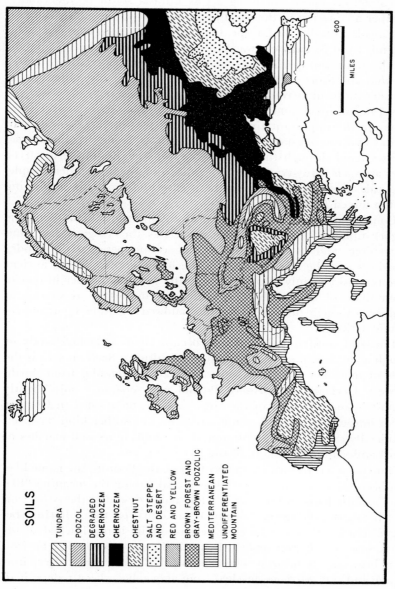

A. Generalized Map of European Soils.

SOILS

TUNDRA

PODZOL

DEGRADED
CHERNOZEM

CHERNOZEM

CHESTNUT

SALT STEPPE
AND DESERT

RED AND YELLOW

BROWN FOREST AND
GRAY-BROWN PODZOLIC

MEDITERRANEAN

UNDIFFERENTIATED
MOUNTAIN

of coniferous forest extending across Eurasia south of the tundra. Further adaptation of the word has applied it to the coniferous belt in Canada as well. In Europe, the taiga or northern coniferous belt extends from Norway eastward to the Urals and, except in extreme northeastern Europe, is composed chiefly of Norway spruce (*Picea excelsa*) and Scots pine (*Pinus sylvestris*). Farther east other species become more numerous: Siberian spruce (*Picea obovata*), Siberian fir (*Abies sibirica*), and Siberian larch (*Larix sibirica*). Spruce and pine are the important timber and pulp trees of the Scandinavian forests and are of enormous economic value. Some deciduous trees are scattered through the taiga, but—except in the southern parts— they are such hardy types as birch, alder, and aspen. Linden, maple, and oak appear toward the southern edge and signal the beginning of the mixed forest.

Coniferous forests are also found in areas outside the taiga on the higher uplands of central Europe, such as the Vosges, Harz, and Erzgebirge, and in the higher Alpine section between the tundra meadows and the mixed forests of the lower slopes. These ancient forests consist mainly of pine, spruce, and larch, but differ in species from those of the north. They are still important as sources of timber, although lumbering is overshadowed by other types of economic activity.

Lowland coniferous forests also occupy many detached sandy or rough areas that are not suitable for agriculture. Such an area is the belt of moraines and sandy outwash plains extending from northwestern Germany to northern Poland and separated only slightly from the southern edge of the taiga. As was mentioned in Chapter 4, an interesting lowland coniferous forest of another kind has been artificially created by afforestation of the sand dunes and marshes of Les Landes along the shore of the Bay of Biscay.

The taiga has its own characteristic soil, the Podzols, the name having been given by Russian pedologists and having the meaning "like ash" (*zola* is Russian for "ash"). The name describes the A horizon just below the surface mat of raw organic matter, the A horizon being characteristically light gray because of its being leached of organic matter and iron oxide. Beneath the gray, leached A horizon is a brownish B horizon where some of the organic matter, iron oxide, and clay particles, leached from above, have been redeposited. The Podzols tend to be sandy on the surface and are strongly acid, especially as a result of the percolation of rain water made acid by the raw coniferous needles on the surface. Plant nutrients are generally low, although sufficient for spruce, pine, and fir trees and for heather. For agricultural use, the Podzols must be limed to correct acidity and heavily fertilized, especially with phosphorus. Along the southern and western border of the Podzol zone of soils, where the longer growing season encourages agriculture, intensive fertilization has given rise to a highly profitable agriculture, as will be shown in the next chapter. In the northern portions of the Podzol zone, peat bogs are numerous and in some places cover more than half the area.

It is important to notice that the Podzols cover a greater area than do the coniferous forests. The Podzols of the taiga are, of course, somewhat different from those that develop under mixed forest vegetation, but the soil-forming processes are roughly the same. The slightly higher temperatures of the mixed forest zone produce more humus in the soil, but the relationship is established through leaching of the soils in both areas under similar conditions.

Mixed and Deciduous Forests (III). Between the taiga to the north on the one hand and the steppes to the east and Mediterranean vegetation zone to the south on the other hand is the largest European vegetation belt, that of the mixed forest. In its most characteristic development, it coincides rather well with the Western and Central European types of climate and thus reflects the influence of the Atlantic Ocean. In the more continental climate of eastern Europe it narrows into a long wedge until it practically disappears at the Ural Mountains.

The mixed forest displays great complexity as a result of microclimatic differences, relief, and soils. On the whole, broad-leaved hardwood trees predominate over softwoods, except on the northern border and in the uplands and sandy soil areas. In areas of loamy soils, hardwoods crowd out the conifers to form a true deciduous forest. Among the deciduous species, beech (*Fagus sylvatica*) and oaks (*Quercus robur* and *Q. sessiflora; Q. ilex* in western France) are the most typical; however, whereas the oak is found throughout the belt, the beech cannot grow under highly continental conditions and finds its limits in southern Sweden and Ruthenia. Other common deciduous trees in the belt are the maple (especially *Acer platanoides*), hornbeam (*Carpinus betulus*), ash (*Fraxinus excelsa*), linden or basswood (*Tilia cordata*—widely used for woodcarving because of its excellent workability), various elms, the chestnut, walnut, willow, and poplar. In European Russia, the order in which deciduous species disappear from west to east is beech, hornbeam, ash, oak and maple, and finally the hardy linden—which actually crosses the Urals into Siberia.

Soils of the mixed and deciduous forests are varied, ranging from true Podzols in the north to Degraded Chernozems in the south; but the characteristic and most widespread soils are the weakly podzolized Brown Forest, Brown Podzolic, and Gray-Brown Podzolic groups. They are related to the Podzols in that the upper horizon is leached, but in them the leaching is not so great as in the Podzols, acidity is generally not so high, loaminess is greater, and the humus content is higher. Whatever the zonal group of soil in the mixed forest zone, the specific soil is usually capable of producing good crops with fertilization. The map indicates that on the east side of Great Britain, in Skåne in southern Sweden, and in the Danish islands, the weakly podzolized Brown Forest soils have developed in the slightly drier continental conditions typical of those areas. The intensive agriculture of these three regions indicates the possibilities of agriculture in the soils of this zone.

Wooded Steppe (IV). In one sense, the wooded steppe is actually little more than a transitional zone between the mixed and deciduous forests and the treeless steppe, but because of its extensive development in eastern Europe—specifically in the Soviet Union—it deserves particular mention. As the name indicates, it combines the vegetational types of both the forest and the grassland and comprises scattered clumps of deciduous trees (although the pine is found in sandy areas) and alternating grass areas. In general, the appearance of the zone is similar to that of the western part of the American prairie. The trees are characteristically oak, the grasses including feather grasses, hairy oat, meadow brome, and others.

There is a gradation of soils from north to south, but the characteristic one is the Degraded Chernozem, which is formed by the leaching out of carbonates and humus from the true Chernozem and the appearance of other signs of slight podzolization. However, the Degraded Chernozems are very fertile and have virtually all been put under the plow.

Steppe (V). The lower actual or effective precipitation in southeastern Europe and in such areas as Spain and the Hungarian Plain results in lack of trees and the resulting dominance of herbaceous plants. In Europe, the most extensive development of grassland is in the east, particularly in the area north of the Black Sea. The steppe vegetation is at its best in spring, when the flowers of many perennial bulbs and tubers make the plains like a colorful carpet. However, in the hot, dry weather of midsummer, even the grasses lose their green color; and the steppe turns yellowish brown under the scorching sun.

The number of herbaceous species, chiefly grasses, that grow in the Russian steppe is quite large; and there is, in addition, a sequential arrangement of species, with certain ones appearing first in spring and others later in summer. Narrow-leaved grasses are typical, the main components being feather grass and needle grass, comprising several species of the genus *Stipa;* and subordinate grasses are fescue (*Festuca sulcata*), June grass (*Koeleria gracilis*), and crested wheatgrass (*Agropyron cristatum*). Different species characterize the Mediterranean steppe (where esparto grass is typical) and the Hungarian Plain, but the general appearance and ecological factors are similar.

It is in the steppe that the famed Chernozems (literally "black earths") reach their greatest development. The formation of Chernozems is entirely different from that of Podzols, since under subhumid conditions there is insufficient rainfall to leach completely the upper horizons of the soil. Grasses, feeding heavily on calcium, return large amounts of it to the surface, and the soil is therefore lime-accumulating. The Chernozem is black to very dark grayish brown to a depth of 1.5 to 3 feet, then grades through a lighter-colored soil to a light-gray layer of lime accumulation. Humus content is high, and the deep soil is very fertile by nature. The chief limitations on crop production are those of climate, specifically rainfall—not soil fertility or structure. Texture is good, and because the Chernozems are associated with plains regions, they are easily cultivated. Furthermore, the main Chernozem region north of the Black Sea is mantled with texture-improving, lime-rich loess, which also blankets an east-west zone north of the Central European Uplands and gives the soils of that zone some characteristics of Chernozems.

The vast expanses of waving grasses on the steppe have almost disappeared, since man long ago discovered not only the fertility of the soil but the ease with which cereals could be grown on it. Vast fields of wheat cover the region where once the Tatar wandered with his herds and flocks. Of the Hungarian Puszta, only a small part is left as natural grassland; the rest has been brought under cultivation. In the same way, the Spanish steppe with its esparto grass and roaming herds of merino sheep is witnessing the invasion of agriculture based on dry farming. Only on the drier steppes does cattle grazing still prevail.

Because the zones of the salt-steppe and desert vegetation and soils are on the very fringe of extreme eastern Europe, only mention of their presence will be made (VI in A94). They cover only a small area of Europe as a whole, but they will be discussed in the chapters on the Soviet Union.

Mediterranean Region (VII). In general, the Mediterranean zone of vegetation and soils lies south of the Alpine folds and corresponds rather well to the area of Mediterranean climate. The peculiar vegetation is a response to the region's mild, rainy winters and hot, dry summers. Where it is present, the forest bears small-leaved, leathery, evergreen foliage and includes such characteristic trees as the cork oak, laurel, several pines (*Pinus maritima, P. pinea,* and *P. halipensis*), cypress, cedar, and—especially in the artificial groves— the gray-leaved olive. Most of the present trees of the types named have been artificially planted, but originally wild trees covered thousands of square miles in the Mediterranean region. The primeval forest was long ago removed to permit cultivation of the land, and soil erosion on the slopes has been severe for centuries. Many slopes have been abandoned to bushes and low scrub—the *maquis* and *garrigue.* It is a mixture of evergreen and deciduous plants, beautiful in spring when the warmth and last rain of the cool season bring forth innumerable flowers, but brown and lifeless during the unrelieved summer drought. On the higher slopes and in the moister northern areas of the Mediterranean zone, the chestnut is the characteristic tree, and, still higher up, beeches form an extension of the central European hardwoods.

The endless complexity in relief and exposure and the variety of parent materials make the soils of the Mediterranean zone highly diverse. A soil typical of the region is the reddish soil termed *Terra Rossa* ("red earth"), found on limestone parent materials in such areas as southern France, Italy, and Greece. Friable, relatively permeable, and slightly alkaline, the Terra Rossa yields well under the management given it by the skilled Mediterranean farmer. Young volcanic soils are found in small areas, such as that around Naples and in eastern Sicily. Alluvial soils are common in some of the valleys—as, indeed, they are in other parts of Europe—although some of them have developed mature profiles, as in the western and central Po Basin. The expression "Mediterranean Soil" often applied to the soils of this zone is, therefore, chiefly a comprehensive term of convenience.

· 7 ·

Use of the Land
and the Ocean

Fundamental Importance of Agriculture in Europe

Agriculture is still Europe's first economic enterprise, and the number of people engaged in it is approximately double that in manufacturing. Nevertheless, there is a strong difference between Europe A and Europe C. In Belgium, as an example of Europe A, more than twice as many people are engaged in manufacturing as in agriculture, and in the United Kingdom the ratio is almost seven to one. In Rumania, exemplifying Europe C, for each person engaged in manufacturing, thirteen practice farming. Table B102 indicates the relative importance of agriculture and manufacturing among the countries of Europe from the point of view of people involved. The following countries have a larger percentage engaged in manufacturing than in agriculture: Belgium, Western Germany, Luxembourg, the Netherlands, Sweden, Switzerland, and the United Kingdom.

It is revealing to compare the map of intensity of agriculture (A102) with the table of the percentage of people engaged in agriculture (B102). However, Table B102 also includes fishing and forestry, which become important in some of the northern countries. In Norway, for instance, 7 per cent of the population is engaged in fishing, which reduces the 34 per cent to 27 per cent for agriculture and forestry. The 45 per cent for Iceland gives an erroneous impression, since few are actually engaged in agriculture and stock raising as such, and fishing is the main occupation.

In general, the areas of high agricultural intensity correspond to those in which the percentage of people engaged in agriculture is relatively low (below 30 per cent). In Britain the percentage is extraordinarily low (only 6), but in the Low Countries also it is below 20. The line of 40 per cent, if drawn, would extend through southern France, northern Italy, around Austria, western Czecho-

101

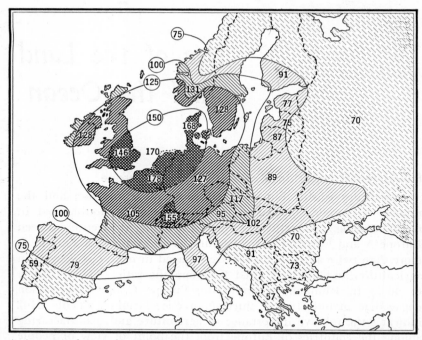

A. Intensity of Agriculture in Europe.   The index of 100 is the average European
yield per acre of eight main crops: wheat, rye, barley, oats, corn, potatoes, sugar
beets, and hay (1937 political boundaries).

TABLE B

PERCENTAGE OF ACTIVE POPULATION ENGAGED IN AGRICULTURE AND MANUFACTURING

	Agri-culture	Manu-facturing		Agri-culture	Manu-facturing
Austria	39	24	Luxembourg	26	40
Belgium	17	36	Netherlands	19	24
Bulgaria	80	8	Norway	34	20
Czechoslovakia	38	35	Portugal	49	16
Denmark	28	25	Rumania	78	6
Finland	55	16	Spain	52	18
France	36	23	Sweden	24	29
Western Germany	29	39	Switzerland	21	34
Iceland	45	17	United Kingdom	6	40
Ireland	48	10	Yugoslavia	79	11
Italy	47	21			

Dates of census vary from country to country.

Other activities include such items as mining, transportation, commerce, administration, personal services, and professional services.

slovakia, and eastern Germany. In the Mediterranean area, percentages are about 50, with increasingly low intensity southward; and in the Balkans and eastern Europe the high percentage of 80 is reached. In Europe A, the low percentages do not mean that all other people are engaged in manufacturing, since such economic activities as commerce and "services" also employ many people.

Intensity of Production

The relative number of people involved does not, however, tell the whole story, because of the much larger production per farmer in Europe A. This is illustrated in Map A103, which shows the

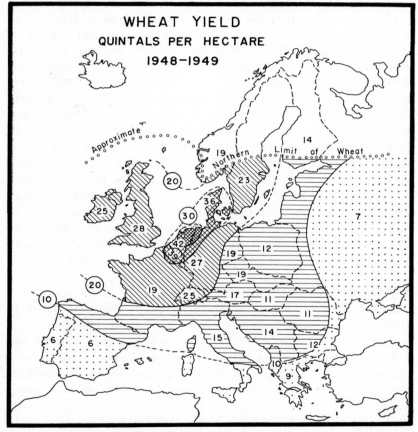

A. Wheat Yield in Europe in Quintals per Hectare (1 quintal = 220.46 pounds; 1 hectare = 2.47 acres).

average yield for one crop—wheat. A more complete picture is offered by the map of intensity of agriculture in Europe (A102). It shows the productivity of the land per acre on the basis of eight very widely raised crops: wheat, rye, barley, oats, corn, potatoes, sugar beets, and hay. For each crop, the average yield per acre for Europe as a whole is taken as an index of 100, and the specific yield in each country is calculated accordingly. It is possible that, if data were available for grapes and olives, the position of the Mediterranean countries might be improved, but the change would be insignificant. The outstanding fact is that Holland and Belgium lead in intensity, with Denmark, Switzerland, and England closely approaching them. A surrounding ring of countries, comprising the rest of Zone A, also ranks above the general average for Europe as a whole. Europe B, from Finland around through Hungary to northern Spain, falls a little below the average, and Europe C falls far below. In Russia, Rumania, Greece, southern Italy, and southern Spain, the farmers—on an average—get only about one third as much per acre as do those of the region immediately around the North Sea. The differences shown on the map of intensity are due to several factors, such as careful crop rotation and selection of seed. Another factor is the use of fertilizers, which in some of the western countries has reached such a high level that it almost seems that the chief function of the soil is to keep the plant upright and serve as a "carrier" for the various fertilizers, which actually feed the plant and make it grow. This is, however, truer for horticulture than for the raising of cereals. For example, in comparison with the United States, the Netherlands consumes 10 times as much nitrogen fertilizer per unit of improved farmland, and for phosphoric acid and potash the figures are 7 and 9.

Reliability of Crop Yield

Among the causes of variations in prosperity from one region to another the reliability of crop yield is of great importance. A farmer who gets 24 bushels of wheat per acre one year, then 15, and 9 the third year, averages 16, but he is not so well off as one with the same average who gets 18, 16, and 14 bushels per acre in three successive years. The first never knows how well off he is going to be: one year he feels rich and spends extravagantly, or more likely pays up old debts, but another year he does not even make expenses and runs badly into debt. The other farmer knows what to expect, lives on about the same scale all the time, and can save a little each year.

Map A105 shows such a difference between Europe A and Europe C. A small figure means high reliability, that is, only a little variation in the yield of crops per acre from year to year. The map shows the percentage of deviation from the average yield during the

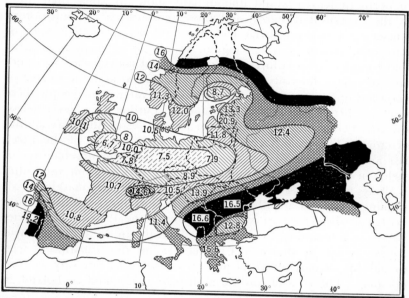

A. Variability of Crops, Expressed as Average Percentage of Departure from Normal, 1927–33. Recent data not available. (Political boundaries as of 1937.)

period 1927–33 on the basis of the weighted acreage and value of wheat, oats, rye, barley, corn, potatoes, grapes, and flax. For any individual crop the variation is far greater than for many crops combined. Moreover, 1927–33 (recent data for such a comparison were not available) were not years of extreme variability. The figure for Spain is probably too low, because the statistics there are somewhat unreliable and because northern and southern Spain have such different climates that good crops in one region often cancel bad ones in the other. The same sort of balance between the north and south lowers the Italian percentage. Irrigated regions, such as the southern parts of Spain, Italy, and Greece, do not, however, suffer from unreliability of crops so much as do the more continental regions farther north.

Rumania, in Europe C, with a variation of 16 per cent, reflects conditions that entail low standards of living if the agricultural population is dense. Russia is so huge that good crops in the wheat region, for example, often cancel bad ones in the rye region. If data for the individual climatic regions were available, conditions in northern Russia would undoubtedly show up worse than those in the eastern Baltic area, and those in southern or southeastern Russia (or European Soviet Union) would be worse than those of Rumania. In the Caspian region, variability of crops is so great that complete crop failures are common. Of course, the low standards of tillage intensify agricultural difficulties, and the degree of variation in Europe A would doubtless be greater if the people there used no better methods than those of Europe C. Nevertheless, the continental climate is the main factor causing the unreliability of crops. The great variability in the region north of the Black Sea and northwest of the Caspian illustrates the unreliability of yields in areas of low precipitation, where precipitation variability is always greatest. The same risks exist along the dry margins of all farming areas and are illustrated by the Dust Bowl conditions that existed in the American wheat belt during the 1930's. The Soviet Union is attempting to stabilize agriculture in its great semiarid region, as will be shown in Chapter 45; but the climatic obstacles to stability of agriculture of any great degree of intensity are formidable. The core of low variability from England to Poland in A105 is noteworthy.

A Contrast

The result of the greater reliability of precipitation, and therefore of crop yield, in northwestern Europe, considered along with other advantages, is that the farmer in Europe A is much better off than the farmer in Europe C. His annual income is three to four times higher. Moreover, he is generally his own "boss," although in many countries he is a member of co-operative organizations for buying as well as for selling. In Europe C, large landholdings, often under absentee landlords, were the usual type of ownership until after World War I, when agrarian reforms initiated breaking up those properties into small units; and in some areas that process is still going on. This breaking up of large holdings, although beneficial in some ways, did not solve the entire problem, especially in those areas where the difficulty was greatest. The new owner was often not financially strong enough to overcome the handicap of bad years or low prices. Behind the Iron Curtain in eastern Europe, individual properties began to be gradually abolished after 1946, and large government collective farms were organized in their place. Whereas in a co-operative the farmer is still his own boss, in a collective farm the farmer loses his individuality completely and is only an "employee" of a huge concern dominated by the state.

Present Status of Land Utilization

Arrangement of Crops. The agricultural revolution of the eighteenth and nineteenth centuries and the importation of food from across the sea have introduced a new arrangement of crops in Europe. Before 1800 the crops were arranged very closely in harmony with the soil and climate. In other words, the crops raised in each region were those that grew best there and thus furnished the most food with the least work and the least uncertainty. Accordingly the various types of crops were arranged in broad zones stretching from southwest to northeast as in A108. This simple pattern was altered slightly by the efforts of each country to grow within its own borders the entire variety of agricultural products that it required.

The new regime of industrialization and overseas competition altered all this in western Europe and sometimes changed the zones beyond recognition. The farmers in many sections no longer raised the crops best adapted to the soil and climate but those whose bulk, perishable nature, or high value made them best able to compete with products from across the seas. This meant, of course, a still further intensification of agriculture in the regions near dense industrial populations. Hence roughly circular zones became established around the industrial centers. The immediate urban fringes were devoted to market gardening, dairying, and other forms of intensive agriculture, and the outlying rings to extensive agriculture, stock ranges, and forests. Some of the small countries, such as Holland and Denmark, shifted almost entirely from subsistence crops to dairying and truck farming. They sold their products in the rapidly developing urban markets of the near-by industrial regions of England and Germany. Where the industrial centers were fairly close together, the zones often conflicted and overlapped, with the result that stock ranges and forest areas were largely relegated to the more remote and rural regions and especially to Zones B and C in the economic-cultural map of the continent. This change in the general distribution of agriculture is illustrated by the contrast between A108 with its strips and A102 with its concentric arrangement around the North Sea.

Agricultural Regions of Europe

Map A108 shows the agricultural regions of Europe, greatly simplified; in order to present a more complete picture, the individual zones will be discussed. The map shows quite well the general

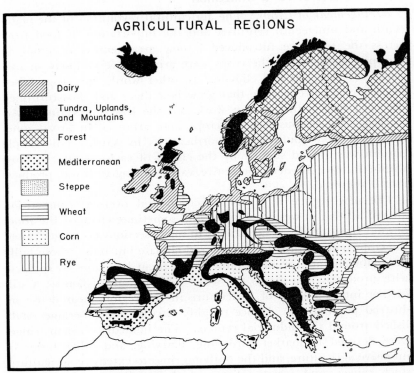

A. Generalized Agricultural Regions of Europe.

sequence from north to south and from west to east. The tundra zone in the north is followed by the taiga or subpolar zone of conifers, both described in the preceding chapter. To the south is the dairy belt, which in turn is succeeded by the region of wheat and rye, and still farther south corn comes to the foreground; finally, there is the zone of Mediterranean agriculture. The broad zonal arrangement is, of course, complicated by mountains, hill lands, and valleys, which form islands whose land use differs from that of surrounding areas.

Forest Zone. The first zone of any significance is the taiga, which starts on the eastern side of the Scandinavian Highlands and continues eastward into Russia and thence into Siberia; only on the coastal plain of the Bothnian Gulf does dairying come to the foreground. For practical purposes, the Småland Plateau of southern Sweden, although different in the composition of its forest, and Les Landes on the French coast of Biscay—a man-planted forest of pines —are added to this forest zone. The vast northern area of softwood is of enormous value to the European economy, and it is carefully controlled in order to avoid depletion. Not only is it a source of fuel, timber, and paper pulp, but it is also a base for cellulose fibers as well as alcohol and even fodder for cattle. The forests, then, provide almost a complete economy whose importance becomes especially great in times of war when imports are cut off.

Other forest areas of Europe, described in the section on mixed forests in Chapter 6, cover many of the uplands as well as some of the poorer soils of central and western Europe. However, they are secondary to other types of land use within their respective agricultural zones, although they are carefully tended.

The Dairy Belt. The dairy belt combines various types of specific land use; however, all these types have in common the predominance of the dairy industry and associated branches such as the raising of pigs and chickens. Climate is the most important factor influencing its location and shape, both of which in turn show its relationship with the ocean; and it is characterized by mild winters, cool summers, and plenty of moisture. However, the intensity of the use of the land is also greatly influenced by the large, near-by markets that absorb those products. In structure, it varies from a simple grass economy with grazing cattle and the cutting of hay to a specialized fodder economy based on the effort to get the greatest amount of fodder value out of a unit of land. Whereas bread grains are increasing in importance, especially under the influence of war conditions (Ireland and Britain are good examples), and potatoes are quite important, the emphasis is on oats, barley, and root crops. Horticulture—the raising of fruits and vegetables— comes to the foreground in certain suitable areas, especially in the Netherlands, and hothouses replace open fields if the climate does not permit the ripening of a product that the market demands. Thus, from the point of view of intensity of production, some parts of the dairy belt have first ranking. Yields are high, partly because of the great use of fertilizers and scientific planning of the use of the land; thus, the most has been made of an area that certainly offered many natural advantages but nevertheless owes its agricultural productivity to the ingenuity of man. A separate dairy zone is found along the northern foot of the Alps, extending from France through Switzerland and southern Germany into Austria, which uses the high Alpine pastures for summer grazing.

Fluid milk, butter, cheese, bacon, and eggs are typical products of the region. The Camembert of Normandy, the Cheddar of Britain, the Gruyère of Switzerland, the Edam and Gouda cheeses of the Netherlands, the Danish blue cheese, and the brown cheese of Norway—these are only a few of the cheeses justly famous in the western world and produced in this dairy belt of Europe.

The Wheat-Rye Zone. Although on the map a clear differentiation is made between the wheat zone and the rye zone, it is possible to combine the two in discussion. The zone starts on or near the west coast of the continent and forms a broad belt extending eastward into Russia, interrupted only by upland areas. Generally, rye is grown where winters are more severe and the soils are sandier and less fertile; in other words, it is generally east and north of the wheat belt. Wheat is also grown in those parts of Germany included in the rye area, but rye prevails there over wheat. Similarly, the wheat zone includes areas of crops other than wheat, as in the European part of the Soviet Union; in the western and central Ukraine the land use is of a great variety, with such crops—besides wheat—as oats and potatoes, horticultural produce, and pasture for dairy cattle. Here is also a great area of sugar beet production, the easterly extension of the zone reaching from northern France through Belgium and the Netherlands, along the northern edge of the German uplands, north of the Carpathians, and eastward into the Ukraine. East of the Baltic Sea, flax is an important industrial crop. Included in the wheat zone are also the semiarid basins of the Spanish Meseta, once the land for sheep but at mid-century gradually developing a wheat economy based on dry farming.

The Corn Belt. The definite climatic base of the European corn (maize) belt is twofold: it is warmer in summer than is the area north of it, and at the same time it receives more summer rain than does the Mediterranean climate zone south of it. It is really a combination zone for corn and wheat, but corn, in contrast with wheat in the neighboring regions, is the characteristic crop, although wheat often prevails locally. In the eastern Danube plains, corn and wheat are the dominant grains; and in the western Danube plains they almost exclude other crops. In the corn belt in general, however, there is a great deal of variety, and it includes fruits and vegetables, pasture along the rivers, and even rice under irrigation. Rice is typical of parts of the Po Basin.

The Region of Tundra, Mountains, and Uplands. This is a composite area of great variety, but a common characteristic is that the climate and generally the relief are not favorable for intensive use. In the Arctic tundra there is only a short summer period when reindeer grazing prevails; otherwise it lies bleak, frozen, and snow-covered. Mountains vary greatly in their use. In the British Isles they are frequently boggy, and their principal use is for sheep grazing. In central Europe most of the mountains are densely forested, whereas the higher elevations carry meadows that are used for summer grazing. In the Mediterranean region, the uplands stand out as patches of green in the scorched summer landscape; olive, chestnut, and cork oak trees are frequently found on the lower slopes; and, higher up, grazing again becomes important, chiefly for sheep and goats. This does not mean that man, under the pressure of necessity, has not tilled many of the less steep slopes and that fruit trees and plots of grain have not replaced many former forest areas. In the French Alps, cultivation can be found in spots up to 7,000 feet. However, in contrast to the surrounding area, mountains appear as a symbol of the difficulty man has faced in attempting to meet a less hospitable environment.

The Mediterranean Region. In the Mediterranean region, all aspects of agriculture are strongly stamped by the unusual climate with mild, wet winters and dry, warm (even hot) summers. Summer is the dormant period for most vegetation, and only where irrigation water is available can crop raising be continuous. The irrigated areas are the gardens of the Mediterranean, growing almost anything from citrus fruits, grapes, peaches, and apricots to nuts and even rice. Southern Spain around the Sierra Nevada, the Valencia Plain, southern France and the Italian Riviera, Naples and northern Sicily, the Dalmatian Coast and southern Greece—all have been famous for their horticulture since ancient times. However, the irrigated sections cover only a small part of the Mediterranean region. Beyond them are the fields of wheat and barley, harvested in early summer, and groves of the drought-resisting olive trees, which cover the slopes of the hills. Pulses such as beans and peas are also part of the Mediterranean agriculture.

Europe's Agricultural Balance

The existence of the Iron Curtain limits the exchange of products between the two parts of Europe. The Danubian countries formerly compensated some of the grain deficit in western Europe, but, even if they could have exported to the west in 1950–51, their surplus would have been small because of postwar agrarian difficulties.

The eighteen countries that belong to the Organization for European Economic Co-operation (including every country west of the Iron Curtain except Spain and Yugoslavia) were, in 1950, self-sufficient in potatoes, vegetables, milk, and eggs. Cereals, however, they had to import up to an amount of 5 million metric tons, although they produced 11 million tons. Their sugar deficit was 2.5 million tons, that for meat was 1 million tons, and for oils and fats 1.75 million tons. Deficits also existed in fruit, cheese, and butter. The United Kingdom needed the major share of these imports, and it seemed apparent by 1951 that, except for Britain, western Europe could be self-supporting in almost all foods except grain, oils, and fats, with surpluses of some countries balancing the deficits of others. A unified agricultural policy in Europe, which was under consideration for western Europe in 1951, would greatly help to improve the agricultural situation. Britain, however, will always remain vulnerable.

Trends in Europe's Agricultural Production

A comparison between the acreage for grains and potatoes in 1923 and in 1947 permits certain rather interesting conclusions. In general there has been a decrease in grain acreage, apparently because of a shift toward dairying and horticulture; also, in some countries, marginal areas have been taken out of production. However, grain acreage increased in a number of countries, notably in Ireland and the United Kingdom, with increases of 42 and 26 per cent, respectively. In both cases the increase is due to government policy to decrease the grain deficit. In Ireland the increase is chiefly due to a much larger wheat acreage, which was helped by relatively warm and dry summers during the 1940's. Switzerland, with an increase of 76 per cent, has also shown a determined effort to decrease its grain deficit. The increases in Denmark and the Netherlands are to a large extent the result of the putting into production of formerly unproductive moorland areas, whereas in Greece the increase has resulted from the enlarged farm area in Macedonia.

On the whole, the tendency in European agriculture has been away from cereals toward more intensive use of the land for dairy products, fruits, and vegetables. Such a tendency is also reflected in a shift toward barley in some of the dairy countries (Denmark, the Netherlands, and Switzerland) because of its feed value.

Fishing

The coastal waters of western Europe are teeming with fish, and conditions for fishing are excellent: many factors combine to make this one of the richest fishing grounds of the world. The extensive continental shelf that permits trawling, the abundance of plankton, the warm water of the North Atlantic Drift that permits fishing in winter beyond the Arctic Circle, and the tides and currents that prevent stagnation of the water are the most important of these factors. These fishing grounds form a continuous zone from the Arctic to Morocco (Map A114), varying only in relative importance and type of catch—the latter varying in turn with the seasonal migration of the species. Changes in these migrations may influence the life of nations; for example, the shift of herring in the fifteenth century from the south coast of Sweden to the North Sea was an important factor in the growth of the Netherlands, and, when in the years after 1945 the sardine disappeared from the Portuguese fishing grounds, the economy of Portugal suffered greatly. The shift in 1950 of herring from their normal grounds south of Iceland caused that country deep concern, since the herring migrations had been somewhat abnormal for several years.

The Mediterranean lacks some of the attributes of a great fishing ground. Deep water prevents trawling, and the catch has none of the uniformity so typical of that of the west coast. Nevertheless, it is always fascinating to see the fish brought ashore in the Mediterranean because of the great variety of shapes and colors.

Fish Catch. Norway exceeds Britain slightly in amount of fish caught; thus, the per capita catch is sixteen times as high in Norway as in Britain. Iceland ranks first not only in Europe but in the world in per capita catch, which reaches the almost unbelievable quantity of 6,600 pounds per year; however, fish is almost the only basic asset in the Icelandic economy. Other high producers are Spain (with the northwest corner, Galicia, famous for its fishing),

Portugal, Denmark, Sweden, the Netherlands, and Germany. Despite lack of statistics, there is no doubt that the Soviet Union fish catch is enormous, especially cod in the Barents Sea. Cod and herring are the two ranking species of the northern catch; sardines prevail in the south. Exports of fish from such surplus-fish countries as Norway

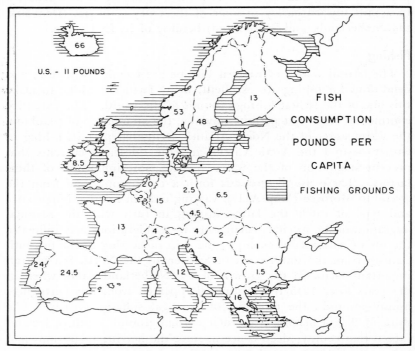

A. Fish Consumption (in Pounds per Capita) and Fishing Grounds in Europe. Note figure for Iceland.

are in a variety of forms—fresh, dried, frozen, canned, and processed (for oil or meal).

Fish Consumption. Map A114 shows that, contrary to the view that Catholic countries eat more fish than do Protestant ones, fish consumption is highest among the Protestant nations in northwestern Europe. In Iceland the per capita consumption is 66 pounds a year, an amount surpassed only in Japan. In the United States the average consumption is about 11 pounds, but it varies a great deal from region to region and in New England may reach the average of some western European countries.

Diet and Food

Under *normal* conditions the European diet is everywhere sufficient in calories, but it varies markedly in structure. The basic
diet of Europe A is similar to that of the United States, with a
nice balance between cereals, roots, tubers, and sugar on the one
hand and fats, pulses, meat, fish, eggs, and milk on the other. In
Europe C, especially in southeastern Europe, cereals comprise the
bulk of the diet and make it unbalanced in comparison with the
diet of Europe A.

The present food consumption, if compared with that of the prewar period, shows some changes. Typical, for instance, is Britain,
where the marked decrease of sugar and meat is offset by a 50 per
cent increase in consumption of milk and potatoes. Austria is
representative of the nations that suffered from postwar difficulties:
except for potatoes and cereals, consumption of all items is much
lower. For western and southern Europe as a whole, milk consumption increased substantially, whereas meat consumption dropped.
The trend seems to be toward a diet of more milk and vegetables
and less meat and sugar. Even in 1952, some actual shortages still
existed, but food supplies were at least adequate in most areas.
Hunger in such countries as Greece and Italy was probably no
more than that—sadly enough—typical of prewar years. The United
Kingdom, because of its "austerity program," probably suffered from
lack of a varied diet as much as any other western European
country.

Geography textbooks in general do not talk about food itself, yet
there is a great deal of geography in national food and drink habits
and local specialties. Despite a desire to try famous French foods,
most American tourists unfortunately do not discover the fascinating "geography of foods" in Europe, since one large hotel is rather
like another in so far as food is concerned, and the average American is conservative in his food habits and does not like to try dishes
or beverages that are unknown or unusual to him. Of course, extensive traveling and knowledge of the best restaurants are invaluable
to an appreciation of the local *cuisine,* but even the inexperienced
traveler can, with very little effort, find in all European countries
charming restaurants that serve local dishes behind which are centuries of tradition and achievement. Practically all of them represent the local environment. They are part of the local life, and

as such they are part of geography. In Europe, meals are not a necessity simply to be tolerated, but family functions that consume a relatively great amount of time that is justified by the family conviviality that is stimulated. The concept of cooking—especially the preparation of local dishes—as an art is typical of Europe.

began to absorb the surplus just beginning to appear. The United States exported millions of tons of coal to Europe during the severest shortage, but decreased shipments to only 370,000 tons by 1949. British coal production climbed steadily after 1945 but had not returned to prewar levels by 1951; and despite strenuous efforts on the part of the nationalized coal industry, coal available for export was in 1949 less than half that exported in 1938. Poland, on the other hand, with the former German Silesian coal deposits, has doubled its prewar production and has become Europe's main exporter of coal. Of the major countries that are not coal exporters, France—with the addition of much of the Saar output—produces a major share of its needs but is still forced to import. Italy, however, has very little coal and is dependent on imports—a handicap that was emphasized during the Second World War. When Britain ceased permitting Italian ships loaded with German coal to pass through the English Channel bound for Italy, all coal shipments from Germany to Italy had to move by rail over the Alps at a time when freight cars were at a premium for the German war effort.

Taken as a whole, the coal production of Western Europe approximately equals that of the United States, and each of them has nearly twice the production of that of Russia and her satellites (Table A7). The Soviet Union has a 1960 goal of coal production approaching that of the United States. However, American coal production can be substantially increased, and the Ruhr is only slowly returning to full capacity. On the other side, Great Britain has difficulty maintaining its production: exhaustion of the better coal seams and operation at great depth in many of the British mines are limiting factors.

In probable hard coal reserves, the richest individual field in Europe is the Ruhr, after which come the southern Polish deposits (former Upper Silesian field) and the Donets Basin in the eastern Ukraine. Each field has sufficient coal for continued output over hundreds of years at the present rate of production, and each has large supplies of coking coal, although the percentage is lowest in the Polish fields. Other major fields are those of the Saar (with its extension into eastern France), the almost continuous field extending from northern France through Belgium and into the Aachen region of Germany, the several fields of the United Kingdom (South Wales, Yorkshire, Durham-Northumberland or Newcastle, Midlands, Lancashire, and Scottish Lowlands), and the Ostrava-Karvinná field of Czechoslovakia. The Moscow Basin contains primarily lignite.

Germany also possesses enormous lignite deposits in the middle Elbe region and in the lower Rhineland.

Petroleum

Except for the Soviet Union and Rumania, both of which are behind the Iron Curtain, Europe has very little oil and depends almost completely on imports, either from the Middle East or from the Americas. Although the total production of Russia and Rumania was in 1950 only about 43 million tons, compared with 270 million for the United States, it is of course of great significance in Russia's potential strength, especially since private consumption is quite low. Map A118 shows the location of the Russian oil fields and pipelines. Besides the well-known fields of Baku, Groznyy, and Maykop, the new fields north and northeast of the Caspian and west of the Urals are developing rapidly. Rumanian production declined after 1945 to about one half of what it was in the peak years of 1935–36.

In western Europe great efforts have been made to increase production, from both wells and oil shales. Western Germany and the Netherlands have the greatest yield of petroleum from wells in western Europe and together produce an amount equal to about one-half the Rumanian output. The Soviet Union controls the small production of Poland (most of the Carpathian wells are now in Soviet territory), Austria, and Hungary. Synthetic petroleum products, for which Germany was the major producer before and during World War II were of little significance in the first few years after 1945.

Water Power

In proportion to its available supply, Europe uses its water power far more fully than does any other continent. This is especially true of western Europe, where countries like France, Germany, and Switzerland have developed virtually 100 per cent of their basic potential—as has Italy. The distribution of water power in Europe is, however, as uneven as that of almost everything else. Germany, although endowed with plenty of coal, uses more water power than does Spain, and the United Kingdom uses more than Yugoslavia. Although water supplies only 8 per cent of the total power within Europe A, it is of outstanding value in regions that lack coal but in which the relief of the land and the rainfall are conducive to water power development. The Alpine mountains are especially good for this purpose, because the main valleys are often bordered by hanging side valleys from which the water falls in cascades or tumbles down through narrow gorges. The glacial topography of Scandinavia is also suitable for hydroelectric development, since there the rivers provide a sequence of waterfalls and rapids as they flow from the high divide toward the coast. The rounded hills of central Europe, among which artificial dams may be constructed to provide the necessary hydraulic head, have certain topographic advantages for the location of smaller power plants; and plentiful precipitation is rather evenly distributed throughout the year. The mild winter temperatures at low altitudes cause only infrequent freezing and consequent lack of flow for power generation. In summer, on the other hand, the melting of the snow and ice on the high mountains increases the water supply.

In proportion to population, Norway, Switzerland, and Sweden rank first in the use of water power. Not only is their power generation based on hydroelectricity as much as possible, but also they will probably export power when plans for power transmission have been realized; initial steps in this direction have already been taken on a small scale. In Switzerland, water power provides an annual volume of energy equivalent to that which would be derived from 6.5 million tons of imported coal. Here, as in the north, conditions are favorable for export of power. In actual energy derived from water, Italy ranks first among European countries (Table A450), and hydroelectricity is the power base for the great industrial development of the Po Basin. By intensifying the development of the great hydroelectric potential of its Alpine streams, Italy is attempting to decrease its heavy importation of coal. France (especially in the Alpine region), Germany, Poland (in the Carpathians), Spain (in the Pyrenees), and the Soviet Union complete the list of countries with developed water power exceeding one million horsepower.

It is difficult to evaluate Soviet hydroelectric development, because few data are available, and there is little certainty about what has been constructed and what is merely planned. However, major Soviet efforts have been devoted toward utilization of available water power, both because of the great requirements for power in the Soviet industrialization program and because of the great concentration of coal deposits, which would necessitate long rail shipments of coal if other power were not available in areas far from coal fields. The famous Dneproges Dam on the bend of the Dnieper was the first great Soviet hydroelectric development; other dams have been constructed on the upper Volga at Shcherbakov (formerly

Rybinsk) and on the Svir River between Lake Ladoga and Lake Onega. In early 1952, major power stations were in construction along the middle Volga and also at Molotov (Perm) on the upper Kama. The per capita output of kilowatts of hydroelectricity is, however, still low.

Metallic Ores

In view of their method of origin, metallic ores cannot be expected in any substantial quantity in the great lowlands of Europe, where the old geologic structure is covered by young materials. Nor can they be expected in large and easily worked quantities in the Alpine regions, where the complex structure makes the ore zones very discontinuous and difficult to exploit. Much more favorable conditions are found in the crystalline rock of old blocks like that of Scandinavia with its iron and copper, Cornwall with its tin (now exhausted), and Bohemia, Spain, and Sardinia with their various metals. The same is true of former piedmont slopes of these old mountains, as may be seen in the Mesozoic basins of England and France with their iron ores.

Iron Ore. As the basic raw material in steel production, iron is the most important metallic ore in modern industry, and prospecting geologists are still actively exploring for more and better fields. Discoveries of great new iron deposits in Europe cannot logically be expected any more, except possibly in the Soviet Union, and supplies will gradually become exhausted. However, at present Europe is well off. Excluding the Soviet Union for the moment, the most productive iron ore area of Europe is the Lorraine district of eastern France and Luxembourg, in the heart of industrial Europe. Second in production is Sweden, with great resources of rich ore north of the Arctic Circle at Kiruna and Gällivare. Great Britain ranks third, with its principal deposits east of the Pennine Chain. However, Britain has an appreciable iron ore deficit and depends to a large extent on imports from foreign sources, primarily North Africa and Sweden. Germany ranks next, but the production is only one-fourth that of France; and, to an even greater degree than Britain, Germany is dependent on imports, especially from France and Sweden. Minor but nevertheless locally important producers are Spain (chiefly for export), Austria, Czechoslovakia, Yugoslavia, and Norway. Retreating German armies totally destroyed the iron mines in northern Norway, but in 1950 production started again. Turning to the Soviet Union, iron ore production in 1950, if the goal was

reached, exceeded that of France, Sweden, and England combined.
The major source is in the Krivoy Rog area west of the bend of the
Dnieper River, although there are several other major sources in
the Urals (especially at Magnitogorsk), and a number of smaller
producers, including those of Soviet Asia.

Bauxite. Bauxite (aluminum ore) is named after the small town
of Baux in southern France, and France has remained the top producer for Europe, even including the Soviet Union, although the
Russian claim for a metallic aluminum production in 1950 of 180,000
tons might indicate a rapid increase in her bauxite production.
Other European bauxite producers are Hungary, Yugoslavia, and
Italy—named in the order of their importance.

Copper, Lead, Zinc, Tin, and Nickel. For most other metallic
ores, Europe is a minor producer, and for some of them the major
production is behind the Iron Curtain and is not available to the
western nations. For copper, for instance, the Soviet Union claimed
in 1950 a production of 213,000 tons, while that of the United States
and Canada together was about 900,000 tons. Outside Russia,
European copper production is quite small: Scandinavia (Finland,
Norway, and Sweden) 56,000, Yugoslavia 38,000, and Spain 6,700
metric tons in 1949.

For lead ore the situation is still worse. In 1949, Russia claimed
144,000 metric tons, compared with 600,000 in the United States
and Mexico. The next producer is Yugoslavia with about 72,000
tons, followed by Germany (chiefly in the Russian zone), Spain, and
Sweden. Zinc ore production is also low. Before the war Germany
was a fairly important producer, but now its Silesian zinc mines are
in Polish territory. The matter of European tin exploitation brings
up memories of ships from Tyre and Sidon sailing in ancient times
past the Gates of Hercules to the British Isles in search of tin. But,
after 3,000 years, the Cornwall tin deposits are virtually exhausted,
although they were mined during World War II. Nickel also is
practically absent, except in Russia, and even the formerly Finnish
nickel mines in the Pechenga (Petsamo) Corridor are now in Soviet
hands.

Alloys. Whereas in peacetime alloys can be bought on the world
market, in wartime the battle for alloys becomes a vital struggle;
there is the necessity not only to buy but also to prevent the enemy
from buying. Portugal and Spain, for instance, received fantastic
prices for their tungsten during World War II and even during the
Cold War by playing one side against the other. Spain and Portugal

are still the major tungsten producers in Europe, but in greatly reduced quantities compared with the war years; Sweden and France
also produce some tungsten. Chromium is another valuable alloy
for wartime industry, and great efforts were made during the Second World War to prevent the Turkish production from falling
into the hands of the Germans. In Europe itself, only Yugoslavia
produces fair quantities, and Russia is well off with major production in the Urals. Molybdenum is found in small quantities in
Finland and Norway. Because some manganese is required in all
steel, Soviet dominance in the production of manganese is of great
significance; the vast Russian resources in the area of Nikopol west
of the Dnieper bend and in Chiatura in Georgia give the Soviet
Union a major share of the world's known manganese resources.
The rest of Europe has no production of any significance, and only
the rather small production in India, Brazil, Union of South Africa,
and Cuba prevents a complete Russian domination of that product.
For years it has been the problem whether to buy Russian manganese ore in exchange for strategic materials the Russians need or
try to do without it.

Miscellaneous (Uranium, Platinum, etc.). Missing in statistical
yearbooks is the production of uranium, base for atomic power.
Frantic efforts made by the Russians to mine pitchblende on both
sides of the Erzgebirge between Germany and Czechoslovakia seem
to indicate that Russia does not have important deposits in her own
country. There are small uranium deposits in the Central Plateau
of France and in Portugal. One metal for which Russia is the top
producer is platinum, which comes from the Ural region. Soviet
gold production is also very high—probably second only to that of
the Union of South Africa—but no figures are available. Finally,
most of the world's production of mercury comes from Europe, particularly from Italy and Spain; and Yugoslavia, which took over
from Italy the famous Idria mines in Istria, is now an important
producer. These three together produced in 1949 four fifths of the
world's production.

Nonmetallic Minerals

Even for nonmetallic minerals, Europe is, with one or two notable
exceptions, not a great producer. Various building materials, such
as stone, clay, sand, and gravel, are present in large, quality deposits
in many parts of Europe, as is indicated by the customary use of
stone or brick not only in urban buildings but in even the most

modest farmhouses outside the Alpine regions. The potash deposits of Europe are the greatest known in the world; and those of Germany, located around Stassfurt (and the major share of which are in the Soviet zone), are conservatively estimated to be sufficient to meet the potash demand for more than a thousand years. The much more limited but still large potash deposits near Mulhouse in southern Alsace are sufficient for more than another century's production. The large, constant demands for fertilizer by all central and northwestern European countries make the German and French potash deposits a very great asset to European agriculture. Europe's large salt production is primarily for the highly developed chemical industries, especially in western Europe. Salt is taken not only from mines in the rock salt form (for which Germany is the largest producer) but also from underground brine and, along the French Mediterranean coast, from the sea. The richest German salt mines were included in the Soviet zone of occupation, but production is still high. The United Kingdom and France are the other two leading producers.

European sulphur production is limited. Italy (Sicily) is the only appreciable producer of native sulphur, and even its output in 1949 was only one-third that of prewar years. Prior to discovery of the great American Gulf Coast deposits, Sicily was the world's principal source of native sulphur, but after World War I its share of world production was small. From pyrites, however, Europe obtains a substantial supply of sulphur. Spain, Italy, Norway, Sweden, Germany, and Finland are the leading producers of pyrites in terms of sulphur content. The magnesite production of Austria is the highest for any country in the world, with the possible exception of the Soviet Union. Postwar Austria has reached the highest level of output in its history as one way of increasing its exports. Magnesite is especially useful in the manufacture of refractory materials.

· 9 ·

Manufacturing

Importance of Manufacturing in Europe

Manufacturing in northwestern Europe reflects the intensity of economic-cultural development shown in Map A15. Not only is it an indicator of the application of human energy toward exploitation of the various resources, but also it helps to explain how such a dense population is supported on a relatively high standard of living. Such intensive industrial development was, indeed, responsible for astonishing population increases in several northwestern European countries, as is shown in the last section of this chapter. Continued evolution of manufacturing in western and central Europe, from the time of the Industrial Revolution until the mid-twentieth century, produced the most compact and varied large industrial region on earth. As has already been indicated, European manufacturing has been seriously challenged by the rise of industry elsewhere, especially in the United States, but western and central Europe still produce a very large share of the world's fabricated goods; and the share produced by the Soviet Union is constantly increasing.

Map A127 indicates the percentage of actively engaged people employed in industries (excluding construction). The percentage varies from 40 for the United Kingdom and Luxembourg to less than 10 for some of the Balkan countries. Countries high in percentage (above 30 per cent) are Belgium, Czechoslovakia, Western Germany, and Luxembourg, with Sweden almost reaching 30 per cent. All other nations of Europe A show from 20 to 30 per cent of their actively engaged population in manufacturing. Denmark, with 24 per cent, is a good example of an economically advanced country of Europe A that has local industrial activity but that lacks intensive general development on a scale great enough to make it an industrial nation. In France and Italy, with 23 and 21 per cent, respectively, certain areas with intensive industrialization—such as northern and eastern France and the Po Basin of Italy—are offset by areas in which industries are poorly developed. This contrast is indicated by the fact that parts of both are not included in Europe A. For some countries, recent figures are not available, and older data were employed. The 10 per cent shown for Ireland has undoubtedly recently increased. The Polish percentage should probably be higher also, since all of former Upper Silesia is now Polish and since communist Poland made strenuous efforts to expand manufacturing after 1946. Russian data are not available but the percentage of people engaged in manufacturing has increased rapidly and should now be somewhere between 20 and 30, but even that is a guess.

Industrial Europe

The extension of what might be called "industrial Europe" is shown on Map A129. The line delimiting this most intensively industrialized part of the continent coincides rather well with the boundaries of Europe A, which is logically to be expected. Of

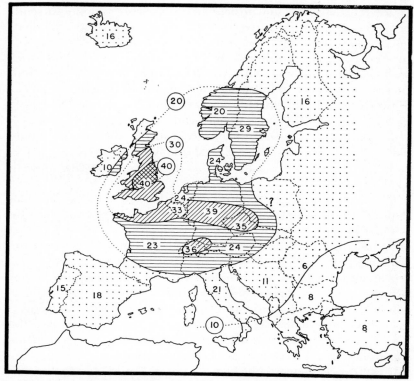

A. Percentage of Actively Engaged Population Employed in Manufacturing, 1949.

course, industrial sections exist outside the main area, but they are a more local type of development. The industrial areas of the Soviet Union are difficult to evaluate and to designate on the map, since pertinent data are scanty and personal observation is impossible. However, so far as evidence permits, the principal manufacturing regions are shown.

Industrial Regions

In Europe A the cores of the major industrial regions generally reflect the existence of the more productive coal fields. This is especially true of the zone from England to Silesia. Most of the regions, to be sure, that are now intensively industrialized had rather highly developed home industries before the Industrial Revolution, and these served as the basis for the modern development. Nevertheless, the existence of coal in such areas as the English Midlands, central Belgium, and the Ruhr has caused many industries to move toward the coal fields and to become vastly more complex in both their processes and raw materials. The English coal beds surrounding the Pennine Chain, complemented in many places by beds of iron ore, happened to coincide roughly with the greatest industrial development before the Industrial Revolution, and it is this coincidence that helped stimulate the present tremendous development of Lancashire, Birmingham, and Yorkshire, and of the Newcastle region farther north. In lowland Scotland and southern Wales a similar, although less remarkable, coincidence of human activity and coal wealth is found. All these industrial sections, as well as those that are discussed later in this section, may be identified in A129.

The line of coal fields continues southeastward along the foot of the central European uplands and can be followed on the map by the sequence of large industrial regions. Northern France around Lille, the Sambre-Meuse zone of Belgium, and the Rhine-Westphalian region of northwestern Germany are all manufacturing areas depending on an almost continuous zone of coal deposits. Grimy factories, chimneys, smoke, and a scarcely interrupted procession of industrial cities characterize all of them. Signs of wartime destruction, especially in the Ruhr, were evident for several years after 1945, but, even by 1951, clearing away of debris and reconstruction erased most of the evidences of World War II damage. Some signs will, of course, remain for many years. Southeast of the Harz Mountains is the Thuringian Basin, where the industrial development is more localized, succeeded eastward by the Saxony region, where lignite to a great extent replaces coal as the source of power. Southeastward, across the Erzgebirge, the Bohemian industrial region displays similar conditions. Finally, the end of this tremendous industrial zone appears in the Silesian coal fields, which were after 1945 united under Poland, after having been split between Ger-

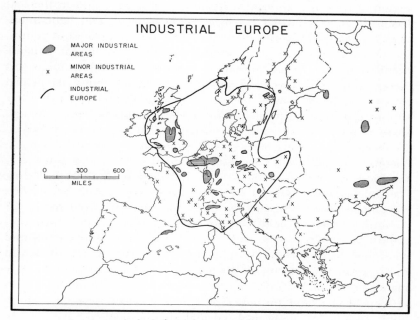

A. Industrial Areas of Europe.

many and Poland from 1921 to 1939, except, in both instances, for a small section in Czechoslovakia. Far to the east in the Soviet Union the Donets Basin may be considered an outlier of this same central European coal belt. In all these regions, the so-called "heavy" industries are dominant, primarily fabricating producers' goods. Blast furnaces, steel-rolling mills, and foundries are located close to the coal mines and furnish vast amounts of steel of all types, shapes, and sizes. Glass and pottery works are located not far away. Around these, and more removed from the grime of the heavier industries, are textile and chemical factories that require a smaller supply of fuel.

Outside the coal fields, but not far from them, many cities and their surrounding districts form active manufacturing concentrations that use some coal but manufacture principally the lighter types of goods. They specialize in consumers' goods in great variety. A string of such places along the western and southern borders of the coal fields begins with Belfast and Dublin in Ireland, expands in Bristol, and reaches huge proportions on both sides of the Channel, around London and in the lower Seine valley. In the Lorraine region of eastern France, with its minette iron ores, and in the coal basin of the Saar farther east is a region of heavy and light industries. The Upper Rhine Plain combines the advantages of central location and excellent river transportation with that of a dense population and hence abundant labor. The rather important Neckar industrial district shows how local home industries helped by modest water power, energetic organizers, and a good water supply can be transformed into modern industries even though there is no coal and only an inadequate supply of water power. Farther east this string of industrial centers is continued in Munich, Vienna, and Budapest. Separated from these by a long interval is the industrial region of the central and eastern Ukraine, including the Dnieper water power development, the Krivoy Rog iron center, the Donets coal basin, and the Stalingrad industrial center.

North of the coal fields and not far from them a similar string of industrial centers begins with Antwerp and the Dutch cities and continues through Hannover and the huge industrial unit of Berlin to the great cotton factories of Łódź in Poland and the more diverse manufactures of Warsaw. Farther north are the industrial centers of Copenhagen and the cities of central Sweden, especially Stockholm, famous for the beauty and high quality of their varied goods. Farther east the minor center of the less varied Baltic industries is found at Riga. The precision industries of Leningrad and the varied industries of the great Moscow Industrial District complete the northern series of manufacturing centers, unless the expanding Ural district on the borders of Asia is also included. In contrast to these new northern centers of manufacturing there are in the south at least three centers where old industries still survive and have expanded. Barcelona is the core of the only large manufacturing district in Spain. Florence and the Arno Basin and Naples have handicrafts as well as some modern factories whose products attain small volume but considerable value although requiring very little power for their production.

Finally, in and surrounding the Alps are industrial areas in which water power is a factor of the first importance in manufacturing.

Such power is now the basis of a great industrial development in southeastern France, Switzerland, and Northern Italy. Although little coal is available to these centers except by transportation over long distances, water power has made it possible to concentrate the old industries in modern plants and to create new industries. In France the tremendous development of water power in the Alps around Grenoble intensifies the importance that this region gained originally through the silk industry at Lyon. The Swiss industrial regions from Geneva to the Boden See (Lake of Constance) and especially around Zürich are an unusually good illustration of the way in which skillful specialization in products that need little power can overcome the handicap of lack of raw materials and coal. The Po Basin represents the industrial efforts of a great old nation to maintain its competitive position in the modern world. But, whereas Venice was once the main center of manufacturing, that function has now moved nearer the Alps, to Milan and Turin. In addition to these areas of Alpine water power utilization, there are also water power areas in the Scandinavian Peninsula and Finland. Here the plants are so scattered that many little crosses appear in A129, but there are a few large centers of production as well as many small ones. In much of Scandinavia the electricity is widely used to operate pulp and paper mills, but in some localities the abundant power has attracted chemical and metallurgical plants.

Europe's Advantages and Disadvantages in Manufacturing

The foregoing discussion reveals certain strengths and weaknesses in European manufacturing, and there are others that merit mention. Europe's advantages in industrial activity include: (1) a long history of production, first by hand and later by power-driven machine; (2) a large supply of highly skilled labor; (3) a large supply of power; (4) an appreciable local supply of certain (but not many) raw materials; (5) a superb system of water, rail, and—in many areas —road transportation for movement of coal, other raw materials, finished products, and labor; (6) a large *potential* market on the continent itself and highly developed trade with many foreign countries; (7) a progressive policy in nearly all countries for increased industrialization—with the eastern countries, which have traditionally been the least industrialized, making unusually vigorous efforts to increase manufacturing.

These seven advantages are somewhat offset by certain disadvantages in industrial production: (1) the rather worn and frequently outmoded machinery in many of the long-established factories of Europe (a liability that, curiously enough, was somewhat offset by the installation after 1945 of new machinery in the many war-damaged and destroyed plants—a step made possible in several of the countries by the supply of United States Marshall Plan funds); (2) limitations on the degree of great, economically feasible expansion of power facilities except in a few areas (Norway, Soviet Union); (3) a relatively limited supply of "risk" capital (with some exceptions)—a limitation that has developed primarily since 1930 and that the United States attempted to help offset in Western Europe after 1947; (4) a local shortage of certain raw materials, most of which can be obtained from foreign sources only so long as a high rate of exports can be maintained; and (5) finally, one of the most harassing handicaps of all, lack of economic unity in Europe, resulting from the large number of political units, each of which feels compelled to be as nearly self-sufficient as possible for fear of wartime dislocations.

Lack of economic unity—or at least of economic co-operation—is considered such an obstacle to the full development of Europe that one of the most important aims of the various postwar programs has been to bring about greater economic integration, at least of Western Europe. Eastern Europe behind the Iron Curtain presents special problems. Briefly stated, the difficulty in all Europe has been—and, despite some progress, still is—that imposition of tariff restrictions and quotas by each country on every other country's goods restrains trade and tends to restrict the market of any one producing country. The next chapter presents more details on this point, but the effect on manufacturing of such restrictions is significant as one of the disadvantages under which European countries carry on their industrial activities.

Post-1945 Recovery of Manufacturing

After the decreased tempo of production during the 1930's, European industries rallied in the latter part of the decade, partly as a result of preparations for impending war. During World War II, industrial production was at a record height in many areas of the continent, whereas it languished in others. Bombing and ground fighting inflicted incredible damage on such major manufacturing areas as the Ruhr, the Ukraine, the Saar, parts of the English Midlands, and many others. Equally serious was the damage inflicted on transportation facilities—especially railway marshaling yards, bridges, and ports, particularly by aerial bombing. The complex readjustments attending the defeat of Germany and the termination of fighting further disrupted production and the flow of raw materials and finished goods. Labor supply especially was chaotic. Different conditions existed in different parts of the continent, of course, but most of Europe experienced the situation just described.

As was brought out in Chapter 1, the staggering economic losses suffered by many countries caused the prospects of any quick recovery to appear dim. Germany, second most industrially productive country of Europe before the war, appeared to be economically crushed. Yet industrial life had to be restored—even in Germany— if Europe was to be rebuilt and if its people were to have a livelihood. With help from the United States, not only in money but in the more important raw materials, Europe in 1947 (excluding the Soviet Union) saw its industrial production reach 82 per cent of that of 1938—an amazing recovery. However, even more amazing was the attainment by Europe in 1950 of 124 per cent of the 1938 level! Germany naturally lagged farthest behind, but in 1950 even it was approximately 90 per cent recovered, and it was the only country that had not reached at least 100 per cent of its 1938 level. The east European satellite countries claimed great advances over their 1938 levels of productivity; and there should be little doubt of such advances in view of the relatively low productivity of most of them in 1938 and the type of efforts made by the communist governments after World War II. Therefore, Europe at mid-century was producing at a rate 25 per cent greater than in 1938. However, the Soviet Union increased its output 73 per cent over that of 1940, and the United States' production was up 125 per cent over 1938. Europe's recovery was slowest in the production of such items as building bricks, iron ore, coal, and wood pulp, and greatest in tractors (605 per cent of 1938 in 1950), commercial vehicles, rayon, and electric power.

Broadly speaking, there has been no significant change in the general industrial pattern of Europe for several decades, with the notable exception of the Soviet Union's new centers of production (described in Chapters 44 through 46). Even before World War I, most of the major industrial concentrations of Europe had taken form. However, a significant change has been taking place over much of Europe since about 1900, and, indeed, it is a continuation of the trend that started in western Europe with the Industrial Revolution: as the factory became more efficient and mass-produced goods became cheaper, handicrafts and home industries were made uneconomical, and home workers moved to the factories. This shift was accelerated on a large scale in eastern Europe only after the advent of the communists, and part of the great rise in official production has been at the expense of the home industries, whose output is not usually recorded in official statistics. The detailed shifts will be brought out in the chapters on specific countries.

Historical Development

The Origin of Manufacturing. Manufacturing, like other more complex cultural activities, developed first in the eastern Mediterranean region and then progressed toward the northwest. It arose in the home, where the self-sufficing primitive family produced for itself all that it needed in the way of weapons for defense or hunting, tools for building shelters, clothing for protection and adornment, and household utensils for personal convenience. The methods and results of these early industries were extremely primitive. Weapons and tools were made of stone, and clothing was fashioned from animal skins to be worn when the severity of the weather made it necessary.

This stage of manufacturing has existed throughout most of the history of mankind. It was characteristic of both the Old and the New Stone Ages, which were vastly longer than the period since the dawn of civilization. It still exists in remote parts of every continent except Europe. In Europe its disappearance began when the civilization of the river lowlands of Egypt and Mesopotamia spread westward across the Mediterranean. Manufactured products became more elaborate and were better finished than hitherto. The pottery of these earliest civilizations shows a skill and artistic sense that indicate that it was made with a purpose beyond mere necessity. Garments were woven out of wool, which was the most available product because wandering flocks of sheep had already become a feature of these regions with their long, dry summers. Life had more material comforts than were possible in the earlier days of the cave dwellers. Bread was made out of flour, oil pressed out of olives, and wine made from grapes. Nevertheless, the family remained the industrial center, and people of all classes worked with their hands. The kings and chieftains of the Homeric period worked with their slaves and followers in the fields, and turned their hands, when need arose, to the manufacturing of furniture, implements, and arms. The queen spun and wove with the women of their households and did not disdain to superintend the washing of the family linen or even to participate in it.

Home industries still continue in Europe to a degree unknown in the United States. They have indeed declined as a result of cheap mass production and the specialization of city life, but it is surprising how much is left. In the villages of eastern Europe the home is still the center of most of the manufacturing so far as this is based on local raw materials. Nothing pleases the Bulgarian peasant woman more than to have her guests admire the woolen rugs and blankets she has made. The Latvian housewife takes pride in her linen curtains and dresses made from her own flax. Her husband may be at work on a homemade cart or ox-yoke. Even in western Europe, so proud of its highly developed industries, a great amount of primitive manufacturing is still carried on in homes in the villages. Besides supplying their own household needs, the villagers often specialize locally in certain products to be sold elsewhere. The women of southern France and Flanders, sitting in front of their houses, work patiently on the beautiful handmade laces that American tourists purchase. In Switzerland the long, agriculturally unproductive winters are used by the men as a time in which to carve the well-known cuckoo clocks, toys, and other wooden articles. Even in European cities it is surprising to see how many people make jewelry, leather goods, pottery, and all sorts of little articles in their own homes. Often only two or three people, all relatives, are at work in a home "factory." In France, Italy, and all parts of the zones called Europe B and C this has long been the practice, although now it is disappearing, especially in Russia.

Ancient Manufacturing Cities. Although the ancient city people originally based their manufacturing on local raw materials, an increased demand for their goods and a better development of trade led them to import not only raw products but likewise skilled labor in the form of slaves. Consequently ancient manufacturing expanded most rapidly in centers of transportation, especially in those located on harbors. In the old Greek world Athens and Corinth were the most important manufacturing centers. In them there were pullers and dyers, workers in cloth factories, hatmakers, leather manufacturers, jewelers, builders and masons, furniture and cabinet makers, potters, and manufacturers of shields, spears, bows, knives, helmets, breastplates, and wagons. Corinth owed its importance to its location on the isthmus between the Aegean Sea and the Gulf of Corinth; it had harbors on both sides and a kind of tramway to transport goods across the isthmus.

After the breakdown of the Roman Empire, the center of manufacturing swung back to the east, and Constantinople took the place of Rome. Here flourished all the crafts of antiquity, together with some new ones. Great silk factories worked up the products of Syria and Greece. Besides the thousands of craftsmen making articles of luxury that would first strike the eyes of the European observer, there were makers of textiles, metals, weapons, and other wares.

Medieval Industries. Throughout the rest of Europe, manufacturing declined with the decline of the cities during the Dark Ages. Not until the Crusades opened the minds of northern Europe to a less simple life after A.D. 1100 did a new awakening ensue. Then manufacturing resumed its northwestward progress, and northern Italy became the nucleus of an industrial renaissance. Florence, Milan, and Genoa were famous for their manufactured products. Venice became the main industrial center. The Venetians introduced the silk industry from Byzantium (Constantinople), wove woolen and cotton goods, and had extensive glassworks and iron and brass foundries. From the east, probably, they took the idea of a rigid guild system, which later spread to western Europe. This system had long been practiced in Byzantium but was there based on slave labor, whereas when brought to the manufacturing cities of Europe it was carried on by free craftsmen. At the same general time southern Spain under the Moors had its period of industrial progress. Thus the northern Mediterranean was the center of the world's industry—a region of production and also of trade where the products of both eastern and northern Europe were exchanged for its own fine wares.

Meanwhile the northwestward progress of manufacturing continued. Northern Europe was awakening to a new life. Along the trade routes that led from Italy the cities of France and Germany became centers of industrial development based on the guilds. Then the Hanseatic League arose on the shores of the North Sea and the Baltic and intensified the growth of many commercial and industrial cities. This development was especially strong in the cities of Flanders, with Bruges as the center. The long-established woolen industry gained wide importance, for in the Middle Ages wool was still the chief clothing material. Other industries did likewise. While this was happening, the Italian and Spanish cities lost their supremacy through the breakdown of the Italian overland trade from the Mediterranean eastward and through the decline and final collapse of the Moorish cities in Spain. When this happened, Flanders was ready to take the lead and become the main industrial region of Europe. Bruges, Ghent, and later Antwerp not only were the centers of manufacturing in the Europe of the fifteenth century, but dominated trade and commerce. Thus the center of industrial activity had at last reached the same general North Sea region where agriculture was also approaching its highest development.

Location of Manufacturing at the Time of the Industrial Revolution. Within the North Sea area as a whole, there was still room for a considerable change in the distribution of manufacturing. The second part of the sixteenth century and especially the seventeenth century saw the relative decline of Flanders. Political factors were mainly responsible. Spain and later Austria controlled the land. The newborn Dutch Republic blockaded the outlet of Antwerp, which had succeeded Bruges, where the harbor had become filled with silt swept along the coast by the currents. Many Flemish Protestants, representing the better class of the population, had fled to Holland. Together with French Huguenots expelled by France, they brought new industrial development in this country of seafarers. But Holland was too small to become the industrial leader.

France and England were especially well fitted for such leadership. France, then at the peak of its power, was long the first industrial country of the world. But its many wars, not always successful, impoverished the country, and the rigid political system and the conservative temperament of the people prevented the industries from having the freedom they needed. In England the factors making for success were much better. Skilled and in some cases wealthy immigrants, fleeing from political turmoil or religious persecution in Flanders, France, and elsewhere, brought new skill and energy to British industries. They modernized the local home industries and made England the world's leader in the production of woolen textiles, which were then the most important type of manufactured goods. Within the limits of England the greatest industrial development first took place in the eastern lowland. By the middle of the eighteenth century, however, a further shift had occurred toward the source of the wool supply, toward a poor region where agriculture offered little competition in procuring labor, and toward harbors facing America and its growing colonial market. Meanwhile, being isolated on an island and therefore little affected by wars like those that continually embroiled France with its continental neighbors, England gained greatly in political strength, especially after the decline of the Dutch Republic. Its trade increased rapidly; new lines of communication with the rest of the world were established. Colonial conquests opened new markets for its products, and the atmosphere was ready for a new era—the Industrial Revolution, which began in the second half of the eighteenth century and reached its height in the nineteenth.

The great features of this revolution were the invention of machinery, the consequent use of power based on coal, and hence a great increase in the use of iron and other metals. All these things were responses to a demand. They were not the result of chance or of the stimulus offered by the mere presence of coal and iron, as is often supposed. The demand for machinery, and hence for coal and iron, arose in England because by 1750 the manufacturing industries of the world had reached their highest development in the same general sections of Europe where they are now most highly developed. The same conditions that caused the old hand industries to reach so high a stage led inventors to make new machines and seek sources of power to run them. By sheer accident it happened that the very regions that were the leaders in this had some of the world's best supplies of both coal and iron. This naturally afforded a great stimulus to the new kind of manufacturing. It also caused some shifting of the centers of activity within the general industrial region of western Europe, together with the growth of many new cities to carry on the heavy industries connected with the production of iron and with other processes, like the making of glass, that require much fuel.

The essential point is that before the Industrial Revolution the progress of industry, agriculture, trade, and civilization in general had given western

Europe and especially the parts near the North Sea the unquestioned supremacy of the world in industry. Within this region, quite without respect to coal and iron, England, the Low Countries, northern France, and the neighboring sections of Germany held the lead. Among these countries England stood first. Hence there the demand for better methods was strongest and the incentive to invention greatest. Accordingly, in that country, almost on top of large deposits of coal and iron, there came to pass an industrial revolution that gave to those beds a wholly unexpected significance. Where England led, the other countries followed suit, and Europe in the nineteenth century entered a period of hitherto unknown industrial progress. As one goes away from the North Sea center, the force of this revolution becomes less and less. This is one reason why the Soviet Union's attempt to do in a few years what England did in a century and a half is of such absorbing interest.

Trade

Bases for European Trade

Geographically, Europe—especially western Europe—possesses many of the basic factors that lead to trade. For instance, climatic differences lead to exchange of products because of differences in regional agricultural production. Timber from the northern forests, wheat and corn from the Danubian states, dairy products from the Netherlands and Denmark, wines from France and Italy, and citrus fruit and olive oil from the Mediterranean are examples of products that as regional responses to climate are extensively shipped from one European country or region to another. Likewise, diversity of relief, which tends to diversify production, leads to exchange, and many cities have developed on the line of contact between mountains and lowlands. Mineral resources such as coal, oil, metals, and other minerals are generally only partly used in the country where they are exploited; many of them are available for export. For instance, in northern Sweden the iron ore of Kiruna and Gällivare, mined under the disadvantage of a climate inside the Arctic Circle, is transported to the Atlantic and the Baltic for export, and food and other articles must be brought in for the mining population. Another stimulus to trade is the stage of industrial development of different regions, which leads, for example, to the exchange of products between the highly industrialized country in western Europe (Europe A) and the agrarian country in the east and southeast (Europe C). Finally, national differences in artistic sense and taste, and the development of industries based on these, are another factor in promoting exchange. Paris is a good example of the way in which French culture has developed a concentration of industries producing a surplus of articles that reflect the French artistic ability. Vienna owes part of its commercial importance to similar conditions; and the importance of the china of Copenhagen and Dresden, the glass of Venice, the lace of Flanders, and the embroideries of Switzerland is in large measure based on the artistic capabilities of the population.

Post-World War II Trade Situation

Despite the logic and geographical soundness of these facts, the European trade situation at the middle of the twentieth century was far from encouraging, although there were a few bright aspects. What was the trouble? First of all, the years of war—with their destruction, constant use of machinery without repairs, drop in food production because of lack of manpower and fertilizer, and perhaps most important the aftermath of lack of human energy and a feeling of hopelessness—produced in most countries tremendous deficits in food, raw materials, and manufactured products. Financially, most countries were unable to import the products needed to re-create a normal economy, and, in spite of American help through loans and gifts, they had to take special steps to avoid bankruptcy and a fatal drop in living conditions for their citizens. Moreover, strenuous efforts were made to protect the value of the national currency. Such steps required strict government control and a closed economy in which only the government permitted foreign trade, and that only if such trade was essential to the nation.

Imports had to be restricted, although they still remained high because of sheer necessity. Exports were encouraged, but there was often not much to sell and not much of a market. Moreover, all countries attempted to follow the same trade strategy at the same time. Strange conditions resulted, and trade to a large extent stopped being geographically logical. For example, Britain vigorously attempted to increase its export of motorcars—and was quite successful for a period; but at the same time automobiles were scarcely available in the country itself. Stores in New York sold Dutch chocolate and beer, but no chocolate was obtainable in the Netherlands, and the beer there was watery. It was the doctrine of "stooping to conquer," but the conquest often did not come.

In the typical European country in 1951 the balance of trade—except for such countries as Sweden and Switzerland, which escaped the worst consequences of war-torn economies—shows a large figure on the debit side, because the difference between value of imports and value of exports is not offset by such items as income from tourism, services, and investment dividends. Despite the persisting unfavorable trade balances in most European countries, in 1950 the export-import ratio reached 0.80 among the countries participating in the Organization for European Economic Co-operation, compared with 0.75 in 1938. Thus, the average balance of Western European countries had by 1950 at least returned to that of pre-World War II years. Even so, the trade situation, as part of the general economic situation, was extremely delicate, and only American help, extended because the United States could not allow Western Europe to collapse economically into chaos and Soviet communism, carried Europe through the postwar years. Aid by the United States was given in the hope and expectation that the recipient nations would be enabled to return to a relatively stable economy. Whatever the arguments pro and con the "Marshall Plan" or European Recovery Program, the fact is that, during the most crucial years after World War II up to 1952, no member nation was lost to communist domination nor did any suffer fatal bankruptcy.

One of the most marked—and, strictly economically speaking, most unfortunate—changes in the pattern of European trade from prewar years is the decrease in trade between eastern Europe and western Europe. Most of the same factors that made the postwar level of trade within western Europe lower than the prewar level also affected east-west trade. The political differences between East and West created an additional handicap to trade between the two areas. Western Europe needed the east's grain, timber, and other products, and eastern Europe needed the west's machinery and other manufactures; but mutual agreement on terms of trade was difficult to reach. However, by 1948 the money value of east-west trade slowly climbed toward prewar levels, although physical volume of trade lagged far behind money value; in other words, inflated prices made trade appear to be greater than it was. Trade with the Soviet Union itself fared less well than that with the satellite countries—especially Poland and Czechoslovakia. However, in general, east-west trade was gradually reviving when, in 1950, the Cold War strategy led the Western Nations, especially the United States, to call for a restriction of exports to the Soviet Bloc. During 1950, therefore, east-west trade decreased appreciably, and in 1951 the decrease was marked. Britain felt obliged to maintain trade relations with eastern Europe, including the Soviet Union, since it needs grain and timber from the area. The dilemma of Germany, divided and torn between East and West, was revealed in the fact that its exports to the east rose in 1950, whereas those of nearly all other western countries fell. The fact was that Germany needed trade partners, and the western countries were unable to fill the role.

Attempts at Economic Integration

The economic disruptions attending the end of World War II emphasized the obstacles that the European countries themselves had long imposed on their own trade relations. Almost every political boundary was also a customs boundary, and the highly complicated system of protective tariffs and export taxes created a virtual chaos in exchange of goods during the confusion that followed World War II. Sheer necessity led to some surmounting of the obstacles, but not until 1948 was real progress made. It was in 1948 that the "Marshall Plan," or, officially, the European Recovery Program (ERP) primed the European economic pump with billions of dollars. The Soviet Union and its eastern European satellites were originally invited to participate in the Marshall Plan, but all declined except Czechoslovakia, which first accepted, then hastily withdrew its acceptance. Out of the ERP there developed an economic organization of western European countries called Organization for European Economic Cooperation (OEEC), whose title reveals its purpose. The OEEC was, of course, a necessary counterpart of the ERP, since the original suggestion by the then Secretary of State George Marshall in 1947 called for closer integration of the European economies. Naturally, both ERP and OEEC affected many aspects of European economic life in addition to trade. But certainly OEEC, with the help of ERP funds, contributed materially to the revival of western European trade on a rational basis. In 1950, another organization, the European Payments Union (EPU), was constituted to ease the exchange problem.

These larger programs overshadowed more limited but still significant efforts. For example, in 1947 Belgium, the Netherlands, and Luxembourg set up the organization *Benelux* on the basis of agreements reached in London in 1944. The ultimate aim was a complete customs union and a common foreign policy. Benelux made appreciable strides, but the Netherlands' economic difficulties and other factors kept the union from achieving the hoped-for results as late as mid-1951. In 1948 France and Italy also took preliminary steps toward a customs union.

One of the most revolutionary suggestions for economic co-operation came from France in 1950 in terms of the "Schuman Plan" for pooling of French and German coal and steel production as a prelude to pooling western European coal and steel production. The scope and significance of the Schuman Plan can be seen in the following quotation from the original proposal:

The peace of the world can only be preserved if creative efforts are made which are commensurate, in their scope, with the dangers which threaten peace.

The contribution which an organized and active Europe can make to civilization is indispensable for the maintenance of peaceful relations. France, by championing during more than twenty years the idea of a united Europe, has always regarded it as an essential objective to serve the purposes of peace. Because Europe was not united, we have had war.

A united Europe will not be achieved all at once, nor in a single framework: it will be formed by concrete measures which first of all create a solidarity in fact. The uniting of the European nations requires that the age-old opposition between France and Germany be culminated: the action to be taken must first of all concern France and Germany.

To that end, the French Government proposes that immediate action be concentrated on one limited, but decisive point:

The French Government proposes that the entire French-German production of coal and steel be placed under a joint high authority, within an organization open to the participation of other European nations.

The pooling of coal and steel production will immediately assure the establishment of common bases for economic development, which is the first state for a European federation, and will change the destiny of these regions which have long been devoted to the production of arms to which they themselves were the first to fall constantly victim.

The community of production which will in this manner be created will clearly show that any war between France and Germany becomes not only unthinkable, but in actual fact impossible. The establishment of this powerful production unit, open to all countries that wish to participate in it, will give a real foundation to their economic development, by furnishing on equal terms to all countries thus united the fundamental elements of industrial production.

This production will be offered to the entire world, without distinction or exclusion, as a contribution to the raising of living standards and the progress of world peace. Europe, with its resources thus increased, will be able to pursue one of its essential tasks: the development of the African Continent.

This will quickly and easily bring about the fusion of interests which is indispensable to the establishment of an economic community and introduce a leaven of broader and deeper community of interest between countries which have long been divided by bloody conflict.

By pooling basic production and by creating a new high authority whose decisions will be binding on France, Germany, and the other countries who may subsequently join, this proposal will create the first concrete foundation for a European federation which is so indispensable for the preservation of peace.

The quotation reveals that the plan envisages far more than increased effectiveness of European industries. It had been initialed by the foreign ministers of the participating countries (France, Western Germany, Italy, and the three Benelux countries) by late 1951, and by the end of April, 1952, both the French and the German parliaments had ratified the plan. Naturally, refusal of the United Kingdom to enter the plan imposes certain handicaps on its effective operation—if it is finally accepted by the parliaments, but Britain's aloofness does not mean inevitable failure of the pooling. It is important to realize the line of thinking in western Europe at mid-century as shown in the proposal.

Per Capita Income

The mid-century impoverishment of Europe cannot be easily shown in figures. Map B16 indicates the national income per capita in Europe; however, it does not tell the whole story, because prices vary greatly from country to country, and buying at the time (1949) to which the figures refer was still restricted; nevertheless, some conclusions can be arrived at from the map, especially if it is compared with Table A144. By taking the per capita income in Switzerland,

TABLE A

PER CAPITA INCOME IN PERCENTAGE OF THAT OF SWITZERLAND

	1928	1948		1928	1948
United Kingdom	107	94	Belgium	61	69
Netherlands	107	59	Norway	?	41
Switzerland	100	100	Spain	44	23
Denmark	78	81	Italy	41	28
Sweden	75	92	Ireland	31	49
Germany	73	37	Portugal	24	29
France	68	57	Greece	19	15

which probably has been least affected by changes, as a base (100) for both 1928 and 1948, and relating the income in a number of other countries to the Swiss 100, the results shown below are obtained.

Impoverishment is shown in the Netherlands, Germany, Italy, France, and the United Kingdom, all of which suffered severely during World War II. Improvement is shown in neutral countries such as Sweden, Portugal, and especially Ireland. Denmark, also, did not suffer much, and Belgium even had a postwar boom. Spain is still in poor condition, the result of the civil war and long-standing misery. Eastern and southeastern Europe were always poor and are still poor, with the figures for Greece showing an extreme example. Fortunately, the situation revealed in Table A144 improved somewhat after 1948, but complete data were not available for purposes of comparison.

Trade

Table A145 shows the exports per capita of the European countries. Exports were selected because, although not actually "normal,"

TABLE A

EXPORT VALUE PER CAPITA IN 1949

	Population	Export (millions of dollars)	Per Capita (dollars)
Albania	1.17	?	?
Austria	7	301	43
Belgium-Luxembourg	8.9	1,769	190
Bulgaria	7.1	86	12
Czechoslovakia	12.4	806	65
Denmark	4.2	672	160
Finland	4	398	99
France	41	2,715	66
Western Germany	47	1,123	24
Greece	7.8	115	15
Hungary	9.2	165	18
Iceland	0.137	40	292
Ireland	3	222	72
Italy	46	1,107	24
Netherlands	10	1,312	131
Norway	3.2	396	124
Poland	24	533	22
Portugal	8.5	157	18
Spain	28	380	13
Sweden	5.9	1,059	153
Switzerland	4.6	804	175
United Kingdom	50	6,831	136
Yugoslavia	16	192	12

they give a better picture of European trade than would imports, which are still not back to normal after war conditions. The table indicates the usual pattern of high values around the North Sea countries and a decrease in all directions—except for Switzerland, which is also high. In 1949, Iceland ranked highest, followed by the Belgium-Luxembourg customs union, Switzerland, Sweden, Denmark, Britain, the Netherlands, Norway, and Finland. The drop from the zone of high exports is quite sharp.   Ireland, France, and Czechoslovakia have average positions, and the scale decreases to a low in Spain and the Balkans.   Germany and Austria are also very low, but their positions —especially Germany's—will have more trade when normal conditions are re-established.

It is interesting to see how much of the trade of the various countries is with regions outside the continent.   In percentages, the pattern is totally different from most of the preceding related data. Only Britain, France, and Portugal have more trade outside Europe than with the European countries, a fact traceable to their trade with their overseas territories.   Southern Europe also has a relatively high percentage of trade outside Europe.   In Spain the total trade is small, but the percentage of exports to the Spanish possessions is relatively high.   However, Argentina ranks as the principal buyer; and for Greece the United States and the United Kingdom are principal buyers.

In contrast to those countries that engage in intensive trade with overseas areas are those whose trade is primarily intra-European. From Ireland, as an extreme example, 92 per cent of all exports go to Britain and Northern Ireland, with an additional 7 per cent to other European countries.   Denmark sends 44 per cent of its exports to Britain and an additional 48 per cent to other European countries. All eastern European Soviet satellite countries, except Czechoslovakia, send nearly all their exports to other European countries; and after 1950 the receiving countries were primarily other satellites or the Soviet Union.   From Bulgaria, for example, 90 per cent of the 1949 exports went to other European countries; and, of this 90 per cent, 50 per cent went to the Soviet Union and 36 per cent to other satellites.

The Development of European Commerce

Ancient Mediterranean Trade.   In the ancient Mediterranean period it was so difficult to transport goods by land that trade was carried on mainly by water along the seacoast and up the rivers.   The Mediterranean Sea had incomparable advantages for such traffic.   In the first place, it extends from east to west, so that the same general kind of weather prevails everywhere, and only one type of seamanship, as well as one type of clothing and equipment for both ships and people, is needed.   In the second place, numerous promontories and islands offer shelter in stormy weather.   This is fortunate, for the irregular topography of the coastal zones impedes overland movements and drives people to the sea.   Then, too, the main products lend themselves to trade.   Salt, wine, grain, and olive oil, which were abundantly produced close to the seacoast, are easy to preserve and to transport, and hence were among the first articles of trade. In early times the Mediterranean was bordered on the east by countries that led the world in cultural development and that had a correspondingly keen interest in the contacts of foreign trade. Thus a great number of factors combined to cause trade to develop more rapidly by sea than by land.

Most prominent among the old seafaring people were the Phoenicians and the Cretans, whose main source of wealth was traffic by sea. The Greeks, however, were perhaps still more important in later days, and even the Romans depended on the sea relatively more than do the modern Italians. Colonies of the Phoenicians (such as Carthage), of the Greeks (such as those in Sicily), and later of the Romans (such as those in Spain) maintained contact with the mother countries by sea routes. Bold sailors circumnavigated the Spanish peninsula to reach the Scilly Islands off the southwestern tip of England. In Egypt a canal connected the Nile with the Red Sea, thus giving a water route from the Atlantic to the Indian Ocean. Battles between the Mediterranean powers were often sea battles, and the victory carried with it the mastery of that sea and also of the means of transportation.

Athens and Corinth were the foremost European harbors of the pre-Roman period. They mark a northward and westward movement in the location of the centers where trade was most active. Their commerce included many products. The Sea of Marmara and the Black Sea, especially off the mouth of the Dnieper, furnished immense quantities of salt fish; and next to bread this was the staple article of diet in Athens. Much of the bread of that city was made from Scythian grain brought from the northern and western shores of the Black Sea. The Scythians also sent cattle to Athens in exchange for oil, bronzes, and especially wine. Besides these staple products, the Scythian tombs have yielded fine specimens of Athenian pottery, jewelry, and other artistic objects. Many slaves were also sent from Scythia to Athens. The imports from the Black Sea also included flax, hemp, timber, tar, and charcoal. Since wood was scarce on the Greek coasts and hard to transport over mountain trails from the interior, the forests on the immediate shores of Asia Minor and close to the course of the lower Danube were used to supply the deficiency.

Not all the trade of this time was carried by water. On every market day a long stream of donkeys laden with grain and other farm products poured into cities like Athens from the surrounding country. More expensive goods such as the famous cloth dyed with Tyrian purple, copper vessels, pottery, jewelry, and weapons were transported long distances by land. Only articles of high value and small size—luxuries, not necessities—were carried far by land, as is still the case in vast regions such as the interior of China. Some very precious goods were transported long distances by overland trails; such were gold from the Urals and amber from the Baltic. But such transportation by men or animals was slow and dangerous, and the trails were scarcely recognizable as such. The sea trade was also beset by many dangers. Piracy was frequent from the oldest period, when the Aegean Islands were hotbeds of pirates endangering the merchant fleets of Sidon and Tyre, until finally in the nineteenth century the last stronghold on the Algerian coast fell before the power of modern weapons. Thus, many circumstances combined to cause the trade per capita in ancient times to be very small except in a few main cities.

The importance of the Mediterranean Sea for transportation continued during the Roman period, but the center of activity moved still farther north and west to Rome. Ostia, the harbor of Rome, saw boats from all over the Mediterranean connecting the Roman colonies with the mother city. The extension of the Roman Empire beyond the realm of the sea caused a new and important factor to enter into commerce: the famous Roman roads, which more or less remained the basis of the European road system up to the eighteenth century. These roads opened up the interior to a degree hitherto unknown. They were directed primarily toward ports on the Mediterranean Sea and thus toward Rome. Along them marched the Roman legions and also the Roman traders. Roman settlements became important centers of trade, exchanging local products for the many articles of commerce that Rome and the Mediterranean towns had learned to supply, while the frontier towns provided commercial contact with the Germanic lands beyond the border.

The Medieval Situation. The breakdown of the Roman Empire destroyed this development. The center of activity swung back toward the east. Trade became centralized in the eastern part of the Mediterranean and did not extend so widely as before. Unstable political conditions and numerous wars interrupted former trade relations; roads were neglected, and the prosperous old Roman settlements declined in importance.

Only when the Crusaders brought northern Europe into contact with the Mediterranean and Asiatic world was there a revival of trade. Products of the Near East and India—such as spices, sugar, pearls, and precious stones, or perfumes, silks, carpets, and glass—were brought from the harbors of the Levant to Venice and Genoa. These Italian cities became the great centers of commerce, thus marking another step northward and westward in the movement of centers of culture. From them, overland roads carried a part of the eastern products to northern Europe, where the demand was increasing. The Alps interposed a formidable barrier to this trade, but the Rhône Valley provided a narrow route around them toward Paris and the Rhine; and from Venice the Brenner Pass made it possible, although not easy, to go directly to Munich and other newly developing towns of southern Germany. Fairs became the usual means of bringing people together for trade and were a characteristic feature of the Middle Ages, especially from the twelfth to the fourteenth centuries.

While Italy's city republics, Venice and Genoa, were at their peak, the next step in the northern and western movement of the centers of trade was in process of development. Northern Europe, now gradually settling down from migrations and wars, began to develop its own trade, using the Baltic and North seas as a means of transit. The Hanseatic League, a rather loose but powerful organization, combined the coastal and inland settlements of the Netherlands and northern Germany with those of the Scandinavian countries and extended its influence even into Russia (Novgorod). Visby in Gotland was its Baltic center. Lübeck and Danzig on the German Baltic coast became the leading commercial cities. The trade was rather complex, with southern Europe exporting wine, salt, oil, fruits, silk, and sugar; Russia exporting furs, hides, leather, grain, and wax; and the Scandinavian lands exporting timber, iron, copper, furs, livestock, blubber, fish, meat, and grains. These were exchanged for more finished foodstuffs, cloth, wines, manufactured wares, and the usual southern European imports.

Meanwhile, the fall of Byzantium and the impossibility of continuing Asiatic trade by reason of the invasions and wars of the Turks, Mongols, and others caused the northern Mediterranean region to decline. Flanders, the richest section of the Hanseatic League, at length overshadowed it. Thus in the fourteenth century Bruges rivaled Venice as the great commercial and industrial center of Europe, and at a later date the fleet of the Netherlands, with brooms at the mastheads of its ships, dominated the North Sea. Trade between the Mediterranean and Flanders was small, since the route by sea is long, and by land the traders were attacked by robbers. The robbers were often in league with feudal landlords who lived near the main roads in castles like the ones whose ruins along the Rhine and Rhône now have such a romantic attraction for tourists.

The Modern Era. The trade of Europe entered a new era about A.D. 1500. This time the shift in the location of the main centers was mainly westward because of the discovery of America. Where this shift took place in Mediterranean latitudes its impetus soon came to an end, for the greatness of Spain and Portugal declined rapidly. Farther north it began most strongly in Great Britain, but finally affected all the regions touching the North Sea. After Columbus discovered America the gold and silver of the new continent provided a tremendous source of income. Portuguese merchants, sailing around Africa, had discovered the road to India and the Spice Islands. Lisbon took the place formerly occupied by Venice and Genoa, and the Dutch and English went there to buy Asiatic products and distribute them throughout northern Europe.

Meanwhile a great change had come over the North Sea and Baltic area. The successful revolt of the northern provinces of the Netherlands—later the Dutch Republic—broke the glory of Flanders, which remained under Spanish control. Flanders was then blockaded by the Dutch fleet and deprived of its commerce. The European center of trade shifted from the Mediterranean and the Baltic to the Atlantic shores, facing a world that had been newly explored. Dutch and English fleets took the American trade away from the Spanish. Finding for themselves the way to India, they there assumed the place formerly held by Portugal. The Dutch and English East India companies became the world's commercial leaders. Colonies were founded along the African coast and in the West Indies and the Americas. The French joined the Dutch and English in this effort. Thus by the beginning of the seventeenth century the world was fairly well-known, its economic value had been explored, and the center of trade had become firmly established around the North Sea. It is worth noting that this region had forged to the head before the discovery of America and of the route around Africa. These discoveries temporarily gave Spain and Portugal great importance, but this waned after a century or two. Thus, although the North Sea countries do not occupy so favorable a position in respect to the two Americas and Africa as does Portugal, they have nevertheless received the greatest benefit from these newly known parts of the world.

For a long time the European trade with these new regions was extremely one-sided. Except in a few cases where white colonization took place, as in North America, the trade mostly took the form of bringing native products to Europe, with little exchange of European products in return. Of course, there was some export of small European articles that had value in the eyes of the natives, but most of the trade was forced on the natives under the guise of political protection or under threat of punishment. Consequently, ships sailing from Europe usually had to sail in ballast as there were no bulky European exports. The general increase in European productivity, which finally resulted in the Industrial Revolution of the eighteenth century, helped to change this situation, especially in England and France. The growth of the colonies, those of England in particular, worked in the same direction. This in turn led to a demand for better and speedier means of transportation and started that tremendous increase which resulted in the present conditions. The change, however, was gradual, and modern means of rapid, luxurious transportation are only of recent date.

· II ·
Transportation

Europe's Advantages for Transportation

Europe is especially favored from the standpoint of transportation. Its peninsular character, with inland seas extending deep into the continent; its well-developed coastline, with numerous bays, gulfs, and islands protecting the coast from the ferocity of ocean gales; its many navigable rivers, with drowned outlets permitting an easy transition from ocean to continent—all these are factors in its favor. Even the relief does not offer insurmountable difficulties. On the lowlands, canals connect the river systems, and railroads form a dense network. Moreover, the uplands usually offer convenient passages. In the few places where real barriers exist, the energy and intellect of man have found ways to cut tunnels through the mountains, as in the Alps and Pyrenees, or to carry roads by easy windings over obstacles, as on the Norwegian fjeld between Bergen and Oslo. Thus in most parts of Europe not only do difficulties of transportation no longer greatly hamper trade, but easy means of transport also actually invite it. One has to go to remote corners of the Balkans to find places untouched by modern means of transportation.

Means of Transportation

It would be instructive if all the transportation facilities of each region could be presented in one map, with the proper weight given to each. It would be necessary to include oxen, horses, mules, asses, carts, automobiles, trolleys, trains, airplanes, canal boats, river boats, coastal steamers, and ocean vessels. To complete the picture of European trade and commerce it would be necessary to add data about the number of people and the amount of freight carried by the railways, the volume of foreign commerce, and the amount of internal trade, although there are no good statistics for the last item. To combine all these in a single map is impossible, but separate maps of many of them can be made.

To begin with the part played by animals, although no map of
oxen is here given, it is interesting to note that all through central
Europe from central France to Bulgaria their use to draw carts as
well as plows is common. This indicates not only a much slower rate
of work and lower standard of living than in most parts of the
United States, but also a correspondingly mild development of trade.
The use of horses, mules, and asses is very widespread. Naturally,
the number of these animals is relatively low in proportion to the
number of people in the main manufacturing regions—less than 6
per 100 persons. Nevertheless where the people of the zone called
Europe A depend mainly on agriculture, as in Denmark, a country
may have a large number of horses per capita in spite of a large
urban and industrial population and a great use of motor vehicles.
Ireland vies with the eastern Baltic lands and with Russia as the
European region where horses are relatively most important. This
indicates that in these regions the other and more modern means of
transportation are not highly developed. In southern Europe the
abundant donkeys and mules are like oxen in indicating a relatively
low degree of commercial activity.

In A159 the distribution of railways shows the opposite side of the
picture. Compared with other parts of the world, including even
the United States, the main part of Europe is abundantly supplied
with railroads. Note how extremely numerous the railroads are in
Europe A, and especially in the main industrial section. A few relatively open areas show the effect of relief in places like Czechoslovakia and Switzerland, but the extraordinary fact is that so many
railroads cross not only the British Highlands, the German Uplands,
and the Erzgebirge between Germany and Czechoslovakia, but even
the Alps themselves. In Europe B, however, the railroad net becomes less dense; in Europe C it is quite open, and many spaces are
without railroads. Some small spaces of this sort are due to mountains like the Carpathians, Pyrenees, Apennines, and Balkans, although these are really much easier to cross than the Alps. Far
larger spaces are due to the cold climate of northeastern Russia and
the dry climate of southeastern European Russia. The reason for the
contrasts in the density of the railway net is that Europe A, by reason of its climate, crops, and industries, produces a surplus that is
not only huge in the aggregate, but also large per capita, a factor of
special importance. The trade of Europe C, on the contrary, is relatively small not only because the physical advantages there take the
form of soil and level plains rather than climate, minerals, and water-

ways, but likewise because the people cultivate only a little land per farmer and do not work very effectively in the factories.

A map showing the number of persons per automobile (A163) looks about like maps of the yield of wheat per acre, or of health, income per capita, actively engaged people employed in manufacturing, and the use of coal per capita. This is natural, for these maps represent the fundamental sources of the surplus that makes it possible to use automobiles. Exceptional countries like Holland, where the number of automobiles is low, simply illustrate how one factor may supplement or displace another. Holland still carries on such active commerce by canal and river that it does not need so many railways, roads, and automobiles as do its neighbors. All things considered, the facilities for transportation are about equally well developed all around the North Sea except where rugged relief interposes difficulties, as in northern Scotland. On the other hand, the gently undulating plain of northeastern Russia contains an area larger than France and Germany with only one or two railroads. Albania also has only 62 miles of railways, and Yugoslavia, although the same size as Great Britain, has only one third as many miles of railways.

The situation in respect to transportation by water is similar to that by land. Great Britain, being an island near the most active part of Europe, has 20 times as great a tonnage of merchant vessels as Russia with its continental position in the less-favored part. Norway, where the geographic environment is stimulating and marine, but inhospitable, has many times as much shipping as Russia in proportion to the population, and it has almost 4 times as much in absolute tons. France, although 13 times as populous as Norway, has a far smaller tonnage of merchant vessels. Yet so active is commerce in all parts of Europe A that even in France the tonnage of merchant vessels per capita is twice as great as in Portugal and 4 times as great as in Yugoslavia, both of which have long and deeply indented coasts.

Water Transportation

Merchant Marine. The world's merchant marine still belongs mainly to western Europe. The United States has increased its share of world shipping remarkably since World War I, and especially during and after World War II; but its share is only one-third the total for the world. The United Kingdom has the second largest merchant fleet, with about one-fifth the world total tonnage. Norway, third in world ranking, has about 6 per cent of the world total. Panama, artificially high in rank, comes next and is followed by France, the Netherlands, and Italy, each with more than 3 per cent of the world total. Sweden, the Soviet Union, Greece, Japan, and Denmark have 2.5 to 1.5 per cent of the total. Germany lost nearly all its merchant marine during World War II or as a result of Allied seizure. Its share of world tonnage was still very small in 1951, but shipbuilding activities had been resumed on an appreciable scale in Germany. Whereas in normal years the North Sea-Skaggerak countries own more than half the world's shipping, in 1950 their share was approximately 43 per cent. However, all except a small percentage of the world's shipbuilding in 1950 was being done in North Sea-Skaggerak countries.

Harbors. It has already been shown that the relative importance of European harbors has changed considerably since the days of ancient Greece. Even where the harbors themselves are still suitable, the changes in the location of markets and in the relative productivity of the hinterland have often joined with political factors to alter their importance. In other places, even where natural conditions were unsuitable, these same factors have led to the construction of artificial harbors. Some of the harbors that were formerly most favorable cannot admit the large modern vessels without extensive dredging or perhaps the construction of entirely new channels. Dock space has had to be increased constantly to satisfy the demands of modern transportation.

Among the present harbors, four are of outstanding international importance, for each receives shipping to the extent of over 20 million tons in normal years: London, Hamburg, Rotterdam, and Antwerp. Each is located at a river outlet, but only Hamburg and Rotterdam have an open waterway far inland. London, including the subport of Southampton, still comes first in spite of its eccentric location in regard to the English industrial regions. The three others are strong rivals for central European trade. Hamburg looks toward the densely populated section of central Germany and, before World War II and until trade was disrupted in 1950, toward Czechoslovakia. Though heavily damaged during World War II, it and its outport of Cuxhaven were extensively repaired and used by the Allies. Rotterdam, with its canalized river, is most favorably located with regard to the Rhine region, but Antwerp on the Scheldt also tries to gain the trade of the Rhine in combination with that of its nearer hinterland in Belgium and northern France. Antwerp gained an advantage over Rotterdam as a result of Rotterdam's destruction and the earlier opening of Antwerp toward the end of World War II.

The other European harbors that receive 10 million tons of shipping or more in normal years are Liverpool, Genoa, Marseille, and Cherbourg. Liverpool combines with Manchester to form the great industrial harbor of Great Britain, but it has lost part of its former passenger traffic. Genoa and Marseille not only combine Mediterranean with transatlantic trade, but also have much traffic with Asia through the Suez Canal. Cherbourg was mainly a passenger harbor for transatlantic steamers before World War II, but it was heavily damaged in 1944 and has yielded its place to Le Havre. Other minor harbors, which nevertheless are locally significant, will be discussed in connection with individual countries.

Rivers. Navigable rivers have played a considerable part in European transportation. Those north of the Alps have a decided advantage over those of the Mediterranean region. The great plain extending from the North Sea eastward into Russia offers few obstacles to the quiet flow of the water, and the equable distribution of precipitation causes a well-balanced water supply. Only in the east does a cold, icy winter limit the practical use of rivers for transportation. Although the rivers of France have only local importance for navigation, those entering the North Sea, the Baltic, and the Black Sea afford easy entrance to the continent. This is especially true now that small obstacles have been eliminated, the channels carefully marked by buoys, the many river tolls abolished, and regular inland harbors developed in advantageous locations.

The Rhine River is probably the world's best-developed inland waterway. In normal years more than 100,000 boats cross the border between the Netherlands and Germany by way of the Rhine. Duisburg-Hamborn, where the Ruhr industrial region touches the Rhine, was, before 1940, the world's greatest inland harbor. Mile for mile the Rhine carries many times as much freight as the Mississippi. At present the Rhine is navigable to Basel on the border of Switzerland. It is under international control, since four countries share its navigable portion. The long Rhine barges, pulled by tugboats, show by their variety of flags the international character of the trade.

The Elbe is navigable clear across Germany and is the logical trade road into Czechoslovakia; Hamburg at its mouth offers special harbor advantages. The Oder is open for small boats from the Baltic to the Silesian coal fields, and the Vistula is navigable especially below Warsaw. Political tensions upset the normal flow of trade on the Elbe after 1945.

Among the rivers flowing to other seas, the Danube has all the advantages of a great artery of traffic. Because of its wide bed and fairly stable water supply it offers few difficulties, and it has been possible to overcome these few, as at the Black Sea delta and in the Iron Gate, where the river cuts around the Transylvanian Mountains in a gorge. Although the Danube empties into a nearly closed sea far from the world's main lines of trade, the river itself affords a great variety of economic possibilities. One would expect to see on it a constant stream of boats carrying grain from the east to the west and manufactures in the other direction. But the beautiful Danube by no means shows the expected traffic. The breaking up after World War I of the Austro-Hungarian Empire into new states, jealous of each other and not willing to co-operate, and the lowering of the Iron Curtain right across the Danube after World War II have made the river even less useful than formerly. The primary difficulty, however, is that the Danube, like the Mississippi, runs in the wrong direction. At one end, to be sure, it touches Germany, Austria, and Czechoslovakia, but at the other end a ship on the Danube finds itself in the least active and progressive part of Europe.

The Russian rivers, because of the gentle relief, are navigable far toward their sources. When not frozen, they give the Soviet Union a natural transportation system that as yet has by no means been equaled by the railroads and roads. The Volga, in spite of its outlet in an inland sea, is Russia's greatest river commercially as well as physically. Sentimentally it takes the same position in Russia that the Rhine takes in Germany. Although not quite so lonely as the Mississippi, it has no such traffic as the Rhine because it does not connect regions of high industrial and commercial activity.

Canals. The inland waterway system of Europe (A157) is extended and completed by numerous canals. These are mainly the product of the last centuries. In Holland, however, the Romans are supposed to have dug a canal giving the Rhine its northern outlet through the IJssel. In later centuries barges there took the place of the wagons of other lands, and towboats to some extent supplanted coaches for passenger travel. In the eighteenth century the increased demand for transportation and the advantages of using the available rivers brought canals strongly to the foreground. France started the work with some canals that now form part of a very extensive system connecting all the rivers and penetrating all parts of the country. The latest addition is the canal from Marseille to the Rhône, which tunnels the hills separating Marseille from the Rhône delta. In

Great Britain the development was along similar lines, but after a few decades most of the canals lost their significance because of railroad transportation. The only large British canal, the Manchester Ship Canal, makes Manchester a seaport. (For French canals see A398.)

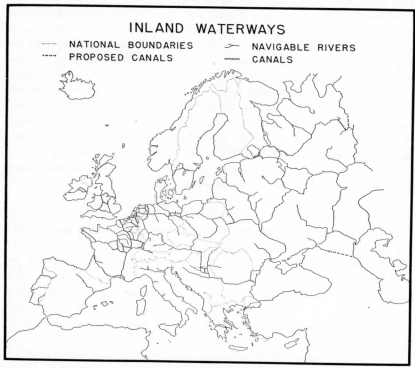

A. Principal Navigable Rivers and Canals of Europe.

In the Netherlands more than in any other country inland water transportation (A364) still continues to be highly important. The North Sea Canal gives Amsterdam a direct outlet to the North Sea; another canal, which also crosses the dunes along the seacoast, makes the Hook of Holland the outlet of the Rhine and the outer port of Rotterdam. Belgium has also built a canal system connecting the distributaries of the Schelde in its delta with the Meuse and the rivers of northern France. In Germany the development of canals began later than in the Low Countries and is not yet completed. West-to-east canals connect all the rivers from the Rhine to the

Vistula. The Rhine-Ems Canal was intended to divert the Rhine traffic through Essen and Dortmund to Emden on the North Sea just east of Holland, but this attempt at a purely German route has not been very successful. Another canal between the Main and Danube rivers via Nürnberg gives an uninterrupted inland waterway between the North and Black seas, but this, too, is used only moderately. On the other hand, the Kiel Canal, cutting off the Jutland Peninsula and providing a direct route between the North and Baltic seas, ranks next to the Suez and Panama canals in the tonnage of its traffic, but cannot rival the inland waterways of the Rhine and the Sault Sainte Marie. Most canal connections in Russia date from the nineteenth century, but several have been widened and deepened by the Soviets, and several have been added. Canal boats can now go from Moscow to the White Sea, to the Baltic, and to the Caspian. Furthermore, the Soviets were rushing to complete the long-dreamed of Volga-Don Canal in 1952. With the opening of this canal, Moscow will be a port of "five seas"—with the Azov and Black seas added to the three already named.

Land Transportation

Railroads. The demand for better transportation that began during the Industrial Revolution combined with the invention of power-driven machinery to cause the first line for steam locomotion to be constructed in 1825 between the English towns of Stockton and Darlington. This supposedly dangerous means of transportation met with general distrust and opposition, especially from the canal companies, which then enjoyed a virtual monopoly in England. Early progress was therefore slow, though certain. Today, however, in the British lowlands it is difficult to get beyond the sound of locomotives (A159). During the Second Empire and under Napoleon III the French railroad system began with a weblike construction having Paris in the center. In Germany the first line began to operate in 1832 between Nürnberg and Fürth. Bismarck was the man who developed the German state railway system. Today these countries and their adjacent small neighbors have so dense a railway net that one needs a magnifying glass in order to study it in A159. In other European countries the beginnings of railway development came likewise during the same period, but in A159 it may be observed that difficulties resulting from rugged relief on the one hand and from severe climate on the other have retarded the building of railroads. The St. Gotthard Tunnel, 9.3 miles long, and constructed in 1882, was the first large tunnel. It opened a new era in railroad development. The Mont Cenis, Simplon, and Lötschberg tunnels followed suit in the Alps, and two railroads have since crossed the Pyrenees.

In contrast to the dense railway net north of the Alps, one may

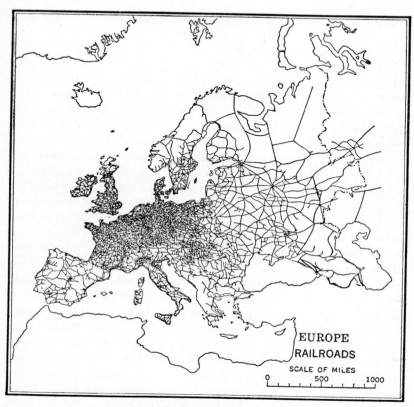

A. Railways in Europe.

note the sparsity of railroads in the north, east, and south of Europe. Even Italy, outside the Po Basin, has a railway net less dense than that of equally rugged parts of France, Germany, or Switzerland. Spain, the Balkan states, Russia, and the cool, rugged parts of Scandinavia and even Scotland are conspicuously lacking in railroads. In fact, the region with a dense railway net is almost identical with Europe A; whereas Europe C has relatively few railways even where it has a dense population. Even in the plain of Hungary in Europe B the net is less dense than in France and Germany. Belgium has the most elaborate railroad system of the world. If local lines are included, it has about 1 mile of track for every 2 square miles of area. The rest of Europe A generally has approximately 1 mile of track for every 5 square miles. Switzerland stands higher in this respect than its relief would lead one to expect, for it has built many mountain lines for tourists. The contrast between such countries and Europe C is very strong. Greece, for example, shows only one-seventeenth the railroad density of Belgium.

The progress of transportation in Europe has led to constant changes and improvements. Many waterways are now used in conjunction with the railway system. Fast steamers connect Great Britain with the continent and Ireland. Ferries carry entire trains across the Baltic and join the railroad systems of Sweden and the larger Danish islands with that of Germany. Speed and convenience have become so important that international trains make long runs, crossing the continent in all directions. The Orient Express runs from Calais to Istanbul, via the Simplon Pass, Milan, and Belgrade, passing through seven countries. Communist Bulgaria continued to cause some difficulty to free passage of the Orient Express in 1951. Electricity has replaced coal as a source of power in many mountain regions that are poor in coal but rich in water power. On the Swiss railroad system coal is practically eliminated, and electric power from plants using not only water power but also coal runs many trains in the Dutch and German lowlands. The competition of motorcars and buses has recently necessitated still higher efficiency, so that in some respects European railroads surpass those of the United States. A train between London and Glasgow makes an 8-hour run at the rate of 70 miles an hour without stopping. Even in Spain, radically new types of trains are tried out. There is still room for improvement, however. A tunnel under the Dover Channel would speed up transportation appreciably; its construction is prevented by the fear of the British that their isolation will be ended, rather than by technical difficulties.

Modern Highways. The transition from the wretched roads of former times to the smooth highways of today is seen mainly in Europe A. It is the work of not much more than a century. It began in France, where Napoleon, like the ancient Roman Emperors, saw the importance of good roads for merchants as well as for his armies. The famous *Routes Nationales* of France, paved with brick and lined with poplars, are in large part his work. England soon followed suit with good macadamized highways. Germany did not do much before 1850. Today even the minor roads in these countries and their small neighbors are largely hard-surfaced. Even in the remoter parts of Scandinavia and in Finland the main roads, though narrow and winding, have a hard surface of compacted gravel. Elsewhere the building of roads has been much slower. Spain has a fine system of main roads between the large cities, but the rest of the roads are poor. Italy has many admirable roads in the north, but few good ones in the south. Poland, Yugoslavia, and Bulgaria have few hard roads, and dust, mud, or frozen ruts, according to the season, make travel very unpleasant.

Progress in such fields as road building is not likely to anticipate popular demand. An early demand arose because of the growing use of stagecoaches as a means of travel. Bad roads often made the passengers extremely uncomfortable, and bruised passengers clamored for better highways. The coming of railways helped materially, for the increasing reliance on the main routes made necessary a system of roads connecting the rails with all parts of the hinterland. Market towns saw the necessity of bettering the surrounding roads to induce the rural population to drive their carts to the cities on market days. Increased security also helped to stimulate the use and improvement of roads. Holdups and robberies have gradually disappeared; they are now limited to the remote corners of the Balkans.

At the end of the last century the bicycle did much to make good roads popular and to make people more critical about their condition. Even now, in some lowland countries like Holland and Denmark, the bicycle is still highly important. Nearly everyone in these two countries rides a bicycle. This phase of transportation is one that Americans rarely understand. In the United States the bicycle created a great furor for two decades or so at the end of the last century, but was mainly a pleasure vehicle. Before it had found its place in the economic system the automobile had displaced it, leaving it as little more than a useful toy for children who are not old enough to drive cars. In Europe A the economic situation is such that the vast bulk of middle class and working people cannot afford motorcars but can afford bicycles. Moreover, the roads were already good before the bicycle was invented, and in large areas there were no hills. Hence the bicycle was very widely adopted as a means of going not only to school, but likewise to work and to market. All over Europe A the bicycle is far more common than in any part of the United States. In the flat, prosperous countries of Holland and Denmark one sees signs forbidding the parking of bicycles. In the rush hours these machines so throng the streets that the motorist must reduce his speed to theirs, and must stop whenever a cyclist, without looking back, holds out an arm indicating a desire to make a turn. In Europe C, on the contrary, bicycles are less numerous than in the United States. Instead of being ridden by children, they are the much-prized treasure of middle-class men who have laid by enough money to afford them.

The most marked change in the roads has of course come with the motorcar. Motor traffic, to be sure, is a small matter in Europe compared with that in America. All Europe, with four times the population of the United States, has only one fourth as many motor vehicles. Nevertheless, motor traffic continues to increase steadily all over Europe, although the rate of increase is very slow in Europe C compared with Europe A. Passenger cars, heavy trucks, and, more recently, regular bus lines compete with the railroads, although in some places, as in France, the buses are run by the railroads. All this has contributed to an increase in the number of roads and to marked improvement in those already existing. The road system of Great Britain, for example, is considered in no way inferior to that of the United States. It is different, however, for huge trunk highways with four or six lanes of solid concrete are rare in England, whereas the minor country roads with a gravel surface average much better than corresponding roads in the United States. On the other hand, Italy, with much poorer roads than England on an average, has built some splendid speedways in the Milan region. During the 1930's Germany created a magnificent network of "parkways"—four-lane concrete highways with a strip of "park" down the middle—in its *Autobahn* system. The *Autobahnen* were constructed primarily for military purposes, but they have been of great value for passenger and truck travel, although they connect only the larger cities. They may best be compared with the Pennsylvania Turpike in the United States, except that they were never toll roads.

Motor Transportation (A163). The motor vehicles of Europe, as well as the roads, show differences from those of the United States. One such difference appears in the fact that in the United States, aside from motorcycles, there is 1 motor vehicle for every 3.5 persons, whereas in Europe the number ranges from 1 for every 17 in France to only 1 for 640 in Yugoslavia (trucks are included in all figures). Another is that the percentage of the various types of motor vehicles differs greatly from country to country and is nowhere the same as in the United States. For example, in Great Britain, in proportion to the population, passenger cars are only one fifth as numerous as in the United States. Moreover, a large percentage are much smaller and less powerful than in the United States. Motorcycles, on the

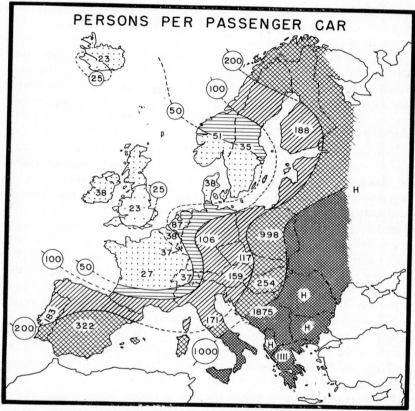

A. Persons per Passenger Car in Europe, 1949 (H = High).

other hand, are relatively much more numerous than in the United States—more numerous, in fact, than in any other country in proportion to the population. Such a situation, together with the numerous bicycles and the less pretentious highways, is in accord with the denser population and lower incomes of England as compared with the United States.

In Germany there is an accentuation of these same conditions. Passenger cars are less numerous than in Great Britain. Motorcycles, on the other hand, are 14 times as numerous in proportion to the population as in the United States and are almost as numerous as in England. Germany has about 55 per cent more motorcycles than passenger cars, because the country contains a great many people who can afford this cheapest form of motor transport but cannot afford regular automobiles. Farther southeast, in Hungary, a typical country of Europe B, there is only 1 passenger car for the same number of people who have 40 in the United States; 1 truck or bus where there would be 34 in America, and 3 motorcycles where the United States would have 2. For the Soviet Union, the most reliable figures obtainable indicate that there are about 200 people for each motor vehicle, including passenger cars, trucks, and buses.

Air Transport

No map of airlines is given in this book, because the airways pattern is changing rapidly and the network would appear almost as complex as the railway map. It, too, would be very dense in western and central Europe, with only comparatively few lines in the north, east, and south. The pattern would be further complicated by the intercontinental lines, chiefly those to the Americas, to India, and to the Far East; many of them are American lines that cross Europe on the way to the south and southeast.

Some idea of airways in Europe can be given in terms of the distance flown by individual companies, although the figures include distances flown *outside* Europe by airlines registered in the respective countries. The United Kingdom comes first with a mileage of about 44 million, France is second with 26 million, the Netherlands is third with 18 million, and Scandinavia is fourth with 14 million miles; other important ones are Belgium and Switzerland. Germany undoubtedly will regain its former important position when it is once again allowed the use of planes, since it had one of the most highly developed airways nets in the world before World War II. The Soviet Union has also developed a far-flung airlines network, which assumes special importance because of the relatively low development of railways and roads. No data are available on distances flown by Soviet airlines, but the total length of all routes flown was, in 1950, approximately 100,000 miles.

Large modern airfields, comparable to the most prominent American fields, are found in all large European cities. Shannon, in Ireland, and Prestwick, in Scotland, as well as Lisbon, are main steppingstones for the transatlantic flights, although flights also go directly to London and Paris. Small towns, it is interesting to note, that formerly could be reached only by long train or boat trips are reached easily by air. For instance, a local line starting at Oslo connects all the major settlements on the Norwegian coast up to the Russian border. Formerly that trip took a week by boat; now it takes only a few hours.

Air cargo is becoming important, and mail is now carried more by plane than by railroad or boat. Planes are used also for excursions, just as buses are used. In Amsterdam the Dutch airlines run a mystery flight for people who want a vacation and will take a chance on the flight's destination.

· 12 ·

Peoples and Political Units

The Concept of Race

The human frailty of wishing to feel superior has led many people to seize on certain physical differences among people as criteria on which to build a system of "superior" and "inferior" "races." A desire to attribute superiority to one's own group and consequently to oneself seems to be present among most of the world's peoples. The names originally given some primitive groups by themselves may be translated *"the* people," thus implying that all other peoples (those who look different or speak a different language or have different customs) are abnormal or actually not quite human. The same feeling persists in many persons even in the most "civilized" and "educated" groups today, despite the fact that scientific evidence has dispelled once and for all the concept that any "race" or group of people is inherently endowed by nature with a superior set of physical or intellectual characteristics.

Physical anthropologists who have honestly attempted to discover what groupings of human physical characteristics exist in the world have never been guilty of making exaggerated claims about the intellectual qualities that accompanied certain physical types. But less scientific men sometimes extended the concept of "race" to include inherent intellectual qualities; and the Nazis of Germany under Hitler distorted the entire field of racial investigation so that their political aims might seem to the uncritical mind to have "scientific" validity. The wide circulation of Nazi racial propaganda increased the confusion that had long existed regarding the validity and meaning of race. On the other hand, scientific anthropologists were challenged by Nazi race propaganda, and their answers (based, of course, on research that had been done years before) to the Nazis showed to all who took the trouble to study them that color of hair or skin pigment has no determining influence on intelligence or personality.

Hitler's "Aryans" are actually people who speak Indo-European or "Aryan" languages, and the term has no meaning in connection with biological types or psychological traits. The Jewish "race" that Hitler persecuted is actually simply a cultural group whose members acknowledge the Jewish religion. The term "Nordic," of which the

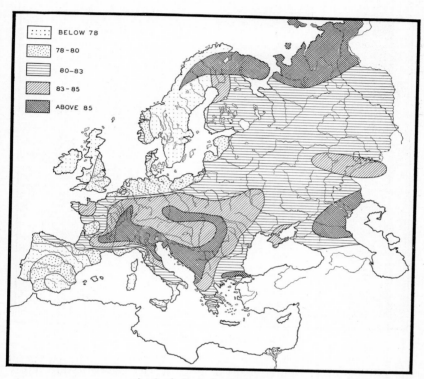

A. Cephalic Index in Europe.

Nazis were so fond, is, indeed, used by some physical anthropologists as a name for the fair-skinned, blue-eyed, tall, and long-headed people of northern Europe. However, no careful anthropologist attaches any inherent superiority of any kind to this particular physical type, and not only is the type found in many parts of Europe other than Germany, but also it is not the dominant group even in northern Germany!

In this discussion of the peoples of Europe, little attention is given to race even if the word is narrowly defined as a group of people with fairly uniform physical characteristics. The physical traits

are, indeed, of interest and sometimes of significance—much of which
has certain geographical applications—but linguistic-cultural groups
are more specifically identifiable and are of greater significance in a
study such as this. Those who are interested in detailed investigations into European physical groups will find suggested readings in

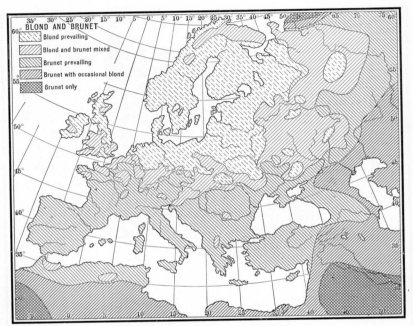

A. Complexion in Europe.

the Bibliography. Three maps of physical characteristics are reproduced (A167, A168, and A169) to show groupings that exist in cephalic
index (ratio of head length to head breadth, obtained by dividing
length into breadth multiplied by 100), complexion, and stature. All
are interesting in the evidence they contribute toward an understanding of the migrations of peoples in Eurasia.

Ethnographic Groupings

Ethnographic units are groups of people bound together by linguistic, cultural, and social ties and are, in actuality, more significant
for the purposes of this study than racial or biological units. The
groupings of peoples into cultural units presents its own difficulties,

of course; and such a classification lacks some of the objectivity even of racial classification. However, linguistic groupings are fairly readily measurable (although some occupants of transitional zones are bilingual), and it is more on the basis of language than on any other single criterion that the units of A171 have been classified.

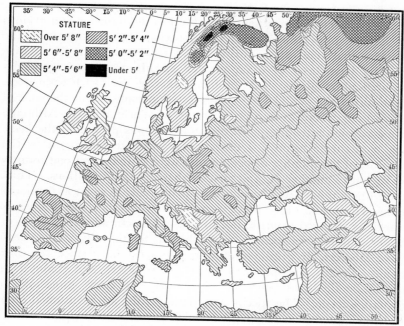

A. Stature in Europe.

Lack of correspondence between linguistic groups and national groups is noted where significant departures exist.

The greater number of European peoples (the word "people" being used for an ethnographic unit) are not of one race or biological group but have been developed through repeated intermixture. Their languages are in many instances not those of the strongest racial factor in the population. A country often speaks the tongue of some small group of conquerors who, though small in numbers and therefore weak in biological influence, have held political power sufficient to force their language upon the conquered population. Thus in time the conquered have become mixed with the conquerors as an ethnographic unit. Sometimes, too, the contrary has occurred, and the conquered population, often on account of its higher cultural standing, has possessed sufficient vitality to dominate. The divide between Germanic and Romance languages still for the greater part follows the limit to which the Germanic tribes, who invaded the disintegrating Roman Empire, were strong enough to enforce the use of their language. To the west of that line they ruled politically but did not change the Romance character of the culture.

A171 represents an attempt to classify the countries and regions of Europe into ethnographic units, taking into consideration the changes that took place during and after World War II. These changes have been of a far greater magnitude than is generally realized, although the "D.P. problem" that received such wide attention during the period 1945–50 suggested to some extent the scale of human migrations in Europe as a result of World War II. Although the confusion attending most of the migrations prevented the keeping of accurate records, a conservative estimate (based on partial records) of the number of people who were shifted from one country or region to another on a permanent basis is 12–14 millions. Thus, the ethnographic pattern of Europe—principally in so far as Germans, Poles, Finns, and other Baltic peoples are concerned—has been substantially changed from that of prewar years. In addition, equal or larger numbers of people were shifted temporarily as refugees, slave laborers, or prisoners of war, and most have since returned home. Finally, the prewar ethnographic pattern was changed in details by the mass execution of Jews by the Nazis, especially in eastern Europe. The specific population shifts are mentioned later in this chapter or in the chapters on the various countries.

Germanic Groups (1–7 in A171)

The ethnographic groups that are Germanic-language speakers are found in central, northern, and northwestern Europe and include such strikingly different cultural groups as the Austrians and the Icelanders. Germanic or Teutonic languages, like the Romance languages, have many similar aspects and show clearly enough their common source. Persons talking Swedish, Norwegian, and Danish can mutually understand one another. Dutch and the allied Flemish dialect of Belgium are closely allied to German and are not greatly different from the Scandinavian tongues. English is different from the others because it contains a large Romance element brought by the Normans, who themselves had given up the Norse language for that of France.

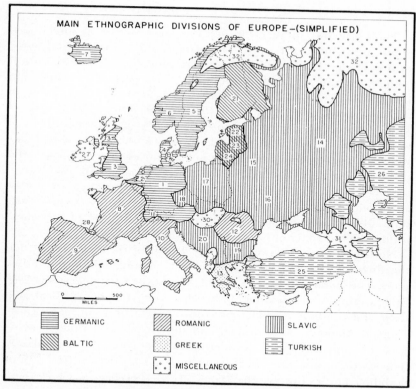

MAIN ETHNOGRAPHIC DIVISIONS OF EUROPE –(SIMPLIFIED)

Legend:

GERMANIC   ROMANIC   SLAVIC

BALTIC   GREEK   TURKISH

MISCELLANEOUS

A. Generalized Map of Ethnographic Groups of Europe.

Germanic:
1 Germans
2 Dutch, Flemings, Frisians
3 English
4 Danes
5 Swedes
6 Norwegians
7 Icelanders

Romanic:
8 French
9 Spaniards, Portuguese
10 Italians
11 Rhaeto-Romans
12 Rumanians

Greek:
13 Greeks

Slavic:
14 Great Russians
15 Belorussians
16 Ukrainians, Ruthenes

Slavic (cont'd):
17 Poles
18 Czechs, Slovaks
19 Bulgarians
20 Serbs, Croats, Slovenes

Baltic:
21 Finns
22 Estonians
23 Latvians
24 Lithuanians

Turkic:
25 Turks, Azerbaidzhani
26 Kirghiz

Miscellaneous:
27 Bretons, Welsh, Scots, Irish
28 Basques
29 Albanians
30 Magyars
31 Georgians
32 Lapps and others

The Germans (1 in A171) form a very compact and nation-minded group in the heart of Europe. The language has certain variations— such as High, Middle, and Low German—and extends across political boundaries into Austria, Switzerland, Alsace, part of Lorraine, and Luxembourg, with dialect differences in nearly every case. One of the most marked changes since 1945 in the ethnographic map of Europe has occurred in regard to the Germans, at least 10 million of whom were shifted from Poland, former East Prussia, Czechoslovakia, Hungary, Rumania, and other countries into Germany, and primarily Western Germany. Thus, the German *Drang nach Osten* that had been going on since the thirteenth century came to at least a temporary halt; and the German front actually retreated substantially. The Oder-Neisse line (the eastern frontier of Germany) is now the boundary of German settlement in the east.

Northwest of the Germans are the Dutch of the Netherlands and the linguistically and culturally related Flemings of northern Belgium (both indicated by 2 in A171). Across the Channel are the English-speaking British people (3), evolved from complex physical mixtures and combining numerous cultural influences—ancient Briton, Roman, Anglo-Saxon, Norman, and others. Dialect differences reflect the large number of invaders who have come into the islands. The Celtic groups are discussed below. In northern Europe, four Scandinavian groups are the Danes (4), the Swedes (5—who extend across the Gulf of Bothnia into the Åland Islands and coastal Finland), the Norwegians (6—who, despite a high degree of cultural uniformity, face a linguistic battle between the Bokmål and the Landsmål), and the Icelanders (7).

Romance and Greek Groups (8–13 in A171)

The western Mediterranean peoples, who occupy the part of southern and southwestern Europe that was subject to the political and social influence of the Roman Empire, speak languages that still have a Latin base. The Iberian Peninsula is shown as a single Romance unit, except for the Basques, because the differences between the Spanish and Portuguese are more political than ethnographic. The Portuguese and Spanish languages differ, of course, although they have a great many similarities; and there are, in addition, different language elements in the Galician of northwestern Iberia and the Catalan of the east and on the Balearic Islands. Basque is considered later.

Italy is occupied by people who are, in part, the direct descendants of the old Romans. North Africans, Normans, Albanians, and other peoples have come into southern Italy, and Lombards have entered northern Italy, but all were absorbed culturally and are now Italian-speaking. Many dialects may be heard, however, and an Italian from Sicily has some difficulty in understanding a Florentine. A number of ancient dialects of Latin survive in the central and eastern Alps. Closely related to each other, they include Romansch (or Rhaeto-Roman, 11) in the Grisons Canton of Switzerland, Ladin in the Upper Adige Valley of northern Italy, and Friulian in north-eastern Italy. Old customs, like the old dialects, have survived among the speakers of these languages.

The Greeks do not speak a Romance language, but they have much in common, in customs as well as in culture, with the people of Iberia and Italy, partly because of the common geographical environment and the Greco-Roman historical ties. In France, out of the ultimate mixture of peoples came a strong ethnographic-national unit marked by its Romance language, with extensions even into southern Belgium (Walloon) and western Switzerland (Swiss French). As in Italy, dialects exist in France, with some influences of the old language of the south (*langue d'oc*—as distinguished from the *langue d'oïl* of the north) still persisting in rural areas and surviving strongly in the Provençal and Catalan of southern France. These linguistic variations do not, however, detract from the strength of the French ethnographic group.

The Rumanians form an isolated eastern unit related linguistically to the Romance group but composed of people whose language is much more Roman than their civilization, which is largely Slavic. The Roman imperial province of Dacia covered most of modern Rumania, but much of the Roman influence probably came later from Byzantium, the eastern Roman Empire of the Middle Ages. Whatever Romance culture has existed has been concentrated mainly in Bucharest, which was proud of its former cultural ties with France. Now a Russian satellite, Rumania is becoming still more oriented toward a Slavic culture. The little enclave of Magyars within Rumania on the plateau of Transylvania is due to arbitrary colonization. The formerly large group of Germans ("Saxons") in Transylvania and in the Banat was reduced after World War II by mass expulsions, but thousands still remained. Nomadic herders speaking a variety of Rumanian are found in Macedonia and are called Vlachs (Walachians).

Slavic Groups (14–20 in A171)

At least until establishment of the Soviet regime, the Slavic peoples of eastern and southeastern Europe had many cultural traits in common other than language. Even at mid-century, they also had in common a communist form of government, although Yugoslavia had declared its independence from Soviet domination. The Orthodox religion, with certain notable exceptions, was also general among the Slavic peoples. The larger grouping of the Slavs is split into two parts by a wedge of the Austrians, Magyars, and Rumanians: the Great Russians (14), White Russians (Belorussians—15), Ukrainians (16), Poles (17), and Czecho-Slovaks (18) comprise the northern Slavic branch; and the Bulgarians (19) and Serbs, Croats, and Slovenes (or Yugoslavs—a Slavic word meaning "South Slavs"—20) the southern. A small group of Slavic people, the Sorbs or Wends, is found in the Spreewald south of Berlin and was left behind in the protected Spree marshes by the larger Slavic group when it retreated eastward centuries ago in the face of advancing German settlement. Another Slavic group, the Masurians, voted to remain with Germany in the Allenstein-Marienwerder plebiscite of 1920, but they were given to Poland at Potsdam. The Ruthenes, occupying the Carpathian slopes in the territory formerly included in the eastern "tail" of Czechoslovakia, are akin to the Ukrainians.

Baltic Groups (21–24 in A171)

Usually, this group is shown in two divisions, the Lithuanians and Latvians in the south and the Estonians and Finns in the north, but such a division is perhaps too linguistic and hides many traits they have had, at least, in common. The Finns (21) greatly dislike the suggestion that they are of Mongolian origin and related to the Lapps as is frequently shown on maps. Their language, however, is derived from an Asiatic language group (Finno-Ugric) and is related to the Magyar language of Hungary (30) and the Estonians of the Estonian S.S.R. (22). None of the three is Indo-European. The Finns have been culturally strongly affected by the Swedes, who occupied Finland until 1809 and thousands of whom still live in the southwest, and the Finns likewise show a strong admixture of physical characteristics of other Baltic peoples. The Latvians (23) and Lithuanians (24) speak languages that, though different from each other, are both closely akin to the old Aryan, and simple Sanskrit can be understood in both Latvia and Lithuania. All three of the former Baltic states, absorbed into the Soviet Union in 1940, have been influenced from several directions—from Scandinavia, from Germany, and from Russia. After 1945, Russians came into the Baltic S.S.R.'s in large numbers, and the freedom-loving inhabitants of the former states were shipped out in large numbers.

Turkish-Tataric Groups (25–26 in A171)

The Turks (25), once prominent in southeastern Europe, are now limited to a small area between the Bosporus and the Greek boundary. Peoples linguistically related to the Turks, such as the Tatars and Azerbaydzhanians, still occupy the steppes around the Caspian Sea, with the Kirghiz (26) occupying a particularly large area toward the north and northeast.

Miscellaneous Groups (27–32)

The members of this classification have no interconnection. It simply combines some smaller groups difficult to put in special categories. The Celtic-speakers (27) of Ireland, Scotland, Wales, Cornwall (where Celtic has virtually disappeared), and Brittany are peoples who remained protected and isolated and retained their old dialects as well as customs and, in some cases (Brittany and highland Scotland), costumes. In Ireland, Gaelic has had something of a revival in the period since the creation of the Irish Free State in 1921. Elsewhere, the Celtic is on the wane. The Basques in the western Pyrenees are an interesting remnant of an ancient group, but it is difficult to say where they came from. Likewise, the Albanians (29), often regarded as descendants of the ancient Illyrians, are something of a puzzle. More numerous is the unit of the Magyars (30) in the Danube basin; once conquerors on horseback coming out of Asia, they still form a definite ethnographic group with strong national feelings, which do not fit into the pattern east of the Iron Curtain. The region of the Caucasian Isthmus (31) contains one of the most complex ethnographic patterns in the world, a fact that may be largely ascribed to the location of the rugged Caucasus in the path of great human migrations. Many villages or valleys have their own language or dialect, and in the mountains of Daghestan alone are found thirty different peoples. The Georgians and the Armenians are the two largest groups in the Caucasus, along with the Azerbaydzhanians, already named. The nomadic Lapps, wandering reindeer herdsmen of the tundra in the northern Scandinavian Peninsula, and a number of Asiatic peoples of northeastern European Russia

(Nentsy—formerly called Samoyeds, Khanty—formerly called Ostyaks, and Mansi—formerly called Voguls) are designated by 32.

One ethnographic group in Europe that is scattered over the continent and that has received a great deal of attention, especially as a result of Nazi persecution of them, is the Jews. Although in pre-1939 times they were largely concentrated in the "Jewish Pale," extending from Lithuania to Rumania, they were present in varying numbers in every country in Europe. More than 4.3 million Jews left Europe during the century 1850–1950, and, of those who remained in 1939, 5.8 millions were exterminated by the Nazis and 200,000 were killed in battle. Between 1945 and 1950, 530,000 emigrated, 350,000 of them to Palestine (or Israel). Of the 2.75 million Jews left in Europe in 1950, most were in the Soviet Union. Rumania furnished a very large proportion of the emigrants to Israel, but all countries furnished a share. Thousands more awaited permission to leave their home country or permission to enter Israel. The result is that Europe at mid-century had only 25 per cent of the world's Jews, whereas in 1850 it had 88 per cent, and the center of Jewish influence has left Europe.

Religious Alignments

Some definite relations exist between the ethnographic structure of Europe and the areal distribution of religions, but it is dangerous to come directly to conclusions while studying the map (A177). The western boundary of the Orthodox Church, for instance, is not based on the Slavic character of the population but on the cultural influence of Byzantium, which spread from the Balkans into Russia, whereas to the west the influence of the Church of Rome prevailed. The boundary between Protestants and Roman Catholics is often a political one; the decision of the ruler during the Reformation often swung the religion of the population to one side or the other. However, it can be said that the Germanic people to a large extent are Protestant, and the Protestant concentration around the North Sea and Baltic is quite evident on the map. The Polish possession of the Baltic coast from former East Prussia to the outlet of the Oder now breaks that Baltic encirclement, since Roman Catholic Poles took the place of the Protestant Germans. The religious pattern of the Netherlands, Germany, and Switzerland, which has been much simplified on the map, can be understood only if the historical background of the numerous political units that once existed in those parts of Europe is taken into consideration. Also in Hungary are small enclaves of Protestants that have not been subdued through political action. The Catholic part of Europe forms a half-circle around the Protestant core, extending from Ireland through France and the western and central Mediterranean, northward through the Danube countries into Poland and Lithuania.

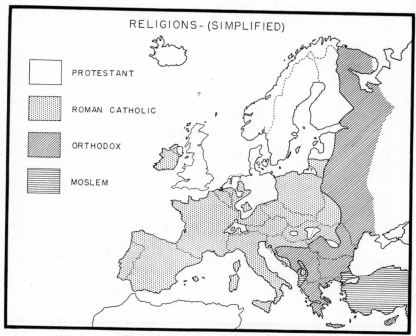

RELIGIONS- (SIMPLIFIED)

PROTESTANT

ROMAN CATHOLIC

ORTHODOX

MOSLEM

A. Simplified Religious Divisions of Europe.

Beyond the Iron Curtain, the church—Catholic, Protestant, and especially Orthodox—has been weakened through government interference. Control by Rome of the Catholic clergy has been seriously interfered with, and, especially in Russia, the tendency has been to regard religion as anachronistic and to replace it by a cult of the communist heroes, Marx, Lenin, and especially Stalin. The Turks are Mohammedans, and, as a remnant of the times of former Turkish influence in southeastern Europe, many Albanians and Bosnians also adhere to the Moslem faith. Small groups of other Moslems may be found in many isolated valleys and basins in the Balkan Peninsula.

States of Europe

For non-Europeans who do not know intimately the historical background, the political map of Europe is a great puzzle. It would be most interesting to discuss the rise and often the decline of the

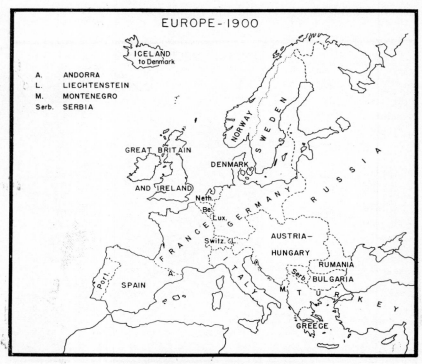

A. Political Divisions of Europe in 1900.

nations of Europe, but that would be a book by itself and not suitable to our purpose. However, it is possible to discuss the sequence of events of the last 50 years and to relate that study to the ethnographic structure.

Europe in 1900 (A178). The Europe of 1900 was still essentially the political Europe constructed at the Congress of Vienna and was largely the result of the interplay between five great powers: Russia, Prussia, Austria, France, and Britain. In 1815, Turkey, although weakened, still controlled the Balkan Peninsula, while Italy was still divided into small political units. Although the nations in western Europe were already well established and had developed their ethnographic bases, boundaries in central and eastern Europe had been drawn according to political consideration without much regard to population structure. The nineteenth century saw the separation of Austria from the German Federation, followed by creation of the dual state of Austria-Hungary, the unification of Italy, the gradual retreat of Turkey, and the separation between Belgium and the Netherlands.

Except for the Balkans, which were in flux, the map of 1900 is a fairly simple one. In the center was the strong German Empire, which extended ethnographically into territory occupied by Poles (eastern Germany), Danes (Schleswig), and some French (Alsace-Lorraine). The Austro-Hungarian Empire was a conglomerate of various ethnographic groups, such as Czechs, Slovaks, Poles, Ruthenes, Rumanians, Slovenes, Croats, Serbs, and Italians, besides, of course, the two dominating groups, the German Austrians and the Magyars. Russia occupied most of the transitional zone that extended from the Arctic to the Black Sea and that included Finns, Estonians, Letts, Lithuanians, Poles, and Rumanians. In the Balkans, four political units had been created: Rumania, Serbia, Bulgaria, and Greece (Montenegro had existed before), but Turkey still controlled the central part from the Adriatic to the Bosporus. Unified Italy was interested in the Italians outside her boundaries, especially the Austrian section of the Istrian Peninsula and of the Trentino. In the west, boundaries were approximately as they are today. France still sought an opportunity to regain Alsace-Lorraine, lost in the Franco-Prussian War. Ireland was trying to gain some kind of autonomy, while Iceland was still under Danish rule and Norway was united with Sweden.

Europe after World War I (A180). The map of Europe after World War I shows great changes in the political pattern of 1900, primarily in central and eastern Europe. The main events responsible for those changes were the defeat of Germany, the disintegration of the Austro-Hungarian Empire, the temporary weakness of Russia, and the new era in the Balkans, with Turkey limited to a small bridgehead across the Bosporus. Another important element was the introduction of the idea of the right of self-determination of peoples that President Wilson had enunciated as a leading principle for the new political map and that he strongly championed at the peace discussions.

The post-World War I map, if compared with the ethnographic
pattern (A171), shows some interesting correlations. At the expense
of Russia, Germany, and Austria-Hungary, a zone of countries that
had been created or enlarged extended from the Arctic to the Mediterranean. These countries were Finland, Estonia, Latvia, Lithu-

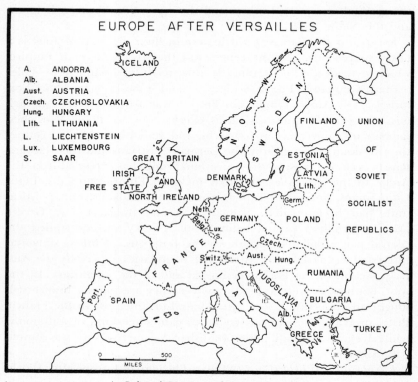

A. Political Divisions of Europe in 1924.

ania, Poland, Czechoslovakia, Rumania, Yugoslavia, Bulgaria, Albania, and Greece. Each state was relatively coextensive with an
ethnographic group ("nation"); however, because in eastern Europe
ethnographic groups were not sharply separated but mingled and
sometimes merged on the peripheries, minority groups were inevitably left inside the new states. In some cases, also, criteria other
than ethnography were used for boundaries: some were economic,
some strategic. Poland, for instance, extended far into territory
occupied by Russian people, and severely treated Hungary found

many Magyars living outside Hungary. However, from an *ethnographic* point of view this pattern was a great improvement over the one before the war, although some of the new countries, especially Czechoslovakia and Yugoslavia, had complex ethnographic structures. Yugoslavia contained Serbs, Croats, and Slovenes, and Czechoslovakia combined Czechs, Slovaks, and some Ruthenes. Differences in cultural background among the groups precipitated appreciable trouble and weakened the new national units.

The other changes in the political pattern were comparatively minor ones. Italy received what she called her "Irredenta" in the Upper Adige, the Istrian Peninsula, and other small areas in the eastern Adriatic; France recovered Alsace-Lorraine; and the Saar was administered by the League of Nations until 1935, after which it was returned to Germany. Belgium received as compensation for war damage the small area of Eupen-Malmédy; and Denmark, after a plebiscite, pushed her Schleswig boundary southward. Germany, having lost her Polish territory, found East Prussia disconnected by the Polish Corridor; and the Free City of Danzig was created to give Poland a harbor and still preserve the German character of the population. Iceland broke away from Denmark, although still accepting the Danish king. The Irish Free State was born in 1921 after a long and bloody struggle, but Northern Ireland (Ulster) refused to join. Norway had broken her ties with Sweden in 1905. And finally the little country of Montenegro ceased to exist and was absorbed in Yugoslavia.

The effort to correlate ethnographic structure and political freedom was not an unsuccessful one. Had events permitted, the new boundaries would probably have matured and minority problems would have gradually been solved. It had been a step forward that peoples had been asked what they wanted and that, in several instances, they were able to express their desires in plebiscites. That the new structure failed was due to the fact that many of the new nations were economically weak and that great powers such as Hitler's Germany and, later, Stalin's Soviet Russia would not accept the new political pattern.

Europe at Mid-Century (A182). Ignoring the short period during World War II when Germany occupied much of Europe, a study of the political map of Europe at mid-century reveals some interesting points. Changes from the map that evolved during the early 1920's are not so great as those that resulted from the treaties ending World War I, and all extensive changes occurred along the western

frontier of the Soviet Union. Some of the changes were in areas of
overlapping ethnographic groupings, but other changes—several of
which resulted from Soviet ultimatums issued before World War II—
were backed only by political-military power and the advantage of
geographical proximity. Every country in eastern Europe that

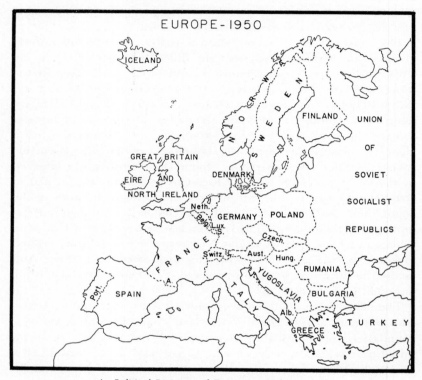

A. Political Divisions of Europe at Mid-Century.

touched the Soviet Union in 1938 was forced to surrender some territory to the Soviets by 1945. Some of the territory taken by Russia
was inhabited by peoples who might feel as much at home in Russia
as anywhere else—the Ruthenes, for example; but in most cases the
inhabitants were even non-Slavic. It is significant that most of the
territories taken by the Russians in the period 1939–45 were part of
Russia before World War I (compare A178 and A182) and were assigned to the various eastern European countries in post-World War
I treaties that the Russians did not sign. It is also important to keep

in mind that direct Soviet influence extends far westward over the Soviet western frontier to the line of the Iron Curtain (A19).

As distinguished from the map of the interwar years, the map of 1950 shows that the Soviets absorbed the Pechenga (Petsamo) Corridor, the Salla district, and the Karelian Isthmus (all three areas from Finland), the Baltic states, eastern Poland, the northern part of East Prussia, Ruthenia, and northeastern Rumania. Its new boundaries give it a long Baltic shore, a connection with the Hungarian Plain across the Carpathians, and access to the outlet of the Danube. Again Russia includes numerous minorities, but this time the policy seems to be to replace them gradually with Russian settlers and to transport the native population, in so far as they are not "reliable," into the interior.

In 1945 Poland was shifted bodily from east to west, losing its eastern territory to the Soviet Union and gaining smaller but more valuable land in the west, at the expense of Germany, up to the Oder-Neisse line, with a bridgehead across the lower Oder at Szczecin (formerly Stettin). Almost no more minorities exist in Poland as a result of population shifts. Germany, amputated in the east, consists of two parts: the German Federal Republic in the west (coextensive with the British, American, and French zones of occupation) and the communist German Democratic Republic in the east (coextensive with the Soviet zone of occupation); in addition, Germany's former territory of East Prussia was divided between Poland and the Soviet Union, and the Saarland was separated from the French zone of Western Germany and set up as a *de facto* autonomous area, linked economically with France (A429). Minute *de facto* changes were also made along the western boundary of Germany. The peace treaty with Germany, which had not been signed by early 1952, might alter the status of any of these former German territories, especially that of the Saarland. Czechoslovakia lost its eastern extension (Ruthenia) and cleared itself of its former German minority. Austria retained its boundaries intact, and Hungary lost only 25 square miles of the Bratislava bridgehead to Czechoslovakia. Rumania lost Bessarabia and the northern Bucovina to Russia and the southern part of the Dobruja to Bulgaria. Greece received from Italy the Dodecanese Islands off the coast of Asia Minor, and Yugoslavia took over Italy's former territories on the Dalmatian coast and all of Istria except the Free Territory of Trieste. The remaining boundary change shifted five small areas from Italy to France. Iceland freed itself from any ties with Denmark in 1944, and Ireland likewise became an independent republic in 1949.

If the new boundaries, which through population shifts of great magnitude have also become fairly good ethnographic ones, have a chance to mature, it is possible that they can become relatively permanent. One question, however, cannot be answered: will Germany accept the loss of her former eastern provinces or will she strive for their return? Absorption of the Baltic states by Russia just as they had begun to enjoy their new independence was strongly frowned upon by the western world, but restoration of their independence remains a question mark. The major political problem—as well as economic problem—of Europe is the separation between east and west, which is geographically indefensible and greatly harms the European politico-economic structure, as has been brought out in preceding chapters. But, more than on any other point, the fate of the political map of Europe—as well as the fate of everything else about Europe—hangs on the outcome of the all-pervading East-West "Cold War."

Plans for Political Unification

Plans for political co-operation among European countries have existed for a long time, but they came especially to the foreground in the 1920's. First came the Pan-Europe movement led by the Austrian Count Coudenhove Kallergi, and then the Briand proposal in 1928. Since World War II still more serious efforts have been made to take the first steps toward a measure of political integration. Out of these efforts came the creation of a Council of Europe, which met for the first time at Strasbourg in the summer of 1949. In 1950 there were fifteen members: Britain, France, Italy, Belgium, the Netherlands, Luxembourg, Sweden, Norway, Denmark, Ireland, Turkey, Greece, Iceland, Western Germany, and the Saar. Its aim is "to achieve a greater unity between its members for the purpose of safeguarding and realizing the ideals and principles which are their common heritage and facilitating their economic and social progress." Although it is premature to judge the Council's success, it is interesting to note that many Europeans—statesmen and ordinary citizens—favor the creation of a federal European state. However, there is a great deal of opposition to that idea, and Great Britain especially, with her Commonwealth ties, is reluctant to enter such a federation. Nevertheless, progress has been made; and, except for Switzerland, which is against any foreign commitment, and the two Iberian nations, all other western European states are active members, and a council headquarters has been built in Strasbourg.

Of course, real unity in Europe as a whole can be achieved only if the eastern as well as the western countries join the effort toward greater co-operation. However, so long as the Iron Curtain splits Europe into two opposing camps, any such harmony between east and west is precluded. Ironically enough, it is this very division of Europe that strongly influenced Western Europe to seek greater unity.

· 13 ·

Population:
Problems and Distribution

Although there are, under present economic conditions, apparently too many Europeans or not enough Europe, war and destruction have played havoc with prewar population predictions; and, even six years after the end of World War II, it was difficult to get a clear picture of trends in the demography of Europe. However, certain facts and tendencies can be seen and will be treated in this chapter. The second half of the chapter deals with patterns of settlement and distribution of population.

Rate of Increase

The rate of increase in the population of Europe has changed greatly in recent centuries. So far as can be judged from fragmentary records, the population had remained almost static for a long time before 1700. This was due in part to failure to exploit new resources and in part to the extremely high death rate. Not only was medical science of the sketchiest sort, but what little knowledge existed was concentrated in a few intellectual centers.

Epidemics were especially effective in retarding the growth of population. Cholera, smallpox, bubonic plague, tuberculosis, and typhus caused the death of millions of people. In spite of the best efforts of modern medicine, the influenza epidemic of 1918 and 1919 took a terrible toll of lives, as is clearly shown in the sharp rise of the lines in A190 at that time. It is easy to understand how, in earlier days when doctors relied on "dragon's blood" and the burning of aromatic herbs and knew nothing of the laws of sanitation, epidemics swept from country to country, decimating the population. The most famous of these epidemics was the Black Death, or bubonic plague, which came from Asia. From 1348 to 1350 it ravaged all the countries of Europe in turn. It carried off two thirds of the population of central Italy; a third, a half, and in some places two thirds of the inhabitants of Lombardy, northern Spain, France, England, the Low Countries, and Germany; and a half or two thirds in the Scandinavian and east European countries. The towns were attacked with special severity. Venice lost two thirds of its population; Bologna, four fifths; Florence, 80,000 to 100,000 people; Majorca, 30,000; Paris, 30,000 at one time. There were 800 deaths a day in Paris. The disease reappeared nine times in Italy, four times in Spain, five times in England. As far as can be calculated, it cost from 24 to 25 million human lives.

A second factor in retarding the growth of population was the frequency of wars. These not only claimed many lives on the battlefield and through disease, but in addition involved the ruin of crops and so brought starvation, for pillaging and burning were a part of war. The wars attending the great migrations that began in the third century and led to the final fall of the Roman Empire may serve as an example. They left a trail of ransacked towns, burned villages, and trampled fields. It was centuries before Europe again showed signs of cultural and economic progress. Likewise, during the Thirty Years' War in Germany the loss of life and property was enormous. In Bohemia the population fell from 3 million to 800,000.

A third factor restricting the population was the economy. Lack of adequate transportation, together with inability to preserve food, made the peasantry depend for subsistence solely upon the crops of each year. Crop failures, which were by no means uncommon, especially in eastern Europe with its relatively unreliable climate, often led to such disastrous shortage of food that starvation claimed its victims in millions.

The eighteenth century saw the beginning of, and the nineteenth century substantial progress toward, changes that helped to minimize these destructive forces. The development of agriculture and manufacturing stimulated trade, which in turn furthered improvements in transportation. Scientific study and the effective application of its discoveries went far to combat disease. Mortality decreased rapidly, first in the more advanced states of western Europe where medicine was first put on a scientific basis and later in eastern and southern Europe, although the rate of infant mortality (A188) still shows a sharp contrast between Europe A, where in Sweden only 23 out of 1,000 babies die before they reach one year, and Europe C, where the figure is well over the hundred mark. Moreover, certain economic factors that once limited population are to a great extent

eliminated; rapid transportation and the spirit of international co-
operation shown, for instance, in the help given by the United States
to starving Europe after World War II make it possible to furnish
effective relief to acute distress anywhere.

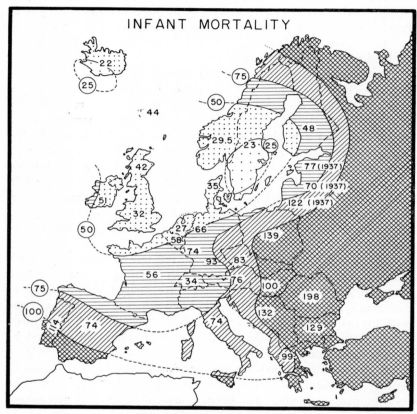

A. Infant Mortality in Europe, 1949.

Table A189 compares the birth rates of 1929–30 and of 1949 in
most European countries. There are some similarities and some
interesting dissimilarities between the two periods. If the birth
rate of 20 infants per 1,000 people is taken as the dividing line between a low and a medium national birth rate, the lower group included in 1929–30 all of western and northwestern Europe, with
the exception of the Netherlands; roughly, then, it comprised Europe
A. Europe B was well represented by the intermediate group (20–30

births per 1,000 people), which included Spain, Italy, Hungary, Czechoslovakia, Finland, and, in the southeast, Greece. Very high (above 30) were Portugal and eastern Europe and the rest of the Balkans, with the Soviet Union reaching the astonishing level of 42.7; that was Europe C.

TABLE A

Birth Rate per 1,000 Inhabitants

	1929	1949
Austria	16.7	15.8
Belgium	18.2	17.2
Bulgaria	30.1	24.0 (1947)
Czechoslovakia	22.4	23.3 (1948)
Denmark	18.6	18.9
Finland	22.6	25.8
France	17.7	21.0
Germany	17.9	16.5 (western part)
Greece	30.6	27.0 (1948)
Hungary	25.0	19.1
Ireland	19.8	22.0
Italy	25.2	20.0
Netherlands	22.8	23.7
Norway	17.7	19.6
Poland	32.3	28.8
Portugal	32.3	25.0
Rumania	34.3	22.4
Spain	28.8	21.4
Sweden	15.2	17.4
Switzerland	17.0	18.4
United Kingdom	16.7	17.0

In 1949 the situation was different. The main changes were a general increase in Europe A, where Ireland and France now joined the intermediate group, and a sharp decrease in Europe C (figures for Russia were not available), where no country exceeded the mark of 30. In other words, the disturbing contrast between Europe A and Europe C was somewhat diminished. Loss of potential fathers during the war may partly explain the decrease in the east; but the tendency existed before World War II, and there were equal losses of potential fathers in the west.

Population trends in Europe A are graphically shown in A190 and A191, which give the death rates and birth rates for five western European countries for more than one hundred years. Study of the death rate curves reveals the following sequence: a persistent drop

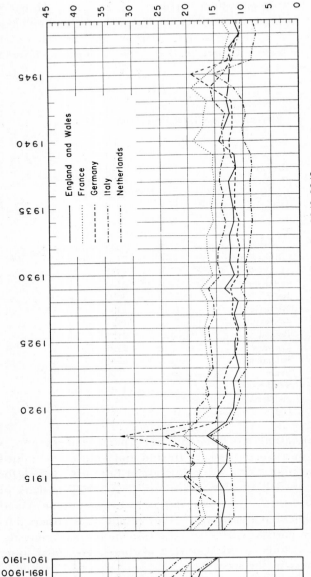

A. Changes in Death Rates in Five European Countries, 1840–1949.

England and Wales: 1929 to 1934, figures are for all the United Kingdom; 1940 to 1947, rate computed on civilian population.

France: Excludes deaths of military personnel during World War II.

Germany: 1939 to 1943, excluding deaths of military personnel; excludes civilian deaths during World War II; 1944 to 1948, averages of available figures from zones of occupation.

Italy: Excludes deaths in zones of military operations (World War II) and on foreign soil.

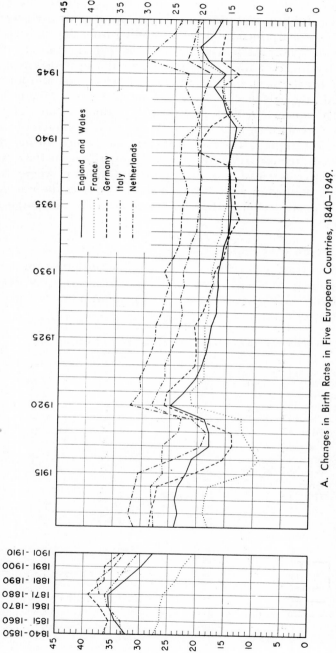

A. Changes in Birth Rates in Five European Countries, 1840–1949.

England and Wales: 1929 to 1934, figures are for all the United Kingdom.
Germany: 1944 to 1948, averages of available figures from zones of occupation.

extending from the 1860's up to the time of the time of the First World War (1914); a slight increase during the war years, especially in Germany; a sharp increase in 1918 resulting from the epidemic of influenza; an equally sharp drop to a level lower than before the war; a general leveling off until a new rise occurred during World War II, with a top for Germany in 1945, the year of defeat, and also for the Netherlands, the year of starvation; and finally a drop to the former level. The sequence in birth rates is quite a different one: after a rise, a very pronounced drop from about 1870 until the end of the First World War (note the low birth rate for France during that entire period); the usual postwar increase, with a peak in 1920; then a gradual decrease, with the exception of Germany, where Nazi propaganda resulted in more babies; a sharp rise after the war; and finally a gradual decline. However, rates were still comparatively high in 1950.

Natural Increase of Population

The net increase of population in Europe (not including the Soviet Union) is about 3 million a year, with a rate of 9 per 1,000 inhabitants. Table A192 gives the distribution of the rates of increase.

TABLE A

DIFFERENCES BETWEEN BIRTH RATE AND DEATH RATE IN 1949

	Birth Rate	Death Rate	Difference
Austria	15.8	12.6	3.2
Belgium	17.2	12.9	4.3
Bulgaria	24.0 (1947)	13.4	10.6
Czechoslovakia	23.3 (1948)	11.5	11.8
Denmark	18.9	8.9	10.0
Finland	25.8	11.3	14.5
France	21.0	13.8	7.2
Germany (Western)	16.5	10.0	6.5
Greece	27.0 (1948)	12.4	14.6
Hungary	19.1 (1948)	11.2	7.9
Ireland	22.0	12.7	9.3
Italy	20.0	10.4	9.6
Netherlands	23.7	8.1	15.6
Norway	19.6	8.8	10.8
Poland	28.8	11.5	17.3
Portugal	25.0	13.8	11.2
Rumania	22.4 (1947)	21.1	1.3
Spain	21.4	11.4	10.0
Sweden	17.4	10.0	7.4
Switzerland	18.4	10.7	7.7
United Kingdom	17.0	11.7	5.3

Although the general pattern is distinctly one of lower values in western and central Europe and higher values in the south and east, the map shows some interesting details. Poland has the highest increase of all countries, and the Netherlands, with the highest density of population and a grave population problem, is next. The Dutch always like to have large families, but another reason for the rapid increase may be the very high birth rate among the Roman Catholics. The rate for Rumania is quite low, but that may be only temporary if the country has a chance to achieve stability. From the point of view of contrast with prewar conditions, the most striking example is France, where the increase rose from almost nothing to 7.2 per thousand. Could it be a sign of new life in a rather old nation?

The table of population increase does not tell the story of population pressure—which, however, cannot be shown in simple table form. Such a study should take into consideration the standard of life and the question of whether that standard is dropping. Another criterion would be the amount of unemployment; but even that is not very reliable, because some countries are still in the process of reconstruction after the war and display artificial conditions of employment. Unemployment was quite high virtually everywhere in Europe during the 1930's, and it became a chronic illness. In 1950, countries with a large number of unemployed were Germany and Italy, with 1.5 million (Western Germany only) and 1.8 million respectively. Both countries have high population pressure. The large unemployment in Germany is due to a great extent to the fact that about 10 million Germans were dumped by Poland, Czechoslovakia, and other countries into a Germany greatly reduced in size, having lost territory east of the Oder River, and in industrial capacity, having been heavily bombed and shelled during the war.

Population Structure

To understand the population problem of individual countries, it is necessary to look at the population structure by age and sex. Under ordinary conditions the number of men and women do not differ greatly. In the ages below 20 years there are more males than females, but in the older age groups the females are more numerous, although the differences are relatively small. Loss of men through war interferes with age structure, a fact dramatically illustrated by the population pyramid (A194) for Germany (the figures are taken from the census of the British zone of occupation in 1946). Starting at the bottom with the young children (1–5 years), the number is rela-

tively small because of the drop in birth rate after the defeat; but
the relative number of boys and girls is normal.   The larger number
in the group between 5 and 10 reflects the high birth rate during
the Nazi period, and the decrease between 10 and 15 reflects the
lower birth rate in the early 1930's.   The relative number of males

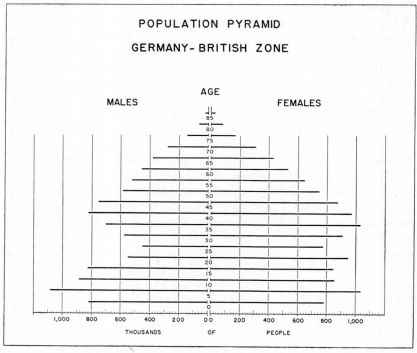

A. Population Pyramid for British Zone of Occupation of Germany, 1946.

and females is still normal.   Then comes the great drop in the number of young men, reflecting the decimation suffered by the males
of this age group during World War II, and in this group the ratio
between female and male is almost two to one.   It is understandable
that such conditions at the marrying age are abnormal and are most
unhealthy for the nation.   The increased proportion of men at
about the age of 45 is formed by those who were too young to fight
in the First World War and were too old to do the heavy fighting in
World War II.   The decrease at about the age of 55 indicates the
loss of men in the First World War; after that the ratio becomes

again almost normal. The pyramid for Germany is, of course, an extreme example, but it is not unique. Similar conditions probably prevail in Russia, but no data are available.

Overpopulation

Whether or not a region or country is "overpopulated" depends, of course, not upon the number of people alone but upon the relationship between population and developed resources. Thus the relatively dense population of western Europe should not be considered "overpopulation" simply because it is dense. Furthermore, whether or not a region is "overpopulated" depends upon the philosophy of the person making the evaluation. An American, accustomed to the high average standard of living and to the high landman ratio of the United States, might consider Belgium overpopulated; but a Belgian might not consider his country overpopulated. Poor economic conditions might seem to make a region overpopulated—that is, would decrease the number of available jobs—during such periods as that of the Great Depression; but, in the same area, good economic conditions would create a shortage of labor. Sometimes the situation is mixed, as it was in Great Britain after World War II, when both a critical shortage of manpower and a distressing economic situation existed. Certainly the balance between population and opportunities in industrial western Europe is a delicate one.

However, there is also strong population pressure in many of the agricultural regions, especially in eastern and southern Europe. Annual farm income per man was already, before World War II, dangerously low; in fact, a farmer in Russia or in the Balkans had only one-fourth the income of a farmer in Belgium. The communist policy of breaking up large properties and of introducing collective farming, which has been generally followed in the satellite countries, may or may not improve the situation. Improvement on any appreciable scale is doubtful, but only time will tell. The flow of surplus labor from the more highly mechanized farms will, of course, reduce pressure on the farms, provided, however, that such surplus labor can be satisfactorily absorbed in the new and expanded industries.

Conditions of population pressure in Europe after World War II varied greatly from country to country and changed appreciably during the first few years. Disrupted agricultural production, transportation, and industrial activity in 1945–47 created a situation in which most countries felt great pressure of the population, but such a situation was most certainly abnormal. By 1949, the pressure was eased except in such countries as Italy, Spain, Portugal, and Western Germany. This is, from one viewpoint, just another way of looking at the state of the general economy, but there is an added significance: will the population capacity of European countries be adequate as economic conditions stabilize at a normal level? The answer seems to be that, under approximately existing conditions, Europe will not be able to support its population of, let us say, 1975, unless there is a marked decrease in net population increase or in standard of living or both. One evidence for such an answer is the fact that even when Western Europe was almost booming in 1951 with production for rearmament against possible aggression, unemployment still existed in many areas and marginal living conditions characterized many more areas.

Migration. Migration seems at first sight the suitable answer to overpopulation. During the nineteenth century it was supposed that emigration in conjunction with manufacturing would solve Europe's problem of growing population. This hope has proved illusory in spite of the fact that millions of people have left the continent. During the first half of the nineteenth century about 5 million people went overseas; nearly half of them came from Great Britain and Ireland, and a fifth from Germany. More than half of all these went to the United States. During the second half of the century, and in the years before the First World War, this emigration reached a tremendous figure. At the beginning of this period most of the emigration was from Great Britain and Germany (about 700,-000 yearly); later there was a gradual but definite shift toward eastern Europe, producing a new flood that just before 1914 amounted to about 2 million a year. Yet even this left a surplus of about 7 million new inhabitants in Europe each year.

The First World War interrupted this emigration and thus caused the population of Europe to increase about as much during the war as it had during the years of peace immediately preceding. Of course, the war occasioned great loss of life through hardships imposed upon civilians as well as through battle casualties, but this scarcely balanced the checked tide of emigration.

Although emigration played a part again after the war, it was on a considerably smaller scale, amounting to only about 500,000 a year until it was virtually stopped by the depression that began in 1929. One of the chief reasons for this decrease was the policy of restriction adopted by several important foreign countries, particularly the United States, in order to protect their own economic and social structures. Then, too, some European governments themselves discouraged emigration. In Italy, Mussolini inaugurated a policy of intensive domestic development that would engage all the nation's young manpower. The Soviet Union stopped all emigration. In addition, the practice of paying dole to the unemployed of countries like England and Germany doubtless served to keep at home many people who would otherwise have been disposed to emigrate. Thus, after World War I, the pressure of population in Europe increased more than ever, especially with the onset of the depression of the 1930's.

Desire among many persons to emigrate was again strong after World War II; especially was this true of the Displaced Persons ("D.P.'s"), mentioned in the preceding chapter. These unfortunate people—mostly Estonians, Latvians, Lithuanians, Poles, Ukrainians, and Yugoslavs—had either been slave laborers in Germany or had fled their homes to escape Soviet domination; and at the end of the war they had no place to go. They struggled for their own existence until some organization was possible, when the International Refugee Organization (IRO) assumed care of them. With no desire to return to their former homes so long as the communists were in control, and with little opportunity to be absorbed by the economy of the countries in which they found themselves (Germany and Austria, in most cases), the D.P.'s sought homes in overseas countries. The Jews went to Israel in large numbers, but they and other groups also went to the United States (which accepted about 400,000 of them), Canada, and Australia. Other emigrants also—British, Dutch, and others—went to Australia and the Americas. But the reduction by emigration was, in total, small.

Seeking Other Remedies. Other remedies for overpopulation in Europe involve three possibilities: an increase in production, a new system of distributing the products of labor, or a decrease in population. The first has been in operation for nearly two centuries— ever since the beginnings of scientific agriculture and the use of power for machinery. Even if there had been no colonization of new lands, the increased productivity per acre and per man would have permitted a considerable share of the fourfold increase of population that actually occurred during the past two centuries. Doubtless, there are still appreciable possibilities of improvement along this line. The land can be made to yield more per acre, and with modern machinery some new land is worth cultivating—even in Europe. The continent could more than feed itself if it had to. Moreover, there are plenty of places outside Europe where food and also raw materials like rubber, cotton, and oil can still be obtained in exchange for manufactured goods. The productivity per man in manufacturing can also be increased enormously. The overpopulation of Europe, then, is not due to any lack of productive ability.

Such being the case, it seems clear that the trouble must lie in the way in which products are distributed from producer to consumer. One trouble, peculiar to Europe, is the small size of the countries and the consequent innumerable tariff walls. This, however, is a small matter compared with the world-wide difficulty arising from the fact that the methods of buying, selling, paying wages, and dividing profits are full of cumbersome features inherited from a wholly different age before there were any such things as modern industry and transportation. Soviet Russian administrators think that they have found a remedy for this by eliminating middlemen and private profit, but western Europe seems disposed to accept this system only with great modifications.

Economic co-operation among countries west of the Iron Curtain looks more promising than it has in former years. Since the war, efforts in that direction have been numerous. The attempts at creation of the Benelux Union of Belgium, the Netherlands, and Luxembourg; French-Italian plans for a customs union; discussions between Britain and the Scandinavian countries on closer economic co-operation; and the partial acceptance of the Schuman Plan are examples of the trend. A complete European economic union, a dream that may come true, would cause some hardships in some individual countries, but it would undoubtedly improve the general economic situation and give more work to more people. It would mean a larger home market and a better distribution of products based on natural advantages and not on tariff protection. Although it would not solve the European population problem entirely, it would certainly alleviate some of the economic hardships faced by the large population at mid-century.

The last and most drastic remedy of overpopulation lies in limiting the number of births through some system of birth control. Discussions earlier in this chapter show that this control has actually been used to some extent, not only in western and northwestern Europe, but also in other parts. Even Catholic southern Europe—Portugal, Spain, and Italy—shows such a definite decrease that it cannot be due to natural causes alone. However, whereas birth control should certainly be helpful in solving the problem of overpopulation,

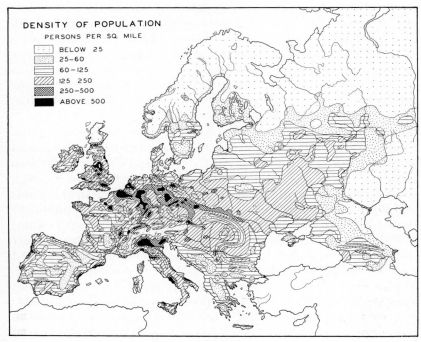

A. Density of Population in Europe.

it also raises in many minds the danger of an overturning of the social structure. There is no particular evidence that any European country will adopt stringent birth control measures.

Distribution of Population

A199 is a generalized map of the density of population with both rural and urban people taken into account. Except in the south and in Holland the areas of very high density coincide with the urbanized major industrial regions. This is one of the most notable and also most recent features of the distribution of population. In these industrial regions, shown specifically in A129, favorable conditions of location, transportation, mineral wealth, and climate have lent themselves to intensive development of manufacturing and an accompanying dense population.

The fertile loess soils extending east-southeastward in an almost continuous belt across the continent from northern France to the Ukraine, and called the Börde Zone in Germany, have long been occupied by a relatively dense population. It was only incidental that this same belt across Europe happened to possess coal wealth that furnished a power base for industry. Relatively fertile alluvial soils in the Po Basin likewise supported a large population before manufacturing stimulated a great increase in density. The gardens of Italy, which reach their fullest development on the rich volcanic soils of the Campania around Naples, show purely agrarian densities approaching those of the Far East.

A combination of good soil, favorable relief, and advantageous location also permits a very dense population on the coastal plains of Spain and Portugal and in most of Italy. In Italy, however, the map gives little indication of the detailed contrasts between the high density where the garden type of agriculture prevails in the plains and valleys and the emptiness of some of the uplands and unhealthy coastal regions. An example of the last is the coast of Tuscany, northwest of Rome, although now malaria has ceased to be a danger there as a result of work by the government in draining marshes and eliminating the mosquitoes. The irrigated coastal plains of Valencia, Murcia, and northern Portugal with its corn-wheat climate, also show a very high density of population. Holland and Flanders likewise show a similar condition, a result of intensive fruit and truck farming together with well-developed activity in manufacturing and commerce.

Mountains, marshes, and arid regions, on the other hand, stand out because of their sparse population. Examples of this are seen in the Alps, the Pripet Marshes east of the border between Russia and Poland, and the dry Spanish Meseta and Caspian Plains. The general density of population also decreases rapidly toward the north of Europe because of the short growing season even where there are no mountains.

Representation of the density of population in the Balkans in A199 is deceptive, because the map does not show the great complexity of the contrasts between the dense population of the narrow coastal plains, the river valleys, and the mountain basins on the one hand and the sparse population of the rugged and hence almost deserted mountain blocks on the other hand.

Cities

Their Location. The present European cities had their dawn in the early Middle Ages after migrations and wars had led to a total breakdown of a great urban period under the Roman Empire. Very often the old sites of the Roman cities were used, but the cities developed in new ways. This was natural, for the same conditions that had been favorable for cities in Roman times were favorable in the Middle Ages. Harbors and river ports where good land routes met navigable waterways were highly desirable. Many of the large cities shown in A202 are seaports, and about the same number are located on navigable rivers. Another very desirable location for a city was one close to fertile plains or lowlands forming a hinterland whence food could be easily brought and where a prosperous agricultural population needed a center not only for trade and government but also for the concentration of the simple industries of that day. The need of good routes of transportation as well as for a prosperous hinterland meant that cities had to be located at a low elevation. The highest of the large modern cities is Madrid, 2,300 feet above the sea; but such altitudes are rare, and even Madrid is on a comparatively level plateau.

Another factor, namely a location that could easily be defended, was much more important for cities in medieval days than now. Thus it happened that many cities grew up in defensible sites under the protection of a church, monastery, or castle. Outgrowing in many cases its need of protection by church or castle, the medieval city at length presented a marked contrast to the villages. Its citizens were free. Its public buildings, such as town halls, churches, and guild houses, and even some of its houses, were beautiful; it had schools, and in many cases universities; and it became the center of cultural development. This fostering of intellectual life is perhaps one of the most important contributions that the growth of cities has made to European civilization. Political life also made progress in the cities, for the free burghers had no such respect for the feudal lords as had the peasants.

Former Size of Cities. In spite of their cultural and political importance, the cities, before the age of manufacturing, comprised only a small part of Europe's population. In the fifteenth century, Paris, with a population of about 300,000, was the largest city in northern Europe. Flanders, however, was by far the most highly urbanized region. It is actually described as a continuous city. Bruges, Ghent, and Ypres have been estimated at 100,000 or even twice that figure, but it is doubtful whether any of them had over 50,000. Even in Flanders 25 per cent would probably be a generous estimate of the proportion of town dwellers. London, which in the fifteenth century followed Paris and the towns of Flanders in size, had only about

40,000 inhabitants.   No other English town appears to have had as
many as 15,000, although perhaps a dozen had over 5,000.   Aside
from Paris the population of the larger French towns ranged from
5,000 to perhaps 25,000.   In Germany, Nürnberg and Cologne had

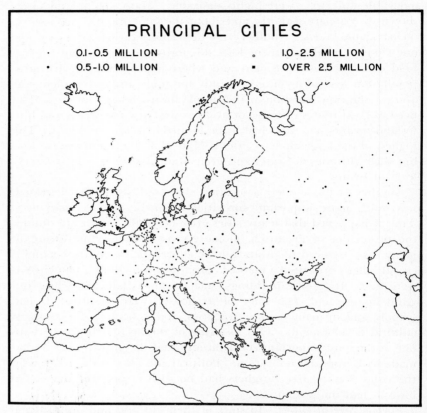

A. Distribution of Principal Cities of Europe.   (For names and populations, see
Appendix.)

about 20,000, but cities as famous as Frankfurt and Basel had well
under 10,000.   The bulk of the population of northern Europe lived
in villages of 300 or less.   In whole English counties, two thirds of
the people were found in villages of less than 120 inhabitants.   City
life was important chiefly because of the changes it was destined to
produce rather than the numerical size of the population.

Until the Industrial Revolution in the eighteenth century this
picture of a rural population dwelling in little villages, and with

only the beginnings of urban life, did not change very much. At that time Paris and London, being the capitals of Europe's most progressive large nations, had each attained a population of about 750,000, but they stood head and shoulders above the other cities. Others like Amsterdam, Vienna, and the three Italian cities of Naples, Palermo, and Rome had between 100,000 and 200,000 inhabitants. All the other cities that now boast large populations were small, and many were still in the village stage. It is obvious that, in order to have attained their present size, European cities must have grown almost as fast as those of America did several decades later.

Modern European Cities. The combined influence of manufacturing and commerce caused the growth of the modern European city and changed rural western Europe into its present urbanized form. A202 shows how closely the distribution of great cities is correlated with that of the manufacturing regions (A129) and how outside those regions urban centers are greatly scattered. The percentage of the population living in great cities varies from 44 in Great Britain to 4 in eastern countries such as Yugoslavia and Bulgaria. Even the Mediterranean countries, in spite of their urban traditions, have only 12 to 15 per cent of their population in great cities, which is far below Germany's 27 per cent. Of the cities of the world with more than 1 million inhabitants, Europe has 21 (see Appendix), of which only 9 are in northwestern Europe, with the rest scattered from Madrid to Moscow. The astonishing increase since 1930 in the number of Soviet cities with populations exceeding 100,000 reflects the growing industrialization of Russia. Except in the eastern Ukraine, the pattern is a scattered one, but the number is, nevertheless, large and increasing.

The modern European city has lost a great deal of its former aspect. The old walls and moats are gone, or have been used for parks and boulevards as the city increased beyond the old limits. The center, used for shopping and commerce, still shows the ancient condensed character, with solid blocks of houses where dwellings, shops, and stores are intimately mingled. The population, however, has spread out over what were once rural districts. These, although urbanized, do not show the compact character of the center. Nevertheless, the city people mostly occupy small apartments or tenements in big blocks of buildings four to six stories high. Such buildings often rise directly from the fields where the peasants are still cultivating the land, as in Vienna and Madrid. Suburbs in the American sense, where great numbers of people live in separate houses with lawns around them, are rare in Europe: only in Scandinavia are they highly developed. In England, to be sure, a great many people live in two-story individual houses on the outskirts of the cities, but the houses usually touch one another or are separated merely by alleys and have only the tiniest lawns or gardens in front of them. In some places—not only in England, but also in other parts of western Europe —attractive "garden suburbs," as they are called, have grown up in the American style, with plenty of trees, lawns, and shrubs. These, however, are common only in the North Sea countries. Elsewhere they are the homes of only a few relatively prosperous people, as in cities like Vienna or Riga. In central Europe, especially Germany, this scarcity of real suburbs has led to the growth of a system whereby people acquire little garden plots outside the cities, build tiny shacks there, and go out for weekends in summer. In Germany these plots are marvelously well-kept, each with its flowers and vegetables.

The character of the development of European cities, with modern industries being added to the peripheries, has necessitated careful city planning. Such planning had some precedents in the designing of cities that had been done by court engineers or by such military engineers as Vauban, especially during the nineteenth century. Planning in European cities during the twentieth century has achieved remarkable results in many places. The poor health conditions that once made the cities death traps for the people who migrated thither from the surrounding agricultural villages have improved steadily. Slums have been replaced by workmen's homes of modern hygienic architecture, and large parks break the monotony of the sea of houses. Nevertheless, it is still true that when people come from the rural districts to work in the cities their death rate greatly increases. In most European cities, if allowance is made for the large proportion of young people, the death rate is still so high and the birth rate so low that the city population would dwindle if it were not replenished from the country. Some of the worst conditions are represented by Łódź, in Poland, a dirty, ugly manufacturing city, a compact mass of smoke-colored houses, with scarcely a redeeming feature. In Bucharest, an attractive modern center contrasts strongly with the still medieval conditions in most of the surrounding parts of the city. Copenhagen, on the contrary, with its beautiful central portions, its thousands of little suburban houses set in gardens, and its throngs of bicycle riders, represents the opposite extreme.

Rural and Village Types of Distribution

In the parts of Europe where the climate and soil were suitable, the art of agriculture developed long ago. This took place especially in subtropical and semiarid regions. There rivers flooded their plains in the winter or spring, leaving moist soil free from weeds and ready to promote rapid growth of crops. The Mediterranean part of Europe was doubtless the seat of widespread agriculture long before this art became feasible in the cooler forested lands farther north or in the moister type of grasslands like the prairies of the Ukraine. The reasons for this can readily be seen. In the first place, primitive people with implements of stone, bone, and wood cannot easily clear forests, nor can they dig up large tracts of sod, especially if they have not yet learned to use draft animals for plowing. In the second place, crops like wheat, barley, rye, and oats, which are especially easy to raise and to preserve, are all found wild in the eastern Mediterranean region. Thirdly, cultivation is easy there, because in large areas the dry summers prevent the growth of heavy sod and of forests, so that even with very crude tools the ground can be prepared for seed. Then, too, the dry summer greatly facilitates the storage of the grain after it is harvested. And, finally, natural irrigation is easily available in many areas where the Mediterranean climate prevails, and this is especially helpful in the more primitive stages of agriculture.

Many considerations led the early European farmers to live in villages rather than in isolated houses, and this has continued until now. The love of sociability, the desire to obtain protection from enemies, and the necessity of being near a supply of water that does not dry up in summer are among the powerful factors that have led agricultural people to live in villages. To an American or Scandinavian, who is accustomed to seeing the farmers living in isolated farmhouses on their farms, it is a surprise to see how few of the agricultural people of Europe live in this way. In the Mediterranean countries practically all the peasants live in villages and walk to their work, just as they have done for thousands of years. The same is true of the rest of Europe, except in Scandinavia and among a relatively small number of people in areas like England, northern France, and northern Germany. Isolated farmhouses are also seen in various rugged regions like Switzerland where it is hard to find arable land for a whole village within easy walking distance of any one spot.

Even so, tiny villages are often nestled in small valleys in many parts of the Alps.

Such a development of scattered homes is greatly favored if there is security for both man and beast. In Europe nature has provided such security from the earliest times in regions like the Alps and the Frisian marshes of Holland. In Sicily the Arab civilization at one time reached so high a level, both in security and otherwise, that the farmers began to live in scattered dwellings among the fields. Then the introduction of Norman feudalism destroyed security and ruined this system. So the population again became concentrated in villages, where the people were protected by feudal lords to whom in return they rendered service. A more recent example is found in Sweden, where the rigid village communities were more or less purposely broken up near the beginning of the nineteenth century. This caused the peasants to move out to their land, leaving the villages merely as the centers of religious, commercial, and social contacts. The breaking up of great estates in eastern Europe after World War I caused a similar development of farm homes outside the villages. The establishment of Soviet-style collective farms in the satellite countries after World War II tended to reverse the process, since the collective farmers were kept in villages. In the Soviet Union itself, steps were taken in 1950–51 to establish *agrogorods,* or agricultural towns. In most parts of Europe the peasants still live in villages that are set in the midst of fields where one sees no houses and not even any fences. Fences around fields and pastures are mainly a phenomenon of the New World, and, except in Britain, where they are common, are practically unknown in Europe. They are expensive to build; they occupy valuable land; and labor is so abundant and cheap that at least a child or an old person can always be found to keep the animals from straying when at pasture.

Appearance of European Villages. So far as outward form is concerned, the present European villages show a great variety of types. Even in a small country like England there are many different styles of architecture. The ugly, square, two-story, stone houses of Cornwall are utterly different from the pretty, one-story, whitewashed, thatched cottages that still persist near-by in Devon. Both are quite different from the more varied villages of Kent, where relatively modern houses surround an old stone church and stand half hidden among fruit trees and gardens. Across the North Sea the villagers of northern France likewise have houses of stone or brick standing among orchards and gardens and surrounded by hedges. In the peat regions of Holland some villages stretch for miles along the roads at the foot of the embankments on which are the canals. In central France many villages show little except forbidding stone houses rising from narrow streets paved with cobblestones and without sidewalks. In Baden a similar condition is made still less attractive, because small paved courtyards wide open to the street are used for storing manure from the stables that stand behind them. Not far away in Bavaria a lovely type of village is found where the houses stand separately in little gardens, fruit trees are trained on their walls, boxes of flowers hang below each window, and the cattle are kept well back from the street. In the southern Alps of France some villages consist of stone houses four or five stories high. Belgian and Italian villages suggest small cities. In Belgium a village often comprises a row of closely spaced houses on each side of a paved road so that one seems to be driving through a city although all the land behind the houses is cultivated as far as the eye can penetrate. Many Italian villages are perched on hilltops and consist of stone houses three or four stories high built in regular blocks like those of cities.

The tree-shadowed villages of Holland are built around the church and have well-washed brick houses and brick streets. The long villages of eastern Prussia stretch along the street for miles, showing Germanic colonization in a Slavic environment. No less interesting are the huge agricultural villages of Hungary, as large as cities, but full of little gardens and orchards surrounding small one-story houses. Equally large villages are found in Spain, but there each street is bordered by a solid wall of whitewashed adobe with doors here and there through which one looks into a paved courtyard where mules, goats, and pigs are standing, or perchance into a richer house with a "patio" surrounded by flowering shrubs and fruit trees. Far away in the northern parts of Poland and Russia the village houses take the form of whitewashed log cabins. In Turkey and southeastern Russia whitewash largely disappears and the villages become clusters of gray adobe walls and flat roofs of dried mud. Greater security and freedom may cause the farmers in many regions to live in more scattered settlements, but the village remains overwhelmingly the most frequent type of settlement among Europe's rural population.

· 14 ·
The March
of Civilization*

The Migration of Centers of Culture

The center of civilization in Europe and neighboring regions has moved from southeast to northwest. This shift has been discussed in regard to agriculture, transportation, and industry. It occurred similarly in art, science, government, education, and other phases of human progress. Five or six thousand years ago the earliest great civilizations flourished in Egypt and Babylonia. At a later date great centers arose in Crete, Syria, and Assyria, four or five degrees north of the earliest centers. Then Greece took the lead, another two or three degrees to the north and farther to the west. Rome, still farther north and west, came next. During the Dark Ages and the great recession in human progress in Europe, the lead passed to Constantinople in the east, but it was soon overshadowed by Venice, Florence, and Genoa, even farther northwest than Rome. These in turn gave place to Vienna, Paris, and other cities, still another five degrees to the north. Even here the northwestward march of progress did not stop, for London, Amsterdam, and Berlin represent regions that came to the forefront still later. Last of all, in the present day, Stockholm, Copenhagen, and the Scottish cities represent extremely northerly or northwesterly regions whose extraordinarily high standards are universally recognized. Thus in four thousand years the center of human progress—that is, the greatest center—migrated more or less steadily for 2,500 miles from Egypt and Babylonia to the region around the North Sea—from latitude 30° to 50° or more, and through 40° of longitude.

At each stage in this migration there have been zones of culture. In the center new inventions, institutions, and ideas have arisen;

---

*This chapter, with only minor emendations, is reproduced as it was written by the late Ellsworth Huntington. It is offered here as a memorial to Professor Huntington and as an example of his broad thinking.

political and military power has reached the highest levels; industry has been most active; and art and science have flourished most steadily. Farther out in each case there has been an irregular zone of moderate progress, and outside that a relatively backward zone. The size and form of the zones have varied according to the shape and location of seas, rivers, mountains, plains, and deserts; according to the character and migrations of races; and according to the nature of new inventions, habits, and institutions. The point to be stressed, however, is the persistent way in which cultural centers and zones have existed throughout historic times, and the systematic way in which the centers have migrated northwestward.

Causes of Cultural Migration

The causes of this migration of culture present one of the most fundamental problems in both geography and history. The migration has emphatically not been a movement of peoples, for the torch of leadership has passed through the hands of Egyptians, Sumerians, Akkadians, Phoenicians, Aramaeans, Cretans, Jews, Persians, Medes, Greeks, Macedonians, Romans, Italians, Franks, Goths, Anglo-Saxons, Vikings, Teutons, and others. Nor has the migration been merely the moving outward of ideas, although this has occurred on an enormous scale. The dominant fact seems to be that the people at the center of culture have invariably possessed unusual energy, initiative, and power of leadership compared with the people around them. This has shown itself in their inventiveness, their ability to utilize the work of their predecessors, their power to control other people, and their ability to elaborate and maintain new methods in ethics, religion, art, science, industry, commerce, politics, war, and other activities. This active quality seems to be the keynote of the whole problem.

The activity and progress of the great centers of civilization seem to be due to the combined effect of three great factors. One is the innate ability of the people, arising often from a rigorous selection resulting from migrations in which the physical and mental weaklings have been exterminated. This involves so many disputed points that it will not be elaborated; it will be assumed that people like the Greeks of the "Golden Age" actually did possess an unusually high type of biological inheritance. The second factor is a favorable geographical environment; and the third is the inventions, discoveries, and new ideas that follow as the result of the contact between the people and their environment.

The Birth of Civilization

At the dawn of civilization, perhaps ten thousand years ago, Egypt and Babylonia appear to have been inhabited by people of more than average ability. The reason may have been that the climatic fluctuations of glacial and postglacial times had here subjected mankind to a peculiarly strenuous process of migration, selection, and possibly mutation. In the course of their wanderings these people had doubtless picked up most of the good ideas of their neighbors, although at that time the world's cultural inheritance was still very small. The floodplains of the Nile and the Euphrates furnished an almost ideal environment for the new art of agriculture, which they or their neighbors invented. In the steppes around them, which appear to have been much more grassy then than now, they found the ass, horse, and camel, and presumably the sheep inhabited neighboring regions. In this same general region wild wheat, barley, oats, and rye all seem to have existed at that time. This means that the resources needed to encourage the early growth of civilization were here grouped together in remarkable fashion, just as today the resources for the modern type of civilization show a remarkable grouping around the North Sea.

The climate also was highly favorable. This statement may seem to contradict what has previously been said about the nature of the optimum climate. There is really no contradiction, however, when two important points are considered. One is the fact that the optimum climate is not the same for all stages of civilization. The other is the fact that at the end of Neolithic times the climate of the eastern Mediterranean regions seems to have been more favorable than now. Previous discussions of climate have described the optimum for the highly civilized, modern type of life. The optimum for people in lower stages of civilization is quite different. The early men who first practiced agriculture were very primitive. So far as can be determined, clothing was to them little more than the adornment of the rich; their shelters were apparently mere wattled huts of sticks; fires were made only in open hearths, usually outside the huts; windows were unknown; and there were doorways rather than doors. At the dawn of the historic era in Egypt and Babylonia conditions like these prevailed among all except an insignificant fraction of the population. Even the rich had no adequate protection against cold or wet weather.

Under such conditions the optimum temperature was obviously higher than for people who enjoy modern methods of protection against cold. Among people on the lower rungs of the ladder of civilization one of the things that most limits productive activity and comfort is the temperature of winter. Even today an average January temperature of 50° F in Sicily leads to a far greater rise in the death rate than does one of 25° in Sweden. The Swedes not only know how to protect themselves from cold and wet weather, but also have to do so in order to live. The Sicilians, on the contrary, not yet having learned to protect themselves properly, shiver, suffer, and die in temperatures that seem warm to the Swedes. The ability of the early Egyptians and Babylonians to protect themselves from the cold was even less than that of the modern Sicilians. Accordingly the climate that was best for their stage of civilization was one in which the winter had no really cold weather. The average temperature of the coldest month for day and night together ranges from 54° to 60° in Egypt, and from 49° to 52° in Babylonia. This is about as low as people in the old Egyptian or Babylonian stage of culture can stand without suffering seriously in health and efficiency.

Unfortunately, the summers in these earliest centers of civilization are extremely hot, the warmest month averaging from 79° to 95° in Egypt and 93° to 95° in Babylonia. Nevertheless, to people in the early Egyptian stage of culture such heat apparently does less damage than does low temperature in winter. The effect of the heat is mitigated by the dryness of the summers, so that a given temperature is by no means as debilitating as in China, for example, where the summers are humid as well as hot. Moreover, there is considerable evidence that in ancient days, although the temperature was about as now, the amount of storminess and hence the variability and stimulating quality of the climate were appreciably greater than at present. This, to be sure, is disputed, and cannot be stated positively. Even if the climate has remained constant, however, the river plains that provided the physical basis for the earliest centers of civilization were located where the climate approaches fairly closely to the optimum for the low stage of culture that then existed.

Thus both the people and the geographic environment of Egypt and Babylonia appear to have been unusually favorable to the evolution of civilization—more favorable probably than in any other part of the world.

Inventions That Overcome Low Temperature and Humidity

The greatest factor in the systematic process by which the center of civilization in the eastern Mediterranean lands and Europe migrated to the northwest appears to have been the inventions and discoveries that have given man greater and greater ability to withstand cold and rainy winters. Such inventions are almost innumerable and of great variety. Some have to do with fire. These include the invention of the hearth and in much later times of chimneys, fireplaces, stoves, and finally furnaces for central heating. The invention of the ax and of matches and the discovery of the way to use coal have also made it much easier to live in cool climates. Other inventions and discoveries have helped mankind to prepare warm clothing. The domestication of sheep, the invention of spinning and weaving, the art of sewing, the use of power for making cloth, and improvements in the preparation and use of leather and rubber have all helped to make it more and more easy to keep both warm and dry in cold, damp climates.

Improvements in architecture have been equally important. A hut of sticks wattled with mud was a truly great invention in its day, but man has gone on to walls of mud, brick, and stone, to the use of lumber, shingles, and stucco, and to structures in which the inhabitants in winter at least have little inkling of what the weather may be unless they look outside. Another very important set of inventions has made it possible to have light and the right degree of warmth at the same time, even in winter, a thing impossible in early days. From a lamp consisting of a smoking wick floating in oil, man has progressed through candles, whale oil, and kerosene to gas and electricity. Window glass has perhaps been of even greater importance than these other methods of obtaining light. Water supplies, sanitary appliances, and medical care have also played a tremendous part in making it feasible to live comfortably and healthfully in cold or wet climate. Compare the stage in which women carried water on their heads from a distant spring and in which toilet facilities were absolutely unknown with the modern stage of automatic washers and tile bathrooms. The contrast represents a tremendous advance in making life comfortable in cold, wet weather.

Still another phase of man's conquest of cooler climates is found in inventions dealing with the use of the land. The cooler parts of the habitable earth are naturally covered largely with dense forests or with thick grass of the prairie type that forms a sod. This is very different from the open forests and thin bunchy grass of regions with the Mediterranean and desert types of climate where civilization first arose. Until iron tools were invented, it was exceedingly difficult, and, on a large scale, almost impossible, to clear a forest for agriculture. Until some sort of harness for oxen or horses, and a plow that would turn the sod, had been invented, it was extremely difficult to plow tough sod and to use many kinds of grassland for farming. These things seem so simple now that it is hard for us to appreciate how slowly and with what pains they were elaborated.

Consider again how necessary it has been to have a long series of inventions in order to make transportation in cold, wet regions as easy as in those that are warm and dry. In Egypt and Mesopotamia, one can travel almost anywhere at any time and with little equipment and no made roads. Rain is scarce and so is mud outside the irrigated areas. It is rarely too cold or wet for the traveler to camp in the open, as is still done very commonly. Long wet storms, snow, and ice are almost unknown. Except in the steepest places the uncultivated land can be easily traversed in any direction on foot or with animals, and in vast areas even with wheels. The motorcars that connect Damascus and Baghdad need no road in the desert. But how far could any kind of wheeled vehicle, or even a loaded horse, get in the forests of Europe without a road? Transportation in regions where the optimum climate for the present kind of civilization prevails became as easy as in ancient Babylonia only when man had learned not only to protect himself and his goods from the rain, snow, and mud, but to make inns and prepare roads with reasonably dry surfaces. He had to learn also to travel on the snow with sleighs, snowshoes, or some other device.

Consider lastly the art of preserving food. It is easy to preserve food in a warm, dry climate. In Egypt grain will keep six months or a year when simply piled in a heap on the ground and covered with a few inches of mud that quickly dries into a hard crust. To preserve it equally well in a cold, wet climate required experiment after experiment until man learned to build corn cribs, grain bins, and finally grain elevators. Grass for fodder can be left where it grows in dry climates, and is still good after six months. The hay of cool, wet regions must be carefully cut, dried, and stacked under a roof or in a barn.

This list of inventions and discoveries that have gradually enabled mankind to live comfortably, healthfully, and actively in regions with cold winters and much rain or snow might be indefinitely expanded. The present skill in these respects has been acquired only through the combined efforts of millions of men and through thousands of years of experiment. From century to century it has become more and more feasible to live comfortably and work creatively in cool, wet, stormy climates. Moreover, with each step toward the northwest on the way from Egypt to England, the stimulating and health-giving qualities of the climate have increased. Thus each new center of civilization has had the double advantage of the knowledge and skill passed on by its predecessors, and of a more stimulating climate than any of those predecessors enjoyed.

The Case of Greece. It is interesting to see how this theory of the migration of centers of civilization applies to Greece. According to the theory, the first step in making Greece the center of civilization was prolonged migration and consequent selection of an especially able group of people who ultimately invaded that country and became dominant in a region with reasonably good natural resources. For some centuries a rigid system of restricted marriage preserved the original high ability of the dominant groups, especially at Athens. The presence of such people helped the Greeks to profit by the inventions made in other countries as well as to make new discoveries of their own. Hence the Greeks were better able to protect themselves against a January temperature averaging about 48° than the Egyptians had been against a temperature 10° or 15° warmer. Baghdad, however, has essentially the same winter temperature as Athens. The really significant difference between the winters of Greece and of the older centers lies in the rainfall. From October to March even dry Athens gets 12 inches of rain; Petras on the west coast of Greece gets 21, and at Sparta the figure rises to 24. Baghdad, on the contrary, gets only 6 inches and Cairo 1. Thus the problem of protection from chilly winter rains is very real in Greece, but negligible in Babylonia and Egypt. The Greek climate must have involved great discomfort and ill health in winter until the art of building houses and making clothing had reached quite an advanced stage. This in itself would apparently have been enough to delay the full flowering of Greek civilization considerably after that of Egypt.

Another significant advantage of the more northerly location of Greece is that human health and activity are much less handicapped by a temperature averaging only 81° F in July than they are by a temperature 10° to 15° higher in Babylonia and upper Egypt. Since Greece is dry in summer, its temperature is only a moderate handicap. Moreover, because Greece consists of so many islands and peninsulas, the heat is mitigated by sea breezes, which are unknown in the continental areas of Egypt and Babylonia. Thus the intimate contact of Greece with the sea affords an advantage in climate as well as in opportunities for trade and for stimulating contact with other types of culture.

Still another decided advantage of Greece over Babylonia and Egypt is that even in the present day the storminess of Greece, and hence the stimulating variability of the climate, are decidedly greater than in the earlier centers of civilization. Moreover, there is some evidence that from 1000 to 500 B.C., when Greece was preparing for its great outburst of mature glory, the storminess and rainfall were relatively high and that this continued with little change until well after 300 B.C. If this was actually the case, both agriculture and human health and activity must have benefited. In connection with agriculture, it is worth noting that when Greece rose to its highest level a long series of improvements had gradually made it possible to cultivate not only alluvial floodplains where irrigation was easy, but dry plains and slopes where there was no irrigation. Greece could not rise to the vanguard of civilization until this stage of progress had been reached.

In summing up the Greek situation, it will be assumed for the sake of argument that the leaders of Greece and Egypt were originally of equal innate ability. On this basis, it would be expected that in 500 B.C. Greece would have risen above Egypt in the scale of civilization for the following reasons: (1) Greece had the advantage of Egyptian and other cultural discoveries as well as her own. (2) Being less favorable than Egypt for primitive agriculture and for primitive human occupation in general, Greece had not become overpopulated as had Egypt. (3) Greece, having long been merely on the edge of the cultural zones that centered in Egypt, had been especially subject to the inroads of fresh migrants who had come a long way. On this account the percentage of people who were descendants of the energetic, selected type of ancestors was presumably large. (4) The progress of the arts enabled the Greeks to live with reasonable comfort in cool, rainy weather that would have been most unpleasant as well as harmful to people with shelter and clothing as poor as those of the Egyptians. Thus they were able to enjoy the stimulus of a climate that is much more healthful and invigorating than that of Egypt.

Great as these advantages were, they did not prevent Greece from eventually declining. Overpopulation and the growth of a poor proletariat, the introduction of lower ideals of living, the breaking down of the old marriage restrictions among the more competent sections of society, the dilution of this same old stock by slaves, the restriction of its birth rate because of wealth and luxury, internal wars and the inroads of enemies, a deterioration in storminess and rainfall especially in the second and third centuries before Christ, and the introduction of the scourge of malaria all seem to have played a part in causing Greece to lose its old power, and hence to decline in population, wealth, and influence. In this process, just as in its rise to the pinnacle of fame, the biological, geographical, and cultural elements are so inextricably mingled that it is often impossible to disentangle them and useless to attempt to say which is more important.

Other Examples. A similar line of reasoning applies to Rome as compared with Greece. An average January temperature of 44° at Rome and a winter rainfall of 24 inches make a combination considerably harder to deal with than the 49° and 12 inches at Athens. But a July average of 77° in comparison with 81° helps to promote energy and the spirit of work much more than is often supposed. A greater prevalence of cyclonic storms and a more wholesome degree of humidity have a similar effect. Genoa, Florence, and Venice differ climatically from Rome much as Rome differs from Athens, or Athens from Cairo. The northern Italian cities, therefore, did not become the most favorable localities until still greater cultural progress had been made. Vienna with an average temperature of 67° in July and 29° in January shows a still further improvement of climate but demands a corresponding development of the technique of living. There, however, the winter becomes so cold that even our present methods do not adequately cope with it.

Berlin with average temperatures of 65° in July and 31° in January, Paris with 66° and 37°, and London with 63° and 39° come still closer to the optimum for people with the present European ability to protect themselves from the harmful effects of climate. The fact that these three greatest cities of Europe, rivaled only by New York, Tokyo, Moscow, and Chicago elsewhere, have climates so close to the optimum is highly significant.

The case of London is especially noteworthy. Today the Old World's largest city and greatest commercial, financial, and political center is found in the very spot where the geographic conditions would suggest it should be expected. It will be remembered that, so far as human material is concerned, southeastern England has re-

ceived repeated incursions of people upon whom migration, persecution, or war has imposed a drastic selective process. Angles, Saxons,
Norse, Vikings, Danes, and Normans; persecuted Flemings, Jews, and
French Huguenots; ambitious Irish and Scots; and in the twentieth
century expatriated but able Russians and Germans—all brought
real elements of strength to this part of the world. Culturally the
situation is as favorable as it is biologically. Each of these migrant
groups, as well as many another, has brought its own contribution in
the form of some special kind of skill, such as that of the Flemish
weavers. The island position of England and its location on the
Atlantic border of Europe and thus relatively near to America have
also tended to bring cultural ideas and material wealth from everywhere. The basis for a great nation in natural resources such as agriculture, coal, and iron is also broad, even though food must now be
imported.

It should be remembered, also, that the climate of London is
close to the ideal for health and activity in spite of the fogs. The
ideal climate should be one in which summer temperature and humidity are the optimum for physical health and the winter should
show the optimum for mental activity. This is just what London
has. So far as can be judged from measurements of health, factory
work, comfort, and activity in many parts of the world, London's
July average of 63° could scarcely be improved. The January average of 39° is almost exactly the outdoor temperature at which the
people who have thus far been investigated in both the United States
and Europe appear to do the best work intellectually. With such a
temperature, often frosty, but not cold at night, the body can be kept
in excellent health by means of clothing, shelter, and other modern
methods, and the maximum stimulus comes from the constant but
not excessive changes that people experience by going in and out of
doors, by opening or shutting windows, and by varying the degree
to which they protect themselves against the outside air. And finally
the storminess and humidity of southeastern England come close
to the ideal.

This sketch of the progress of civilization from Baghdad to London indicates that at each stage of history the center of culture has
been located where migration, physical selection, natural resources,
and climate have combined to make people most competent in cultural achievements. Thus not only the location of the earliest great
centers of civilization, but also the march of these centers northwestward, appear to be the consistent result of the interplay of geographi-

cal environment, man's innate biological characteristics, and the accumulation of a great heritage of human culture.

What of the Future?

At this point the question of future centers of civilization arises. Will the center shift still farther north to Scandinavia? Will it move eastward to cooler regions such as the Soviet Union? Will it stay where it is? Or will it perchance move once more to lands that are warmer? In answering these questions the following major results of the preceding pages must be kept carefully in mind. First, although the centers of civilization have shown a tendency to migrate to cool regions, there has been an even stronger tendency toward regions that are stormy. The most desirable condition appears to be an abundant but not excessive rainfall evenly distributed throughout the year, and constant but not extreme changes of weather from day to day. Such conditions are the best both for agriculture and for human health. The only part of the world that surpasses the North Sea region in the variability arising from cyclonic storms is the northeastern United States, but there the extremes of temperature both in summer and winter may counteract whatever gain arises from greater storminess.

Second, in the earliest days of civilization the optimum climate was determined by the conditions of winter, but now summer is more important. In other words, the earliest centers of civilization arose where the winters were as cold as the people could comfortably stand. The summers, so to speak, were left to take care of themselves. To-day the main centers of civilization are located where the summers are most nearly ideal, and the winters are taken care of by artificial means of heating. If man should learn to protect himself perfectly from cold, dry weather, his health and activity might be as good in Russia as in England, but thus far the best efforts still fail in this respect.

Third, although data are still scanty, the climatic optimum for mental activity appears to occur at an average outside temperature of about 40°. The regions near the North Sea, Puget Sound, and New Zealand, and some islands like Nantucket are the ones where there is the closest approach both to the optimum temperature for physical health in summer and the optimum temperature for mental activity in winter. It is difficult to see how any other part of the world could rival them in temperature no matter how fully man may learn to control his physical environment artificially.

The fourth feature of the discussion is that the centers of civilization tend to grow up not only in regions with stimulating climates, but also in those where recent migration into relatively unoccupied areas has led to an intensive process of natural selection. In this respect new lands like the United States, Canada, and Australia seem to be the logical successors to the North Sea region.

Finally, new cultural conditions have played an indispensable role in determining the march of civilization. It is possible that a new social and economic system in a country like Russia or China might be so superior to the present systems that those countries would forge to the forefront of civilization. It appears to be the rule, however, that all sorts of new ideas, no matter where they originate, are used most effectively in the regions where the combined effects of innate biological character and climate lead to the greatest activity. If such is the case, it is probable that western Europe and the United States will quickly seize any advantages that may accrue from a new social system or other improvements in Russia or anywhere else.

In view of all this, it may be legitimate to conclude that in its progress to cooler and stormier climates the center of civilization is now in course of jumping across the Atlantic to the northeastern United States. Nevertheless, although this part of the world is wealthier and more active than the North Sea region, there is no proof as yet that it is superior either in climate or human material. The most that can be said is that in both climate and people the two differ more than is usually realized, but that in spite of this they form a single great center of civilization broken in two by the Atlantic Ocean. They are united by the storm belt that sweeps across them both and is here more highly developed than in any other habitable region. When the advantages of mineral resources, agriculture, and waterways are added to those of climate, it is hard to see how any other large region can surpass these two unless some great change takes place in the innate ability of the people.

·15·
Fennoscandia
as a Unit

The Fennoscandian Unit

The Scandinavian core, consisting of Sweden, Norway, and Denmark, can be expanded to include Finland in a unit frequently referred to as Fennoscandia. A further extension may be made, especially on a cultural basis, to bring Iceland into the grouping. In this general chapter, the discussion will be centered on the three countries of the Scandinavian core, but the other two units will be brought in in so far as they share in the topic under study. Although there are individual chapters on the specific Fennoscandian countries (with Iceland discussed in the chapter on Denmark), an over-all treatment such as this has the advantage of presenting in one general study the aspects common to all Scandinavia, plus the advantage of showing also the differences that exist.

People

Scandinavia is the homeland of the people often called the "Nordics": tall, blond, blue-eyed, fair-skinned, and long-headed. They moved into the area 4,000–5,000 years ago and largely replaced a shorter, darker people of whom remnants are found especially in western Norway; a small percentage of brunet, brown-eyed people is found in several parts of Scandinavia, and the percentage is rather large in Finland. Since migration into the fairly severe environment of Fennoscandia has been almost nonexistent, the original physical type has been kept almost unmixed—certainly to a greater extent than is true of any other considerable area of Europe. The Scandinavian languages (A221) are closely related, but Finnish is of entirely different stock. Though varying locally, a sufficiently uniform culture has developed throughout the area for it to be referred to as "Scandinavian"; and one cultural institution, the Lutheran church, is the same throughout Fennoscandia.

In relation to the population, the number of Scandinavians who have achieved distinction is very high, and the fields in which they have excelled have been varied: music, painting, architecture, theater,

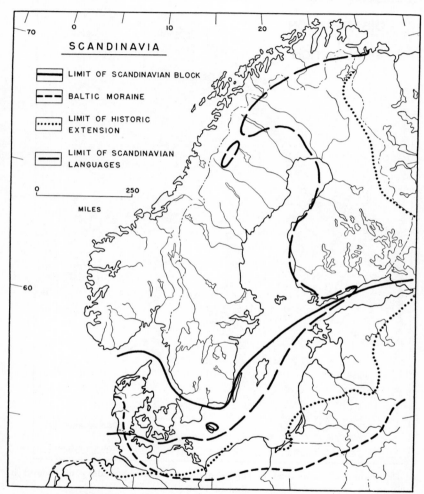

A. Geographical Correlation of Several Aspects of Scandinavia.

literature, science, politics, sports, and others. The birth rate is low, but infant mortality and the death rate are also low. There is virtually no illiteracy, and education is a serious matter for all. Iceland and Finland are democratic republics, whereas the other three coun-

tries are kingdoms with elected parliaments. The socialist element
is strong in all five and is reflected in the trend toward a security

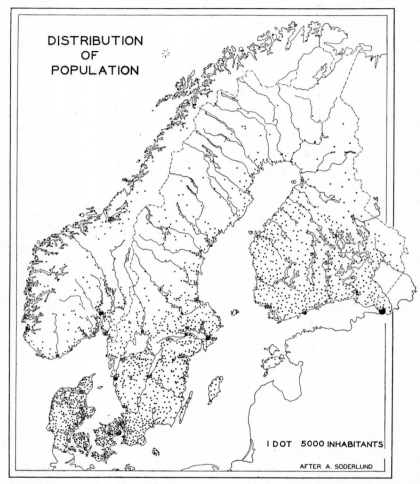

A. Distribution of Population in Fennoscandia. (Eastern boundary of Finland is that of 1940.)

state. Even among the socialists the kings of Denmark, Norway, and
Sweden are popular. The Scandinavian countries have almost eliminated poverty, especially in the more urbanized sections; and, although isolated farmers or fishermen may be poor, they are not destitute. Strenuous efforts to meet the conditions of the severe environ-

ment have led to the accomplishment of much to make life comfortable—an accomplishment that is revealed more in the large cities. An especial trait of the Scandinavians is their blending a spirit of individual independence with a respect for law and a faculty for co-operative enterprise; co-operative organizations ("co-ops") are common in almost every field of economic activity. As lovers of outdoor life, the Scandinavians excel in sports, especially track and winter sports, and are great hikers.

Latitude and Situation

All Scandinavia lies north of 54° N—a parallel that runs through central Labrador and the Kamchatka Peninsula. Oslo and Helsinki are almost on the parallel of 60°, Stockholm is just south of it, and Reykjavík is at 64°. These latitudes might be compared with those of 41° for New York, 38° for San Francisco, and 58° for Juneau, Alaska. Such high latitudes for Scandinavia cause long winter nights and long summer days, but the winter season is long and the summer short. Large areas of Norway, Sweden, and Finland experience 24 hours of darkness a day in winter, and Iceland has only a few minutes of sun in a winter day.

The three core Scandinavian countries are located on peninsulas: the Jutland Peninsula of Denmark separates the North and Baltic seas and joins central Europe, whereas the large Scandinavian Peninsula, jointly occupied by Norway and Sweden, has its connection with the rest of Europe in the far north. Denmark's extension over islands east of Jutland, Iceland's insular position in the North Atlantic, and Finland's semi-peninsular situation are harmonious with the situation of the other areas. All Fennoscandian countries except Finland have longer seacoasts than land boundaries, and little of the land anywhere is far from the sea and its influences.

The situation of the Scandinavian countries around the fringes of the Baltic and the adjoining North Sea has aided the development of a community of culture and interests. Maritime activities are highly developed in all three of the core countries but are especially developed in Norway, the country with the greatest contact with the open sea.

Physiography

The Fennoscandian Shield. Except for extreme southern Sweden and Denmark, Scandinavia and Finland lie, geologically, on the Fennoscandian Shield (A221), a block of extremely ancient, strongly metamorphosed rocks such as gneisses and granites similar to those of the Laurentian Shield of Canada. These old, Pre-Cambrian rocks were eroded down almost to a plain ("peneplain") before the Paleozoic Era, and more Pre-Cambrian and Cambro-Silurian deposits were laid down on the erosion surface, then folded, uplifted, and eroded again to a peneplain. In the west, the younger (but still ancient) deposits were folded down into the Pre-Cambrian surface so deeply that they may still be found there as the Caledonian System in Scandinavia—structurally related to the folded system of the Caledonian originally named in Scotland. In the east, however, the late Pre-Cambrian and Cambro-Silurian deposits were completely removed, except for small "outliers" that attest to their former existençe.

Apparently no deposits of later age than the Silurian were laid down on the Fennoscandian Shield, and the block remained stable through geological ages until it was tilted by pressure exerted during the period of Alpine mountain building in Tertiary times. This pressure tilted the block up in the west and simultaneously cracked the rigid mass in many places. The shield thus displays rather high mountains in Norway; their barren summits still exhibit the rounded forms of the second peneplanation, and the northeast-southwest trending structure of the Caledonian folds is still preserved. This ridge along the Norwegian-Swedish boundary is called Scandinavia's Kjølen ("keel"). To the east, the surface slopes gently to the Gulf of Bothnia. The Finnish portion of the shield is mainly a low, rolling surface that is believed to be the best example of an existing peneplain, somewhat spoiled, however, by surficial glacial deposits.

Toward the southern part of Scandinavia, the old rocks of the shield disappear under younger deposits in Skåne and Denmark, and only in the island of Bornholm do the ancient rocks make a final appearance. Iceland has entirely different conditions from those of Fennoscandia: it is an island on which volcanoes have played a leading role in building up the surface and on which volcanic activity is still strong.

The Ice Age and Its Influences. The uplands of the Scandinavian Peninsula were the feeding grounds for the great continental ice sheets that, during approximately 1 million years of the Pleistocene Ice Age, expanded over northern Europe and then melted back at least three and probably four times. The sheet with the greatest extension (the second advance, called in Europe the Mindel) reached the uplands across central Europe (see Map A63), although the last sheet (Würm) is responsible for the vast amount of moraine deposited over northern Europe. The black arcs in A63 represent terminal moraines and recessional moraines that were dropped at the edges of the ice when it was in equilibrium for extended periods. Brilliant research by Scandinavian glacial specialists led by De Geer has shown that the Würm ice sheet began its retreat from the plain of northern Europe approximately 25,000 years ago and that the retreat lasted 16,000 years until the last remnants of the ice were left in the Swedish highlands near Lake Ragunda. A few scattered remnants may still be found on higher elevations in Scandinavia today.

The effects of the last ice sheet are especially marked in Scandinavia. Debris dropped by the ice in the form of ground moraine blankets much of southern Scandinavia, especially Denmark. The recessional moraines already mentioned rise above the general level in long ridges several hundred feet in height. The recessional moraines in central Sweden and southern Finland mark the limit between the Gotiglacial and Finiglacial stages of the melting of the ice sheet. Long, winding ridges (eskers—called *åsar* in Swedish), similar in general appearance to moraines but formed of gravel deposited in tunnels under the ice sheet, are found in great numbers in central Sweden and in Finland and generally trend north-south. Also present are low whaleback hills (drumlins), small conical hills of gravel (kames), outwash plains of sand and gravel, dry beds of former ice-dammed lakes, and other depositional evidences of recent glaciation similar to those found in such parts of the United States as Wisconsin, northwestern New York, and New England.

In most of Scandinavia, glacial erosion or ice-scouring was more operative. Vast areas were scraped clean of their soil cover, and thousands of depressions were scoured out by the ice and are now occupied by lakes. Some parts of the scoured region have a thin, stony moraine scattered over the surface. The material scraped from northern and central Scandinavia was transported by the ice to the southern portions; a Dane visiting in Norway or northern Sweden may jokingly thank his Norwegian or Swedish friends for sending their soil to Denmark by the ice sheet. Descent of tongues of ice down the former river valleys following the steep western slope of the Scandinavian block widened and rounded the valleys. Subsequent development of these valleys is discussed in detail in Chapter 17. Large areas in northern Fennoscandia were left polished by the hard materials carried at the foot of the ice; and, in places, scratches (striae) mark the surface and show the direction of ice movement. Knobs of rock were rounded by the ice sheet to form *roches mouton-*

nées, common in parts of Sweden, the Åland Islands, and mainland Finland.

Melting of this vast continental glacier, with its ice thickness of several thousand feet toward the center, released the water that had been locked in the frozen mass and returned it to the sea, causing a rise in sea level of many feet. Simultaneous melting of ice sheets in other parts of the world contributed equivalent amounts of water to the sea. Much of the meltwater from the Scandinavian sheet poured into the depression now occupied by the Baltic Sea, but this basin had to pass through several stages of development before the sea attained its present outline.

With the melting of the ice edge northward and the outpouring of meltwater, the Baltic Ice-Dammed Lake was formed in the Baltic depression, with outlets eastward across Finland to the White Sea and northwestward through the depression now occupied by the Øresund between Sweden and Denmark. Further retreat of the ice uncovered the depression in "central" (actually southern) Sweden now occupied by lakes Vänern and Vättern and opened a connection with the North Sea. The salt sea that then came to occupy the Baltic basin is referred to as Yoldia Sea. It not only flooded vast areas in central Sweden and Finland but likewise drowned parts of the present Jutland and the Danish islands. Continued retreat of the ice naturally subtracted from the load of ice that had for thousands of years weighed down the Fennoscandian Shield and had depressed it below its normal level. Therefore, the rise in the level of the land began to match the rise in sea level. This new adjustment closed the connection to the North Sea and changed the salt Yoldia Sea into a fresh-water lake, referred to as Ancylus Lake. It overflowed westward through a channel across the same region in central Sweden that had previously served as a broader connection with the North Sea. Further rise of southern Scandinavia, however, closed this outlet; and as the fresh water lake level rose it found its next outlet through the Great Belt of Denmark between the present islands of Fyn and Sjælland. This same rise in lake level caused Ancylus to submerge the coastal areas of Scandinavia, especially those of Sweden and Finland.

The rising sea level eventually caused re-establishment of connections between the salt water and Ancylus Lake; this second salt-water stage of the Baltic basin is referred to as the Litorina Sea. Central Sweden, however, had by this time risen to a height sufficient to prevent its being greatly flooded. Continued rising of the land, which

is still going on, in the Scandinavian Peninsula and in northern
Jutland has brought about the existing relationships between land
and sea in the Baltic area.

Those parts of Scandinavia and the mainland coasts that were

POSTGLACIAL OCEAN EXTENSION

A. Greatest Extent of Late Glacial and Postglacial Lakes and Seas.   Dotted lines
indicate present shore lines.

submerged by the waters of any of the lakes or seas of late glacial
and early postglacial times are shown in A227.   Not only did the glaciation and the flooding of the coasts exert profound influences on
the landscape of Scandinavia, but also those parts that were submerged
were mantled with marine sands and clays that are of enormous value
in Scandinavian agriculture today.   Soil-forming processes have operated on the marine sediments to produce fertile and easily cultivated

loams that give high yields under the progressive agricultural practices characteristic of Scandinavia. Thus, the glacial history of Scandinavia is important not only in the physical geography but also in the human and economic geography of the region.

Climate (A228, A229, and A230)

The unusually high latitude of the settled parts of Scandinavia, mentioned earlier in this chapter, would seem to preclude any ap-

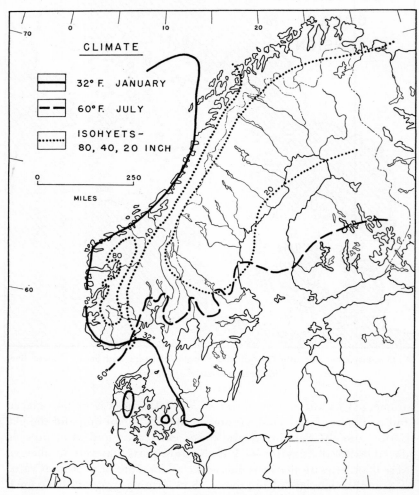

A. Aspects of the Climate of Fennoscandia.

preciable development of human activity. However, as was shown in Chapter 2, unusual controls operate to make northwestern Europe not only habitable but also favorable for human occupance. From the Atlantic comes a sequence of cyclonic storms bringing humid

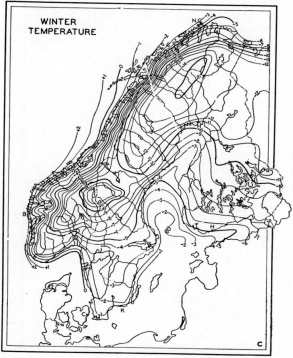

A. Winter Temperature of Fennoscandia. (Eastern boundary of Finland is that of 1940.)

and relatively warm Atlantic air masses. Such influence is especially strong in winter, since the Norwegian Atlantic coastal waters are abnormally warm in relation to the latitude because of the flow of the North Atlantic Drift along the coast and because of the constancy of westerly winds in bringing the warmth inland. The imported heat of the North Atlantic Drift produces a positive temperature anomaly of 50° in January near the islands of Lofoten, which means that the temperature is about 32° in January instead of the −18° that is the average for that latitude.

In Denmark and southern Sweden, where cyclonic storms cross frequently, winters are relatively mild and summers are fairly cool;
rainfall adequate for agriculture is well distributed through the
year. Steep slopes along the west coast of Norway lift the moisture-
laden winds and receive heavy orographic precipitation. Only on

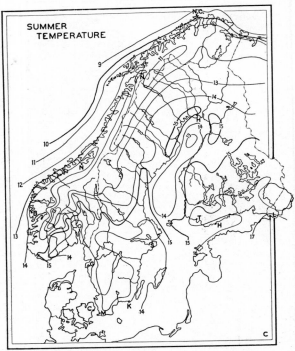

A. Summer Temperature of Fennoscandia. (Eastern boundary of Finland is that
of 1940.)

the eastern slopes of Scandinavia and in Finland does leeward location lessen the marine influence and produce colder winters, with
appreciable snow, and relatively warm summers. The total precipitation is lowered in leeward locations, and at times it falls below the
amount required by crops. Irrigation is actually practiced in some
protected Norwegian valleys. On the whole, therefore, the climate
of Scandinavia, especially in its southern portions, is not only livable,
in contrast to northeastern North America at the same latitude, but
is quite suitable for a specialized agriculture and is conducive to
human health and energy.

Economy

The land of the three Scandinavian countries and Finland is used principally in two ways: for forests and for dairying (A108), the

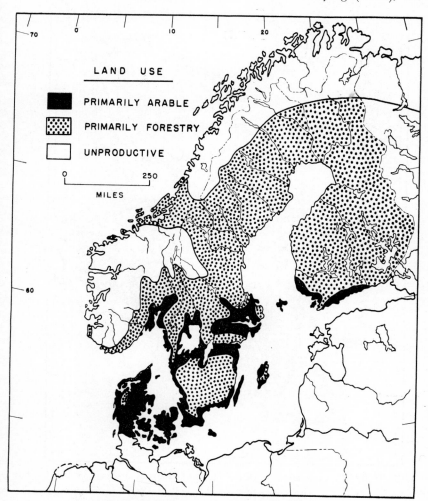

A. Generalized Land Use in Fennoscandia.

former an extensive use of the land and the latter an intensive use of the land. The vast coniferous forests that cover most of Sweden and the Oslo region of southeastern Norway are the most westerly extension of the Eurasian taiga and are a response to the relatively conti-

nental climate and thin soil of the eastern slopes. The dairy industry, on the other hand, with its crops of hay and coarse grains, is
found chiefly where the more marine type of climate prevails and

A. Used Land in Fennoscandia. Only the shaded areas are cultivated. (Eastern
boundary of Finland is that of 1940.)

especially where such a climate is combined with good glacial soils
and a near-by market. In Denmark dairying reaches a level unequaled in any other part of the world. Food grains, however, are
not sufficient to feed the population in any of the three countries and
must be imported in large quantities to supplement those produced
locally. Sweden is, however, approaching self-sufficiency.

Mining, especially of metals, is one of the most important of the Swedish economic activities and is also important in Norway; it plays no role in the Danish economy and only a small one in that of Finland. With certain notable exceptions, the main industrial development in Scandinavia is based on products of the soil and especially on those from dairying and forestry. Sweden especially, but also Norway and Finland, have developed metalworking industries. In addition, local community industries, such as printing and food processing, are highly developed, as in all the more progressive countries.

The general significance of forest products in Sweden and Finland, and to some extent in Norway, deserves special mention. It is amazing to discover what the Scandinavians and Finns can do with their forests. Of course they can use their wood for building and for fuel, but they can also use it for paper and can even dress in it (cellulose). In case of necessity, they run their cars with wood and feed it to the cattle. They can extract alcohol from it and drink it or extract sugar and eat it. Moreover, it is the major export. It is no wonder that forestry has reached such a high level of efficiency and planning in Fennoscandia.

History and Traditions

For hundreds of years, the Fennoscandian countries have shared many aspects of political and cultural life. It was from all three of the core Scandinavian countries that the Vikings (Norsemen, Normans) moved outward during the approximate period 750–1050. The earliest Scandinavians to migrate and engage in conquest were apparently the Danes, who in the eighth century established themselves in eastern Britain. It is possible, if not probable, that the Jutes, who had invaded Britain two and three centuries earlier, were also originally inhabitants of Jutland. Shortly after the Danes began their conquests, the Norwegian Vikings, rugged warrior-seamen with high-prowed ships, sailed westward and southwestward. In the ninth century they reached Iceland and Greenland, both of which they colonized, and by the year 1000 reached the northeastern coasts of North America. Those Vikings who sailed southwestward settled Scotland and Ireland, settled northern France (Normandy), and attacked deep into France and as far south as Sicily and North Africa. Also early in the ninth century, Swedish Vikings (Varägians or Varangians) attacked the Baltic coast and moved southeastward on the rivers, gaining great power in Novgorod and Kiev, and even reaching Constantinople.

For the next several centuries, Denmark was the most powerful of the Scandinavian countries, controlling Norway and varying amounts of Sweden. However, Sweden won its independence in the sixteenth century, despite continued Danish control of part of southern Sweden; but Norway continued in union with Denmark until 1814, when it formed a union with Sweden. Swedish power ex-

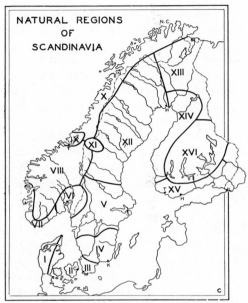

A. Natural Regions of Fennoscandia. (Eastern boundary of Finland is that of 1940.)

tended over the Baltic lands during the sixteenth to eighteenth centuries, but was finally pushed back by the growing German and Russian power. Even Finland, which Sweden had penetrated for many years, was lost to Russian control in 1809. The Swedish-Norwegian union was dissolved in 1905, ending political interconnections in Scandinavia. However, the effects of these centuries of common history are still influential, although no bitter memories of wars remain.

In recent years Scandinavian interrelations have been quite close, and all three generally co-operate in the international sphere. However, there is one point of difference: Denmark and Norway generally look toward the West and, especially after the period of Nazi aggression, have decided to give up their former policy of neutrality by signing the North Atlantic Pact. Sweden, with its Baltic orientation, faces the east, including Russia; and with the power of Germany, on which Sweden built her policy of protection against Russia, gone, Sweden tries to offset the danger of Russian aggression by official neutrality. At the same time, it has increased its military strength and has become the strongest military nation of Scandinavia. Iceland followed the example of Norway and Denmark and signed the North Atlantic Pact, which provides for American air bases on its territory. The case of Finland is quite different. Although the Soviet Union could crush Finland at any time, strangely enough the Russians have permitted Finland a great deal of freedom, politically as well as economically; and Finland is still a democratic republic outside the Iron Curtain.

· 16 ·
Denmark (Danmark)
and Iceland (Ísland)

DENMARK

General Foundations

Denmark resembles the Netherlands, Belgium, and Switzerland in being one of the small European countries that are true representatives of the high cultural and economic level of Europe A. With an area of 16,576 square miles and a population of approximately 4.2 millions, it is also similar to the other three countries in respect to the influential position it holds among other countries of the world all out of proportion to its small size and population. In other ways, however, Denmark is very different from the other three countries: it does not have the superb location at the mouth of the Rhine that the Netherlands does; it has no coal to aid it in an industrial development like that of Belgium; nor is it endowed with Alpine splendor to attract as many tourists as Switzerland does. Denmark is, in fact, poor in resources other than the natural advantages of good climate and soils that respond to intelligent management, although some advantage is gained from the location between the North Sea and the Baltic and between southern Scandinavia and mainland Europe.

The prosperity of modern Denmark is based on its cows, pigs, and chickens, which provide the great Danish export products: butter, cheese, bacon, and eggs. Such an economy may sound rather prosaic, but in few places do cows give more and richer milk, nowhere else has bacon reached such perfection, nowhere else is the freshness of the eggs so universally shown by stamping them with the date on which they were laid. Such specialization in animal industry has been possible largely through co-operation among producers and marketing agencies, which guarantee every pound of butter or bacon and every egg, giving Denmark a reputation for products of high quality. In no country in the world have agricultural and marketing co-operative organizations taken such a prominent place in the economic life.

Naturally, the specialized nature of Danish production contains some elements of danger in view of its lack of diversity and flexibility. Export of most of the products to Great Britain means that any closing of the British market, such as British assigning priority to Dominion breakfast products to the exclusion of Danish ones, would react disastrously on the Danish economy. The post-World War II austerity program in the United Kingdom was reflected in the decrease of sales of Danish products to Great Britain in comparison with prewar years. There is some truth in the jocular suggestion that Denmark would do well to ask for inclusion in the British Commonwealth.

Politically, Denmark, like the Netherlands, owes its independence primarily to the fact that it controls the outlet of an important body of water. For the peace of Europe it is important that a neutral power control the Baltic gateway. In the naval aspects of World War I, Danish neutrality was a significant factor, since it made it more difficult for the German fleet to enter or leave its secure Baltic retreat except by way of the Kiel Canal. It was easier for Great Britain to patrol the mouth of the Elbe than the Skagerrak. In World War II, Nazi occupation of Denmark and Norway placed Germany in a more advantageous position in North Sea naval affairs than it was in World War I. In former days Denmark levied dues on all ships entering or leaving the Baltic, usually through the Øresund, which runs between Sjælland and the Swedish coast. The practice has long since ceased, and many ships pass through the Øresund without stopping. Nevertheless, the growth of Copenhagen was greatly stimulated through the centuries by its location on the Øresund, and many ships still stop and in one way or another contribute to the wealth of the city. Considered in a still larger setting, Copenhagen is located at one of the important focal points of world trade.

Denmark is unusually fragmented in shape, lying partly on the Jutland (Danish: Jylland) Peninsula, which contains approximately two thirds of the area, and partly on a dozen main islands lying between Jutland and the Skåne Peninsula of southern Sweden; the outlying island of Bornholm is located farther west in the southern Baltic. The fragmented shape of Denmark has required a high development of coastal shipping for adequate communications, although in recent years great bridges have been constructed to connect Jutland and Fyn and to link Sjælland and Falster. Ferries ply the waters of the Great Belt and connect the railways of Fyn and Sjælland.

Relief

The entire surface of Denmark is either flat or at most gently undulating. The highest point in the entire country is only 535 feet above sea level. Such low elevations and gentle relief are due to the fact that the Danish surface deposits were laid down by the Pleistocene ice sheet on a low-lying foundation of sedimentary rocks. Ground moraine, or till, is the typical deposit mantling the surface of Jutland and the islands.

Western Jutland (I in A234)

Although all of Denmark was covered with ice during earlier glacial advances, the western half of Jutland was not invaded by the last ice sheet, the margin of which ran north and south through the center of the peninsula. During the time that the ice margin occupied such a position, meltwater poured westward toward the North Sea, carrying with it a large amount of sand and gravel that was deposited in outwash plains among the higher areas of moraine left from earlier glaciation. Thus, western Jutland has two types of landscapes and soils: the low-lying flat areas of sandy outwash plains and the slightly higher and more undulating areas of old glacial till. The higher standing areas are referred to as "hill islands" (Bakkeøer) and in some cases cover relatively large expanses of territory. Dunes and heath are common. Eastern Jutland, on the other hand, is mantled with moraine having a hilly aspect and is less subdued because of the more recent origin of the glacial deposits. There is a marked change in the landscape along the line of the former ice margin. The eastern hills, often with lake-filled depressions between them and small forests of beech, fir, and pine on the slopes, lend variety to one of the most attractive parts of a country that is otherwise very flat.

The west coast of Jutland is bordered by a row of sand dunes. The dunes were formed on sand bars built by currents as the land rose slightly in relation to sea level after the glacial period. The lakes that exist behind the dune belt are lagoons but are unlike the lagoons that exist along the North Sea coasts of Germany and the Netherlands: except in the south there is none of the fertile marine clay that accumulated in the lagoons between the dunes and sandy uplands in those two countries. Along the southern extension of the west Jutland coast the line of dunes disintegrates into a number of islands with passages between them. Constituting part of the North Frisian Islands, they mark the northern extension of a chain that extends in a sharp arc southward and westward along the German and Netherlands coast. Many of the islands are utilized as summer bathing resorts, and because of their wide sandy beaches they are excellent for the purpose. These Danish islands, built up as offshore bars, are comparable with the islands around Cape Hatteras on the North Carolina coast and, like them, have a sheltered channel behind them. Lying at their northern end, on Jutland proper, is the only significant harbor on the west coast of Jutland: Esbjerg. The harbor is actually artificial and was built at great expense in the last quarter of the nineteenth century as an export point for products to be sent by fast ships to the United Kingdom. It has also become the main fishing center on the west coast for Danish activities in the North Sea fisheries.

In the north the Lim Fjord cuts entirely across the peninsula and creates North Jutland Island. In the west, Lim Fjord is wide, shallow, and winding, but in the east is deeper and narrower. This, like the other Danish fjords, should not be confused with those of the type found in Norway: the Danish fjords are often drowned tunnel valleys. The entire course of the Lim Fjord is useful as a passage only for small boats, but it plays an important role in the plaice, eel, and oyster fisheries. At the head of the narrow eastern channel is located Denmark's second most important port, Ålborg, with important cement works. At the northern tip of North Jutland Island a long sand spit, Skagens Odde, has dunes and sandy bars resembling those of Cape Cod in Massachusetts. Continued accumulations of sand cause Skagens Odde to extend seaward between the deep Skagerrak, on the west, from the Kattegat, the sea between Jutland and southern Sweden.

On North Jutland Island the changes in sea level after the ice began retreating in late Pleistocene times are clearly revealed. Two distinct marine terraces represent the former bottom of Yoldia Sea (upper level) and Litorina Sea (lower level). These terraces, as well as other parts of Denmark, are especially interesting because of the evidences they give of early human occupation. The relation of the old sea and lake shores to the location of Stone Age artifacts reveals that early man followed the ice sheet edge northward as it retreated. The dating system worked out by the Scandinavian glaciologists permits the assignment of a rather exact date to the earliest human invasion after the last ice sheet: 7–8,000 years ago. First came the Reindeer people; then there developed the Maglemose or River Valley culture, which gave way to the Ertebølle culture. The Ertebølle culture is well represented by the kitchen middens, or heaps of shells, piled along the old shoreline of the Litorina Sea. Finally came Neolithic cultures, with agriculture first making its appearance. When agriculture and herding were introduced, possibly by a new influx of people, use was made of the lighter soils of the moraine country and outwash plains for agriculture. Later on, the agriculturists moved into the region of the heavy, loamy soils of eastern Jutland and the islands that became, as they still are, the most productive part of the country. Much of western Jutland was left as a domain of forest or else of heaths where sheep browsed on the heather.

The soils in western and central Jutland vary in fertility but are for the most part rather sandy and poor. However, the modern use of fertilizers and the growth of the dairy industry have now made it worth while to cultivate much of this sandy area. In order, the main crops—excluding hay and grass—are oats, barley, mixed oats and barley, swedes (rutabagas), potatoes, and rye. As in the rest of Denmark, little of the crop is used for other than animal feeds. Wheat finds a limited place in the marine climate of western Jutland. Dairying predominates, and sheep still retain a place in rural activity. In spite of increasing productivity of western Jutland, the intensity is not so great as that of eastern Denmark. The less intense land use is also reflected in the relative sparsity of population. Except for the port of Esbjerg, there are no outstanding cities in the region. The southern part of the Jutland Peninsula is politically a part of Germany. Between 1864 and 1919 the boundary was farther north than at present. In the first few years following World War II concentration of repatriated Germans in southern Schleswig (Danish: Slesvig) created some alarm in Denmark.

Eastern Denmark (II in A234)

East of the moraine margin the landscape changes. The margin itself, though evident, is not marked by the prominent terminal moraine that is so conspicuous in the landscape of the Baltic mainland in northern Poland and the Baltic east coast. Eastward the relief is rolling, with low hills reaching heights of 350 to 450 feet, all formed of ground moraine. An interesting and significant feature of the landscape of eastern Denmark is the relatively large number of valleys, usually trending roughly east and west, that were formed by streams under pressure flowing beneath the ice during the last glacial period. These "tunnel valleys" are found on both Jutland and the islands of Denmark and have had significant influences in the

A. This is Denmark: A farm built in a square with garden and trees amid fields of fodder and grass. Courtesy of Hærens Flyvertropper Eneret.

location of modern drainage, communications, and settlement. Remnants of the former universal beech forests on the lower hill slopes, little lakes in the depressions, deeply penetrating arms of the sea, and comfortable, neat, low, white farmhouses embowered in trees are typical of the regional landscape.

The eastern Danish islands are all that remain of the former land bridge that existed between Jutland and Sweden during the period of the Yoldia Sea and part of the Ancylus Lake period described in the preceding chapter. The land bridge was first breached when the former outlet of the lake through central Sweden to the Skagerrak was damned by continued rising of the land and it found its way out through the Great Belt. The complex physiographic history of the Danish islands has given them an extremely irregular outline. Some of the irregularity is due to old tunnel valleys and river erosion channels now partially submerged by the sea. The Little Belt, the strait between Jutland and the island of Fyn; the Great Belt, farther east between Fyn and Sjælland; and the Øresund or "Sound" between Sjælland and Sweden are, therefore, partially erosion channels and partially depressions in the moraine deposits formed by ice lobes during the retreat of the glacier.

Eastern Jutland and the islands constitute the most productive part of Denmark. There are extensive good meadows and, in relation to western Jutland, appreciably more productive fields of two-row barley, fodder beets, sugar beets, oats, and wheat. The presence of wheat and sugar beets in the east indicates the existence of better soils and less marine conditions than in the west. Per acre yields of wheat and barley as high as 60 bushels show not only good soil and very intensive, intelligent cultivation and the breeding of high-yielding varieties, but also a very favorable combination of rainfall and temperature.

Co-operative organizations started in western Jutland after the model of the British co-operatives made great strides in helping all Danish farmers in the second half of the nineteenth century. During the same period they enabled farmers to meet the growing difficulties arising from increasing competition of cheap grains from the Americas and Australia, the temporary loss of Schleswig-Holstein, and the new protective tariff of Germany, which until then had been one of Denmark's principal export markets. Co-operatives have virtually made Denmark one great farm specializing in a few agricultural products for export. Only a very small percentage of the Danish farmers do not belong to one or more of the co-operatives for the export of dairy products, bacon, and eggs, or for the import of stock feed and fertilizer.

Eastern Denmark also contains most of the main towns, the chief of which are Copenhagen (Danish: København), on the east coast of Sjælland, Århus on the east Jutland coast, Ålborg in northeast Jutland, and Odense on Fyn. All these cities except Ålborg have populations of more than 100,000. Copenhagen, with one million inhabitants—one-fourth Denmark's total population—is not only the principal Danish city but also one of Europe's chief cities. In no other country except the rump state of Austria—not even in France —does the capital play so large a part in the country's economic, political, cultural, and social life. It is Denmark's chief port and center of manufacturing. Its industries produce high-grade china-ware or porcelain, margarine (used extensively instead of butter, even in such a great butter-producing land), beer, and a variety of other goods.

With its rich architecture, in some instances showing traces of foreign influence, and pleasant suburbs like those of American cities, Copenhagen possesses great charm and appeal. Suburbs of this kind, where one-family houses stand among lawns, trees, and fenced gardens crowded with colorful flowers, are rare in Europe. Here, as in Stockholm and Amsterdam, tens of thousands of people ride bicycles to and from their work. Attractive parks with famous sculptures, such as those by Thorwaldsen, enhance the beauty of the city. Numerous historic castles in the vicinity lend interest to the area: in northeastern Sjælland at Helsingør is Kronborg Castle, the "Elsinore" of Shakespeare's *Hamlet*. Europe's most famous pleasure garden, Tivoli, is a kind of Copenhagen Coney Island.

Danish Possessions

From the peak of Denmark's power in the Middle Ages, when Danish possessions included not only Norway and parts of Sweden but also part of Britain and a number of north Atlantic island pos-sessions, and, later, the Danish Indies, relatively little territory re-mains. The largest possession is that of the island of Greenland, which Denmark is wisely attempting to develop slowly to a modern level of culture. The only other present Danish possession is the Faeroes (Danish: Færøerne, "Sheep Islands"), lying southeast of Iceland. In their political relationship with Denmark they are some-what comparable with the Isle of Man in its relationship with the United Kingdom. They are an integral part of Denmark in certain respects, but in other ways they enjoy local government; they have their own flag and local parliament, but their foreign affairs are con-ducted in common with Denmark. The Faeroes are made up almost entirely of Tertiary basalt with individual layers as much as 100 feet thick. Younger beds of sedimentary rocks overlie the basalt, and the surface was glaciated during Pleistocene times. The main eco-nomic activity is fishing, especially for cod, but in recent years a few hardy crops, mostly potatoes, have been cultivated. Sheep graze the lower grassy slopes. Thorshavn, located in a protected situation on the southeast side of the main island, Strømø, is the capital and principal fishing center.

ICELAND

Although apparently settled originally by Irish seamen, the development of Iceland really began with the Vikings, who came about A.D. 850. For more than a thousand years thereafter the island was politically affiliated with either Norway or Denmark or both. Icelandic love of independence led it in 1918 to declare itself a separate state, but with a common king with Denmark. Even this link was broken in 1944, when a plebiscite showed overwhelming desire of the Icelanders for an independent republic.

Although Iceland is more than twice as large as Denmark, it has only about 1 inhabitant for every 30 in Denmark; no other civilized country is so sparsely populated. The reason for this is that Iceland has had practically no natural resources except grass and fish, although water power and local hot springs are now being utilized. A large part of the island is too rugged and volcanic for occupation, even if the climate would permit. The main trouble, however, is that high latitude and high altitude combine to make most of Iceland too cold in summer for any vegetation aside from Arctic lichens and mosses typical of a tundra region. Around the coast, however, and in the lower valleys there is a belt of grass. There are very few trees, although reforestation is restoring some trees, chiefly birch, in the protected locations that permit their growth. Vigorous efforts in the line of plant breeding and technique of cultivation are gradually expanding the limited agriculture that has had to rely on such crops as potatoes, turnips, and cabbages. The most common and reliable way of earning a living on the land is by using the grass as pasturage for sheep and cattle in summer and storing up hay for winter feed for them. Accordingly, Iceland has 3 cattle for each 10 persons and—showing the importance of sheep—35 sheep for each 10 persons, more sheep per capita than any other country except Australia, New Zealand, and Uruguay. The export of sheepskins, wool, and mutton to Europe helps the Icelanders pay for food and practically everything else from abroad.

The waters around Iceland are rich in fish, especially cod, and the cool climate makes it easy to preserve them. The many little bays, the wealth of fish in the sea, and the inhospitality of the treeless land tend to drive the Icelanders out to the sea for a living. Hence fish not only form an important part of the Icelandic diet but also provide virtually all the exports. Out of the annual catch of nearly 0.5

million metric tons, a large proportion is exported as frozen, salted, or iced fish or as fish oil or meal. Thus, for a thousand years fish and sheep have been by far the most important Icelandic products. Several poor herring catches in post-World War II years, of which 1950 was one of the poorest, and a decreasing market in Europe for fish imposed severe economic hardships on Iceland by 1950. To off-set these difficulties, Iceland devalued its money and attempted to attract tourists to add to the national income.

Exploitation of sulphur almost ceased with discovery of the sulphur deposits of Sicily, and the bog iron ore formerly smelted with charcoal from the limited trees is no longer exploited. However, during the third and fourth decades of the twentieth century greater use of Iceland's resources was undertaken: the numerous swift streams were exploited for water power, and the water of the equally numerous hot springs was piped into homes and buildings for heat.

Occasional catastrophes have made life in Iceland precarious through the centuries. During certain periods, such as the four-teenth and eighteenth centuries, exceptionally cool, wet summers made curing of hay for the winter impossible. Hundreds of thousands of sheep therefore died. At the same time the increased storm-iness made fishing unusually difficult and dangerous, so that the food supply was low. Among numerous volcanic eruptions certain severe blasts poisoned large tracts of grass and also killed thousands of sheep. Plagues such as the Black Death, famines, and even attacks by pirates have thus decimated the population, sometimes to the extent of more than half of the inhabitants, and economic conditions were truly abject.

In spite of all this, Iceland, for a thousand years, has stood in the forefront of intellectual progress. Long ago, the famous Icelandic Sagas, some of the world's choicest literary masterpieces, were written here. From the introduction of Christianity down through such steps of progress as the invention of printing, modern hygiene, and the use of electricity, the Icelanders, in spite of their poverty and isolation, have on the whole kept pace with their Scandinavian relatives in Europe. Today with a population no larger than that of the little metropolitan district of Paterson, New Jersey, Iceland main-tains an unusually good system of universal education which has long made illiteracy virtually nonexistent. No country in proportion to its population does more in the way of scientific research, historical criticism, and social reform.

Located in southwestern Iceland, Reykjavík, the capital, is the only large town on the island and contains more than a third of the island's 141,000 inhabitants. Growth and economic activity of Reykjavík increased appreciably after 1940, especially under the stimulus of the installation and operation of Keflavík airport just outside the city. The presence of the airport reflects the strategic position of Iceland for both military and civilian aircraft near the Great Circle route from the northeastern United States to northwestern Europe; and Iceland's membership in the North Atlantic Treaty Organization indicates Icelandic recognition of her strategic role and also her dependence on her more powerful friends.

An analysis of the basis for the high standing of Iceland in spite of its poverty of resources indicates that there are apparently two chief reasons for such a standing. One is that Iceland was chiefly settled by a selected type of people, the stronger and more resourceful among the upper classes of the Vikings, together with the more reliable of their retainers whom they chose to bring with them. Few other immigrants have come to Iceland, and the life there has been so strenuous that weaklings in either mind or body have been eliminated; hence the present population is of unusually high quality biologically. The other reason is that the climate, although too cool for agriculture, is excellent for man and especially for intellectual activity. Because of the North Atlantic Drift the winters on the south coast where most of the people live are milder than in New York. The summers are indeed too cool for all except certain crops, but they are the kind that keep people very active and vigorous. Thus Iceland furnishes an unusually good example of the part played by diverse factors in fostering civilization. An isolated location off the main lines of travel and in stormy seas, a rugged relief with many volcanic eruptions and earthquakes, a climate too cool for most agriculture, and a great dearth of mineral resources are factors that retard Iceland economically and prevent its having a dense population and its having great influence on the world as a whole. On the other hand, the high biological quality of the people, a climate that is unusually stimulating to intellectual activity, and sufficient contact with the rest of the world to bring in new ideas have enabled the country not only to do great things in proportion to its population, but even to advance steadily and remain in the forefront of civilization.

· 17 ·
Norway (Norge)

Introduction

Except for Iceland, Norway is Europe's most inhospitable land, 73 per cent being unproductive and 24 per cent in forest, leaving a mere 3 per cent of cultivated land and pasture (A232). The relatively barren nature of most of Norway is discussed in Chapters 3 and 15, and the attraction of the relatively warm, well-protected coastal waters, resulting in fishing and seafaring, has been contrasted with the unfavorable conditions of the land itself. With a total population of approximately 3.2 millions living on an area of 124,556 square miles, the population density is the lowest for all the European countries (except Iceland)—26 persons per square mile. From 883,487 in 1801, population grew to 2.2 millions in 1900 and added another million by 1950. During part of this period, large numbers of both men and women emigrated to the New World; from 1836 to 1935, 860,694 Norwegians left for American countries, especially the United States. The combination of small population and large emigration in such an enlightened country partly reflects the restricted capacity of the environment, but in the case of Norway the emigration also shows the adventurous spirit of the people.

The dominance of "Nordic" characteristics in the population is shown by the fact that among Norwegian army recruits 64 per cent had pure blue eyes and only 7 per cent had brown eyes. The Norwegian language, closely related to Danish and Swedish, has been a matter of concern in Norway for the past century; the strong Danish influence that developed especially after the fifteenth century created some fear among Norwegians in the nineteenth century that no true Norwegian language would evolve. Philologists and educators are attempting to fashion a compromise language between the strongly Danish-flavored *Riksmål* (officially referred to as *Bokmål*) and the more truly Norwegian *Landsmål*. As the educational system trains more and more students in the use of the chosen linguistic forms, a more uniform and more truly "Norwegian" language will be employed.

Contemporary Norway continues the struggle that has been going on for more than a thousand years to establish a reliable economy and an effective political organization in a harsh environment. From the Viking Age until the twentieth century, while most other European nations were achieving unity and independence, Norway found its human and physical resources too limited for it to exist alone. From 1347 until 1814 Norway was united with Denmark, and then for nearly a century was in union with Sweden. In 1905, however, Norway severed her political tie with Sweden and has existed as an independent constitutional monarchy since that time. Therefore, the evidence is that twentieth century Norway has finally achieved a satisfactory relationship between people and setting.

Norwegian freedom was, of course, interrupted by German occupation during World War II. The chief reasons for the German occupation were the necessity for Germany of keeping Swedish iron ore flowing through the ice-free port of Narvik in northwestern Norway and German desire to use Norwegian airfields and employ Norwegian ports for naval vessels. The period of occupation, treated by John Steinbeck in his penetrating short novel, *The Moon Is Down,* was a time of severe trial for the country. Damage—some of it inflicted by the Norwegians themselves—was great at home; and Norway lost about half of its large merchant shipping fleet. Most Norwegian ships were away from their home ports when the Germans occupied the country and, to a ship, joined the Allies.

Landforms

Norway is a country of high mountains, plateaus, and steep-sided valleys. Generally speaking, it occupies the steep western slope of the tilted Scandinavian block described in Chapter 15. However, in the south, Norway includes both slopes of the block—a fact of supreme significance in Norwegian geography—as well as the broad upland between the slopes.

The Fjords. Following the tilting of the peneplaned block during the Alpine period of the Tertiary, rivers established themselves on the steep western slope, generally flowing along and widening old fault planes and joint planes. Much later, Pleistocene ice moving westward from the center of accumulation plowed its way down the pre-existing river valleys and widened and deepened them, changing their transverse profiles from a V-shape to a U-shape. At the lower end of the valleys the plowing action of the glaciers was especially vigorous and caused the ice to scoop out great masses of rock material. Once beyond the restricting walls of the valley near the coast the ice spread out, forming piedmont glaciers, and lost much of its erosive action. At the present time these glacially widened and deepened river valleys are invaded by the sea and form the magnificent and justly famous Norwegian fjords, some of which, like the Hardanger and Sogne fjords, extend far inland. Sogne Fjord reaches eastward 112 miles and reveals a depth of 4,080 feet; as is typical of fjords, however, the water is much shallower at the seaward entrance, where the ice action was less vigorous and where moraine probably was deposited during the Pleistocene. Another consequence of the weakened erosive action of the ice near the coast was the formation by selective ice erosion of rocky offshore islands, outliers of the mountainous mainland, which today border the Scandinavian coasts, not only of Norway but also of Sweden and Finland, by the tens of thousands. The islands, referred to as "skerries," form entire chains in some places, a chain of them being referred to as a "skerry guard" (Scandinavian: *Skargård*). Some of the skerries are merely rocks washed by the surf, but others attain considerable size.

The drowned character of the Norwegian coast must be ascribed not only to these glacial erosional processes but also to the relative levels of land and sea for the past 10,000 years. It will be recalled from the general discussion of Scandinavia that the great weight of the Pleistocene ice sheet depressed the landmass of the region, although absolute sea level also fell with withdrawal of water for ice formation. The rise of the center of the Scandinavian Peninsula can be seen in the uplifted marine terraces that are higher at the eastern or interior end of the fjords than at the western end. By far the dominant sites for settlements in the fjords are the old deltas, built by streams entering the sea when the land was lower in relation to sea level, but now lifted well above present water level.

Thus, the western coast of Norway has a very ragged appearance because of the hundreds of fjord indentations and thousands of skerries. Since the fjords are quite deep, except at their entrances, large passenger ships—many of which carry excursion tourists—can sail far up them and close to the high, steep sides with no fear of striking bottom. Scenic waterfalls descend the great heights of the fjord walls from hanging valleys formed when the main glacier eroded to much greater depth than the glacier tributaries.

The Fjeld. The fjeld (Norwegian: *fjell*) is the high, barren area forming the backbone of the Scandinavian Peninsula. It comprises a rather continuous upland from north to south but is interrupted by two gaps: the Narvik depression in the north and the Trondheim depression near the center. In the north the fjeld is rather narrow and closely approaches the coast, but in southern Norway it constitutes a high, broad plateau displaying generally rounded forms resulting both from the basically peneplain character of the surface and the scouring effect of the Pleistocene ice sheet.

Influences of Landforms. One of the most significant consequences of the nature of Norwegian landforms, considered in conjunction with climate, is that Norway is endowed with a potential hydroelectric power of more than 10 million killowatts. Numerous lakes on the fjeld and summer melting of the ice fields help to give natural regularity to the flow of streams, so that reliable flow can be anticipated. Another result of the nature of the landforms is that communications by land are relatively difficult; and the sea, as a common link between the numerous fjord settlements as well as with the more favorable region in the southeast, has long been relied upon as a medium of transportation. Finally, the barren fjeld has tended to repulse settlement and has acted somewhat as a barrier; therefore, settlement has centered along the fjords and in southeastern Norway, and the fjeld is either uninhabited or only sparsely populated.

Climate

The specific climate of Norway plays such a great role in the country's life that it merits detailed examination. Because Norway extends from south to north through more than 13° of latitude, it would normally be expected to exhibit great differences in climate between the northern and southern extremities; however, the temperature maps (A229 and A230) show that such is not the case. More important than mere latitude are the prevailingly westerly winds and the presence of the North Atlantic Drift offshore, explained in Chapter 15. The two influences not only prevent freezing of the ocean along the full length of the west coast but also increase the supply of moisture falling on the land. As a result, the west coast of Norway has, particularly in winter, an extreme variety of west coast marine climate.

Fruholmen, one of the most northerly climatic stations in the country, located far inside the Arctic Circle, has a mean temperature of 26° F in February, which is there the coldest month because the marine influence causes a lag in the season. Skomvœr Lighthouse in the southern Lofoten records 31° for the coldest month. South of Trondheim the mean temperature of the coldest month remains above the freezing point, as at Ålesund at latitude 62° N, which shows 35° for February. In the mountains back from the coast, lower temperatures, of course, prevail, but in comparison with other regions at the same latitude and elevation there are very mild winters. The Swedish station of Storlien, located in the Trondheim depression, has an average February temperature of 16°, which is appreciably higher than that for surrounding mountain stations, since it is warmed by the inflow of Atlantic air through the mountain gap. The eastern slopes are colder than the western at equivalent elevations. Oslo in the southeast averages 25° in February and shows a combination of east-slope location and marine influence as a result of its fjord location.

In summer the oceanic influence is slight but is still apparent. Thus, the July temperature of Bergen on the west coast averages 60°, while that of Oslo, a little farther south, and east of the mountains, is 65°. The difference in temperature due to latitude is very slight, for the length of the summer days in the far north helps to maintain an average of 55° for July even within the Arctic Circle. Latitude, however, does have a marked effect on the length of the summer, so that the growing season for the hardy cereals grown in the north is quite short.

The rainfall of Norway (A36) is influenced by the same factors that affect temperature. Along the west coast, precipitation is very heavy, especially in the southwestern section, where Bergen has 87 inches annually; but even in the far north it exceeds 25 inches. Distribution is fairly uniform throughout the year in the north, but in the southwest there is a minimum in early summer and a maximum in fall. Precipitation diminishes in the mountains, especially on the eastern slopes. Oslo, with 24 inches, has less than one-third the precipitation of Bergen and has a summer maximum. Bottoms of deep valleys in the south receive as little as 10 inches annually because of the "rain shadow" of the fjeld, and irrigation is actually required in some places.

In addition to temperature and precipitation, the amount of sunshine is of great importance. Following the comparative darkness of winter come the long days of summer; in the northern section the "midnight sun" may be seen in the sky throughout the 24-hour day for several weeks, and even in the south the summer nights are very

short, and crops are thereby considerably favored.   As in other
Fennoscandian countries, town and city planning and architecture in
Norway are significantly influenced by attempts to afford people
maximum sunlight.

Economic Resources and Activities

The fame of Norwegian fishing and whaling activities and the
small amount of arable land might obscure the fact that the foundation of Norway's economic life is, after all, the soil, and that agriculture and forestry continue to be the mainstay of the people, engaging slightly more than one third of them.   Fishing is, indeed, a
significant aspect of Norwegian economic life, as is shipping.   Furthermore, even before World War II Norway carried on a strong manufacturing program, and it has made special efforts since 1945 to take
its place among the manufacturing countries of Europe.   Such attempts to diversify economically are wise for Norway, but the fact
remains that at present the soil is the basis for most of the country's
livelihood.

For agricultural purposes the soils of Norway are generally poor,
since the Pleistocene ice denuded more widely than it deposited.
However, the coastal zone of southern and southeastern Norway contains some marine deposits, laid down at the time of higher sea level
immediately after the melting of the ice, and some glacial deposits,
both of which have yielded soils of relatively high fertility.   The
Oslo and Trondheim regions also possess better soils than the average, and these two areas of good soil are the largest in Norway.
The limited arable land of Norway is devoted primarily to hay and
hardy cereals able to mature in the cool, damp climate and short
growing season—oats, barley, and, especially in the southeast, wheat;
production of rye is only 1 per cent as great as that of oats.   Potatoes
are the main root crop and are extensively cultivated.   As in Sweden,
hay must be hung on racks for curing in the damp climate.   Dairying is a significant phase of agriculture, and Norway has more than
one third as many cattle as it has people and has half as many cattle
as does the Netherlands.   Indeed, it should be understood that here,
as in the rest of Fennoscandia, agriculture revolves mainly around
livestock raising, and most crops are actually fodder crops.   The
saeter system, although gradually declining in practice, is still extensively followed in Norway and is the local form of transhumance
practiced in the Alps and described in Chapter 33; the term saeter

is applied to the hut on the upper slopes in which the dairyman or one (or more) of his family lives during the summer.

Norway is pre-eminently a land of small freehold farms. Only a small percentage of the farms exceed 250 acres in size, and most of them are less than 50 acres. Less than 10 per cent of the farmers are tenants. Such a situation leads to a stable agricultural population. The Norwegian farmer frequently combines forestry or fishing—or sometimes both—with his more regular agricultural activities. Such a practice explains the small size of many farms and also the over-lapping number of men engaged in various economic activities.

Exploitation of the forests has long been important in the country, as evidenced by the construction of the fine wooden ships used by the Vikings more than a thousand years ago. One fourth of the land is in productive forests, nearly all of which are coniferous. The numerous and varied industries based on the Norwegian forests center in the southeast.

Fishing as an activity is most prominent in the fjords and skerries of the west coast, although it is carried on also in the Skagerrak and especially in North Atlantic waters around Iceland and Greenland and in the North Sea. The total catch exceeds 1 million tons a year, about equal to that of the United Kingdom and more than twice that of Iceland. Herring constitute by far the principal fish sought by Norwegian fishermen, with cod, haddock, and mackerel constituting about half as much tonnage as herring alone. Brisling are canned in large quantities as sardines. Fish have always constituted an important part of the Norwegian diet and were especially significant in the years of food shortage during and after World War II. The significance of fishing in the Norwegian economy can be appreciated from the fact that it directly engages 7 per cent of the men, and that fish and fish products comprise one-third the value of the total exports from Norway, even after large amounts of fish are consumed in the country. Whaling, especially in Antarctic seas, continues to be an important part of Norwegian seafaring, as it has been for approximately 400 years. However, increasing efficiency in hunting and killing whales with specialized ships and gear has, in spite of international attempts at conservation, reduced the average daily catch per catching ship in the years following World War II by 20 per cent in relation to prewar years. The whale oil, of which more than 500,000 barrels is recovered each year, is used primarily for making margarine.

Despite the loss, mentioned earlier in this chapter, of one-half its merchant marine during World War II, Norway rebuilt the fleet by 1951 to 5 million tons and was continuing shipbuilding at a high rate. Safely occupying third place among the world's merchant marines, Norway owns by far more tons of shipping per capita than does any other country, although more tons per capita are registered in Panama. Profits from the fleet are a large and valuable addition to the Norwegian national income.

Norway's mineral wealth is limited. The country can boast of no coal, and it has no such great iron ore deposits as those of Sweden, although scattered iron deposits give it reserves equal in metallic content to about one-third those of Germany. The principal mineral production is that of pyrites, some of which contain a high percentage of copper, from the Sulitjelma area (east of Bodø, just north of the Arctic Circle), and other areas in northern Norway. Iron ore is mined at Sydvaranger and is concentrated at Kirkenes, near the Russo-Norwegian boundary; damage during World War II retarded resumption of iron ore production at Kirkenes after 1945, but substantial production was being achieved by 1951. High-grade ores are also found at Arendal and Kragerø on the southeast coast. Electric smelting of iron ore increased pig iron production in Norway even before World War II, and the Norwegians hoped after 1945 to develop an iron and steel industry of appreciable scale, using their own ores instead of exporting them to Germany as they did before 1940. There is some limited production of molybdenum from mines at Knaben, north of Mandal in southern Norway. Therefore, in mineral raw materials of its own, Norway faces a severe problem in any attempt to develop an industrial economy.

However, Norway is rich in hydroelectric potential and has developed about one-fourth her potential capacity of more than 10 million kilowatts. This potential is greater than that of any other European country, although both France and Italy surpass Norway by a wide margin in installed hydroelectric power. Rapid stream flow down steep, rocky slopes and a fairly regular flow create ideal conditions for use of rivers for power. There are, in addition to a few large plants, hundreds of small hydroelectric installations along the west coast and in the southeast.

"White coal" is the chief basis for the existence of any considerable industry in Norway. Electric power and forest products are two resources of which the country has a surplus, and it is only natural that they should play such a dominant role in its industrial life. In the southeast especially, sawmills and pulp and paper mills, process the timber cut from the great forests of the area and use electricity generated from the numerous swift streams. In the southwest, the large power supply and the efficient employment of shipping facilities have led to processing of imported raw or semi-finished materials such as alumina, which are then in turn exported after processing. The result is that, although Norway is deficient in metallic minerals, her main industry in terms of gross output value and number of workers is ironworking and metals engineering.

Natural Regions

Northern Norway. Region X as shown in A234 comprises a sparsely populated, largely barren upland bordered on the west by a rocky coast fringed by thousands of skerries. Forests are limited in Northern Norway because of barren rock surfaces, a low timber line at such high latitude, and low temperatures. The high latitude causes North Cape to remain in total darkness from November 18 until January 23. Lack of level land and unfavorable climate limit agriculture to a little hay, barley, and potatoes around the coastal villages, although vigorous effort is being expended at present to increase production of especially bred types of cereals, especially barley, in the north, where barley ripens in 60 days. In the southern part of Northern Norway, where longitudinal valleys following the ancient Caledonian folds lie some distance inland from the coast, agriculture becomes more important than it is in the extreme north. More than a score of small, scattered ice fields lie at elevations of 3,000 to 4,500 feet and in some cases send glacier tongues to much lower levels. When the regional climate and relief conditions are considered, the population of the fjords and island villages seems to be comparatively dense.

Fishing is the chief economic activity of Northern Norway and dominates the life of the region. Off this coast lie the winter fishing grounds for cod, and the barren islands of Lofoten are the center of some of the world's greatest fishing activity. The principal season lasts from January until late March, a period during which the seas are animated with hundreds of small fishing vessels. Cod are exported partly as *stokfisk*, dried on poles, but more than twice as many are exported as *klipfisk*, dried on the rocks; and salted cod is also exported. Cod-liver oil is extracted and shipped out in large quantities.

The fact that the North Atlantic Drift keeps the fjords ice-free throughout the year has led to the establishment of Narvik, east of Lofoten, as the export port for Swedish iron ore from the great Kiruna mines. The port was a main center of fighting in the early days of World War II, when the Allies attempted to prevent shipment of the iron ore through Narvik to German smelters. The very modern and elaborate ore-loading facilities were damaged dur-

A. The rugged Lofoten, islands fringed by small fishing settlements.   Courtesy of Widerøes Flyveselskap, Oslo.

ing the fighting but were repaired shortly afterward. The iron ore mined in eastern Finnmark near Kirkenes and the pyrites mined in Northern Norway were mentioned in the preceding section. Besides Narvik, the only town exceeding 10,000 population is Tromsø, which is primarily a fishing center and a supply port for Svalbard. Hammerfest and other towns of Finnmark were completely destroyed toward the end of World War II, when Nazi troops, withdrawing from the region after their failure to take Murmansk, burned settlements through which they passed. However, special attention was given by the Norwegian government to rehabilitation of Finnmark after 1945. Of special interest in Finnmark, which lies east of the main divide and has a lower relief than the west coast, is the presence of semi-nomadic Lapps who graze their reindeer in the region.

Trondheim Depression. The Trondheim region (IX in A234) differs markedly from the areas to the north and south of the depression:

elevation is lower in the gap that here breaches the Scandinavian mountain backbone, and the relief is more gentle. The Trondheim Fjord, 81 miles long, is surrounded by rolling agricultural land on a scale unknown anywhere else in the west of Norway. Hay and oats are cultivated in addition to the barley and potatoes that one would expect to find here. Conditions also favor the growth of extensive forests on the slopes of the depression. Large, prosperous-looking farms show that the descendants of the Vikings have solved the problem of living comfortably in a latitude of almost 64° N. Located on the south side of the fjord, the city of Trondheim is an important railway junction of lines leading south to Oslo, east to Stockholm, and the recently constructed line extending far north to the Salt Fjord. This productive district played an important role in the political life of Norway during Viking times and in succeeding centuries, when the town of Trondheim was the capital of Norway. Frequent disastrous fires have destroyed nearly all the wooden structures of the old days of the town's glory, but the magnificent cathedral has been restored as a reminder of the past. The cathedral is the finest in Scandinavia and is by law the place of coronation of the Norwegian kings.

Southern Fjeld. Except for the arms of the fjords penetrating from the west and of the river valleys reaching up from the southeast, the central part of southern Norway (VIII in A234) is a barren region that is largely uninhabited. The surface on the hard rocks of the Dovre-fjeld, the Hardangervidda, and the Jotunheim is barren, ice-scoured, and lake-studded like the similar landscapes of the Laurentian Shield of central Canada. Extensive permanent ice fields, of which Jostedalsbreen north of Sogne Fjord is the largest, indicate the nature of the climate of parts of the southern fjeld. In the peak of Galdhøpiggen, 8,100 feet, in the Jotunheim is found alpine glaciation like that described in Chapter 33; the rounded forms created by the ice sheet here give way to the jagged forms typical of nunataks, or peaks that rise above a surrounding ice sheet and are carved by valley glaciers and frost action. That the fjeld is not a complete barrier is shown by the fact that two railways cross it and connect Oslo with Bergen, the Romsdalfjord, and Trondheim, the lines having required great expense and engineering skill. A secondary rail line extends from Oslo to Trondheim through the Østerdal.

The "West." The region described here extends along the western coast south from the Trondheim depression and does not, therefore,

exactly correspond with VII in A234. Here the fjords reach their
most extensive development, especially in Sogne Fjord and Hardanger Fjord but also in numerous others. The deep penetration
of the drowned glacial valleys into the great elevations of the fjeld
creates spectacular scenery, particularly if viewed from steamers on
the fjord waters. Agriculture is limited to the old deltas now elevated above sea level and to the adjacent valley bottoms. Only
along the coast of the southern part of this region, in Jæren south
of Stavanger, is there extensive cultivated land on the moraine and
marine loams of the lowland. Bergen, lying between Hardanger and
Sogne fjords, is an old, picturesque town that is Norway's second
greatest port and that was a main port of the Hanseatic League,
whose charming old warehouses are still standing along the water
front. Houses extend up the steep slopes back of the town, emphasiz-
ing the small amount of level land available for settlement. With a
population of 110,000, it is a busy center for shipping and fishing.
Stavanger, with 50,000 population, is a center for fishing, which is
of major importance along the coast, and for fish-canning. Lower
hills unfit for cultivation support some forests. Of increasing importance is the utilization of the numerous swift rivers descending
from the fjeld for hydroelectric power, which is generated at scores
of small installations and at a number of larger plants. In spite of
the lack of a significant supply of raw materials in the region, Norway's large merchant fleet and the good port facilities along the coast
combine to permit economical importation of raw materials such
as bauxite, alumina, zinc ores, chromite, and manganese ore for
processing into aluminum, metallic zinc, chromium and ferro-
chrome, and manganese; thus, the wealth of electric power, even
without raw materials, and skilled labor are contributing to the
growing industrialization of the region.

Before 1940 transportation between Oslo and Stavanger depended
entirely on coastal shipping; however, during World War II a rail
line was built between Stavanger and Oslo by German engineers,
who used prisoners of war and slave laborers, hundreds of whom
died during winter construction work. Much of the southwest coast
continues to rely on the sea as a connecting link with the Oslo region
and other parts of Norway.

The Southeast. Southeastern Norway (VI), with Oslo as its center,
contrasts sharply with the rest of the country and contains not only
one third of the agricultural land of Norway but also nearly one third

of the population of the entire country. Structurally, the center of the region around Oslo is a graben in and around which the surface displays a rolling relief. Moraine deposits, fertile soils on eruptive rocks, and marine loams encourage agriculture. Cultivated land occupies much of the region, and here are found intensively tilled fields of hay, cereals, and vegetables. Virtually the only wheat produced in Norway is grown in the southeast, where it occupies a large percentage of the land in cereals. In late summer the hay fields are dotted with racks on which the hay must be hung for curing because of the dampness. On the hilly divides between the valleys that focus on Oslo are found Norway's most extensive coniferous forests, which thrive in the more continental climate of the region. Here, accordingly, are concentrated most of Norway's sawmills and pulp and paper mills.

The valleys of rivers flowing from the north and northwest into the Oslo depression are occupied by numerous hydroelectric stations and processing plants. At Rjukan and in the area around the town are great plants producing synthetic nitrates. Most of the power plants are operated by Norsk Hydro, a large company that built the town of Rjukan and that of Notodden between Rjukan and Skien. Most of the valleys that focus on Oslo are also utilized for the railways that form the densest rail net in Norway: lines extend up the Østerdal, Gudbrandsdal, Valdres, Hallingdal, Numedal, and other smaller valleys to connect with the west coast and with interior mining or manufacturing towns.

Oslo, Norway's capital, at the northern end of the Oslo Fjord, is the geographic center of this most populous part of the country. With a population of 416,000, it has the atmosphere of a modern city and lacks the charm of age of Copenhagen and Stockholm or even Bergen. It is the most important port of the country and possesses a well-sheltered harbor in the fjord and has good rail connections with its hinterland. The University of Oslo engages in intensive Scandinavian and Arctic research. In the municipal park of the Frogner, Oslo has the unique collection of sculptures by Gustav Vigeland, who was commissioned by the city to execute the numerous unusual works.

Farther down the fjord are the whaling towns of Tønsberg, Larvik, and Sandefjord, from which thousands of men sail each autumn to engage in whaling operations in the Antarctic; the naval base of Horten; and, a short distance up the Glomma estuary, the large industrial town of Sarpsborg, which produces carbide, paper, cellulose, and chemicals with its hydroelectric power.

Svalbard

Norway's most important possession is the group of islands in the European Arctic Ocean known collectively as Svalbard, the main group of which is Spitsbergen. The total area of the Svalbard group is 24,095 square miles, of which the single large island of Vest-Spitsbergen occupies more than half. Norway's sovereignty over Svalbard was recognized in 1920. Although the islands are important as a weather observation point and for hunting and trapping, the extensive coal deposits give them their greatest significance. The Tertiary coals around Isfjorden, largest of the fjords on the west coast of Vest-Spitsbergen, yield well over 500,000 tons annually from pits operated by Norwegian and Soviet Russian companies. Rebuilt after World War II after having been destroyed by German troops, Longyearbyen has about 1,100 permanent settlers and is the main town on the islands. Although largely ice-covered perennially and frozen in by ice from October to May, the islands have open water on the west for a long summer season, during which the coal is shipped out. More than half the population is composed of Russians.

Other Norwegian possessions include the volcanic island of Jan Mayen, lying southwest of Svalbard and used as a meteorological station, Bouvet Island and Peter I Island in the Antarctic (both uninhabited), and part of Antarctica.

Having succeeded after a thousand years in establishing a successful political and economic unit and having generally recovered from the destruction, hardships, and dislocations of World War II, Norway is attempting to continue playing a strong role in world affairs, as is shown by the part it takes in the United Nations. Its recognition of its place in western Europe is evidenced by its membership in the Council of Europe and in the North Atlantic Treaty Organization. Norway's persistent and vigorous efforts to industrialize and to establish better interior communications demonstrate an increasing success in exploiting a limited environment.

· 18 ·

Sweden (Sverige)

Sweden's Place in Fennoscandia

Sweden is the largest of the states in the Fennoscandian group in both area and population, and in general displays an interesting and significant combination of the salient characteristics of the other three countries. In some ways it is the most typical of the Fennoscandian states, but in others it is unique. It extends appreciably farther south than Norway and even as far as central Denmark, but it lacks the extreme Arctic extensions shown by Norway and Finland. In common with Denmark it has a well-developed dairy industry in its southern and central parts, where relief and climate are conducive to dairying. Great coniferous forests link those of eastern Norway with those of Finland as the western extension of the vast Eurasian taiga; in extent and economic value Swedish forests surpass those of Finland and by far those of Norway, and wood products of many kinds comprise Sweden's main export. Like the other countries, Sweden engages in coastal fishing but to a much lesser extent than does Norway. The Swedish merchant marine is next to that of Norway in size and is much larger than those of Denmark and Finland.

Physically, Sweden has shared the effects of glaciation with the rest of Fennoscandia. The Pleistocene ice sheet scoured the northern part of the country, rounded the forms of much of the fjeld, glaciated the upper valleys of the rivers of the north, and blanketed most of the southern lowlands with moraine. Furthermore, coastal Sweden was invaded by the higher sea levels after melting of the ice, and the central part was almost completely submerged by waters of the Yoldia Sea. Structurally, Sweden is made up largely of the same ancient crystalline rocks found in Finland, but in the south it also shares some of the younger sedimentary rock types that underlie Denmark.

In one sphere of economic activity Sweden stands quite apart from the rest of Fennoscandia. The well-developed Swedish mining industry, which has long been significant and which is based mainly

261

on iron ore, has led to the associated development of iron and steel plants and especially of machine factories on a scale unknown elsewhere in Fennoscandia. Furthermore, the high quality of the specialized metal and machine products is comparable with that of the finest goods fabricated anywhere in the world. The precision manufactures, combined with such artistic and functional products as Swedish glassware and household equipment, display the premium quality that puts northwestern Europe in the front rank in so many fields, economic and artistic as well as social and scientific.

Primarily as a result of its location on the east side of the Scandinavian Peninsula, Sweden has through the centuries differed—and still differs—politically from Norway and Denmark. It has long concentrated its attention on the Baltic Sea and on the lands eastward and southeastward across the Baltic, as was brought out in Chapter 15. With its slightly detached position and Baltic orientation Sweden has remained aloof from continental wars since 1814. Its success in remaining neutral in both world wars, especially the second, furnished appreciable stimulus to industry and permitted Sweden to escape physical destruction and loss of manpower, although wartime shortages had marked repercussions. After 1945 Sweden suffered some of the less serious dislocations of the postwar period but in general enjoyed great prosperity industrially. The transitional location occupied by Sweden was in a way reflected by its reaction to international organizations after 1945: it entered the United Nations and the Council of Europe, but its fear of Russia, its traditional enemy, caused it to remain outside the North Atlantic Treaty Organization. In its effort to gain neutral neighbors, Sweden attempted in 1949 to form a Scandinavian alliance; however, Norway and Denmark rejected the idea and joined the NATO.

Natural Regions

Skåne (III in A234). Skåne, southernmost part of the Scandinavian Peninsula, is structurally part of the "Fennoscandian marginal zone," so-called because it combines the harder ancient rocks and the younger softer rocks. It is geologically related to the Danish Islands, especially to Bornholm, and is composed chiefly of sedimentary layers —limestones, sandstones, and shales. Through central Skåne, extending northwest-southeast, are six low, narrow, and discontinuous ridges of crystalline rock—true horsts or uplifted blocks of gneiss and granite, which show the relationship of the area with the more typical structure of the Fennoscandian Shield farther north. Much of

Skåne is moraine-mantled, and since the moraine was derived chiefly from the underlying sedimentary rocks it yields a fertile soil. Northwestern and northeastern Skåne contain marine deposits laid down by the late Ice Age high waters. Thus the region has appreciable variety in spite of its essential unity: intensive agriculture on the fertile soil derived from the marine and moraine deposits, beech forests (reflecting the milder climate of this southern region) and conifers on the crystalline ridges, and less intensive agriculture on the northern moraines, which were derived from crystalline rocks farther north. Except for the granite and gneiss ridges, Skåne is exceptionally flat, especially in the south; and only the gentle undulations of the moraine cover betray the glacial origin of the surface deposits, as in Sjælland in Denmark. In some parts of the region, especially along the coasts, as much as 90 per cent of the area is under intensive cultivation, compared with 10 per cent for the average for Sweden. The fields form a veritable mosaic, interrupted only by the many scattered farmhouses and tiny villages. Occasionally there is a large manor or castle, a reminder of the rich past of the region.

In this granary of Sweden the land is used much the same way as in the Danish islands, except that oats rather than barley is the main grain, and wheat is much more widely raised; there are also rye, potatoes, fodder beets, sugar beets, and great amounts of hay. Yield of all crops is very high, reflecting the scientific intensity of production. In terms of calories, Skåne produces approximately one fourth of Sweden's food output, although a dense population is required for the effort.

The population of the interior of the region lives on farms or in agricultural villages, but several urban concentrations fringe the coast. Malmö in the southwest is Sweden's third-largest city, with active industry and commerce. It has long been important as the harbor for ferries connecting Sweden with Denmark, but it became especially important after closing of the ferry line between Trälleborg (farther south in Skåne) and Sassnitz (in northern Germany) when Sassnitz was occupied by the Soviet Union in 1945. Hälsingborg, industrial and commercial center on the coast northwest of Malmö, is also important as a harbor for ferries and is Sweden's fifth-largest city. Many towns along this coast were founded and developed by Danes when the area was part of Denmark until the mid-seventeenth century. Summer bathing resorts are numerous along the coast of Skåne, where sandy beaches replace the skerries that guard virtually all the remaining coast of Sweden. In north-west Skåne is the only coal-producing area of Sweden; however, the coal, of Jurassic age, is present in only small quantities, is of low grade, and is difficult to mine economically. About 500,-000 tons are produced annually, less than one tenth of Swedish coal consumption.

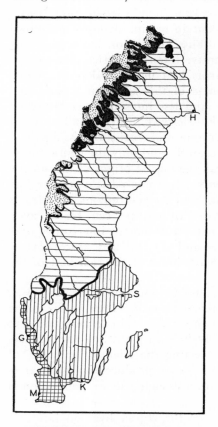

VEGETATION OF SWEDEN

▨ TUNDRA

■ BIRCH

▤ NORTHERN PINE & FIR REGION

▥ SOUTHERN " " " "

▦ BEECH

A. Vegetation of Sweden.

Småland (IV in A234). The Småland Plateau is a detached part of the crystalline northern Swedish uplands, from which it is separated by the central Swedish lowlands. Its gravelly and stony moraine cover, derived chiefly from the acidic crystalline basement rocks, is infertile; and the landscape contrasts sharply with that of Skåne to the south and the lowlands to the north. As suggested in A227, Småland was an island in Yoldia Sea and received no marine loams. Scores of eskers, extending roughly north-south, form typical ridges across the plateau. Hundreds of lakes, some of considerable extent, occupy shallow depressions in the moraine cover, and peat bogs indicate the poorly integrated drainage. The lakes are of especial interest in giving evidence of the rising of Central Scandinavia since melting of the ice: greater rising of the land toward the north has tilted the plateau toward the south and has caused the lakes to "migrate" southward, exposing the lake bottoms at the northern end. Småland's upland character is emphasized by a more severe

climate than that to the west or south. Because of such adverse physical conditions of the environment, agriculture plays a limited role
in the Småland economy, and cultivated areas are small and scattered,
based on occasional patches of better soil on an old glacial lake bottom or in a river valley. Forests, which are chiefly coniferous but
which contain extensive stands of such deciduous trees as beech and
oak, dominate the landscape, although heath and moor break the
forest in many places; therefore, forestry is the main economic activity of the region.

However, three manufacturing activities of world significance are
found in Småland. Making of matches by the billions, chiefly for
export, is carried on at Jönköping at the southern tip of Lake Vättern. Most of the production is of safety matches, a Swedish invention. Preferred wood for the matches is aspen, formerly produced
in Småland but now largely imported from Finland; however, alder,
birch, or fir is sometimes employed. It is curious to note that Jönköping, although the main center of Småland, is economically closely
linked with central Sweden, especially through elongated Lake Vättern. A second industry is that of glassmaking, which gravitated to
Småland because of the supply of glass sands in the area. The magnificent engraved art glass of Orrefors, a small town northwest of
Kalmar, is world renowned, and the less expensive products of Kosta,
west of Orrefors, are likewise exported to many countries. Raw
materials for all except ordinary bottle and window glass are imported; the reason for the continued concentration of glassmaking
in southwestern Småland is the supply of skilled labor. A third
industry, that of furniture manufacturing and cabinetmaking, is
becoming increasingly important with wider acceptance of the
once-radical Swedish designs in furniture. Utilizing the rich resources of both hardwoods and softwoods, the industry is centered in
Nässjö and a dozen other towns on the plateau.

The essentially peneplain surface of Småland drops abruptly on
the west but slopes more gently toward the east, and along the east
coast are preserved Silurian sedimentary deposits, primarily shales
and limestones. In this area of more intensive agriculture is the
port town of Kalmar, from which so many emigrants sailed for America. Across the Kalmar Sound lies the long island of Öland, which,
like the larger island of Gotland farther east, is composed chiefly
of limestone. On Öland the main center is the resort town of Borg-
holm, which also exports wool and mutton from the sheep that graze
the sparse vegetation on the stony plateau surface. Gotland has a

high percentage of arable land and sends dairy and garden products to the Stockholm market. Visby, the main town of Gotland, was the principal Baltic headquarters of the Hanseatic League because of its central location for Baltic trade. Now a quiet tourist town, it preserves much of its medieval charm in its town walls and cathedral. A dozen other limestone churches scattered over the island are now in ruins. Gotland was settled in the Stone Age and has yielded significant archeological discoveries, including such evidence of later commercial activity as thousands of Roman and Arabic coins.

The Central Swedish Lowland and the Göteborg Coast (V in A234). The third of the five natural regions of Sweden is the most important. Between the Småland Plateau to the south and the latitude of Lake Siljan to the north lies the rich and highly varied Central Swedish Lowland, the heart of Sweden and the center of Swedish political evolution. During the early centuries of the Christian era it was in the northeastern portion of the Lowland, around Uppsala, that the powerful peoples known as the Sveas organized an effective political organization. In the south, on both sides of Lake Vättern, were the Goths, occupying what is today Västergötland, west of Lake Vättern, and Östergötland, east of the lake, as well as the island of Gotland. In wars that are partly narrated in the Anglo-Saxon saga of *Beowulf,* the Sveas established dominance over the Goths, and the two were united to establish the kingdom of Sweden.

The underlying rocks of central Sweden are predominantly ancient Archean crystalline gneisses, granites, and varied igneous rocks that have been metamorphosed in differing degrees. Small blocks of younger sedimentary layers, Cambro-Silurian in age, are preserved at scattered points. Even such a variety of rocks does not indicate the full extent of faulting that has occurred in the region. Two main sets of faults, one north-south and the other east-west, are indicated by the orientation of Lake Vättern, occupying a north-south graben, and lakes Mälaren and Hjälmaren, whose general trend is determined by the east-west faults.

The present natural landscape was further greatly influenced by Pleistocene glaciation and results of the Ice Age. Ground moraine blankets much of the area, but at lower elevations it is in turn covered with water-deposited clay loams. A well-marked recessional moraine in the south is a westward extension of the Salpausselkä of Finland. When the waters of Yoldia Sea and the early Ancylus Lake covered the region, clay loams were deposited on those portions that were submerged. Along the northern and southern edges of central

Sweden are "elevated skerry guards"—groups of rocky hills that fringed the coasts of Yoldia Sea when it lay over central Sweden, were denuded of the finer particles of the moraine cover, and were later uplifted when melting of the ice relieved the land of its weight. Such, then, is the background for the varied landscape of central Sweden. Such a varied landscape has elicited a variety of responses. The region is characterized by diversified agriculture, hundreds of mine installations, widespread forestry, highly varied manufacturing, and a thriving tourist industry.

Very large expanses of intensively cultivated land such as characterize Skåne are few and coincide remarkably with areas of marine loams and limestones and shales. Nevertheless, much of the region comprises fertile fields, chiefly on marine loam. Yields are not equal to those of Skåne but are still high under the heavy fertilization and scientific methods employed. Hardier crops, such as oats, rye, barley, and potatoes are much more prominent than in Skåne; and wheat and sugar beets constitute appreciably less of the production. The greater role of dairying is reflected in the larger amount of fodder crops.

Occupying the ridges and less fertile, coarser moraine areas are coniferous forests in which are mixed some oak and other deciduous trees. The valuable softwoods have given the region a principal source of income from lumber, pulp, and paper, all of which are exported in such quantities that Sweden joins Canada and Finland as a main producer of wood products for the world market. Carefully tended woodlands are exploited over much of the lowland: in the northeast is the large pulp- and paper-producing center of Gävle, and north of Lake Vänern are many small towns containing large pulp and paper mills, especially paper mills. Karlstad, on the north shore of Lake Vänern, produces machinery for wood processing and serves as the main port for the large lake. Sawmills and pulp mills are, however, more numerous and important along the coast of the Gulf of Bothnia; paper mills are also located in Småland.

Centuries-old use of the timber from the central Swedish forests for making charcoal to smelt local iron ore gives the forests an added significance. Although use of charcoal for iron smelting was discontinued 150 years ago in most iron districts—such as the Ruhr, Lorraine, and Pennsylvania—in favor of coke from coal, central Sweden still uses charcoal for smelting much of its iron ore. The reason is not only that Sweden lacks coal yet has plenty of wood, but also that she can better utilize her very high-grade ore for making high-quality, special-purpose steel by using charcoal than by using coke. Sweden does, indeed, import both coal and coke for some of her blast furnaces, but only to produce ordinary steel, whereas her finest steel comes from charcoal-smelted iron, although electric smelting is also used.

The central Swedish iron ore, with estimated reserves of 130 million tons (iron content), is found in scattered localities in the Bergslagen district northeast of lakes Vänern and Vättern up to and even beyond the Dalälv (*älv* is Swedish for "river"). More than 500 mines extract the ore, but the principal mining center is Grängesberg; other centers are found around Filipstad, southwest of Grängesberg; Nora, to the south; and Avesta, to the east. The magnetite and hematite ores are of medium iron content, about 52 per cent, which is appreciably higher than the 32 per cent Lorraine minette ores; and most of the Bergslagen ores are very low in phosphorus content, unlike the high phosphorus minette ores. The very finest Swedish ores, and some of the world's best, are those mined at Dannemora, 25 miles north of Uppsala, where the phosphorus content is negligible. It is these central Swedish ores, medium in iron content but relatively free of phosphorus, that are used locally and that contribute to the reputation of the high-quality Swedish production. The higher phosphorus ores, including many of those from Grängesberg, are exported (chiefly from Oxelösund), as are nearly all of those from the Lapland fields, discussed later.

The rock underlying the central lowlands contains not only iron but also a number of other minerals—copper (formerly mined at Falun), zinc (mined at Åmmeberg, north of Lake Vättern), lead, nickel, and even gold—but usually in such small quantities that commercial exploitation is impracticable. The search for large deposits in the region has been intensive for decades and still goes on; but discoveries, except of iron, have been few.

Although central Sweden is one of the world's great manufacturing districts, the factories—unlike those in such industrialized regions as the Donets Basin, the Saar, or eastern Pennsylvania—are not concentrated in a few great manufacturing centers. Rather, they occupy individual sites in scattered small towns that often do not appear on the ordinary map; in this respect the location of industry resembles that of parts of New England. Such a distribution of Swedish industry is traceable to such influences as the widespread distribution of available iron ore in relatively small quantities, dispersed water power sites, and superimposition of industry on a pre-existing pattern of scattered agricultural and home-industry villages and manors.

The variety of manufactures of central Sweden is great; but, except for the wood products industry, the regional specialty is all types of machinery and other metal products, based on the available iron and charcoal and skilled labor. The high degree of Swedish inventiveness has given Sweden and the world many items now considered indispensable to modern progress and now manufactured in large numbers in central Sweden.

Among the specific cities and parts of this region that merit special consideration the first is the capital and largest city of Sweden, Stockholm, and the Lake Mälaren area. Charmingly situated at the eastern end of Lake Mälaren, Stockholm lies on the channel communicating between the lake and the Baltic Sea through which the flow is controlled by locks; however, some summer residences spread over a few of the scores of skerries lying in the sea east of Stockholm (the Hammarbyleden). Such a site, along with its centuries-old significance as a commercial center, has given the city the nickname of "Venice of the North." Located in the richest part of Sweden and yet on the coast, Stockholm developed rapidly, especially during the period of Swedish expansionist interest toward the east, and completely overshadowed Uppsala and other towns as the focus of Svealand. Although it has surrendered first place in export trade to Göteborg, it still retains an active commerce, and its harbor and canals are always busy with shipping. As the political, cultural, and economic center of the country it has many large governmental buildings, museums, theaters, and office buildings that are interspersed with well-kept parks such as the large Djurgården. Equally impressive and revealing of the high social and economic development of Sweden are the numerous large apartment buildings constructed in the striking functional style that Scandinavian architects have both pioneered in and improved. The renowned and magnificent City Hall, located on the shore of the lake, combines traditional and modern architecture. Stockholm speech is considered the most beautiful of all varieties of Scandinavian languages and dialects. Not the least of Stockholm's important aspects is its industry; of particular interest among its highly varied manufactures are telephone equipment, special-purpose stoves, cream separators, chemicals, ships, clothing, and chinaware.

The area around Lake Mälaren is one of dense industrial and residential concentration. Västerås, north of the lake, is one of the greatest industrial towns of Sweden and is one of the few large concentrations of manufacturing; its specialty is electrical equipment of all sorts: generators, motors, appliances, transformers, and electric locomotives, as well as a variety of other metal and mechanical products. Eskilstuna, south of the lake, is the Sheffield of Sweden, producing fine steels and cutlery; its precision gauge blocks are prized in machine shops the world over. Located northwest of Stockholm, Uppsala, ancient capital of Svealand, is revered by Swedes for its rich past, but it is also significant as the location of Sweden's principal university and of the Swedish archbishopric—indicative of the cultural interest that focuses there.

Northwest of Uppsala is a large mining and industrial area divided by the Dalälv. Dozens of small and medium-size towns are sites of iron mines, iron and steel works, and metallurgical works of great variety. Sandviken, west of Gävle near the mouth of the Dalälv, is world renowned for the excellence of its quality steel for such specialized manufactures as watch springs, razor blades, band saws, and similar items. Between Sandviken and Falun, the small town of Hofors has a large iron and steel industry. Southwest of Falun are large metal works in the town of Domnarvet. These are only a few examples of metalworking centers of the region that could be similarly catalogued by the score.

Falun deserves special mention because of the copper mining that began there in the thirteenth century and died out only recently. For 800 years the same company conducted the actual mining operations. During the centuries the extraction of ore produced a huge pit at Falun that was the forerunner of such great open pit mines as those at Bingham Canyon, Utah, and Bisbee, Arizona; but there are, in addition, great underground tunnels and shafts at Falun. The town has a museum of mining and retains a busy industrial atmosphere, producing heavy and light metal products, although the copper ore is virtually exhausted.

Farther south, between Lake Vänern and the shoemaking center of Örebro, is the renowned armaments center of Bofors, which produced innumerable medium field guns for both world wars. Bofors rapid-fire light antiaircraft guns were the pride of the Allied armies and navies during World War II and were also manufactured by the thousands in Allied arsenals under license from the Bofors company. Besides heavy and light arms and ammunition, the works also produces armor plate and heavy hardware.

The principal textile center of Sweden is Norrköping, fourth largest Swedish city, located at a waterfall near the end of a deep indentation of the east coast southwest of Stockholm, where woolens are a specialty. Linköping to the southwest is also a textile center, as is Borås, east of Göteborg.

In the region of Lake Siljan, on the northern edge of the Central Swedish Lowlands, is the region of Dalarna. A curious ring of sedimentary rocks north of the lake gives rise to a soil that is intensively cultivated. Much of the Bergslagen district is in southern Dalarna. However, the particular interest of the province is its transitional character between the uplands north of Lake Siljan and the lowlands to the south. In the valleys and hills northwest of the lake are preserved some of the old customs of Sweden, such as wearing of colorful peasant costumes, especially on Sundays. In this area is found also a type of saeter system. It was among the stalwart peasants of Dalarna that Gustav Vasa, Swedish national hero, first succeeded in arousing the Swedes to throw off the Danish yoke and form an independent kingdom.

One area grouped in this treatment with central Sweden is in some respects a region by itself—the Göteborg coast, which extends along the Skagerrak and northern Kattegat. Dominant in this area is Göteborg itself, second city and principal port of all Sweden. Its hinterland comprises all of central and southern Sweden, and from it radiates the densest rail net in Scandinavia, joining the dense Skåne net. The port developed rapidly during the late nineteenth century as Swedish trade with western Europe and the Americas became of increasing significance. In spite of its busy harbor and its highly developed industry—which includes shipbuilding, machine shops, automobile factories, and especially the world-renowned SKF ballbearing works—the city is a dignified cultural center and maintains attractive parks. The former beech forest of the entire west coast has virtually disappeared, and the marine loams have been put under intensive cultivation in the mild climate. On the Göta älv south of Lake Vänern are the spectacular and significant cataracts at Trollhättan, which because of their hydroelectric power and favorable location are considered the Niagara of Sweden. The electric power is largely wired to other parts of southern Sweden, but some is used locally for the manufacture of machinery, turbines, locomotives, and other equipment. The cataracts are bypassed by a series of locks that permit ships to pass through, and traffic between Göteborg and various ports on Lake Vänern is heavy. The Göta Canal continues eastward from Lake Vänern to Lake Vättern and on to the Baltic Sea, but from its exit from Lake Vänern it accommodates only small boats that spend much of the time required for the trip going through locks. At present the canal is used chiefly for specially built tourist boats that give sight-seers an excellent opportunity to view the delightful countryside along the canal route.

Norrland (XII in A234). Norrland is that part of Sweden that lies generally north of the Dalälv or, more specifically, the latitude of Lake Siljan. It may be roughly subdivided into three parts that run approximately parallel with the Swedish-Norwegian frontier and the Bothnian coast: the fjeld just east of the frontier, the forests in the central band, and the coastal plain along the Gulf of Bothnia. The factor that unifies these three banded landscapes is the system of parallel rivers that flow from the water divide of Kjølen along the frontier southeastward to the gulf. The drainage system is a perfect indicator of the nature of the gradual back slope of the Scandinavian block. The Norrland comprises more than one-half the area of Sweden but has only one sixth of the population.

The inclined surface of old crystalline rocks was thoroughly glaciated during Pleistocene times and was the last part to be uncovered by the melting ice; indeed, a number of small glaciers still exist in the highest parts of the fjeld. The glaciation left the usual evidences of its work: glacial cirques and scoured valleys in the fjeld, a moraine cover over the middle band of forests, a number of eskers, and lakes along the river channels. Moraine and eskers along the middle courses of the rivers dam the water at some points and not only created the lakes that lie in every valley but also forced the water of some rivers to be diverted from the preglacial channels and to return farther downstream in cascades or waterfalls. The divides between the middle courses of some of the rivers are so inconspicuous that bifurcations sometimes occur, indicating indeterminate drainage, and portages, as in Canada and the northern Soviet Union, interconnect neighboring river systems.

The climate displays a true continental character as a result of leeward location at high latitude. The winters are long and severe, and the lakes and rivers are ice-covered for many months—indeed, for as long as 200 days in the far north. Even the Gulf of Bothnia, in spite of its being much warmer than the land in winter (A229), freezes regularly along the whole coast almost as far south as Stockholm, with ice existing in the north from late December until late May. The water freezes at a comparatively high temperature because of its low salt content (three parts per thousand), a result of the inflow of numerous rivers, the low rate of evaporation, and the narrowness of the connection with the ocean. In some years it is possible to cross the ice to Finland.

Agriculture in the Norrland is limited to the coastal plain and lower river valleys where suitable soils have developed on the marine

A. The drying of the harvest in northern Sweden. Courtesy of A. B. Aeronautics, Stockholm.

loams and river deltas deposited when the coast was drowned under the higher waters of the postglacial seas and lakes. Hay, barley, oats, and potatoes are the main crops; the numerous cattle graze on the hillside pastures and are stall fed during the long winters. However, despite the relatively good agricultural production that has developed on the coastal plain and in the river valleys, it was not the fertility of the soil that attracted settlers to the Norrland, especially during the nineteenth century and early twentieth century, but the wealth of the great coniferous forests that occupy three fourths of the area of Norrland. It is these forests that play such a significant role in the entire economy of Sweden and that are most important in permitting the country to achieve a balance of trade by exporting timber and wood products.

Conditions for exploitation of the timber are almost ideal. The trees are cut in winter and are transported by sledge or tractor over the snow to the frozen rivers. The distance from felling point to stream is never great because of the close spacing of the rivers. The logs are either piled on the ice directly in the river channel or in artificially constructed basins that cause a build-up of hydraulic force. Thawing of the river ice in spring proceeds from the river mouths upstream to the higher latitude and elevations, thus permitting the logs to rush downstream in the rapidly flowing water. The opposite condition exists in the great northward-flowing Siberian rivers, in which the thaw proceeds from source to mouth. Timber canals or flumes are built around the larger cataracts and waterfalls to prevent splintering of the logs. If lakes intervene along the timber run, small motorboats are used to move the logs in rafts across the still water to the outlet. Thus, in spring and early summer, the rivers and lakes of the Norrland appear to be a mass of logs rather than streams and bodies of water. At the river mouths in the Gulf of Bothnia are the largest settlements of the Norrland; they contain the great Swedish wood-processing plants—sawmills, pulp mills, veneer factories, and some paper mills—that receive the logs from upstream after they are sorted.

Among the two score rivers that serve as the main timber waterways the Ångermanälv system and the Indalsälv system are the two most important for the amount each carries; accordingly, the two greatest concentrations of sawmills and pulp mills for not only the Norrland but also for all Sweden are located near their mouths, the Härnösand district for the Ångermanälv and the Sundsvall district for the Indalsälv. Sundsvall also receives timber from the Ljungan system, which debouches near the Indalsälv mouth, and it has become the chief processing center of the coast. South to Gävle and north to the Finnish frontier are other small towns built around sawmills and pulp mills. From such port towns flow hundreds of shiploads of lumber and wood products, both to central Sweden and to many consuming centers in western Europe and the Americas.

The timber of Norrland is the region's greatest asset, but there are two others of prime importance. One is the millions of kilowatts of potential hydroelectric power—three fourths of Sweden's capacity—available from the swift rivers that also serve as timber floatways, and much of the power has already been developed by installed power plants. Besides several small power stations in northern Sweden, large plants have been installed on the Luleälv (at Porjus, southwest of Gällivare, and at Harsprånget, south of Porjus), the Indalsälv (Krångede), and the Dalälv at the dividing line between Norrland and central Sweden. The progressive increase of electric-power generation from Norrland rivers encouraged the sawmills and other wood-processing plants to turn from steam, generated from wood scrap, to hydroelectricity; furthermore, the scrap itself could be made into valuable products—pulp in some cases, pressed wood panels in others. Farms in Norrland are almost entirely electrified as a result of the plentiful supply of power. The two railways that extend through most of the length of the Norrland are being electri-fied after installation of the power plants, and for the country as a whole more than 85 per cent of the railways are electric. Plentiful electricity has likewise been a boon to northern mining operations. Finally, the difference in the regime of Norrland rivers and of those of southern Sweden has led to an exchange of power between the two areas: Norrland rivers generate least power in winter, whereas southern Swedish rivers generate least in summer. Long-distance, high-voltage lines link north with south so that a better balance of supply of electricity can be maintained in both areas. Nevertheless, Sweden as a whole is rapidly approaching full exploitation of its readily available hydroelectric power and will soon be forced to develop additional sources of power. If Norway is assisted with capi-tal, it can export appreciable amounts of power to Sweden in addi-tion to the limited amounts that have begun to flow by underseas cable to Denmark.

The third great asset of Norrland is iron ore. One of the world's greatest iron deposits is located at Kiruna in the Norrbotten region of northern Norrland. A solid mountain of magnetite with an iron content of 60 to 70 per cent, Kirunavaara has reserves of 1,400 million tons in terms of metallic iron. The ore lay almost untouched until development in 1878 of the Thomas-Gilchrist process for smelting high-phosphorus iron ore, since phosphorus in the Kiruna ores com-prises between 1 and 2 per cent of the mass. Lack of adequate trans-portation also hindered mining, but since the early years of the twentieth century rail transportation has been excellent. At Gäl-livare, south-southeast of Kiruna, another large iron deposit is ac-tively exploited; here the ore quality and mining conditions are comparable with those at Kiruna, but the reserves are only 160 mil-lion tons, iron content. These reserves might be compared with those of 130 million tons in the Bergslagen district. More than a dozen smaller deposits are scattered over the Norrbotten.

Mining at Kiruna employs both shaft and open-pit methods but is chiefly accomplished simply by removing levels of the mountain with huge shovels, loading ore in special cars, and hauling them downgrade to the railway. Nevertheless, winter conditions impose severe difficulties on the operations, not only because of the low temperatures that come especially with cold waves from the east, but also because of the six weeks of total darkness in December and January. High wages and good housing still do not prevent a high labor turnover. Kirunavaara presents a spectacular sight in the winter darkness, with hundreds of lights shining on the artificial terraces and in the town. Adequate power for such large-scale use of electricity is available from the hydroelectric plants on the Luleälv to the south. Since Sweden lacks the coal to smelt the high-phosphorus iron ore of the Norrbotten, it is entirely exported; and domestic production rests on the purer, though lower-grade, ores of Bergslagen. Kiruna ore moves over the railway to the ice-free port of Narvik on the Norwegian coast, whereas that from Gällivare is exported from Luleå during the summer; therefore Narvik, discussed in the preceding chapter, is of prime significance in Sweden's ore export trade. The entire Narvik-Luleå railway is electrified. Ore is shipped to the United Kingdom, Poland, and even the United States, as well as to other smaller consumers. Production of iron ore for all Sweden averaged approximately 14–15 million tons annually before World War II; and, from a low of about 20 per cent of normal in 1945, production had returned to normal by 1951. Roughly 90 per cent is exported.

Along with the Bergslagen and Norrbotten mining districts, a third significant Swedish mining area is found in the Norrland along the Skellefteälv, where complex ores yield copper, sulphur, arsenic, zinc, lead, silver, and gold. The Skellefte field is Europe's greatest gold producer. Because there is no known use for such large quantities of arsenic as those resulting from the refining of the ores, the poison creates a difficult problem; however, research workers are attempting to discover some large-scale use for it, and it is stored in great warehouses in the hope that it can some day be marketed. Boliden has been the main producing center of the field since it was opened after its discovery by electrical prospecting equipment after World War I. The ore is shipped by rail to the smelter at Rönnskär, north of Skellefteå.

Jämtland (XI in A234). The Jämtland region around Lake Storsjön owes its individuality to two facts: first, preserved in the local structure are soft limestones, similar to those around Lake Siljan, that gave rise to a fertile soil on the local moraine; and second, the Trondheim gap permits marine influences from the Atlantic to extend beyond the divide and to ameliorate the climate. Around Lake Storsjön and smaller lakes, meadows and even crops cover the lower south-facing slopes, although forests prevail elsewhere. Östersund is the main center of the region, and here, as in the smaller but more fashionable resort center of Åre farther west, are numerous hotels that operate the year round. Conditions for winter sports are especially favorable here because of the greater supply of snow resulting from the moist winds from the west; and skiing, skating, and coasting are enjoyed by many Swedes from southern districts.

· 19 ·
Finland (Suomi)

Finland after Two World Wars

As an independent state, Finland came into existence only in 1917, in which year it declared its freedom from Russian control and fought to insure it after having been a Grand Duchy within the tsarist empire for 108 years. After 1917, the new republic strove wisely, valiantly, and successfully for 22 years to build a sound economic and social structure in its rigorous environment; and it gained the respect and admiration of virtually all peoples. However, in 1939, the Soviet Union demanded of Finland the cession of territory that Finland believed, after extended and conciliatory negotiations, it could not reasonably be expected to yield. The Soviets then attacked in the Karelian Isthmus to open the "Winter War" of 1939–40, which, after some setbacks, they won. Not only was Finland forced to surrender territory to the Soviet Union in the treaty ending the Winter War, but also, after joining Germany in the Nazi attack on Russia and again meeting defeat, it was obliged to yield additional lands in 1944. The territorial losses, shown in A182, decreased Finland's territory by 17,783 square miles, more than one half of which was lost in the Karelian Isthmus; and, in addition, 151 square miles on the Porkkala-Udd (*udd* is Finnish for "peninsula") was leased to the Soviet Union for a period of 50 years (dating from 1947) for an annual rental of 5 million Finnish marks. The lease on Porkkala-Udd replaced a lease on Hangö (Finnish: Hanko) Peninsula that had been arranged in the 1940 Finnish-Soviet treaty. Loss of the Pechenga (Finnish: Petsamo) Corridor in the far north deprived Finland of nickel deposits and the Arctic port of Pechenga, but the loss of the Karelian Isthmus area was infinitely more serious. The main urban concentration in the region, Vyborg (Finnish: Viipuri), was Finland's second largest city and was one of its three chief industrial centers; and the surrounding region was one of the most densely settled and highly developed of Finland's territory. As an aftermath of the transfers of territory, 410,000 people, mostly from the isthmus region, had to be resettled in other parts of Finland. And, finally, the reparations that Finland had to agree to furnish the Soviet Union imposed a heavy burden on the country, with its limited population and resources. However, as they proved by their faithful payments of war debts to the United States after World War I, the Finns will find a way; and so remarkable was the schedule of reparations shipments that the Soviets agreed to a reduction of payment balances after about half the shipments had been sent.

The Finns and Their Culture

The prehistoric developments in the area now occupied by Finland have not been as well reconstructed as those in the remainder of Fennoscandia. Therefore, the origin and evolution of the people of Finland are somewhat obscure and have been misinterpreted to some extent because of the apparent incongruity between the biological characteristics of the Finnish people and the Finnish language. The language is one of the two main branches of the Finno-Ugrian linguistic substock to which belong the Magyar of Hungary, the Estonian, and a number of languages spoken between Moscow and the Urals as well as in western Siberia. The Finnish people biologically are not "Asiatic" in appearance as might be expected in view of the well-established route by which the language reached Finland —and, indeed, as they have sometimes been described. Anthropological studies in Finland have revealed some characteristics— high cephalic index, broad figure, and short stature—of the people of the Urals region who speak various types of Finno-Ugrian, but these characteristics have been amalgamated with those typical of the Scandinavian "Nordics" as well as those that appear to have been local on the eastern Baltic shores. A large measure of intermixture has confused the human biology of Finland until at present there is much similarity between the Finns and the Swedes. Approximately 78 per cent of the people of Finland are blue-eyed, and 57 per cent are fair-haired. Cephalic indexes increase from west to east and from south to north—showing increasing round-headedness—and, for whatever significance the fact might have in regard to biological extraction, cultural development generally decreases in the same directions. Thus, southwestern Finland is properly classified as belonging with Europe A, whereas northern Finland falls into Europe C.

Of prime significance in the development of Finland has been the relationship between Sweden and Finland. Early in the Middle Ages, Swedes settled in southwestern Finland along the shores of the

Gulf of Bothnia and the Gulf of Finland. In succeeding centuries Sweden not only colonized the Finnish shores but also exercised political control over the entire area. It was thus through Swedish influence that elements of western European culture were introduced into Finland that laid the foundation for the comparatively high culture that has developed in Finland. The conflict of interests of Russia and Sweden led to numerous clashes between the armies of the two countries on Finnish soil, and in 1809 Swedish power was permanently broken and Finland became a Grand Duchy in the Russian Empire. Nevertheless, the Finns were given a large measure of autonomy under the tsars except in the realm of foreign affairs, and it was not until the end of the nineteenth century that serious attempts were made at Russification.

As a result of such developments, about 10 per cent of the population of contemporary Finland is composed of a Swedish-speaking element, although—in contrast to former times—the Finns have taken over the leadership in most aspects of the life of the country. The Swedish contribution in Finnish culture continued to decline between the two world wars and is perhaps destined to be submerged to that of the Finnish majority. There are, however, still certain distinctions between the Swedes and the Finns, and Swedish is officially recognized as a national language along with Finnish. The Swedish population is concentrated along the southern coast and the coast of west-central Finland; and it also occupies the Åland Islands, in the southwest, which have autonomy within the Finnish state. The former Russian element virtually disappeared after World War II as a result of population exchanges between the Soviet Union and Finland. The Lapps in the north of Finland number less than 2,500, and in their primarily reindeer-herding economy make very little contribution to the life of the main part of Finland.

By far the greater part of the population of Finland is found in the southern part of the country and along the west coast. Such a distribution is firmly rooted in the nature of the environment of the two regions.

Land of Lakes

The Finnish basement rocks are generally even more characteristic of a "shield" region than are those of the Scandinavian Peninsula, including as they do granite of many varieties, gneisses, and crystalline schists. In some scattered localities are small areas of volcanic rocks, and in others are sedimentary rocks that have been preserved.

The granites form the low, rounded hills that are characteristic of parts of the landscape, whereas the schists constitute the elongated rock ridges. These upland areas are actually monadnocks of especially resistant rocks rising above the peneplain formed by erosion mostly in Pre-Cambrian times. During the period of Alpine mountain building during the Tertiary, the old rocks of the shield were subjected to such tremendous stresses that they cracked along lines of weakness, and some relief features were created as a result.

During the Pleistocene Epoch the Scandinavian ice sheet advanced from the northwest over Finland and with a thickness of thousands of feet eroded the soil from the rock, leaving it bare and polished. During the melting back of the ice, the southern edge stabilized for scores of years in southern Finland where a double recessional moraine ridge was deposited in two arcs trending generally east and west. These ridges are the Salpausselkä (*selkä* is Finnish for "ridge" or "heights") mentioned in the section on central Sweden; and, like the recessional moraines of southern central Sweden, they mark the dividing line between the Gotiglacial and Finiglacial stages of melting. Reaching heights of more than 200 feet, the Salpausselkä comprises the most prominent relief of southern Finland and marks the dividing line between the "amphibious landscape" to the north and the much less lake-dotted region to the south. The famous Imatra waterfall, where one of Finland's most important hydroelectric stations has been built, is formed where the Vuoksi River breaks through the Salpausselkä and drains into Lake Ladoga, in Soviet Russia. The railway from Vyborg to Hangö follows the more southern of the two ridges for nearly 200 miles.

During the long period that the ice front was stabilized along the line of the Salpausselkä, meltwater streams flowing from the ice front deposited deltas and varved clays to the south of the ice edge. Since a varve comprises one summer's silt deposit and one winter's clay deposit, the profile or vertical column of many varves permits the accurate determination of the length of time that deposition, and therefore an ice front position, continued. As in other parts of Scandinavia, the area of Finland was depressed by the weight of the ice and was consequently flooded by the waters of Yoldia Sea, and during the Yoldia stage the Baltic was continuous with the White Sea across the Karelian Isthmus. Coastal Finland south of the Salpausselkä and along the Bothnian shores received especially thick deposits of marine clays, which today carry the most intensively cultivated soils of Finland. Rising of the land is continuing at the rate of 15 to 18 inches in the south and 3 feet on the Bothnian coast each century.

The "amphibious landscape" typical of central Finland owes its existence to a number of physical factors. Not only was the general rock surface of the old peneplain relatively flat, but also glacial scouring enlarged joint planes, fault lines, and former river channels

A. Punkaharju, famous forested esker crossing Lake Puruvesi, in southeastern Finland. Courtesy of Finnish Legation.

during the Ice Age, and glacial deposits created new basins and subdivided both the new and the old ones. The ground moraine cover is neither thick—rarely more than 35 feet—nor at all continuous, but it contains numerous depressions on its surface. Also of significance and interest is the enormous number of eskers (*harju* in Finnish) that snake their way in ridges 60 to 200 feet high generally from northwest to southeast across land and lake alike. Composed of sand and gravel deposited by streams running in tunnels at the bottom of the ice sheet, the eskers sometimes demonstrate dramatic continuity: one of them extends for more than 200 miles from Raahe on the Gulf of Bothnia southeastward through Iisalmi to Kuopio. Punkaharju, crossing Lake Puruvesi in southeastern Finland, is one of the world's most photographed eskers and is popular with tourists because of the scenic aspect of the narrow, forested divide it forms across the lake water. As in Sweden, eskers have long served as convenient routes, and villages are often built on the southern slopes in order to gain a little extra warmth from the low winter sun. Drumlins, although not especially important in lake formation, are also prominent features in some Finnish landscapes. The many lakes and the glacial topography afford Finland a large number of waterfalls for water power development, and the lakes also serve as settling basins for flowing water, thus giving the rivers clear water for human use and regular flow for more reliable water power. For the country as a whole, the lakes cover approximately 10 per cent of the surface, but in the amphibious area of south-central Finland the water area is 50 to 60 per cent of the surface.

The only elevations of more than moderate height are found in eastern and northern Finland. The ice-scoured Koli upland in the east reaches an elevation of only 1,000 feet, and the highest point in the country is located in the narrow arm of territory reaching northwestward toward the Atlantic. However, because of the high latitude, even moderate elevations exceed the timber line and produce the barren fjeld.

Resources and Economic Activities

Climatically speaking, it it fortunate that most of Finland, and all the southwestern part, is indeed of low relief. No highland barriers prevent the tempering influence of westerly winds from extending far over the country. Thus the climate is not nearly so severe in southwestern Finland as it is at the same latitude farther east and in northeastern North America, although it is not so mild as it is on the Norwegian west coast. Precipitation falls mainly as snow during the long, dark winter; and the snow cover lasts for 130 days at Helsinki, 175 days in the lake country, and more than 200 days in Lapland.

However, such a climate is, as in the Swedish Norrland, ideal for forests; and, though Finland is called a land of lakes, it is even more a land of forests, since more than three fourths of the country is covered with a dense growth of conifers, the country's "green gold." Pine, spruce, and the deciduous birch account for virtually all the forest growth, and the other scattered deciduous specimens—oak, ash, maple, elm, alder—are found in the southern part of the country. Having a greater percentage of its area in forest than does any other European country, Finland can naturally be expected to have a significant forest economy, especially in view of the suitability of the waterways for easy transportation of logs to points of focus where processing of the wood can take place. As in Sweden, the natural drainage system has been augmented by artificially constructed float-ways across low divides and by wooden flumes around waterfalls to prevent splintering of the logs. However, the greater number of lakes and the gentle gradients of most rivers create less favorable conditions in Finland than in the Swedish Norrland.

Up to 90 per cent of Finland's exports in many years is composed of various wood products—lumber, pulpwood, wood pulp, wrapping paper, newsprint, quality paper, wallboard, and fabricated wood products such as plywood, spools, prefabricated houses, and similar items. The great spruce stands of Finland are especially valuable for the better grades of paper, which are manufactured by the sul-phite process. Thus, on the world market, Finland stands high among the four big exporters of wood products—Canada, Sweden, and the Soviet Union being the other three; however, the Soviet Union has dropped markedly as an exporter and has taken the repa-rations from Finland mainly as wood products. The mills and factories that process the logs felled in Finnish forests are widely distributed over the country, excepting only the north and northeast. The south-central lake country has a number of wood-products mills of all types except sawmills; lumber mills are distributed chiefly along the southern and western coasts at the mouths of the main rivers, which serve as log floatways.

Despite the significance of forests, especially in providing Finland with export products, agriculture is still the economic activity en-gaging the largest number of persons; however, the 51 per cent of the population statistically engaged in agriculture also includes most of the forest workers, since most farmers have a forest tract that they also exploit. The percentage of the population engaged in agricul-ture and forestry is, however, decreasing—from 75 per cent in 1880 to 65 per cent in 1920 and to 51 per cent in post-World War II years—indicating an increasing industrialization. In response to the cool, humid Finnish climate and the damp soils, the crops are mainly hay and hardy cereals: hay occupies more than half of the arable land and oats about 17 per cent. Rye occupies about half the acreage of oats, barley half that of rye, and wheat half that of barley. In tonnage, however, the rank is different: oats is still the leading crop in tonnage, but wheat ranks second and has been steadily in-creasing since the 1930's at the expense of other grains; rye and barley

are appreciably less in tonnage than wheat.   Potato production out-
weighs oats and wheat together, and various root crops exceed the
oats tonnage.   As in the other Fennoscandian countries, most crops
are used for fodder; and the most important phase of farming is
cattle raising.   Food grains must be largely imported in exchange
for wood products, although Finland after World War I increased its
wheat acreage—half winter and half spring wheat—to the point that
one fourth of its wheat needs are satisfied.   Dairy products have increased to the point that appreciable quantities of cheese and butter
as well as eggs are exported.

Finland faces one of the most acute agricultural problems in the
limited supply of arable land, most and the best of which is found
in the south between the Salpausselkä and the coast and in the west
along the Baltic.   Marine loams and higher temperatures are the
principal assets in both regions.   Vigorous and highly organized efforts were sponsored by the government after World War I to open
new agricultural land: some forests were cleared, but most of the gain
was made by draining bogs.   Parts of large estates were expropriated
according to a sliding scale, and neglected farms were taken from
owners or renters.   In all, arable land was increased by nearly 1.5
million acres or 25 per cent of the original area.   However, 740,000
acres of agricultural land was surrendered to the Soviet Union in the
treaties of 1940 and 1944.   The loss obliged Finland to undertake a
program of opening new land and of redistributing land to the 35,000
displaced farm families that required even more vigorous methods
than did the program after World War I.   Again, the creation of new
farmland required draining bogs and additional clearing of the
coniferous forest.   Governmental assistance was given the resettled
farmers in their pioneer homes, with the hope that after a number
of years the new farms would be self-supporting.   Encroachment on
the forest is a point of concern to the entire country, since wood
products are of such significance to the economy of Finland.   The
result of the programs after the two world wars has been that by
1951 agricultural Finland became a land of small farmers entirely,
and the estate is a thing of the past.   Furthermore, every encouragement is given to farmers to own their land, and the small percentage
of tenant agriculturists is rapidly becoming even smaller.

Such a decisive trend toward small landholdings has given added
impetus to the tendency toward co-operative operation of farms and
co-operative marketing of farm products.   The co-operative movement in Finland dates back to 1880, when the country followed the

lead set by England and also followed by Denmark. The movement grew rapidly from 1920 to 1940, until the portion of Finnish economic activity that took place within co-operative organizations was larger than that in any other country: purchase and use of farm machinery, cattle breeding, standardizing and marketing farm produce, retailing goods and services of all sorts (40 per cent of the Finnish retail trade is handled by "co-op" stores), banking, and even forest exploitation and wood processing. World War II created great stresses in the co-operative organizations, in some cases because of losses suffered in war damage or territorial cessions, but the principle is unshaken and seems destined to make even further gains with the return of stable conditions. Finnish people in the United States have initiated strong "co-op" organizations in their localities, as in New England and the north-central states.

Unlike the "shield" rocks of parts of Canada, the Finnish bedrock is not rich in mineral wealth, and the only mining area of significance is Outokumpu in the southeast, where copper is the principal ore. Woodworking industries are highly developed and are concentrated primarily in southern Finland. Although it is necessary for the country to import the raw materials, textile industries and engineering industries are surprisingly well developed and are being encouraged by the government.

Regions and Cities

Southern Finland (XV in A234). As has already been indicated, that part of Finland lying between the Salpausselkä and the Gulf of Finland is in general the most highly developed part of the country. However, the zone of high development also extends northward along part of the Bothnian coast. Marine loam soils, lower latitude and consequently longer growing season, marine influences on climate, closer commercial and cultural contact with other Baltic countries (particularly Sweden), availability of water power, and location of woodworking industries along the rivers draining southward—all are factors contributing to more intensive development of region XV. The total significance of this region was, of course, greater before 1939, when Vyborg and its hinterland were still part of Finland.

Located in the center of the southern coast is Helsinki (sometimes called by its Swedish name, Helsingfors), the capital, main port, and principal city (population: 400,000) of Finland. Situated, like Gibraltar, at the point of a peninsula, Helsinki developed during the nineteenth century, when it became the national capital, gained significance as a cultural center, and became the country's primary commercial city. Its main square is faced by the impressive buildings of the university, cathedral, and government offices, and its railway station was a pioneering adventure into modern functional architecture, a style to which Finland has contributed appreciably. Despite the use of icebreakers, the harbor generally is frozen in winter; and Hangö in the southwest becomes Finland's winter port, since it does not become icebound. In the western part of the region is Turku (Swedish form: Åbo), an old city used as a Hanseatic port. It served as the capital of Finland until the seat of government was moved to Helsinki; however, it still functions as a center for the Swedish population of southwestern Finland and has two universities, a Swedish one and a Finnish one, both established shortly after World War I. The national university, established in Turku in the seventeenth century, was moved to Helsinki in the early nineteenth century.

Bothnian Coast (XIV). The Bothnian Coast region is also mantled by marine loams, but the higher latitude shortens the growing season in this area, especially in its northern part. North of Vaasa, therefore, forestry assumes increasing importance. Hay is the most important crop, and over a characteristic landscape are scattered hundreds of small bins in which hay is stored until winter. Sawmills and woodworking plants are located at the mouths of the Oulu and Kemi rivers in towns by the same names. Metalworking and engineering industries are found in Vaasa and Pori.

Central Finland (XVI). The region of Central Finland comprises the "amphibious landscape" of the lake plateau, where there is as much water in the tens of thousands of lakes as there is land in the divides. It is to such a landscape as this that the Finnish name for the country, Suomi ("Land of Lakes"), applies. Out of the bewildering labyrinth of lakes lying north of the Salpausselkä three principal water systems emerge: in the east is the Saimaa, the largest; in the center is the Päijänne; and in the west is the Pyhäjärvi-Näsijärvi system. Each of the three systems comprises thousands of interconnecting lakes, all of which are quite shallow and dotted with small, low islands; and each system is named after its largest lake. Navigation in the lake systems, an important means of communication in Finland, is a fine art because of the circuitous channels that boats must follow in order to reach their destinations and in order not to become hopelessly lost in some blind inlet in the maze of waterways.

Man is found chiefly along the lake shores where he has cleared parts of the forest for meadows and for crops of hay, potatoes, and hardy cereals and where he uses the lakes for fishing. Three north-south rail lines and an equal number of east-west lines supplement the lake transportation as outlets for the forest and dairy products. Most towns are small, with their wooden houses scattered to prevent large-scale fires. Outside virtually every house, as near the lake as possible, is the Finnish bath house, in which members of the family, frequently as a group, take the famous *sauna,* or steam bath. Steam is generated by pouring cold lake water over stones heated in a wood fire. The Finns find the *sauna* invigorating, especially the beating of the bare, perspiring body with willow branches—an essential part of the bath procedure. The *sauna* is found in all Finland, but the lake country is especially adapted to the custom.

Located in the southwestern part of the region, Tampere is the largest city in Central Finland. It owes its development primarily to its site by a waterfall, created when a stream eroded through the Pyynikki esker separating two lakes. Using water power from the falls, Tampere has become Finland's greatest industrial center, producing textiles, shoes, paper, and metal goods—including iron and steel on a small scale. It is the country's third city, with nearly 100,-000 inhabitants, and is called the Manchester of Finland because of its great textile mills.

Northern Finland (XIII). Most of Northern Finland lies north of the Arctic Circle and, because it is much more continental than the same latitudes of Norway, is only sparsely inhabited and poorly developed. Its widespread forests are owned by the state, but the trees are small and are of limited value. The inhospitable character of the region is increased by the fact that the land rises to an elevation of a thousand feet or more and in the northwestern corner merges into the fjeld. The nomadic Lapps, with their herds of reindeer, create a political problem by their seasonal wanderings across the northern parts of Norway, Sweden, Finland, and the Soviet Union. Loss of Pechenga to the Soviet Union closed this region's outlet to the Arctic. The rail line following the Kemijoki northeastward from Kemi was extended during the 1940's to join the Soviet line connecting Murmansk and Leningrad.   .

Finland and the Soviet Union

The significance of Finland's position at Russia's side door has already been suggested by mention of Russian control over the country during the period 1809–1917 and of the Winter War of 1939–40. The same influences keep the Finns keenly aware of their delicate situation, both politically and geographically: although Finland belongs with the "West" in nearly every sense of the word, it cannot ignore its gigantic neighbor. If Sweden feels constrained to be cautious of antagonizing the Soviets, it is understandable that Finland would feel that it should be even more careful. Having been fortunate enough to keep its population, most of its territory, and most of its industry intact, Finland is following a policy of "correct" relations with the Soviets, hoping for a continuation of its good fortune of being left outside the Iron Curtain. Vigorous communist elements in the country make the independent policy a difficult one, but the Finns as a whole seem determined to continue the effort.

·20·
Factors in Britain's Outstanding Position

"The United Kingdom of Great Britain and Northern Ireland" is the official title of the land often referred to simply as "Britain." It includes England, Scotland, Wales, Northern Ireland, the Isle of Man, and the Channel Islands as official parts, but other island groups are also integral parts of the state: Orkneys, Shetlands, Hebrides, Skye, and Isle of Wight.

Despite the very heavy drain of two world wars, a great depression, and loss of overseas territories, the United Kingdom is still a world power and will always be a great nation. Such a statement, the dubious overtone of which would have been unthinkable a few decades ago, implies some doubt about the future. This chapter treats first the factors that have made Britain great and then discusses some limitations the country faces.

Few people would question that Great Britain has for several centuries occupied a position of outstanding influence in world affairs. There is, however, much debate about the reasons for this. Most authorities agree that insularity, location, climate, and natural resources, as well as the character of the people, have played important parts.

Insularity

The fact that Great Britain is an island and yet lies close to the mainland has been a great help in giving the country a leading position. Because the island has been cut off from hostile or competing countries by a strip of water, it has been able to develop its own peculiar characteristics more freely than have most countries. For example, the need of a strong central government that could act quickly in an emergency has been much less than in countries like France and Germany. This has made it easier for Britain to develop democratic institutions and representative government, two lines in which Britain especially excels. And this in turn has made Britain a refuge for persecuted Europeans who want to think for themselves. Again, the insular quality of Great Britain has compelled the people to use ships in order to engage in any kind of foreign trade. And, once embarked in a loaded, seagoing ship, it is only a little more difficult to go a thousand or three thousand miles than one hundred. This fact became of supreme importance when the discovery of America shifted the center of maritime interest from the North Sea and the Mediterranean to the broad Atlantic. It has been one of the most important factors in helping Great Britain to build up foreign commerce and a great colonial empire.

Location in Respect to Europe and America

Great Britain is also fortunate in being located off the western border of Europe near the meeting place of the Romance and Germanic types of culture. Because of this it has received a highly diverse assortment of ideas and institutions from each type. This is plainly evident in the English language, which combines Teutonic and Latin elements so fully that we can almost say the same thing in two different languages and yet speak English in both cases. For example: "This book tells about one of the best homes of man," or "This volume contains facts concerning an example of the optimum human habitat." British literature, laws, and customs reflect this same duality, and thus make for a richness of life rarely found outside the English-speaking world.

Another advantage of Great Britain is its location between continental Europe and America. Near enough to Europe to be genuinely European, it yet stands so far west that it is a natural steppingstone between the two continents. Ireland, to be sure, lies still farther west, but it lacks contact with the rest of Europe and has other disadvantages that have prevented it from playing the role of middleman that has been vital in Great Britain. This in turn has been one of the reasons why English-speaking people have colonized the best parts of the New World and Australia. Being posted on the edge of the new territory, like prospective settlers in the days when new lands were opened in the western United States, the British rushed in and seized what they wished at the first opportunity. Thus the British Empire partly owes its inception to the insularity and western location of Great Britain as well as to the character of the people and their great ability as sailors.

Another important but less commonly recognized advantage of Great Britain pertains to immigration and the quality of the people. The isolated location and insularity of the country, aided by the cool marine climate, long caused the island to remain not only relatively inaccessible, but almost uninhabited. Interstratified peat bogs and forests, as well as other lines of evidence, indicate that from about 1000 to 600 B.C. Britain was cooler and more humid than now. Even a slight change in this direction, as will be shown later, would make agriculture impossible in most parts of the island. Accordingly, about 2,500 years ago or later the population of Great Britain must have been extremely sparse, and the present population is derived largely from comparatively recent migrants who crossed the North Sea or English Channel after the climate ameliorated. The Celts, Saxons, Angles, Danes, and even the Normans who thus settled in England migrated under difficulties. People who migrate under such conditions usually, if not invariably, include an uncommonly high percentage of the sturdy, vigorous, adventurous, adaptable, strong-willed, and ingenious types. Those who are deficient in these qualities tend to stay at home or to be weeded out through the hardships, exposure, and discouragement of migration. Women and children suffer especially. Hence there is a drastic selection, leaving survivors who form especially good material from which to build a nation. Practically all countries reap some benefit in this way, but Great Britain appears to have profited to an unusual degree by reason of its island isolation, its marginal but not too remote location, and the relatively inhospitable character of its climate until quite recent times.

The benefit thus derived did not end with the Normans. In later days Great Britain has received many other unusually fine types of immigrants. Flemings, Huguenots, Germans, and others have fled thither from religious or political persecution. Competent European artisans have been deliberately brought to England because of their skill; others have migrated thither because they were not satisfied at home, and England offered great opportunities. In the early decades of the twentieth century Great Britain received a large number of unusually able people who left the mainland of Europe because of political and social chaos; and the influx reached a peak during the Hitler era and the aftermath of World War II. Such immigration is encouraged not only by England's position close to the continent, but also by the fact that because Great Britain is an island it has been free from many of the political complications of

the mainland. This has saved Great Britain from the slavish fear
of new ideas and of consequent political upheavals that have often
caused the mainland countries to be afraid to receive freethinking
immigrants.

Climate

Another important element in giving Great Britain its present
status has doubtless been the typically marine climate. From the

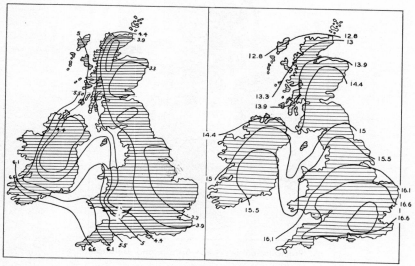

Temperature of Great Britain and Ireland.
A. Winter.   B. Summer.

Temperatures are here given in degrees Centigrade, but the intervals between isotherms are 1° F. Note that 3.3° C = 38° F; 6.6° C = 44° F; 12.8° C = 55° F; and
17.2° C (the isotherm surrounding London) = 63° F.

standpoint of agriculture the climate is good because the winters
are mild, extremes of temperature are rare, and rain falls at all
seasons. Nevertheless, on the whole the summers are too cool and
the rainfall too abundant. Along the west coast where marine influences are strongest, the January temperature (A293) is nearly uniform
from Cornwall in the southwest (44° F) to the Hebrides (42°). In
the Scilly Islands, off the end of Cornwall, subtropical vegetation
prevails; and the winter temperature is about the same as in the
French Riviera, although the Mediterranean sunshine is missing.

Toward the east the temperature decreases, but except in the mountains it almost nowhere averages below 36°. In summer the west and north coasts are cool, ranging from 60° along the west coast of England to 55° in the far north. The central part is warmer, with July averages as high as 63°.

The rainfall (A294) is distributed fairly evenly throughout the year,

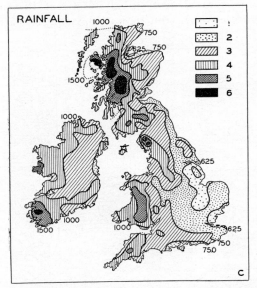

A. Precipitation in Great Britain and Ireland.

Rainfall is here given in millimeters. The shadings have the following significance when expressed in inches: 1 = under 25; 2 = 25–30; 3 = 30–40; 4 = 40–60; 5 = 60–80; 6 = over 80.

with a little less in the spring and a slight maximum in the fall. On the western side of Great Britain and in most of the highlands it is more abundant than is desirable in a climate with such cool summers. Consequently the natural vegetation is largely moors (A295) with a great amount of heather, and the use of the land is almost limited to sheep raising. In certain sections the annual rainfall exceeds 80 inches. Eastern Britain and the Midlands, however, are in the rain shadow of the highlands, and some parts receive less than 25 inches. The humidity is generally high, and cloudiness increases toward the west. On Ben Nevis the sun shines only 17 per cent of the time when it is above the horizon, and even in the sunniest sections along the English Channel the sun shines only 40 per cent of the daylight hours. This means that most of Great Britain is better adapted to cattle and sheep than to crops; the southeast, however, is good for crops.

The outstanding excellence of the British climate lies in its effect on man as distinguished from agriculture. There is probably no part of the world where the climate is more favorable to the health and activity of both mind and body, provided people are technologically so advanced that they can easily provide themselves with proper food, clothing, and shelter.

Chapter 14 discussed how the center of human progress has shifted toward the climates that combine five main conditions: summers that are ideal for physical activity, winters that are ideal for mental activity, a rather high degree of humidity at all temperatures from the optimum downward, a constant succession of stimulating but not excessively severe storms, and a sufficient but not extreme rainfall evenly distributed throughout the year. Even on the basis of investigations in distant lands like America and Japan, the ideal weather appears to be approximately that of London, with an average of 63° in July and 39° in January, and with a constantly high atmospheric humidity, few extremes of heat or cold, constant changes of weather, and moderate rain at all seasons. Fogs are often mentioned as a great disadvantage of London, but as a matter of fact they occur there on an average only about 20 days per year. They are not particularly bad in themselves; their disagreeable quality arises largely because man—even the Englishman—has not yet learned to keep smoke and dust out of the air.

A. Moors of Great Britain and Ireland. Shaded areas are moors.

Natural Resources and the Steps in Their Utilization

Soils, Vegetation, and Animals. No less important than the insularity, location, and climate of Great Britain are the natural resources. Here, as in most countries, numerous natural resources are available among which man is free to choose. Down to about A.D.

1400 the British had not advanced far enough in the scale of human culture to make much use of any resources except those depending upon the soil. There was, to be sure, a little mining of tin and lead; coal was shipped from Newcastle to London as early as the twelfth century; and there was a little trade across the North Sea and the English Channel. All this, however, was insignificant in comparison with agriculture. Wealth lay in crops and animals, and power was almost synonymous with the ownership of the land.

The soil of Great Britain varies greatly, but on the whole it is of only moderate quality. In the north, glacial drift or "boulder clay" (A63) causes the soil to be relatively uniform, although everywhere there is a difference between the much-leached soils of the wet west and the less-leached and more fertile soils of the drier east. In the less-glaciated or unglaciated parts there is much local diversity, and each soil has its special value. In general, the Fens area, around the Wash, where peat and silt have been reclaimed by drainage, is most suitable for potatoes, sugar beets, and other vegetables. The heavy clay soils farther inland are best for wood and grassland, and it is within their limits that the famous English hunting region lies. Loamy glacial soils support crops and fruit; and the light, sandy, limestone soils are used (with the addition of much manure) partly for crops and market gardening and partly for grazing sheep. Wheat and oats, the main cereals, grow best in well-drained loams and clays, but not in peaty soil or sand. Their distribution in Britain, however, depends on climate far more than on soil, as does that of all sorts of crops. Grass and oats are the great crops of the wetter west and cooler north; practically all other crops find their greatest development in the southeast.

This distribution of crops reflects the distribution of the original natural vegetation. The drier eastern sections of Great Britain were originally covered by a continuation of the central European type of forest, but little of this now remains. Timber long ago became so valuable that only small sections, notably the Weald and the New Forest in Hampshire, have been left uncut. At present forests occupy not much more than 4 per cent of the whole area. They are increasing, however, especially in the Scottish mountains, owing to the work of the Forestry Commission.

In the west, natural grassland takes the place of the forest because of the abundant moisture, which is also responsible for the vast extent of moorlands, especially in the mountains above 1,500 feet (A295). The Scottish Highlands are an area of moors as are the

Cumberland Mountains, the Pennine Chain, sections of Wales, and Exmoor and Dartmoor in the Cornish Peninsula. Several sections of the moorland near Morecambe Bay in Lancashire and the Fens south of the Wash are relics of its once greater extension in the lowlands. These vast monotonous areas covered with moss and heather are familiar in many parts of England, and account for the great abundance of sheep—approximately 20 million, together with 10.5 million cattle, in Britain as a whole. They contrast sharply with the cultivated fields of other sections. The Isle of Man in the Irish Sea offers an excellent local example of such a contrast, the mountainous rainy west being devoted to sheep raising, and the drier east, in the rain shadow a few miles away, to agriculture.

In the use of the soil and of the agricultural possibilities described above there has always been more or less conflict between wheat together with other crops, on the one hand, and sheep together with cattle, on the other hand. The secret of this is that Britain lies close to the margin of the region where the climate permits the growth of wheat. If the climate were a little cooler or more humid, wheat would not grow; with a somewhat greater, but still small, change of this same sort even oats, barley, and potatoes could not be relied upon. Because of this marginal quality, the distribution of sheep and especially of cattle presents a most pronounced contrast to the distribution of land under crops. The wet, western portions of Britain, and the uplands everywhere above 1,000 feet, are almost entirely devoted to grass and wild pasturage for sheep and cattle. The drier, lower sections, especially in the east, raise much wheat and other food crops for man, except in regions like the Downs south of London, where poor soil causes the land to be used mainly for sheep in spite of the favorable climate.

Moreover, during such periods as the fourteenth century the repeated failure of the crops by reason of wet summers has sometimes led to a great increase in sheep raising and a consequent disturbance of agricultural labor and the prices of food. In later times the growth of railways in the New World and increased development of oceanic transportation had a corresponding effect, for, when crop foods could be brought more cheaply from beyond the sea than they could be raised at home, there arose a growing tendency to raise mutton, wool, beef, and dairy products instead of wheat. This means, of course, that crops like oats, barley, clover, and turnips, which are fed to livestock, increased greatly at the expense of wheat. This steady trend in decrease in production of bread grains was, however, reversed during World War II, when imports were cut off and Britain had to become more self-sufficient in wheat. As a result, wheat production doubled from prewar years to 1943 and then decreased again after the war to a level one-third greater than that of prewar years. Today Great Britain, with 50 million people, has an area of wheat of 2.5 million acres and produces more than three fourths of the consumption. Oats, however, still outrank wheat in acreage (3.1 million acres), and barley has third rank with 2 million acres. Other feed crops remain important, and large quantities of turnips, mangolds, and even cabbage are raised for livestock. In tonnage, potato production has doubled since prewar years; the British have become potato conscious.

Thus, Great Britain must make constant readjustments in her agricultural programs, responding to developments in the islands themselves and in overseas countries. Britain produces approximately 39 per cent of the calories consumed at home, compared with 31 per cent before 1940. However, the products themselves are highly specialized. Aside from the wheat crop and relatively extensive vegetable crops, contemporary British agriculture has become more of a "processing industry." That is, the emphasis is not only on livestock and livestock products, but also the meat, dairy, and poultry industries are becoming more dependent on imported feed stuffs—to the extent of about one fourth of feed requirements—and the country is even importing store cattle from Ireland for fattening.

The British government is promoting agriculture in a number of effective ways, both direct and indirect. Subsidies are extensively employed to maintain the desired balance. In addition, experiments during the 1930's led to increased appreciation of the practice of "ley farming"; and farmers in many parts of Britain in which the system had not been practiced have been encouraged to adopt it. Ley farming works on the principle that soil improves in fertility during three or four years under grass and legumes for pasture and hay and that higher yields are obtained from sale crops planted in the two or three years after the temporary grass or "ley" is plowed up. Thus, the farmer is encouraged to abolish the distinction between arable land and permanent pasture and to "take the plow around the farm." The same logic has led to encouragement of the practice of plowing pastures every few years even where crop raising is unprofitable so that the soil can be aerated, limed, fertilized, and replanted to pasture. As a result, the acreage of temporary pasture has increased by almost half. Encouragement of ley farming is only one of several progressive attempts that the British have made to improve agriculture. One basic step taken in Britain that is far ahead of any similar effort made by any country of comparable size is the Land Utilisation Survey, which, under the direction of L. Dudley Stamp, has mapped every field in Britain on a uniform system. Thus, the British had a complete survey on which to base their land use planning. The survey found that nearly one third of the combined area of England and Wales, and one fifth of the area of Scotland, are suited to cultivation.

The significance of livestock farming in Britain demands that it receive special consideration. The 20 million sheep are raised for meat rather than for wool, since the humid climate causes the wool to be too coarse for high-grade cloth. Furthermore, wool can be imported from Australia and other overseas areas; therefore at present wool produced in Britain amounts to only one quarter of British consumption. By purposeful breeding, sheepmen have produced a stock of a very heavy, high grade for mutton, but the demand is so great that it cannot be fully met from domestic flocks. In both England and Scotland the sheep are sent from the mountains to the adjacent farming areas for fattening. As a result of scientific cattle breeding, the more than 10 million cattle are of the finest types for their special purposes, and growing emphasis on dairy types has caused a concentration on purely dairy herds, although the total number of beef cattle is still greater than that of dairy cattle. The leading beef cattle breeds are the beef Shorthorn, the Hereford, and the Aberdeen-Angus, and the leading dairy breeds are the dairy Shorthorn, the Frisian, Ayrshire, Guernsey, and Jersey. Dairying flourishes particularly in the mixed farming regions of Cheshire, Lancashire, Derby, and Somerset. Emphasis is put on milk production, in which England is self-sufficient; butter and cheese are imported in large quantities, especially from New Zealand, Australia, and Denmark. Swine, almost 3 million in number, are not very numerous if compared with those of other European countries; but they are of excellent breeds and produce about one half of the bacon consumption. There are about 700,000 horses, many being of types bred for riding, hunting, or racing. The 100 million chickens do not fulfill the demand for eggs.

Fish. A second step in utilizing Great Britain's natural resources began long ago when people first caught fish. Before 1416 the drowned coast and many harbors of the island had been an asset of relatively small value. In that year, perhaps because of a change in oceanic salinity or temperature, the shoals of herring that had previously been found chiefly in the so-called Sound at the western end of the Baltic Sea suddenly appeared in the North Sea off the coast of England. This fact co-operated with improvements in boats and tackle and increasing pressure of population in leading the British who lived around the drowned harbors of the east coast to develop fisheries on a large scale. The North Sea, the harbors, and most of the kinds of fish that are now caught had been there for a long time, but only then did the British reach the point at which they were ready to utilize these new resources on a large scale. The development of the fisheries led in turn to a rapid evolution of overseas trade. As the fishermen went farther afield after fish, they acquired skill and boldness. Then they found it profitable to carry more goods than formerly across to the mainland, and ports began to grow rich through commerce with the continent.

Today, Great Britain is responsible for half of the total catch of fish in the northern waters of the Atlantic, as well as for a catch of smaller importance along the south coast where sardines are taken. Codfish, haddock, and herring are the principal fish caught in the North Sea and around the Shetlands, Orkneys, and Hebrides, and give Britain an annual catch of more than a million tons—almost the same as that of Norway. Kirkwall in the Orkney Islands, and Lerwick in the Shetland Islands, like the Norwegian coastal towns, are busy places in the fishing season. Wick in the far north of Scotland, and Peterhead and Aberdeen farther south, as well as Grimsby, Hull, Fleetwood, and Yarmouth in England, are the main harbors that ship fish to the regions of consumption.

Agriculture and fisheries together occupy less than 6 per cent of the British working population, in contrast to mining and manufacturing, which employ 41 per cent. Thus the industries that were once predominant have sunk to minor proportions.

Ship Timber and Drowned Harbors. During the early days of the fisheries the western location of Britain was a disadvantage so far as commerce was concerned, but with the discovery of America and of the sea route around Africa it became an asset. Fishing has never flourished on the Atlantic coast, partly because of violent storms and great distance from the main markets, and partly for other reasons. But, with the opening of the New World, neglected harbors such as Bristol and Liverpool became even more valuable than most of those on the east coast. Wood for ships and for smelting the iron needed

not only in ship fittings such as anchors, but also in other new industrial activities, also assumed a greatly increased value. At first the
supply was good, and the cutting of the forests went hand in hand
with the reclaiming of new land for agriculture. But by the sixteenth
century there was a serious shortage. Masts and other ship timber
had to be brought from America or Scandinavia, and laws were
passed to limit the use of wood for smelting. But the forests had
done their work in enabling the British to rise to the top in the art
of shipbuilding.

Because of all this, colonial possessions across the seas became a possibility, settlers could be sent there to increase production and thereby
stimulate trade, and Great Britain, by reason of her insularity, her
fishing, her trading, her forests, and her western harbors, had become
the country with the greatest advantages in this respect. So the next
step was the laying of the foundations of the British Empire. This
made it necessary to have plenty of armed vessels as well as merchant
ships. Thus the British navy, with all that it means in respect to
world policy, is the logical outgrowth of the British method of using
a drowned coast, the fish of the sea, the trees of the forest, and an
insular location off the west coast of Europe. Britain took to the
sea by choice and not by destiny, and the history of British seafaring
is summed up in the kinds of ships that have succeeded one another
—herring smack, East Indiaman, three-decker, dreadnought, sub-
marine, and aircraft carrier.

Today the British Empire embraces possessions in all seven continents—North America, Australia, Africa, Asia, Antarctica, South
America, and Europe, if arranged according to the size of the British
possessions outside the mother country, or Asia, Africa, North America, Australia, South America, Europe, and Antarctica if arranged
according to population. In continental Europe the Empire includes
only Gibraltar, and in South America only British Guiana. Being
an island itself, Great Britain has taken possession of a vast number
of islands ranging from New Guinea, part of which belongs to Holland and is claimed by Indonesia, down to mere rocky islets. This
is natural not only because Britain travels by sea, but also because
it needs fueling and watering stations on the way to all its possessions.

Seven dominions—Canada, Australia, New Zealand, the Union of
South Africa, Ceylon, Pakistan, and India—all members of the Commonwealth of Nations, face the mother country on terms of equality.
India is even a republic, but it accepts the British king as the symbol
of the free association of the independent member nations and, as

such, the head of the Commonwealth. The Rhodesians have semi-dominion status, and various forms of self-government and autonomy have been given to many of the colonies. All together, British overseas territories comprise one fourth of the earth's land and one fifth of the world's population.

Minerals and Manufacturing. The last great resource that Great Britain has exploited is its marvelous minerals, especially coal, together with iron ore and smaller supplies of other minerals such as tin. Britain still produces one sixth of the world's coal, but only about 5 per cent of the iron ore. Earlier discussion has shown that the presence of iron ore and coal had little to do with the invention of machinery and the initiation of the Industrial Revolution. In fact during the early part of the eighteenth century, just before the Industrial Revolution, England imported about two thirds of its iron from Sweden and elsewhere. Birmingham got its start as an iron-working town with little or no help from local supplies of either iron or coal. But, when the Industrial Revolution had once begun, the presence of iron ore and especially of coal was of almost incalculable value in enabling industries of many sorts to forge rapidly ahead. The location of the coal close to the seacoast in northeast England, South Wales, and Cumberland also helped to make this product a most important article of export. This enabled England to import food cheaply and profitably and thereby to attain the maximum industrial development.

Of course, the coal and iron did not oblige the British to become a great industrial nation any more than grass obliged them to wear clothes made from the wool of sheep, or than fish and forests obliged them to build a colonial empire. But, when human culture became so advanced that Englishmen were especially eager, and perhaps also especially able, to find the means of supplementing man's puny strength mechanically, coal happened to lie almost under their feet. So the use of a new resource once more revolutionized the course of British history. But it is doubtful whether coal would ever have had such a revolutionary effect if the cool grassiness of much of Britain had not first made the country unusually fit for raising wool, which supplied the best-known means of making clothing fit for the cool, moist climate of western and central Europe. The wool had to be manufactured, but this was a long, slow process of spinning and weaving by hand. When the fishermen made commerce easy, it became profitable to sell woolen cloth in Europe. Then the demand for quicker ways of making cloth urged inventors to apply their abilities to the inventions that brought the Industrial Revolution.

British Character. It has already been shown that the British people as a whole are descendants of very active and alert migrants who reached the island after what seems to have been a long selective process of migration, struggle,. and the extermination of those who were either physically or mentally weak.

In the earliest historical period Great Britain was occupied by people of Mediterranean origin, but with a Celtic civilization. It came in touch with civilized Europe when the Romans occupied it as far north as the Scottish Lowlands and built Hadrian's Wall between Solway Firth and the Tyne. The Romans were attracted by such mineral wealth as tin, iron, and lead, and by the grain and meat of the southeast. Roman roads made traffic easy and gave importance to such urban centers as Londinium, where the main route from Europe crossed the Thames and branched northward to York, northwest to Chester (near modern Liverpool), west to Gloucester, and southwest to Exeter.

After the Roman occupation, commercial and cultural development declined, but a new period began in the fifth century with the invasion of Nordic tribes. Frisians, Angles, Jutes, and Saxons came into southern England. Danes invaded the northeast, and Norsemen the highland north, and eventually pushed back the Celtic population to the western mountains. For some time there was a dual development, Anglo-Saxon in the southwest and Danish in the northeast. These two were combined under a Danish king only to be conquered in 1066 by new invaders, the Normans under William the Conqueror. Since the Normans were descendants of the Norse Vikings, this conquest made little change in the biological composition of the British, although it introduced Franco-Roman culture as well as new and vigorous people. The Celtic population of the western mountains remained apart and independent for many centuries. In succeeding centuries and until the present time, many able migrants came into Britain peacefully, seeking religious, political, or other kinds of refuge. If England had not throughout long centuries received from the continent successive waves of immigrants who brought not only their own ability but also many types of skill evolved elsewhere, it is doubtful whether the country would ever have been able so effectively to exploit first one possibility and then another.

Limiting Factors

So far, this chapter has concerned itself with factors that have contributed to Britain's outstanding position in the modern world. As has already been indicated, certain counter factors have, however, imposed severe handicaps on the United Kingdom. Some of these counter factors have always been inherent in the land of Britain; others have developed with time. It will be seen that limited size and limited resources are the two most effective handicaps at home, and that development of overseas areas is the most important exterior influence on the relative decline of British power.

During the eighteenth and nineteenth centuries the small size of Britain was no particular drawback, and the very high fertility of the population furnished fairly adequate numbers of people for colonization and for military forces. The low ratio of land to population was easily compensated by the traditional practice of importing whatever foodstuffs were needed in addition to the home production. This practice required, of course, a steady rate of exports, which were readily provided by the rapidly developing industries and coal mines; and, in addition, the very valuable "invisible exports" of financial services and foreign investments provided millions of pounds of revenue. The coal and iron resources were enormous for the period in which Britain led the world industrially, and the early start in the Industrial Revolution gave the British a great advantage over other parts of the world that actually possessed equal or greater resources.

By the middle of the twentieth century, 50 million people, even of high quality, and relatively limited economic resources were no longer adequate as a base to permit Britain to compete against the gigantic nations of the world, such as the United States and the Soviet Union, on equal terms of power and prestige. The trouble is, therefore, not so much that Britain has declined but that others have surpassed it. Even in coal production, Britain's chief mineral asset, the United States passed it long ago and now mines more than double the production of Britain, whereas the Soviet Union equals Britain in coal production. Iron ore, once adequate for the heavy industries, at present supplies less than half of the consumption; and wool, the only raw material for textiles that Britain had itself, is now to a large extent imported. Lacking virtually all other minerals, including petroleum, and having only a small water power potential, it is really quite a miracle that Britain continues to do so well. Exhaustion of the more available coal layers and an industry still not entirely geared to modern levels increase the difficulties.

The Influence of the Wars. The two world wars did not produce the relative decline of Britain, but they increased its momentum; and they coincided with and partly stimulated the industrial development of other areas. During World War I, for more than five years Britain had to concentrate on fighting, which for a time went very badly. Not only were losses of young manpower heavy and many ships sunk, but also during that time many other nations started producing for themselves many things formerly bought from Britain. When the war was over Britain found many of its markets gone, and even had to accept the United States as a financial center. The interwar period was one of struggle, a fight against heavy odds, economic as well as financial.

World War II had an even greater influence. Again Britain lost a great number of young men on the battlefields, and again numerous ships were sunk. To pay the enormous costs of fighting, Britain sold foreign investments valued at $2,800 million and accumulated foreign debts of $8,400 million. Thus, not only is the interest from many foreign investments gone, but also debts are staggering to Britain. Furthermore, at home there was a great deal of destruction. The insular position protected Britain from actual invasion, but in air distance Britain was only a few minutes from the continent, and air bombing by the German *Luftwaffe* was intense during the early years of the war. By 1944, robot bombing began. Many British cities—especially London—still show great gaps in their built-up areas. When the war was over, Britain was tired; but nevertheless it was called upon to fight another struggle, this time an economic one. The slogan was then "austerity," and no other nation in western Europe was so much regimented in what it could produce, buy, or eat. On the outsider, especially the American, Britain made a drab impression. Abroad, the colonial empire showed signs of disintegration, partly the result of a more liberal policy at home, but also partly because Britain could not continue all her commitments. The prestige of Britain fell. The United States not only had to aid the British home economy with billions of dollars in financial help, but it also had to assume some of Britain's responsibilities as a stabilizing force on the world scene.

Britain Today

After the middle of the century, Britain showed signs of a new life on the home front. The difficulties had not yet been solved, but there was a feeling of greater confidence that success could be achieved. The drabness was replaced by a more cheerful atmosphere, and the islands attracted many tourists, who became a major source of income. All aspects of production showed great increases over prewar years, and tangible exports were much higher, although income from foreign holdings was, of course, down.

Overseas, Britain's prestige continued to decline, even after the home islands had made a strong recovery. "Twisting the lion's tail" became more than just a phrase. Increasing liberalism, British weakness, and threat of Soviet intervention led such areas as Iran and Egypt to assert independent attitudes. Unrest, much of it communist inspired, continued in Malaya.

Despite the severe conditions that forced Britain to take strong measures after World War II, and despite the unusual sight of a Britain showing many weaknesses, it would be a mistake to mark the United Kingdom off and call it finished. Times have, indeed, changed, and no one is more aware of the fact than a Britisher, but the strength of Britain is far from gone. The following two chapters will show some of the mainsprings of the strength that will long remain in the British Isles.

British Highlands
and Lowlands

Geological Structure and Relief

The main physiographic features of Great Britain have been described in Chapter 3 but may be explained here more in detail. First of all it must be emphasized that the British Isles have always been a part of the continent. They stand on the continental shelf; most of the North Sea is less than 300 feet deep; and both that sea and the Strait of Dover are of comparatively recent origin.

The north and west of Great Britain comprise the old blocks of A308. They belong mainly to the old Caledonian mountain system, a continuation of the folded Norwegian mountains. In the north the Scottish Highlands and the coastal islands consist mainly of gneiss; farther south in the southern highlands of Scotland, as well as in Cumberland and Wales, sedimentary Silurian rocks predominate. Both the gneiss and the sedimentaries, however, are combined with granite.

Debris from these old Caledonian Mountains was deposited in a sea that occupied most of the area that now forms England, and even spread over the lower parts of the Caledonian system into Scotland. Then these deposits, Devonian and Carboniferous in age, were folded into a second mountain system. These Hercynian mountains surround the Caledonian system in the south of Wales and in Cornwall, and form the Pennine anticline in north-central England. Rocks of this same age are also still preserved in certain depressions of the Caledonian system such as the central Scottish Lowlands and the northeastern coast of Scotland. Next, during Mesozoic times, the Hercynian mountains were worn down, and their debris formed marine sediments where southeastern England is now located. These have now been uplifted and form part of a great European Mesozoic basin, one phase of which is the Paris Basin, as described in Chapter 4.

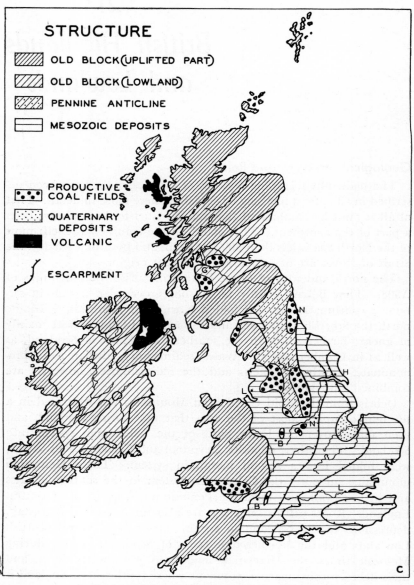

A. Geological Structure of Great Britain and Ireland.

The broader aspects of the present relief of Great Britain are due to pressure from the south and consequent uplift during the Alpine period. The old eroded mountain blocks were raised, and in many places, such as parts of the Scottish Highlands and Wales, their

A. Ben Nevis, highest summit of the Scottish Highlands: rocky, almost bare, slopes but trees and meadows in the valley. Courtesy of British Information Services.

present surface still shows the former peneplain, only slightly affected by the later erosion of running water and glaciers. Here, as in Sweden, new fault lines appeared, or old ones were renewed, and to such fractures are due several transverse depressions of which the narrow cleft of Glenmore extending straight across Scotland is an instance.

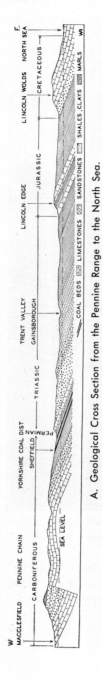

A. Geological Cross Section from the Pennine Range to the North Sea.

The Scottish Lowland may be lower than the Highlands partly because the blocks north and south of the graben were uplifted along the old fault lines, but the main reason is that it consists of limestones and sandstones that are eroded more easily than the older rocks to the north and south. The Highlands now show an erosion landscape with hills representing the harder outcrops and with valleys eroded on softer rock between them.

In the Scottish Highlands the maximum elevation is Ben Nevis, with an altitude of 4,406 feet; the southern uplands of Scotland with their softer, rounded forms, are much lower, their highest part reaching only 2,680 feet. The glaciated and dissected Lake District (or Cumberland Mountains so celebrated for their scenery) reaches 3,210 feet. Very like the Scottish Highlands in appearance is the mountain system of Wales, where Snowdon attains 3,560 feet. In the Cornish Peninsula a few plateaus, notably Exmoor and Dartmoor, are as high as 2,000 feet, with structural depressions between them. These highlands of Devon are a revival of the Pennine (Hercynian) anticline; but in some other sections, where old formations come to the surface, as in the Weald south of London, it is uncertain whether the dome-like uplift belongs solely to Alpine times or is a revival of an older one.

The Pennine Chain, too, shows the old peneplain surface dissected by gaps that are important passages for transportation. Here the plateau rises to 2,000 feet in the south and as high as 3,500 feet in the north, with typical karst erosion on the Carboniferous limestone. On both sides the Pennines fall steeply to the Midland plains, as appears in the cross section, A310. In the central part, north of the cross section, the limestone is replaced by the overlying millstone grit, which assures a supply of soft water and thus has played an important and long-unappreciated part in making it easy to use steam engines, and in the development of the textile industry.

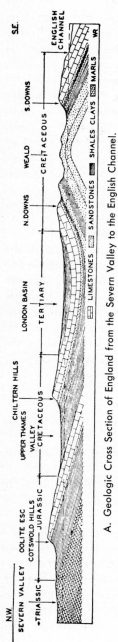

A. Geologic Cross Section of England from the Severn Valley to the English Channel.

During the Alpine disturbances the Mesozoic deposits (Triassic, Jurassic, and Cretaceous) were also slightly uplifted on the flanks of the Pennine anticline (A310) and were exposed to erosion. They are responsible for the typical scenery of the English lowlands. Taking the Pennine anticline with its Carboniferous limestone as a center, and going toward the North Sea or London, one finds first a land of coal-bearing strata near Sheffield. Then one crosses a succession of younger and younger geological formations. The first is hard Permian limestone. This thin layer is at once followed by Triassic sandstone and clay; because of their lack of resistance to erosion, the clays form the vales, or broad, level valleys of the Weaver, Trent, and Ouse river systems with outlets to the Mersey and Humber. Next comes a steep escarpment due to relatively resistant Jurassic limestone and forming Lincoln Edge (600 to 800 feet) in the cross section. Much farther south along the line of the western escarpment in A311 it forms the Cotswold Hills, and it also produces the North York moors. Then follows a band of soft clay forming the depression of the upper Thames and the Ouse River, and extending toward the Wash. The other escarpment of A311 represents the resistance of the Cretaceous chalk to erosion. It includes the Chiltern Hills (800 feet) and the East Anglian Ridge in the south, and continues into the Lincoln and Yorkshire Wolds in the north. On both sides of the dome of the Weald (A311), this formation comes to the surface again in both the North Downs and the South Downs. It also appears in Salisbury Plain, Dorset, and the Isle of Wight. The last low area includes the East Anglian Plain in the north and the Hampshire Basin in the south, with the uplift of the Weald between them.

In the Alpine period Great Britain was still connected with the European continent, and the

North Sea did not exist in its present form. During the Ice Age, Great Britain was covered partly by local glaciers and partly by the western extension of the great Scandinavian ice sheet that moved as far south as the Thames Valley (A63). The mountains were given their typical glaciated features, and the lowlands were partly covered by a mantle of fertile drift. Only after the Ice Age did Great Britain assume its present form. The rise of the ocean because of the melting of the ice partially explains the formation of the North Sea and of the drowned coastline that in western Scotland is accompanied by numerous coastal islands like those that border the coast of Norway. The land connection between England and France disappeared, and Great Britain first experienced the insular isolation that so strongly influenced its eventual development.

The Contrast between the Northwest and the Southeast

Geological structure, relief, climate, and location in respect to the continent all combine to create a strong contrast from northwest to southeast. The differences are well exemplified along a line extending only two hundred miles from the Island of Anglesey in northwestern Wales to London and its suburbs in Kent. Of course, the transitions from one extreme to the other are often irregular and some steps may be missing. Nevertheless, the transition is on the whole so clear that it may be summed up in the form of a list showing the types of changes from northwestern Wales to London:

1. From the oldest rocks to the youngest.
2. From moderately high altitude and rugged relief to low altitude and gentle relief.
3. From thin, poor, acid soils that can be worked with difficulty to deep, easily worked, and fairly fertile soils.
4. From almost uninhabited tracts hundreds of square miles in extent to one of the world's two main conurbations, or urban aggregations.
5. From a very moist climate, with constant rain and cloud and a small range of temperature, to a climate with only half as much rain, more sunshine, and a distinctly greater range of temperature.
6. From an almost purely natural landscape of grass, heather, moors, bogs, and treeless windy wastes to an almost purely manmade landscape of fields, hedges, villages, cities, factories, roads, and railways replacing a natural landscape of deciduous forests with large broad-leaved trees like the oak, elm, and ash.

7. From pastoral agriculture based on sheep and natural pastures to horticulture where orchards and market gardens predominate.

8. From old, long-established, conservative racial stocks to young stocks representing comparatively recent migrations.

9. From almost purely agricultural communities with practically no cities or even villages to a commercial, industrial, and political community embracing a quarter of all the people in the country.

The outside world thinks of Great Britain as a very unified country, but in reality it is highly varied. In the United States the contrast between New York and the southern communities of cotton-raising colored people who live in board shanties with shutters instead of glass windows is perhaps greater than that between London and the shepherds of Wales in their gray stone huts, but one has to travel four times as far to see it. Moreover, there is by no means so great a change in density of population and in scenery. On the continent of Europe, too, it is not easy to find such great and systematic contrasts within the limits of a single country unless one travels long distances as in Russia, or from a high altitude to a low one, as in going from the Alps to the Po Valley. The reason for all this is the marginal location of Great Britain, to which reference has already been made. The country lies close to the border of the favorable portion of the world. Hence, even a small increase in altitude, such as occurs in Wales and Scotland, lowers the temperature and increases the rainfall so much as to alter profoundly the conditions of human existence.

Western Highlands

It has been shown how the old, hard rocks of the Caledonian mountain system (the old blocks in A308) form the Scottish Highlands, the Southern Upland of Scotland, the Lake District, Wales, and the Cornish Peninsula. All alike consist of very ancient rocks, much folded and metamorphosed, which were at one time worn down to a rolling peneplain. Since then they have been uplifted in such a way that in general there is a downward slope of the peneplain from west to east. Thus Ben Nevis, the highest point in Scotland, and Snowdon, the highest in Wales, lie close to the west coast, although the most extensive area above 3,000 feet lies east of the center of northern Scotland. A peneplain also extended across the younger rocks of the rest of Great Britain. It has also been shown that since its uplift there has been a great amount of erosion, and the softer rocks have been extensively worn away, especially in the east where they form the "vales" that are so prominent a feature of England. Nevertheless, the old peneplain still remains intact in many places, with the result that all over Great Britain, even in the escarpments that diversify the lowlands, the hills and mountains usually have broad, flat tops. This quality, together with the low temperature, cloudiness, and rain due to their altitude, accounts for the widespread occurrence of "moors," or high, wet, boggy regions (A295).

The Scottish Highlands. Occupying most of Scotland north of latitude 56° on the west and 57° on the east, these Highlands rise abruptly from the sea in the west, but the old peneplain slopes down to a narrow lowland on the east. Seen from a distance, the individual mountains of the Highlands have smoothly rounded summits because the surface of the old peneplain still persists. In detail, however, the scenery is very rugged. Not only have the streams cut deep gorges, but also the ice sheets of successive glaciations have steepened the valley sides, gouged out long, deep hollows that are now filled by lakes or swamps, and carved precipitous cirques higher up. Flat land is so scarce that there is rarely room for more than a few farms. There is not a single town of any importance, except on the lowland close to the sea. The county of Sutherland in the far northwest has only eight people per square mile, and practically all of these are on the coast. About half of the whole region is actually uninhabited and is rarely visited except by shepherds and hunters. The scenery is bleak, though grand. Trees are found only in the more sheltered valleys. Nevertheless, down at the bottoms of the stern valleys some of the lakes and glens are very lovely. Elsewhere, if the slopes do not consist of bare rock or sliding scree, they are largely brown or purple with heather, or else, on the limestones, green with grass. So wet are the highlands (A294) and so cool (B293) that they are almost wholly covered with moors (A295). If it were not for the sheep that feed on these drizzly moors, the Scottish Highlands would be almost completely uninhabited except in the summer when tourists abound in the more picturesque valleys, and in the fall when hunters from England flock northward for deer and grouse. Nevertheless, compared with regions farther south, the number of sheep is not large.

The Southern Upland of Scotland. This second British highland lies south of Edinburgh and Glasgow and includes the Cheviot Hills on the English border. Here the highlands are lower and less rugged than those north of the graben and are penetrated more deeply by broad, habitable valleys. Nevertheless, the dweller in lower latitudes is amazed at the promptness with which cultivated fields and trees give place to grass and heather as soon as one climbs a thousand feet or so above sea level. Not only are these highlands, and all the others, too cool for crops, but also they are so moist that large sections take the form of swampy moors where it is difficult to travel because of frequent soft bogs. Nevertheless, this treeless Southern Upland with its grass and heather is so well fitted for sheep that in much of it there is more than one sheep per acre of land. Almost nowhere else in the world is the sheep population so dense as in the Southern Upland of Scotland and the Cheviot Hills, and Scotland as a whole has three sheep for every two of its 5 million people.

The Lake District. The third of the older British highlands lies in the northwestern corner of England and has been made famous by Wordsworth and other poets. It is merely a little circle of bare rounded mountains covered with moor grass and moss; but it rises so sharply from pleasantly tilled lowlands that the contrasts are impressive. Moreover, the local glaciers that here, as elsewhere, reinforced the main ice sheet, have carved a wonderful series of long, narrow, steep-sided valley basins now occupied by lakes, including the famed Windermere. The lakes resemble those of the main Scottish Highlands, but lie like a star, with their upper ends pointed nearly toward the famous peaks of Helvellyn and Scafell.

Wales. In Wales there is a fourth repetition of the same bare, rounded, treeless hills, green grass, boggy moors, gray crags, deep valleys, waterfalls, sheep, and the stone huts of shepherds. In some places there are lakes, although these are not so numerous as in the Northern Highlands and the Lake District. As is usual in such areas, the people live mainly on separated farms and not in agricultural villages as do the people in England and most of the European lowlands. In Wales there is not room for many farms within easy reach of any one spot.

One of the most interesting features of Wales, as of the other highlands, is the persistence of old types of people and old customs. A316 illustrates how old habits persist in an inaccessible environment. Almost everywhere in Wales a few people understand the old Welsh language, and in the most rugged and inaccessible parts the percentage rises to 80 or even 100. A revival of the old language takes the form of competitions in singing and poetry. Old physical varieties of man also survive here to an unusual degree, especially a small, dark, rather long-headed, smooth-featured, and slender type much like the

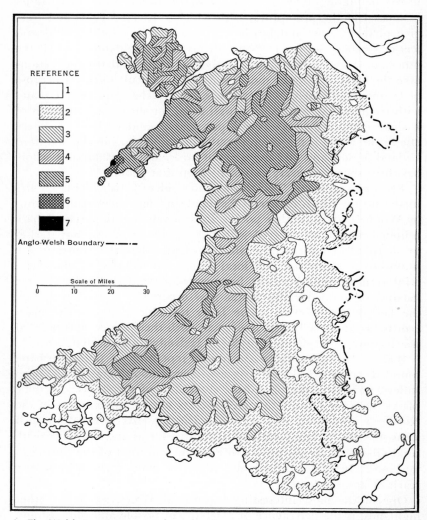

A. The Welsh Language in Wales, after Trevor Lewis. The percentages of persons knowing Welsh are as follows: 1, 0; 2, 0–10%; 3, 10%–30%; 4, 30%–50%; 5, 50%–80%; 6, 80%–100%; 7, 100%. From *Great Britain*, edited by A. G. Ogilvie; courtesy of The Macmillan Co.

Mediterranean peoples. "Old rocks, old stocks" seems to be the case here. Because of their isolation, these people go their own way in many things. That is one reason why nonconformist sects such as the Methodists are especially strong and relatively conservative in Wales.

In spite of all this, Wales is far from being a unit. The relief map shows that the country lies open to England along at least four main river valleys. Thus it is easier to deal with England than with other parts of Wales, and the unity of the country breaks down. Moreover, three fifths of the people are in the southern county of Glamorgan, where the coal mines and Cardiff are located. There a different type of geology and of human life prevails, as the next chapter will show. Most of the remaining two fifths of the Welsh live along the west coast and in the lower land toward England. The higher and more rugged regions here, as in the other British highlands and in regions like New England and New York, are losing population. In many areas, however, tourism is creating a new means of livelihood. The fate of the highlands illustrates the very important geographic principle that the growth of human culture tends to cause people to leave less-favored regions and concentrate in those that are most favorable.

The Cornish Peninsula. A similar situation prevails in Devon and Cornwall. There, however, the elevation is lower than in the other old highlands; the rainfall (A294) is less; the moors (A295) are not so extensive; the lowlands are more extensive; and cattle assume a greater importance than sheep. Part of this difference is due to the fact that in winter (A293) as well as in summer (B293) the temperature here is higher than in the other highlands. This fact would be still more evident in the maps if the temperatures were given as they actually are, instead of being reduced to sea level. The difference that the higher temperature makes in habitability is easily apparent when Cornwall and Devon are compared with the other highland areas as reflected in A318. On the southern coast a very dense population surrounds the port city of Plymouth, whereas out at the end of Cornwall the ancient tin mines, and especially the one really prosperous industry, the mining of kaolin, or china clay, help to make the population dense. Nevertheless, in not much more than fifteen minutes one can drive upward from an almost semitropical southern valley where frost rarely comes, where winter vegetables are raised, and where fuchsias are in blossom, to bare, treeless Dartmoor where there are no houses for mile after mile and little scraggy ponies run wild among bogs and heather.

The Pennine Chain. Although the Pennine Chain is of more recent geological origin than the other highlands, it is geographically like them. In A308 it appears as a lobe of moderately old rocks

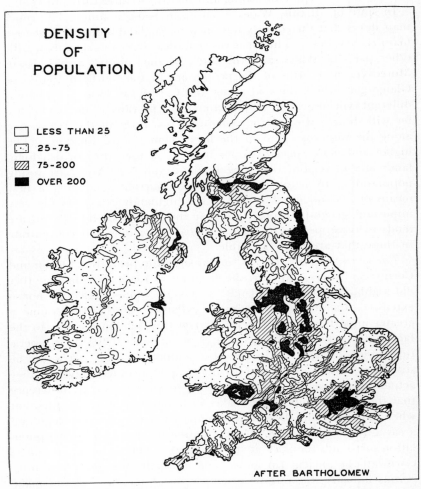

DENSITY
OF
POPULATION

☐ LESS THAN 25
⬚ 25 - 75
▨ 75 - 200
■ OVER 200

AFTER BARTHOLOMEW

A. Density of Population in Great Britain and Ireland. (Persons per square mile.)

extending southward from Scotland. It forms a relatively high region with many moors (A295) and a scanty population (A318). The geological cross section (A310) shows that it consists of an uplifted block of Carboniferous rocks, bent on the east and faulted on the

west. In earlier times the most important geographical fact about
the Pennine Chain was that its high moors made it a continuation
of the great sheep region of the Cheviot Hills. Hence the woolen
industry became highly developed in the habitable regions on its
sides and in the low gaps that cross it at the heads of the Tyne and
Aire rivers. These gaps are important because they permit easy
access from one side of the Pennines to the other, and carry the
lowland type of life into the very heart of the highland. In modern
times the most outstanding fact about the Pennines is the extraordinary contrast between their cool, damp, treeless, rolling, upper slopes,
where shepherds still watch their flocks, and the busy industrial
regions on the coal measures only a few miles away.

Southeastern England

Just as the British highlands stand primarily for sheep raising and
their borders for manufacturing, so the British lowlands stand for
crop agriculture and their seaward borders for commerce. The main
agricultural portion of Great Britain is the low southeastern section
of England and its extension through the Midland Gap to Cheshire
and Liverpool. The lowland is by no means flat. Near its northwestern margin, as has been seen, it is broken by the flat-topped but
sharply defined hills of the Jurassic Escarpment (A308) from the
Humber southward. A second escarpment, composed of Cretaceous
chalk, is seen in A308 and A310 to the east of the Jurassic Escarpment. South of the London Basin, an upward doming of the strata
has produced another chalk escarpment that forms a loop around the
hilly tract of the Weald. The northern arm of the escarpment forms
the North Downs, the southern arm the South Downs, reaching the
English Channel at Beachy Head. Only in East Anglia, southeast
of the Wash, is there found a broad and really flat plain. Elsewhere
southeastern England consists of a pleasant alternation of rolling
fertile vales and low, flat-topped ranges of hills. The hills of the two
main escarpments are generally steeper on the west than on the
eastern slope, which dips with the strata. In the breached anticline
of the Weald the steep side faces inward, and the slopes that fall with
the dip of the rock toward London and the English Channel are
gentler. The hills of the Weald, although not good for agriculture,
make very picturesque sites for residence suburbs for London.

Nowhere is the scenery of the English Lowland grand, but almost
everywhere it has a mild, delightful beauty. This is due partly to
green hills and plains, hedges of hawthorn, and stately trees in old

baronial parks or scattered among the fields. It is also due to rich
pastures full of sleek cattle, to picturesque old gray churches, and to
quiet villages with pretty gardens hidden carefully by walls or hedges.
Fruit trees standing in well-kept orchards or trained against sunny
walls present a comfortable, prosperous aspect; and thoroughfares
and railways alive with busy traffic moving to and from London give
a feeling of energy and power.

A. Farming in Kent (valley of the river Darent). Courtesy of British Information
Services.

This lowland was the dominant part of England before the manufacturing era; it was long the home of the most influential section
of the British aristocracy, and from it came a great many of the
leaders who built the British Empire and gave England its fame in
art, literature, religion, and science. Today the leadership is still
here, but now far more than ever before it centers in London. Such
seats of learning as Cambridge and Oxford, although fifty miles away,
are today practically suburbs of the great metropolis. So, too, are
the slightly more distant ports of Southampton, Dover, and Harwich,
for the vast majority of the people who pass through them are
traveling to or from London.

The southeastern lowlands, especially that part extending south-
southeastward from the Vale of York through the East Anglian Plain
and to the Channel is the great agricultural region of Britain. Drier
and warmer summers, more gentle relief, and rather fertile loam

soils on the old glacial deposits are physical factors conducive to development of agriculture in this area. Here are most of the 2.5 million acres of wheat of Britain, but barley is common on the chalky boulder clays of Norfolk and Suffolk in East Anglia. Oats, though better adapted to the cool, moist west and northwest of Britain, are also extensively raised in the southeast. Little rye is produced, as, indeed, is true for Britain as a whole, although where it is grown it yields as well as it does in Germany, where 300–400 times as much of it is produced. But cereals are not the only crops of the lowland: potatoes, a variety of vegetables, sugar beets, fruits, and berries now supply a large proportion of the requirements for these products in the markets of London and other large urban concentrations. Root crops—turnips, mangolds, and swedes—are raised for winter feeding of cattle. The Fenland, inland from the Wash, is a kind of second Holland: since the seventeenth century the fresh-water fens and salt-water marshes have been gradually drained and the land has been devoted to horticulture. Hops for the breweries are grown in the counties around London, with Kent and Herefordshire producing 90 per cent of the crop. Fruit orchards and berry fields have given rise to a thriving canning industry, an adjunct to the already-established industries making jams and jellies.

·22·
Industrial Britain
and London

Industrial Britain (A323)

In geological age, in complexity of rock structure, and even in relief, as well as in location, the industrial sections of Great Britain stand between the old Paleozoic Uplands and the younger Mesozoic and Tertiary Lowland. They form a more or less transitional zone or borderland because their location depends on coal measures dating from the Carboniferous Period near the middle of geological time. A308 shows that one set of coal deposits is found in the Scottish Lowland, a second on the western side of the Lake District of Cumberland in northwestern England, and a third in South Wales. Far more important, however, is the U-shaped series of Carboniferous beds that swing around the southern end of the Pennine Chain. These begin in the northeast with the Durham-Northumberland coal fields near the sea around Newcastle. They continue southward in the York and Nottingham region. South of the Pennines they swing around to the west in the intensively active Midland section from Nottingham to Birmingham, where the size of the detached coal areas in A308 is no criterion of the amount of manufacturing. The coal fields end in still another extremely active area west of the Pennines around Manchester. Note how clearly these industrial areas, as well as the coal regions of the Scottish Lowlands and South Wales, stand out on the map of population (A318).

Some of the significance of these coal fields in the economic development of Britain has already been mentioned. It should be added that exploitation extending over 150 years has taken most of the readily available coal and that even before World War II output per man-shift was declining in relation to what should be expected from increased mechanization. Even in absolute figures, not until 1949 did output per man-shift equal the level of 1938, 1.14 tons. Thus, future coal mining in Great Britain will be done increasingly in mines sunk in the "concealed fields," whereas that in the past has been from the "exposed fields." Billions of tons of coal reserves remain, but mining it will be more difficult and more expensive. The nationalized coal industry had by 1951 already closed many marginal

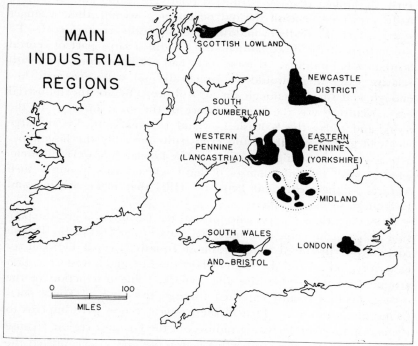

A. Principal Industrial Regions of Britain.

collieries and opened several new, efficient ones. It is almost impossible for the British ever to become again the great coal exporters they were before World War I; however, after the years during World War II when almost no coal was exported, shipments in early 1950 were made at more than half the 1938 rate, although they dropped again in 1951. By 1949, total production of coal in Britain was up to 218 million tons annually, but it was still 30 million tons below the level of the pre-depression years and also well below pre-war years.

Scottish Lowland

In A308 the Scottish Lowland, the most northerly industrial section, stands out clearly as a sunken portion of the old block that in ancient geological times formed a westward extension of Europe. Two facts about the geological structure of this block are especially significant. First, its sunken position permitted relatively young and soft strata to be preserved beneath the old peneplain. Second, these younger strata, which are really of middle age geologically, contain coal. To the softness of the down-faulted strata is due a large part of central Scotland's habitability. If these rocks had not been worn away with relative ease, there would be practically no extensive area low enough and smooth enough for agriculture. Before the industrial era agriculture was the main reliance of the great majority of the Scots, and today the Scottish Lowland is remarkable for its large yields of grain, vegetables, and even fruit—probably the largest per acre anywhere in so high a latitude. The Lowland, however, is somewhat rugged, for large masses of hard igneous rock produce such features as the Ochil and Pentland Hills that make Stirling and Edinburgh so picturesque.

In modern times the presence of coal has permitted a great expansion of both commerce and industry. The 14 per cent of the British coal output produced here is almost equally divided between an eastern region around the Firth of Forth in Fife and a western region around Glasgow in Ayrshire and Lanark. The production of the eastern fields is mainly exported through the Firth of Forth ports facing the North Sea. That of the western section gave impetus to the enormous manufacturing industry of the Glasgow region because the coal seams were intermixed with iron ore and so encouraged the iron and steel industry. The Glasgow industrial development, however, has spread eastward, and agriculture has been gradually overshadowed by manufacturing. Today half of the 5 million people of Scotland are in the Clyde Valley around Glasgow, and another quarter in the rest of the lowland. All but a small fraction of these are urban, or at least suburban, and either industrial or commercial. The suburbs of Glasgow and Edinburgh almost coalesce.

In spite of the eastward spread of industry, the Lowland still has a markedly dual character. Edinburgh on the Firth of Forth stands for an old, aristocratic, agricultural, political, and commercial development with its face toward England and Europe. Glasgow, only 40 miles away on the Firth of Clyde, stands for a modern, democratic, industrial, and commercial development with its face toward America. Edinburgh, because of its eastern location, had all the advantages at first. It is drier and sunnier than Glasgow (A294) and hence better adapted to agriculture. It not only faces Europe, but also is on the same side of Great Britain as London and the richest agricultural part of England. Then, too, the configuration of the hills causes the east coast route from England to Scotland to be the easiest, and Edinburgh stands near the entrance of this to the Scottish Lowland. Thus for many centuries Edinburgh was not only the beautiful capital of Scotland, as it still is, but also the chief city, while Glasgow was still a small cathedral city.

The discovery of America and the invention of power-driven machinery changed the situation. Although Glasgow is only 40 miles from Edinburgh, its sea route to America is fully 400 miles shorter than that from Edinburgh, even if the ships make the stormy trip around northern Scotland. So, when tobacco became the great article of commerce from America, the Glasgow shipmasters imported it at great profit. When the steam engine and cotton gin made cotton a major material for clothing, the wealth amassed in the tobacco trade provided Glasgow with capital for large cotton factories. Many such factories still flourish in some of the suburbs, especially the thread town of Paisley. Then, too, the coal beneath the surface began to be important. When iron replaced wood in ships, Glasgow with its firth (later dredged to accommodate large ships), its coal, its ore, and its wealth was able to become the world's greatest shipbuilding center. Other sorts of engineering works and metal industries have followed shipbuilding, as have chemical works that depend on heavy imported raw materials, such as oils. Glasgow is noteworthy for the great variety and well-balanced quality of its industries in contrast to the specialization that is so pronounced in many of the English cities. This growth has attracted great numbers of Irish as well as other people from outside Scotland. So today Glasgow is wealthy and prosperous, but Edinburgh is much more Scottish, and far more interesting historically and architecturally. Glasgow is famous as a place in which to work and Edinburgh as one in which to live.

Aberdeen and Dundee, north of Edinburgh, illustrate not only the character of the Scots, but also the general principle that success depends upon energy, intelligence, and reliability more than upon natural resources. Having a hinterland that is both too small and too cool for much except grass, oats, cattle, and sheep, Aberdeen's only conspicuous natural advantage is the excellence of its climate for human activity. Nevertheless, the industry of its own people, and the skill of immigrant weavers from Flanders, made its woolen cloth unrivaled in the seventeenth century, and its hosiery in the eighteenth. When the Industrial Revolution and Aberdeen's lack of coal and iron crushed these home industries, wood from Scandinavia was used for shipbuilding, but iron ships soon put an end to this. Next Aberdeen turned to fisheries, and the making of fishing equipment and paper, using Scandinavian wood. Then, as prosperity and wealth increased in Great Britain, it turned to polishing and exporting the granite of its hills.

Dundee illustrates the same thing. Aside from the intelligent activity of its people there is no compelling reason why this city should be pre-eminent in the jute industry and a great center for linen. The raw jute comes from India and the linen from Ireland and continental Europe, and the finished sacking, canvas, ropes, carpets, etc., are sold to the British navy and to many countries all over the world. The same Scottish qualities that hold onto this industry in spite of geographic disadvantages are seen in the growth of educational institutions and the elimination of slums. Dundee is likewise known for its marmalade made from oranges brought north in exchange for fish. The bridge over the Tay at Dundee is famous for its great length of more than two miles.

Newcastle District

The great cities that surround the Pennine Chain form four groups: first, those of Northumberland and Durham, with Newcastle as the main center; second, those of the great county of Yorkshire, including Leeds and Sheffield; third, those of the Midlands in the five counties of Nottingham, Derby, Leicester, Warwick, and Stafford at the southern end of the Chain with Nottingham and Birmingham as the two greatest cities; and fourth, those of Lancastria, including the counties of Cheshire and Lancashire and the great city of Manchester. The basic connection between these four groups of cities is of course the coal, but the fact that the wool of the Pennine Hills long ago stimulated primitive manufacturing in the valleys leading down from the hills must not be overlooked.

Newcastle, the most northerly of the great English cities, lies on the Tyne River, the lower course of which separates the counties of Northumberland and Durham. In many ways it is much like Cardiff in Wales, at the other end of the British industrial section. Its good harbor, the estuary of the Tyne, and the low Tyne gap, which gives easy access to the west coast, have always made the place important, but its main growth was stimulated by the presence of coal almost at the water's edge. With the increasing demand for coal in London and other parts of eastern England, as well as on the continent of Europe, Newcastle has forged steadily ahead. Conditions like those at Glasgow, combined of course with Britain's insularity, its western position, and the fishing industry, have led to a large shipbuilding industry. This in turn has stimulated many kinds of ironwork including the making of machinery not only for ships, but also for mines, railways, and other purposes. Around the coal mines and in such neighboring cities as Gateshead and South Shields at the mouth of the Tyne, important metal and chemical industries have grown up. They use iron brought from the Tees Valley, a little farther south; pyrites from Spain; and salt from many places.

Sunderland at the mouth of the Wear River a little southeast of Newcastle has had a simpler development. Coal is the main export, and timber for mines is an important import. Like Newcastle, Sunderland has a number of shipyards. Middlesbrough, still farther south at the mouth of the Tees, is still another center belonging to the Newcastle region. Although it is farther than the other centers from coal deposits, it has the advantage of being close to the iron ore of the Cleveland district. This explains the special importance of the smelting of iron ore and the export of pig iron and steel to the other metal-manufacturing regions. The presence of salt in the neighboring Triassic strata is the basis for a progressive chemical industry, which is Britain's chief nitrate producer.

Eastern Pennine Industrial Districts: Yorkshire

For more than 60 miles from Leeds to Nottingham, coal deposits come to the surface and dip gently toward the east beneath layers of younger formation. The width of the exposed Carboniferous area narrows from 25 miles in the north to 10 miles in the south. Here is the greatest coal field of Great Britain, mining 25 per cent of the total production.

The industrial development based on coal differs in the various sections. In the north the famous wool industry of the West Riding of Yorkshire is concentrated around Leeds, Bradford, Huddersfield, and Halifax—the industrial focus of more than 2 million people. These cities nestle in the Aire Gap, with the bare moors of the Pennines rising close above them to both the north and south. In this gap, during the early part of the last century, a canal was carried across England, connecting the Humber River and Hull on the east with the Mersey and Liverpool on the west. In some places it goes through tunnels. Its construction seemed justified because it connected two flourishing ports, passed through Leeds and what is still the world's greatest woolen manufacturing district, and was connected by a branch canal with a similar cotton-manufacturing district around Manchester. The canal never paid, however, because railroads soon superseded it, and its use is now limited.

Although most of the wool for these manufacturing cities is now imported, the presence of sheep in the Pennine Chain, together with water power (and, later, coal) and plenty of soft water, was the factor that induced a migration of the wool industry from Norwich to the West Riding. This greatest of wool-manufacturing sections is limited in area because soft water suitable for manufacturing is restricted to the central part of the Pennine Chain where the millstone grit covers the limestone. Here again a strong tendency toward specialization is observable; different communities are noted for special types of work. Bradford is the center for wool-combing and worsteds; Halifax for carpets and heavy woolen; Leeds, which is less essentially a wool city, specializes in wholesale clothing, the production of which occupies one fifth of the workers, but the making of machinery, locomotives, and factory equipment is also important.

Now, as in the past, the growth of the port of Hull on the Humber is intimately bound up with that of Leeds and Bradford. Unlike Newcastle, Hull is not self-sufficient. Without the manufacturing centers at the base of the Pennine Chain it would be merely the center of a small agricultural district and of a fishing industry like that of other places like Grimsby. But coal, as well as manufactured goods from the Leeds-Bradford district and also from Sheffield, together with its own local industries, makes Hull a great and flourishing city, famous for its progressiveness.

Sheffield, farther south, is an interesting example of a city that follows an inherited type of industry even though the original reasons for such industry have long since disappeared. Today, as for centuries, the name Sheffield stands for high-grade cutlery and other small steel goods. Yet tradition and social inheritance are practically the only discernible factors that now give Sheffield any advantage over other places on the coal fields of Britain as a steel manufacturing center. They are so strong, however, that they explain the curious anomaly of an inland town that manufactures many heavy goods from "imported" pig iron and mild steel and is a great center of shipbuilding materials although it is without access to the sea. Sheffield, like several other towns, got its start centuries ago through the smelting of local iron ore with charcoal from the surrounding forests. First the smelting furnaces were located on hills so that the winds might furnish a draft. Then they were moved to valley bottoms so that water power might be used for this purpose. Sheffield is located at the convergence of five upland streams on which 200 dams and water wheels were located. The local iron contains so much phosphorus, however, that the cutlery trade began to depend on iron ore imported at great cost from Spain and Sweden through Hull. Then, in the eighteenth century the supply of wood was practically exhausted and it looked as if Sheffield would have to change its industries. But such conditions stimulated the British to invent methods of using coal as coke with which to smelt iron ore. Since Sheffield happens to be located on coal beds, it still continues to manufacture iron goods, although neither the ore, the forests, nor the water power that originally fitted the site for this industry now has any importance.

Midland Industrial Section

Four great cities—Nottingham, Leicester, Birmingham, and Stoke —around the southern edge of the Pennine Chain form the nuclei of the Midland industrial section. The first two are great hosiery centers, and Leicester, outside the coal district, also makes boots and shoes as well as lace. A third center, Birmingham, less than 40 miles southwest of Leicester, provides other parts of Britain, as well as many colonial and foreign customers, with machinery, hardware, and the iron and steel needed in all sorts of construction. And finally Stoke, scarcely 40 miles north of Birmingham, supplies the needs of dining rooms, kitchens, and other parts of the house in the way of chinaware and pottery. Both Nottingham and Leicester were woolen centers before the Industrial Revolution. Many similar little centers were then scattered over Great Britain, and sheep were raised everywhere. Because Nottingham and Leicester were favorably located in respect to coal fields, they forged ahead and helped to drive the majority of the old small centers out of business. The fact that they concentrated upon hosiery while the Leeds district specialized in cloth and ready-made clothing was more or less accidental. A slight difference in early days might have reversed this.

The importance of the woolen industry is not always understood. Until about 1800, Europeans dressed almost entirely in wool, for cotton, silk, and linen were expensive luxuries, to be used only on special occasions. Moreover, to this day Europeans outside the Mediterranean area wear woolen clothes much more commonly than do Americans. Furthermore, if buying power is slight, as in the days before the Industrial Revolution and in large parts of Europe today, clothing occupies a very important place among the manufactured articles that are consumed. Among articles of clothing none wears out more rapidly than stockings, as almost every mother will testify, and in Europe woolen stockings are still common. Thus, the textile industries have been long established in Europe. On the other hand, the extensive use of iron is of only recent date. Before the days of steam engines almost the only uses of iron were for small things like tools, weapons, nails, horseshoes, hoes, and spades. Even the plow was then made of wood with only an iron tip. The flour ground in local mills was almost the only kind of manufactured food product. Wood and other building materials were almost invariably prepared locally for each individual structure. Almost the only chemical industries were such processes as soapmaking, which were carried on in the house. Although shoemaking has always been important, only within two generations or so has it ceased to be a peculiarly local industry, each village having its own shoemaker using local leather. Pottery-making has also long been important; but, in spite of its breakability, crockery lasts a long time, and no great amount is needed by the ordinary family. Thus, until the last few generations, the making of woolen clothing, including hosiery, was by far the greatest of all manufacturing industries. Hence the woolen industry must be understood if one is to obtain a true historical perspective and understand the present distribution of industries.

In modern times Nottingham has added many other industries to those producing hosiery and other woolen goods. Like Sheffield, it early became famous for its smiths, who used the charcoal of Sherwood Forest where Robin Hood hunted the deer. The presence of coal enabled this industry to thrive and grow. Today Nottingham makes many bicycles, for in Europe, unlike America, these still give rise to an important industry. As might be expected, the bicycle industry was at first associated with the older industry of making wheeled vehicles for both roads and railways, and is now related to the motor-vehicle industry. Derby, near Nottingham, is especially famous for the last, the superb Rolls-Royce cars being made there. Leicester's textile industry, too, has expanded, so that cotton factories and lacemaking are now conspicuous.

Leicester provides an interesting illustration of the way in which agricultural productivity may combine with easily procured coal in giving a special bent to a town. A relief map shows that Leicester lies well away from the Pennine Chain in a rolling, fertile farming region. The fact that coal could be obtained only a few miles away naturally helped to perpetuate the boot and shoe industry here. Other evidences of Leicester's agricultural as well as industrial character are its cattle and sheep fairs, and its huge market place to which people flock three times a week from both city and country. The artificial-silk industry has recently sprung into importance here and in Nottingham.

Birmingham is perhaps even more famous than Pittsburgh and Essen as an iron and steel center. Such centers arise only in conjunction with coal fields. That the coal fields are important at Birmingham is evident from the huge mine dumps that dot the so-called Black Country a few miles west and northwest of the city. Because of the decline in the local production of iron ore, however, and the depth at which many mines are now worked, even the Black Country is no longer a region of blast furnaces where smoke clouds the air by day and huge flames flare upward by night. In fact, although Birmingham still manufactures vast quantities of hardware, it has more and more become a center for all kinds of manufacturing, especially non-ferrous metalworking. Its products include motorcars, bicycles, tires, and other rubber goods, rayon, ready-made clothing, electrical supplies, machine tools, munitions, and even food-products and drinks. Walsall shares the growth and industries of Birmingham, as does Wolverhampton, where ironwork is especially prominent.

Physical circumstances alone do not account for the phenomenal position of Birmingham as a center of British manufacturing. The city does not lie directly on the coal fields; its supplies of iron ore have long required large supplements from abroad; and its location is not especially favorable for transportation. No water communication with the ocean is available, and the city lies nearly 500 feet above the sea on a low plateau. About 160 miles of canals have indeed been made, but they lie at three different levels and are used mainly for carrying coal short distances. Long ago, when Birmingham was only a small agricultural market town, it began to be a center for ironsmiths, but was still insignificant. Its early insignificance con-

tributed to its later greatness. After the restoration of King Charles
II in 1660 the Dissenters who had supported Cromwell were persecuted and made unwelcome, especially in the larger cities. Since
little Birmingham had no city government and no trade guilds, it
allowed many Dissenters to settle there, and the population increased
from 5,000 to 15,000 between 1650 and 1700. The newcomers were
of strong character. When the Industrial Revolution took place,
such people, together with the proximity of coal and the established
reputation of Birmingham in ironwork, caused a very rapid growth
of industry. Today Birmingham owes its reputation to this early
and favorable start rather than to any peculiar advantages of location.

In 1907 six towns in "the Potteries" on the border between the
Midlands and Lancastria united to form Stoke-on-Trent. This
makes a curiously shaped city extending 8 or 10 miles north and
south, but very narrow from east to west. It cannot expand eastward because the ground is so honeycombed by coal mines that it is
not safe to build on it. Westward the old market town of New-
castle-under-Lyme, a typically English name, opposes the growth of
the new industrial city. The primary reason for the growth of
Stoke is that good clay for earthenware, drain pipes, and tiles is
found close to coal. But to these, more than a century and a half
ago, the great Josiah Wedgwood added a stroke of genius when he
established the famous Wedgwood china factory. There local coal
and the skill acquired in firing cruder kinds of pottery have made
it easy to convert fine imported clays into every sort of crockery
from common dishes to superbly beautiful works of art. More than
a third of the workers are engaged in the potteries, and more than a
fifth in coal mining, while many of the rest make brushes and the
colors and glazes needed for the pottery.

Lancastria

The difference between the woolen district of Leeds, east of the
Pennine Chain, and the cotton district of Manchester, 30 or 40 miles
to the southwest on the west of the Pennines, results partly from
slope. Originally the woolen industry was dominant on both sides
of the Pennines. A century or more ago Eli Whitney's gin suddenly
made cotton of great importance for clothing. The British, with
their coal, steam engines, and looms, began experimenting with it.
They soon discovered that cotton thread breaks very easily, especially if the air is dry. The western slope of the Pennines gets more
rain than the eastern slope (A294), and the winds are damper. More-

over, Manchester is nearer than Leeds to the west coast. Since cotton comes to Britain by sea from America, or even from Egypt, the western location of Manchester within 30 miles of Liverpool is also an advantage. In fact, proximity to the sea is so desirable that Manchester now has a ship canal that enables ocean-going ships to unload cotton almost at the doors of the factories, although most of the cotton is still landed at Liverpool. All this makes Lancashire better than Yorkshire for the cotton industry. Lancashire shares three other great advantages with the West Riding (southwestern part) of Yorkshire. One is the presence of good coal, providing about 10 per cent of the British output; another, the freedom of the water from lime; and the third, a climate so cool in summer and warm in winter that injury to health is at a minimum even when cotton factories are artificially humidified.

As the result of all this Manchester now has about 700,000 people and is surrounded by five other cities of at least 100,000, all of which are engaged mainly in the cotton industry. No other part of the world has so many spindles and looms in so small an area. More than 600,000 cotton workers, or 90 per cent of the British cotton operatives, are here concentrated in an area not much more than 30 miles long. But the different cities tend to specialize even here. Manchester and Salford with about a million people between them carry on the larger share of the cotton finishing, but in Manchester other industries and commerce have now become more important. Oldham and Bolton are spinning towns, and Oldham also has important textile-machinery factories, related of course to the cotton and woolen industries. Blackburn in the Ribble Valley is a weaving town that has specialized in cheap cotton cloth for the Indian market; Preston at the mouth of the Ribble is noted for sheeting, long cloths, and fancy cloths; Burnley farther inland produces prints.

Liverpool bears the same relation to the Manchester district that Hull does to Leeds, Bradford, and Sheffield, but the connection is much closer. Moreover, Liverpool also serves Birmingham, so that its hinterland is large and active. The harbor at Liverpool is not good, for the tidal rise and fall is very great and the natural channel at low water is shallow. Fast ocean liners that need to be loaded and unloaded quickly formerly tied up at a huge floating wharf, George's Stage, with a length of half a mile, a width of 80 feet, and many bridges that change their slope as the wharf and the ships that lie alongside move up and down with the tide. Now they use the

newer Gladstone dock, which can be entered at all stages of the tide.
Such conditions, as well as the necessity of constantly dredging the
channel, entail great expense, but they give Liverpool a good modern
harbor. The fact that Liverpool faces west has stimulated growth
here just as at Glasgow, but the details have been different. The
industries have taken forms that are related to the city's position as a
westward-facing port. They include the milling of wheat from
America and elsewhere, sugar refining, the building and repairing of
ships, the making of machinery for export, the extraction of oil,
and the manufacture of margarine, oil-cake, soap, chemicals, tobacco, ship's tackle, foodstuffs, and artificial silk. In the last product
Preston, which was once Liverpool's rival as a port, now is one of the
leading producers of the world, although its harbor is of little use
because it is silted up. South of Manchester and Liverpool in
Cheshire are extensive Triassic salt beds from which the brine is
pumped and used not only for salt, but also for chlorine and other
chemicals needed in cotton bleaching and dyeing. Glass is also
made in South Lancashire.

Lancashire exemplifies some of Great Britain's main problems.
Because of the modern tendency toward concentration of activity in
the most-favored centers, many ocean liners that formerly plied from
Liverpool now go to London or Southampton. In the same way,
many industries slowly but surely gravitate toward London, as is exemplified in the establishment of motor works at Oxford, much to
the disgust of the old inhabitants. A still more difficult problem
arises from the growth of industry in other countries with the aid
of British skill and machinery. America has thus become England's
greatest rival in foreign markets.

Lancashire suffers from an especially acute phase of this process.
Cheap cotton cloth has long been a major item in England's foreign
trade with India, China, Africa, South America, and elsewhere. But
cotton is produced in these same warm countries. Moreover, cotton
machinery has been so highly perfected that the making of cotton
cloth is one of the easiest kinds of manufacturing. Only a few
skilled mechanics are necessary; the rest of the work can be done by
unskilled people who know just enough to tie the broken threads.
Then, too, the packing, storage, marketing, and transportation of
cotton cloth present the minimum of difficulty. Cloth can stay on
the merchant's shelves for years unspoiled. Accordingly, cheap cotton cloth is exactly the kind of goods for manufacture in hitherto
undeveloped regions. Hence this industry has spread not only to

the southern United States and Japan, but even to Brazil, China, and India. The British market has thus been greatly curtailed, as has that of New England. In both cases the problem is like that seen on a small scale at Aberdeen. Can the British, and especially the Lancastrians, shift to some other kind of work? Already they are changing to finer types of cloth that demand more skill than do the coarse grades that predominate in India. They are also engaging in a greater variety of industries, and particularly in specialties and novelties that require much skill both in manufacture and marketing. This is happening in the textile industries of Manchester, as well as in the metal industries of places like Birmingham. Work of this kind demands far greater economic stability than do the older and simpler industries, for periods of depression check the sale of such goods far more than of standard goods like coarse cloth or flour. Hence the development of the resources of other lands brings to Britain a steadily increasing need for freedom from all sorts of disturbances such as war, epidemics, and economic depression.

This brings up the problem of free trade versus protection, which has long been of paramount importance in England. The Manchester School of the last century stood for free trade. Manchester, even more than the other industrial cities, wanted cheap food and no restrictions on foreign trade. Therefore it fought bitterly against all sorts of tariffs. The farmers and landowners naturally objected to this, for cheap American wheat meant low prices for their own products. The industrialists prevailed, and for a long time England throve on free trade. After World War I the policy brought no prosperity. So Empire preference is being tried; that is, the outlying parts of the Empire enjoy lower tariffs than other countries. But the end is not yet.

Northwestern Industrial Region

North of Lancaster the Cumberland coal area on the west side of the Lake District is limited in size, but well situated for coastal traffic since it borders the coast. Whitehaven is the main export harbor, shipping chiefly to Ireland. The south of Cumberland contains deposits of iron ore in an outcrop of Carboniferous limestone. The combination of coal and iron gave rise to an important iron and steel industry, but now most of the iron is imported. The great plant of the Vickers munitions works, for example, imports Spanish iron ore through Whitehaven. Barrow is the chief industrial center.

Bristol and South Wales

In its location in relation to America, Africa, the sea route to
Asia, and the interior of England, Bristol would seem to be the
most favored of British ports. This favorable location is reflected
in the early development of Bristol's colonial trade, and in its substantial old buildings and long-lived commercial firms. The large
ships dock at Avonmouth, but the smaller ones proceed up the narrow gorge of the Avon and anchor beside great warehouses almost
under the walls of the old cathedral. The grain, timber, petroleum,
oil nuts, oil seeds, soybeans, tobacco, ores, phosphates, esparto grass,
canned foods, dried fruits, and bananas that they discharge show
not only that colonial trade is still strong, but also that here, as at all
British ports, the main imports are food and raw materials from
other parts of the world. In spite of all this, Bristol has not held its
own with London and Liverpool. Its hinterland lacks the necessary
people and resources. The abundant coal close by in South Wales
is shipped from Cardiff and Swansea. The manufactured goods of
the Birmingham district are practically the same distance from
Liverpool or London as from Bristol. No great industrial centers
rely upon it as Manchester does upon Liverpool, and Leeds, Bradford, and Sheffield upon Hull. Nor has it great natural resources
of its own like the coal of Newcastle, nor huge and varied manufactures like those of London. So Bristol, in spite of its superb location, must be content to rank with Hull and Newcastle instead of
with London and Liverpool. Yet many people think that in its
quiet solid dignity it is the most attractive of them all. The surrounding country, too, is very charming with its old stone villages
and its air of quiet, agricultural comfort.

Only 20 or 30 miles across the water from Bristol a wholly different
social and economic atmosphere is found in South Wales. There
about three fourths of the 2.5 million people of Wales, as well as
another half million in the neighboring English county of Mon-
mouthshire, depend largely on coal mining and the related occupations of smelting imported ores and exporting coal. The coal is
found in a syncline within the old Welsh mountain system, and the
mining towns are situated in narrow valleys along the small streams.
The coal is of the hard anthracite type and hence of great value,
especially as steam coal on ships. The production supplies one fifth
of the total for all Great Britain. Swansea, Cardiff, and Newport
ship Welsh steam coal all over the world, although the amounts are

greatly reduced from pre-1939 levels. Here once more Great Britain has a combination of coal and iron ore, and Merthyr Tydfil is important in the production of iron and steel. The principal industrial development in Wales, however, has been along the coast, where foreign ores, including tin and copper as well as iron, can be cheaply brought to meet the coal. Tin plate has long been an important export article.

The South Wales coal fields are one of the "Depressed Areas" of Great Britain and are very unattractive, as are most mining regions. Tucked away in barren little valleys or extending up the treeless slopes, the towns have an uncommonly dreary, hopeless appearance. Here the British method of building little two-story, one-family houses in long solid rows is carried to an absurd extreme. Such houses are characteristic of the outer parts of practically all British industrial towns, and, before the rehousing programs of post-World War II years, probably half or more of the inhabitants of England lived in them. Sometimes they are rather attractive, standing in pairs with narrow open spaces between them and pretty little gardens in front. More often they stand in long solid rows where ten or twenty houses form a single solid block as in Philadelphia. Such blocks are the British substitute for the apartment or tenement houses that hold so many of the townspeople on the continent and in the central portions of the larger cities of Britain. They are also a substitute not only for the two- or three-family houses of America in which the families are shelved one above another, but for a large part of the one-family suburban houses that are becoming increasingly dominant in the United States. They are built because they are the cheapest way of giving each family its own individual house, a thing that the British lay great store by. In Wales this type of architecture is carried to such an extreme that enormously long blocks of dingy houses with no front yards or gardens line both sides of streets that run through open pasture land. The congestion, poverty, and lack of ambition evinced by these poor houses on the part of the working people, and the lack of far-sighted public spirit evinced by them on the part of the owners are typical of one of the worst social situations in Great Britain. It is against such conditions that the British "common man" reacted during the Great Depression and especially after World War II, when socialist policies were adopted by the government. The South Wales area and a number of similar mining and heavy-industries areas were made "Development Areas," a name deliberately adopted to offset the implication of

"Depressed Areas." The aim was to diversify industries in such regions so that economic dislocations and technological readjustments would not create mass unemployment and economic distress. Part of the plan also is the erection of better housing, but shortages imposed great difficulties on the housing program.

Metropolitan London

Although London lies in the Lowlands, well back from the open sea, it owes its growth to all four of the parts into which the country is logically divided—the pastoral Highlands, the agricultural Lowlands, the intervening industrial section, and the commercial seacoast.

The metropolitan district—Greater London—now contains about 9 million people, or nearly one fifth of all those in Great Britain. Nowhere else except around New York do so many people live on an equal area of the earth's surface. The quality of these people is even more significant than their number. So far as leaders are concerned, London and its vicinity are at least four or five times as well off as the rest of Great Britain. London is equally conspicuous for its splendid museums, great libraries, huge banking institutions, and organizations for world-wide activity. Paris and Rome may have a longer series of great historical events to look back upon, as well as a greater number of splendid churches, and New York may have more wealth, but none of them rivals London in these other respects. And only New York rivals London in its wide development of a vast variety of modern types of industry.

Another feature of London is the completeness of its transportation system. A perfect network of railways radiates to all parts of Great Britain, and the nationalized railroads are extremely well run. Rapid steamships connect London, and thus Great Britain, with the continent. The chief lines are from Harwich to Hook of Holland, from Dover to Ostend and Calais, from Folkestone to Boulogne, from Southampton to Le Havre, and from Newhaven to Dieppe. The projected channel-tunnel still fails to win favor with insular-minded Englishmen, but if it is ever built it will still further stimulate the growth of London. A number of airlines operate from London to Paris and other continental cities. Within the limits of Great Britain, however, air transport is not much used, probably because of the moderate distances and the perfect railroad system.

The supremacy of London in these many ways is the result of the gradual growth of the city's hinterland. When the Romans came to Britain, London was simply a site where the Thames River could easily be crossed. The estuary of the Thames is an obstruction to northward travel, and the lower course of the river was long bordered by swamps, which were a serious obstruction. So the travelers bound for prosperous East Anglia or any other part of central or northern Britain had to go upstream as far as London in order to find an easy crossing place. There the ford, ferry, or bridge that at successive times afforded means of crossing tended to induce people to stop for the night and made it a good place for merchants, artisans, officials, and others.

From that time onward the history of London has been the history of the improvement in man's technological ability and the consequent growth in the size of London's hinterland. Better boats on the Strait of Dover, a better road to London, the cultivation of more land in East Anglia and elsewhere, and the better cultivation of each acre—all meant more people and more goods passing through London, and hence growth of the town. Political unification, the fishing industry, seagoing ships, and ocean commerce all helped to extend London's hinterland not only at home but also abroad. All sorts of technical progress had a similar effect. Thus, when people learned to burn coal in grates, Newcastle—for this purpose at least— became a part of London's hinterland. The discovery of America and the sea route to India acted as a tremendous stimulant to London as well as to Bristol and Liverpool. London became the head-quarters of great colonial ventures like the East India Company and Hudson's Bay Company, and thus started its career as the world's greatest entrepôt where colonial goods are received for distribution to other parts of the world. Although the Industrial Revolution for a time made other cities grow faster than the capital, London in the long run was the greatest gainer.

The significance of all this is that growth or improvement any-where in England, and one might almost say anywhere in the British Empire, means at least a little growth in London. Transportation illustrates this excellently. The macadam road a century and a half ago and then the introduction of railroads encouraged people to go to London rather than to some nearer but smaller center. Motor roads now have a similar effect. The first to be built radiated from London. Today it is often easier to find the way 100 miles to Lon-don than 10 miles to some little village. The increased size and speed of steamships have had the same effect. Southampton and even Plymouth have become large cities in part because fast liners stop there in order to serve London. Brighton is an amazingly large summer resort because it is near London. Because the ships of modern times need big ports in order to get loads quickly, London has again been the gainer. Airplanes, more than any other type of transportation, have their center in London. In the same way London's share in the foreign trade tends in the long run to increase at the expense of the rest of the country. All these conditions make the city an even more favorable place for manufacturing. So London's industries as well as its other activities have increased greatly. Aside from industries producing heavy iron goods, cotton and woolen textiles, and pottery and glass which have special reasons for centering elsewhere, the metropolitan area tends gradually to absorb a greater percentage of most kinds of business.

More severely than any other British city with the exception of Coventry—England's center for production of electronic apparatus— London suffered from air bombing and "V-2" bombing by the Nazis during World War II. Many square blocks around St. Paul's Cathedral, for example, were leveled, and buildings in many parts of the city were destroyed or damaged. Even the Parliament building itself was hit, although it was completely restored by 1950. Loss of so many housing units caused thousands of people to leave London for shelter elsewhere. Also, the government learned that the great London conurbation was a prime target in any possible future war, especially if the city were attacked with atomic bombs. A policy of decentralization of population and industries has, therefore, been adopted. The vulnerability of not only London but also of all Britain to atomic attack is one reason for British caution in European affairs.

Britain and the United States

These three chapters on Great Britain have attempted to give the impression of a great country still very important in the world even if its world leadership is gone forever. To the United States, Britain —in spite of unavoidable disagreements—remains an allied nation; quarrels can be almost regarded as family quarrels. It is understandable that often the British do not like the idea of American leadership: it is difficult for them to become reconciled to their loss of leadership. On the other hand, in the United States the importance of Britain is often underestimated. It is often difficult for the American mind to associate democracy with nationalization of the major industries and with strong government control of trade, but America has never faced the problem Britain had to cope with, especially in the years after World War II. The majority of the British feel that "limited socialism" is a necessity. But, in a world in crisis, close co-operation between Britain and the United States is essential for world peace. Their futures run together even though each of the two must retain its own characteristics, political as well as economic, and act according to what it believes are its best interests.

· 23 ·

Ireland
(Éire and Northern Ireland)

The Effect of Marginal Location

Although Ireland is politically subdivided into the Republic of
Ireland and Northern Ireland, the geographer must view the island
as a whole. The history of Ireland has been characterized by
peculiarly great fluctuations comparable to those of Greece. The
reason is that Ireland lies on the northwestern margin of Europe
near the moist, cool limit of agriculture, just as Greece lies near the
opposite, or dry, margin. From the fifth to the seventh centuries
A.D., after the days of St. Patrick, Irish culture surpassed that of any
other country in northwestern Europe. The arts and agriculture
were highly developed, and learning flourished greatly. Huge mo-
nastic schools sent out thousands of students, many of whom brought
enlightenment, culture, and Christianity to countries like England,
Scotland, France, and Germany. The old Brehon laws furnish a
picture of a virile, young civilization that seemed to promise high
achievement.

Such a situation was possible because of two especially favorable
conditions. One was that Ireland at that time enjoyed a period of
comparatively dry, warm climate, a stage in one of the long climatic
cycles that occur all over the world. In Ireland this particular stage
was unusually important because that country is typically marginal.
In other words, it lies so far north and is so oceanic that a slight
lowering of temperature or an increase in cloudiness and rainfall is
disastrous to crops. On the other hand, a change in the opposite
direction, which would make little difference to France, for example,
is of almost incalculable benefit to Ireland.

The second favorable condition was that Ireland's remote location
protected it from barbarian invasions. All Europe was in confusion
in those dark centuries; barbarians were swarming into all parts of
the Roman Empire; England was invaded by the Jutes, Angles, and

342

Saxons. Those wild tribes were doubtless very virile and able people—excellent as ancestors—but they brought confusion and retrogression when they overwhelmed the old Roman civilization that had prevailed for centuries in England. Ireland, however, was fortunately so remotely located that it escaped all this, and was free to develop its own characteristic culture.

By the fourteenth century all this was changed. The coolest, most rainy phase of a long climatic cycle prevailed. Agriculture was almost impossible, and cattle raising became practically the sole means of making a living. To make matters worse, the isolation of Ireland had broken down. Danish invaders and then the Normans from England had poured into the country. Their warlike, destructive activities submerged Ireland much as the greatest waves of a mighty tempest at high tide overwhelm parts of the shore that have long been deemed safe. Thus confusion prevailed in Ireland; the population became extremely scanty; and cattle raids, like those of the modern Arabs, were in many ways the dominant, or rather the favorite, activity when the Irish were not fighting with the English invaders.

The end of the sixteenth century saw another period of more favorable climate. The troubles of the British conquest died down, and at last, during the seventeenth century, the Irish population ceased to depend so completely on cattle and began to increase. The early part of the eighteenth century, however, was again cold and wet; progress was checked; and intense misery prevailed all over Ireland, as is so vividly depicted in some of Dean Swift's famous satires. But soon a more favorable climatic phase and the newly introduced potato began to do their work. Hillside land and bogs that had apparently not been cultivated since the good old Brehon days a thousand or more years earlier were reclaimed on all sides. During the century from 1730 to 1830 the relatively favorable climatic conditions and especially the potato, which had been introduced from America, permitted an almost unparalleled change to take place. The population increased from 1.5 million to 8 million. The Irish changed from a nation of cattle keepers, whose main source of sustenance was milk and cattle, to a nation of small farmers depending mainly on potatoes.

Then came another swing of the climatic pendulum. Between 1831 and 1842 unfavorable weather fostered a blight that wrought havoc with the potato crop, and there were six seasons of dearth approaching famine. Then in 1846 the crop was almost a complete failure. Famine and pestilence ensued. About 3 million people were at one time on daily rations from the government. This led to tremendous migration to America. It intensified the social and economic evils arising from unjust laws, religious controversy, and absentee landlords who lived in England and allowed their agents to squeeze rents out of the peasants unmercifully. The final result was that the population of Ireland was reduced by half, and the country returned to an economy in which the potato, although important, is subsidiary to cattle raising. This is to be expected in a country so marginally located and hence so subject to disaster under the impact of even the small climatic cycles of recent centuries. The present increased crop production (especially that of wheat) coincides again with a sequence of fairly warm, dry summers, and it will be interesting to watch what will happen in the future.

Structure and Relief

The relief of Ireland suggests a very irregular and shallow bowl, with a much-broken rim of low, rounded mountains surrounding a central plain. The plain itself is broken by mountains. No part of the country is located more than 40 miles from mountains. The rim consists of a combination of the old Caledonian and Hercynian mountain systems, whereas the central depression is filled with Carboniferous limestone. Evidences of recent Alpine mountain building appear in the physical separation between Ireland and Great Britain, in the accompanying eruptions of basalt that are represented by the Plateau of Antrim in the northeast, in the structural depression of Lough Neagh in that same region, and in the uplift and revival of some of the old mountain systems in the south, especially the sandstone Mountains of Kerry in the far west, which attain elevations of 3,000 feet. The Irish mountains are mostly knobs of especially hard and resistant rock, such as the granite uplands of Wicklow, south of Dublin; Connemara, in the center of the west coast; and Donegal, in the northwest. Any appreciable elevation is a disadvantage to agriculture in Ireland. Not only do elevations above a thousand feet or even less create conditions too cool for agriculture, but mountains promote cloudiness and rainfall, especially on their western, seaward slopes. Such conditions are disastrous to agriculture in so marginal a country.

Another handicap of Ireland is that much of the present topography is the result of the weathering and erosion of soluble limestone, with its consequent unusual forms of relief. The lowland consists almost wholly of limestone, on which have developed vast areas of bog. The central plain is a typical karst region, characterized by underground drainage and numerous sinkholes and other undrained hollows. The largest of these hollows are occupied by numerous low-lying lakes not more than about a hundred feet above sea level; thousands of smaller hollows contain bogs. Thus, large parts of even the lower land are useless for cultivation.

The spread of ice sheets during the Ice Age did not endow Ire-

A. Mount Errigal (2,466 feet), owing its existence to hard quartzites rising above the lowland of Donegal in northwestern Ireland. Small scattered farms reflect the poverty of the moorland with its heavy rainfall and strong winds. Courtesy of Irish Tourist Association.

land greatly. Glaciers of local origin covered the mountains, making them smooth and rounded, and carrying away a great part of the soil. Some parts of the lowland profited from the glacial moraine or "drift" that was thus carried down, but in many places the number of lakes and bogs increased as a result of glacial deposition and disarrangement of drainage. Some variety was given to the lowland landscape by the deposition during the Ice Age of scores of eskers and drumlins (described in Chapter 15). Indeed, both words are of Irish origin.

Climate and Vegetation (A-B293, A294, A295)

The productivity of Ireland is influenced by climate even more than by relief. Ireland possesses an extreme marine climate. Along the west coast the winter temperatures average between 42° and 44° F, and even in the interior they average between 39° and 40°. The summers are cool, the mean July temperature along the west coast being 58° or 59°, and inland 60° or 61°. The difference between summer and winter temperatures is, therefore, remarkably small, particularly in the southwest, where the range between the average temperatures of the warmest and coldest months is no greater than 15°. Rainfall is heavy in the west, where it ranges between 60 and 80 inches; but it decreases toward the east in the rain shadow of the mountains, falling below 30 inches around Dublin. The distribution is fairly uniform through the year.

The influence of regular and abundant rainfall, high humidity, and prevailing cloudiness is shown by the great amount of moorland and bog. Moorland covers the higher parts of the mountain upland as in Great Britain, and parts of the central plain as well. Monotonous lowlands covered by peat are typical of widespread sections, and peat is still the commonest Irish fuel. But, where the drainage is sufficient, the climate gives rise to the grassland *par excellence* that accounts for the legendary green of Erin, the "Emerald Isle." In former times, during the phases of great climatic cycles when the climate was drier, the European forest extended into Ireland. This was the case, for example, at the end of the sixteenth century. Grass, however, was abundant and probably dominated the landscape even then, particularly in the west. The combined result of climatic cycles and deforestation by man has been that only the typical park landscapes of big estates with scattered trees in the midst of grassland remain to show the former extent of the forest. At present only 1.4 per cent of the whole area is in real forest, Ireland having the lowest figure among the countries of Europe.

Use of the Land

Marked changes have taken place recently in the use of the land, and, although pasture still prevails, the shift has been toward more cropland and especially toward an increase in the production of wheat. During the 1930's, Ireland raised about as much wheat as the state of New Jersey, using only 35,000 acres. In the 1940's that acreage climbed to about 600,000 acres for the Republic alone. This increase was distributed over most of Ireland, but the major concentration is still in the drier southeast. Flour imports have become negligible, but hard wheat is still imported in appreciable quantities. Another change, again pertaining only to the Republic, is the increase in the acreage of sugar beets; at mid-century it reached 66,000 acres, although sugar beets were almost lacking in 1930. Oats are, however, still the major grain crop in acreage as well as in production, as would be expected in a cool, moist area. In Northern Ireland, where wheat is still insignificant, oats prevail by far. The acreage in potatoes is still large; it has declined in the Republic but increased in Northern Ireland. In both areas, fodder crops, such as turnips and mangolds, still play a major role, and flax continues to be raised, with the major emphasis in Northern Ireland. Barley is used for the beer industry.

It is understandable that in the Republic the shift toward wheat took place somewhat at the expense of livestock raising. Once the land of butter and bacon, both of which were exported to Britain, Ireland after World War II exported no appreciable amount of butter and very little bacon. This is, indeed, one of the most pronounced changes—albeit on a small scale—in the whole European economy. Decrease in number of dairy cows and increased milk consumption partly for such purposes as production of dried milk and chocolate crumbs (both exported to Britain) accounts for the drop in butter available for export. The number of pigs decreased about one half during World War II, a decrease partly attributable to the decrease in imports of corn used to fatten the pigs. On the other hand, the number of cattle is still equal to that of prewar years (4 million for the Republic), and approximately 375,000 are exported yearly to Britain for slaughter. From the natural mountain grasslands the young cattle are brought down into the plains to graze. The final fattening is accomplished on such rich grasslands as those of Meath near Dublin and those of the "Golden Vale" near Limerick. Horses are also exported in large numbers as saddle horses, hunters, and thoroughbreds for breeding purposes. Sheep have declined from 4 million to 2 million and are no longer of appreciable importance for export. Poultry raising has increased enormously, and exports of dressed poultry and eggs have increased accordingly. The number of eggs exported in 1949 was, for example, 240 million.

Land Tenure

From the earliest times, ownership of the land has been one of the chief troubles of Ireland. During the seventeenth century, when British political power became dominant after prolonged wars, the greater part of the country was divided among British conquerors. The English landlord-and-tenant system replaced the old Irish arrangement. The big landowners either leased the land to the Celtic Irish peasants or exploited the properties themselves by means of hired managers and Irish labor. For more than two centuries a struggle went on between the oppressed Irish farmer, who found himself deprived of his own soil, and the foreign Protestant landlord, who very often looked with contempt on the Irish-Catholic inhabitants. The system of "tenancy-at-will," imposed by the English, was one of the greatest injustices done to the unfortunate Celts. It permitted the landlords to send away tenants whenever they chose.

Although the climate with its effect on potato diseases and thus upon economic conditions in general was mainly responsible for the great collapse after 1846, the hated landlord system seriously aggravated it. The small holdings that were not cultivated directly by the big landlords had previously been subdivided repeatedly because of the increase of population. In this way they became too small for the farmer to earn a livelihood. It was on properties of this kind that potatoes were raised most intensively until the failure of the crops suddenly cut off the principal source of food and threw the entire country into privation.

A change came in the latter part of the nineteenth century when new laws restored a part of the land to the tenants as owners. At present most of the holdings are cultivated by owners, and the rest are leased. Most of the properties range in size between 5 and 100 acres; only 6 per cent of them are larger. The creation of small farms is still going on. New holdings are created from untenanted land, and considerable sums have been lent by the government to finance the development of these small properties. Another part of the program has been the enlargement of very small holdings to the size that will permit them to be profitably operated.

Industries

As a whole, Ireland is not likely to become a country of great manufacturing development. Its coal has not been worth exploiting because of poor quality, excessive depth, and inconvenient location. Peat is the only home-produced fuel. The Republic of Ireland is carrying forward work of developing hydroelectric power, which was first supplied on a large scale in 1929, when the Shannon project was put into operation. The Shannon Scheme calls for additional tapping of the potential water power available in the 100-foot drop in the river. In 1950, Northern Ireland and the Republic agreed on mutual development of a hydroelectric scheme involving the drainage of Lake Erne, in Northern Ireland, and construction of a power station at Ballyshannon, in the Republic. About one-half the Republic's population now have electricity, which means that the rural homes generally still are without it. Factory products are chiefly those based on farm commodities and include dairy products, beer, and whiskey. There are, however, such industries as sugar refineries, flour mills, and apparel shops. The great exception is found in Belfast, capital of Northern Ireland, which combines shipyards and linen-textile industries, both having a world reputation. About 40,-000 men are employed in shipbuilding and engineering, and 90,000 (mainly women) work in the textile plants. Londonderry also has a share of the textile industry.

Transportation

The transportation system of Ireland is directed toward the east. By railroad or waterway, goods are brought to such harbors as Cork, Belfast, and Londonderry. Several rapid-transit lines connect Ireland and Great Britain across the Irish Sea and St. George's Channel. Chief among these are a southern line between Rosslare, near Wexford, and Fishguard in Wales; a central line between Dublin and Holyhead on Anglesey; and a northern line from Larne, north of Belfast, to Stranraer in Scotland. The internal waterways chiefly focus on Dublin, the best-known being the Grand and Royal canals, which provide connection with the Shannon system. Waterways, however, carry only 6 or 7 per cent of the total tonnage of Ireland; railroads are responsible for 93 per cent. The railroad system falls below modern standards because of abnormal use during the time of political disturbances, but much has been done to improve it.

Population and Its Distribution

The population of Ireland remains essentially rural. The proportion living in rural regions, however, has now been reduced to two thirds, both through the growth of cities and through depopulation by emigration. This emigration has caused persons of Irish descent in the United States to outnumber by far those in the home country. Many emigrants have also gone to Great Britain, where large numbers have settled around Liverpool and Glasgow.

Cities. The principal towns of Ireland are all seaports depending upon trade. From Londonderry in the north to Cork in the south they face away from the main Atlantic. The reason is that the major part of Irish trade has always been with England and Scotland, and sometimes with France. Not only is the west coast very stormy, but also it is far from the parts of Ireland in which the climate permits the largest population. Moreover, Ireland has had little in the way of goods that could be sold across the Atlantic. Ireland's new political independence, to be sure, is reflected in a slight increase of trade with foreign countries, but the economic relationship with England mentioned in Chapter 10 is too close to be much changed. For this reason the towns along the western coast, despite their splendid harbor facilities, remain small and show no sign of becoming important. Limerick, at the mouth of the Shannon, Ireland's principal river, is the chief of these, along with Galway and Sligo.

On the east and southeast coast lie the three largest cities: Cork, Dublin, and Belfast. Cork, however, is much smaller than the other two. With its outport of Cobh, where several transatlantic lines touch, Cork is essentially Irish. It is primarily a commercial center, though manufacturing industries increased somewhat during the 1940's.

Dublin, the Irish capital, with more than 0.5 million people, was originally a Norse settlement. The relatively dry climate has always been a great advantage agriculturally. Because of its location facing England, Dublin early became the main Irish harbor. Its advantages as an outlet of the productive central lowlands have been increased by construction of canals connecting with the River Shannon. Hence it is not surprising that Dublin has long been the political and cultural center of Ireland. Its industries are based on domestic materials, notably brewing and distilling, both beer and whiskey being important export articles.

Belfast, with a slightly smaller population than that of Dublin, is the capital of Northern Ireland. It was originally a Scottish settlement and owes its growth largely to industrial enterprises. It is interesting to note that the principal manufacturing section of Ireland is the one with a foreign—that is, Scottish—population. The linen industry and shipbuilding have advanced Belfast from a small town to a great city. On a small scale, Londonderry, the most northern port, has also profited from the industrial development, besides being the commercial center of the northern region.

Density. The average density of population in the entire 32,000 square miles of Ireland is about 130 per square mile, but there is great variation from place to place. The highest density is in the industrial sections of Northern Ireland, which reach 380 per square mile; the average for the agricultural districts of the Republic is about 100 per square mile, higher where the soil is better, and lower in the boglands. In some mountain sections of Connacht and Munster the population is very sparse.

Political and Religious Separation

The present political division between the Republic of Ireland and Northern Ireland dates from 1921, when Protestant Ulster refused to become part of the Catholic Irish Free State created in that year. The division was underlined in 1949, when a vote in Northern Ireland indicated that Ulster still preferred to retain its ties with the United Kingdom, even if Ireland were independent. Thus, after 1949 Ireland as an island was split into two unequal parts: the larger was the completely independent Republic of Ireland, which thenceforth severed the official ties with the Commonwealth that had existed during the period of the Irish Free State; and the smaller was Northern Ireland, which, although it had its own parliament, was also represented in the British parliament.

In the 1949 voting, the areas with an Irish Nationalist majority were those along the southern border in the counties of Down, Armagh, and Fermanagh, as well as on the uplands of Londonderry and Tyrone. Of the total number of votes, the Irish Nationalists received 27.2 per cent against 62.7 per cent for the Unionist Party, which represents the pro-Britain element, and 10.1 per cent for smaller parties, which, however, generally are not in favor of union with Ireland. The percentage of the pro-Irish vote is much lower than that of the Roman Catholics, which is almost 40 per cent, indicating that not all Catholics are in favor of a union.

From an economic point of view, the separation between the two parts of Ireland is illogical, because the essentially rural Republic and the industrial North complement each other. It is understandable that the Republic government would feel that an all-Ireland state is essential. However, the dominantly Scottish-Irish, Protestant Ulster seems to have elected to remain with Britain and not join the Irish, Catholic Republic.

The Republic represents the achievement of freedom that Irishmen have been fighting for against the English for many decades. Growth of the national spirit was evidenced during the 1920's and 1930's, when the old Gaelic language—which had for centuries been gradually decreasing in use and popularity—was revived as an official language to counteract British influence. The attempt was not very successful, and efforts to extend its use have been softened, but not abandoned. Despite the gain of English over Gaelic during past centuries, the Irish have maintained their Roman Catholic religion in the face of contact with the Protestant British, and the religious

difference accentuates other already existing differences, not only
between Britain and Ireland but also between the Republic and
Ulster.   Having gained their complete freedom, the Irish will be
watched with interest in the years to come so that the world can see
how they will fare as an independent state.   By the end of 1951 the
evidence was that they would attack their problems forthrightly, and
improvements in many fields had already been made.   One accomplishment is reflected in A144: whereas the per capita national income in 1928 was less than one-third that of Britain, at mid-century it
was more than one-half.   A center of culture and progress in the
early Middle Ages and then a land of misery for centuries, Ireland
has started to work again toward a high level of achievement.

·24·

The Netherlands (Nederland)

Factors in Holland's Economic and Cultural Growth

The Netherlands, more commonly called Holland, was formerly the outstanding example of a small country that could rise to a high level, economically as well as culturally. It represented Europe A at its best. Its successful blending of agriculture, industry, and trade gave it a standing far above its relative position in size and population. Even a casual visitor was struck by the country's atmosphere of contentment, prosperity, and culture. Aside from the general geographical advantages of western Europe, of which climate is the most important, three factors have had special weight in giving Holland its outstanding position among the smaller nations. The first and foremost is the physical background of the Netherlands and the consequent battle between man and water. The Dutch, like the Swiss, are products of an originally rather unfavorable environment. This they largely conquered and thus, like the Swiss, not only made a living but also converted themselves into a nation of strong individualists purified through natural selection. The discussion will come back later to this physical background in greater detail.

The second factor was the call to the sea. The Dutch, by the very nature of their land, are naturally a seafaring nation; and, although the period of their world supremacy in maritime affairs ended centuries ago, the ocean trade remained important. Moreover, seafaring was the basic factor in the establishment of the great colonial empire, which contained a population of more than 75 million. One part, Surinam or Dutch Guiana, together with some of the West Indian islands, had little value and was in many ways a burden rather than an asset. But the other, the Netherlands East Indies, with their wealth of tropical products, was a great factor in the life of Holland. It supplied an outlet for Dutch energy and a source of national wealth in the form of plantations, which in good years provided a considerable part of the national income. Almost every family in Holland had friends and relatives who spent a great part of their life in "tropical Holland."

The third factor in giving Holland an outstanding position was the country's location not only at the outlet of the Rhine, Europe's most important river, but especially in the center of Europe's greatest industrial area, with its dense population. Holland, exploiting the advantage of that location, developed into a country of intensive land use, raising food for that great market. In contrast to Denmark, it did not become a one-crop country, since dairy products, although important, were balanced by others, such as fruits and vegetables. Holland developed an export economy, buying most of its own needs, such as grain, from other countries. With the help of scientific studies in the qualities of soils and the use of fertilizer, it reached the peak in productivity. Climatic disadvantages, such as the lack of warm summers, were overcome by the use of hothouses. The limited amount of land made every acre count. Here was horticulture at its best, and, indeed, the land became a garden of production. Even manufacturing profited from that location. Besides the normal industries of a prosperous country, some specialized industries developed, producing for export: the outstanding example was the electric industry of Eindhoven, the famous Philips plant, one of Europe's largest.

The Chief Limitation

The chief limitation on the Netherlands can be put in these words: there are so many Dutch and there is so little Holland. Even before World War II, population pressure became a threatening factor. High birth rate and low death rate resulted in an increasing number of people, not balanced by a commensurate addition of new territory through the process of reclamation. In the twenty years from 1930 to 1950, the population increased from 8 to 10 million, and no country in the world equals the Dutch density of population —about 750 per square mile—if England is considered within the United Kingdom and if "city-states" are excluded. This density became Holland's greatest problem, but as long as there was a colonial empire there was at least one good population outlet.

The Netherlands after the War

After the liberation in May, 1945, Holland started to repair the damages of war in so far as repair was possible. During the first part of the war, the suffering had been more mental than physical, except for certain areas destroyed during the short war period of 1940. Such an area was the center of Rotterdam, totally destroyed by the *Luftwaffe*. There was a wartime decline in industrial production, resulting partly from lack of raw materials, and an accompanying drop in agricultural production, resulting from lack of formerly imported fodder and fertilizers. But the real tragedy came during the winter of 1944–45, when the liberation effort of September, 1944, failed and Holland for the first time in its history actually starved while the Germans took away everything of value. The fact that the battle zone ran through the country and that the Germans flooded large areas added to the disaster. However, after liberation day, Holland started on the long road back to her former prosperity. But the energy was there to do the job with hope and confidence in the future.

The Netherlands at Mid-Century

Dutch hopes for recovery were not fulfilled because of the changes that had taken place in the rest of the world. The markets to which Holland once fed a constant stream of products did not ask for so much as in former times, owing to impoverishment and government policies. A second tragedy—as seen from the Dutch point of view— was the political change in Indonesia, the former Dutch colonial empire. Although Indonesia and the Netherlands were in 1952 still somewhat related through a union, Dutchmen are no longer very welcome in Indonesia, and those who are there live under very difficult conditions.

This means that two of the three factors on which the prosperity of the Netherlands was based have greatly declined in importance. Holland is now little more than just another small country. It will always be one of the better ones, largely owing to the energy of the people, but the time of former glory will probably not come back. Holland's major export is now young men, who go out to all parts of the world where they are accepted and start their new homes, carrying with them the reputation of Dutch productivity. Holland will remain a country of color and charm. Its cheeses, hams, chocolates, vegetables, and bulbs will continue to find a place on the world markets; tourists will admire its beauty, cleanliness, and comfort of life, its traditions and art. But, on a world scale, Holland is just a small nation, a minor factor in world affairs. Economic co-opera-

tion with Belgium and Luxembourg in the Benelux scheme may lead
to a greater economic development, and the unit may gain a position
that no one of them alone could reach. However, it is mainly the
difficult situation found by the Netherlands that is, indeed, holding
up full operation of the Benelux union.

The Physical Background

During the Ice Age the thick northern ice sheet (see Chapter 15)
covered northern Holland and extended across the present North Sea
into England. Upon its retreat, the ice left sandy fluvioglacial deposits with many glacial ridges, which now cover eastern Holland
north of the Rhine (A357). At the same time the swift-flowing Rhine
and Maas (Meuse) laid down the sands that now form the uplands
in the provinces of Brabant and Limburg south of the Rhine. These
provinces, as is clear in A358, can be called uplands only in contrast
to the lower western part of the country. Because of their loose, dry
soils, they were the home of the first men who followed the retreat
of the ice. Meanwhile, in the shallow depression that now forms the
North Sea, the rivers at first flowed northward, probably uniting
with others from England and southern Scandinavia to form a single
great stream.

In time, however, the rise of the ocean resulting from the melting
of the ice and the sinking of the land permitted the sea to encroach
more and more. The process of drowning the land culminated only
after the sea had broken the land connection between England and
France. As a result, the sandy uplands became the coastline of the
continent. Along the shore, however, from the protruding Nose of
Calais (*Nez de Calais*) northeastward, the winds and currents formed
a sandy bar, indicated by the heavily dotted strip along the coast
in A357, with a broad closed lagoon behind it. This extended as far
as the low morainic upland of Denmark. The bar in time became a
narrow zone of sand dunes and was broken in many places to give an
outlet to the deltaic branches of the Scheldt, Maas, and Rhine rivers.

The next stage was the gradual filling of large portions of the
lagoon, partly with clay brought by ocean currents and rivers, and
partly by peat, the result of lagoon vegetation. In this way the
lagoon was transformed into a swamp, half land and half water,
which appears in A358 as the area below sea level. In later times,
storms attacked the sandy bar and broke through it at many places,

flooding the swamps beyond and forming inland basins of salt
water. The present map of Holland still shows evidence of this

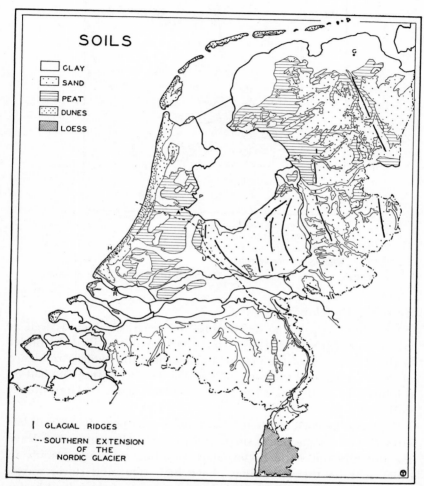

SOILS

☐ CLAY
▨ SAND
▤ PEAT
▨ DUNES
▨ LOESS

| GLACIAL RIDGES

--- SOUTHERN EXTENSION
OF THE
NORDIC GLACIER

A. Soils of the Netherlands. The Northeast Polder is not shown.

process, in the form of the disconnected character of the dune islands
of the northern or Frisian coast, as well as in the central basin of the
Zuider Zee (the combined Wadden Zee and IJsselmeer), and the
ragged coastline of Zeeland in the far southwest.

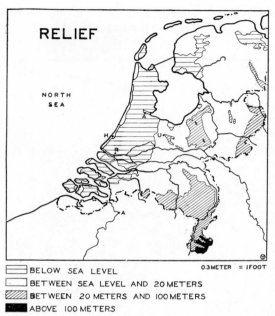

A. Relief of the Netherlands. The Northeast Polder is not shown.

Historical Development

The dune strip, being dry because it is relatively high as well as sandy, attracted early settlers. Here the Romans fortified the outlet of the Rhine west of the present Leiden; here the modern residence of the sovereign and the government (The Hague, H in A358) had its origin as the garden of a count, as the Dutch name, 's Gravenhage, indicates.

The swamp itself, with its many lakes and peat areas, was less attractive. In some places small groups of people ventured to leave the uplands and settle in lowlands, building artificial mounds in order to raise their dwellings above high tides and storm waves. Groups of fishermen also settled along the shores of the inland basins and used the protected inland waters as fishing grounds. Such settlements grew in importance; seafaring as well as fishing became an important occupation; and in the Middle Ages many of the towns thus started became members of the Hanseatic League and traded along the coasts of the North Sea and the Baltic. But man cannot live on fish alone, and the problem of where to get the other necessary kinds of food always confronted the fishing settlements. This led to the discovery that the swamps and even the floors of the shallowest parts of the many lakes and of the inland marine basin contained fertile soils, which could be used for grazing and crops if surrounded by dikes and drained. So the Dutch polders described in Chapter 3 originated. The Dutch lowland (A358) still contains an intricate assortment of these reclaimed floors of former bodies of water surrounded by dikes and drainage canals, into which the surplus water is pumped.

The area reclaimed from the water was at one time an insignificant possession of the German Empire and later of Spain. For a long time it was completely eclipsed by the high culture of near-by Flanders on the south, but the same water that had been conquered with so much difficulty could be used to flood the land once more in case of need, and thus to stop invaders. Aided in this way, the small group of individualists who had made their own land and fought for its freedom gradually gained power until for a short time they became the dominant nation of Europe. A decline soon followed, however, for Holland was too small to maintain the leadership in world politics. Nevertheless, much of the old spirit is still left and is responsible for Holland's present high standing.

Draining the Land

To return to description of the physical background, A358 shows how much of Holland is now below sea level because it consists of the old bottom of the lagoon converted into fertile fields and grasslands. Exceptionally low tides make it possible at fairly frequent intervals to drain much of this low area by means of canals; at high tide closed locks keep the ocean out. The relation between polders, dunes, dikes, rivers, and the sandy eastern region is seen in A360, in which the low places between dikes, including the one marked "reclaimed lake," are polders. The isles of Zeeland in the southwest were reclaimed by means of dikes in this way, as were the provinces called North and South Holland, which lie along the coast from Rotterdam northward.

The greatest task of reclamation was the Zuider Zee project. A large dam-causeway, eighteen miles long, was constructed between the island of Wieringen (see A361) and the coast of the province of Friesland, changing most of the former Zuider Zee into a freshwater lake, IJsselmeer. Of the four planned polders, the Northwest

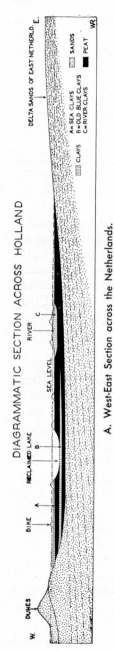

DIAGRAMMATIC SECTION ACROSS HOLLAND

DELTA SANDS OF EAST NETHERLD. E.

A = SEA CLAYS
B = OLD BLUE CLAYS
C = RIVER CLAYS

▨ SANDS
▦ CLAYS
■ PEAT

SEA LEVEL

RIVER C

RECLAIMED LAKE B

DIKE

DUNES

W.

WR

A. West-East Section across the Netherlands.

Polder (Wieringermeer) and Northeast Polder have been completed, and a third was in construction at mid-century. The two present polders have an area together of 170,000 acres— quite a gain for a small country. But the work does not stop once the sea has been drained. Attention must then be given to such procedures as leaching the soil impregnated with salt, selection of the types of land use, selection of the new farming population, and the construction of roads, farms, and villages. Map A362 shows the parts of Holland that were reclaimed partly from the sea but only through the additional diking of numerous lakes and swamps. Map A363 gives an idea of what areas can still be reclaimed, although it will take a long time before all the reclamation can be completed. If all areas shown in A363 are reclaimed, Holland will have added 2.5 million acres of new land—twice the amount of present reclamation.

Natural Regions

The Dunes (A357). Except where the sea has broken through them, the dunes form an almost continuous band. Since the sand is usually fixed by vegetation, they are strong enough to break the furor of waves and winds. On their outer side, a beach, wide at low tide and protected by many stone piers, invites bathing in summer. Many summer resorts line the coast, the best-known being Scheveningen, the beach of The Hague. In addition to the waterways of the Scheldt and Rhine, two artificial shipping canals cross the dunes—the New Waterway leading seaward from Rotterdam on one of the Rhine branches, and the North Sea Canal giving an outlet for Amsterdam (A364). The Rhine outlet itself is of minor economic importance, but the Scheldt opens the way first to the Dutch harbor of Flushing (Vlissingen), the continental terminus of one of the main crossings to England on the route between London and Berlin, and then farther inland to Antwerp, the harbor of Belgium.

The straight Dutch coast does not favor seafaring. Nevertheless, fishing is still important. Steam trawlers have replaced the old flat-bottomed boats, and the fishing has been concentrated in a few important harbors, notably Ymuiden on the North Sea Canal, where herring are the main catch.

A. The great dam, 18 miles long, that divides the former Zuider Zee into the fresh-water Lake IJssel (right) and the salt-water Wadden Zee (left). In the foreground is part of the Wieringermeer polder. In upper right is the coast of Friesland. Courtesy of KLM.

On the inner side of the dunes a zone of sand forms a transition to the polder region. Here the soil is very favorable for the raising of fruit, vegetables, flowers, and nursery stock in the form of young trees and bushes. Near Haarlem are the famous bulb fields, which supply a rather unusual item in Holland's exports. The many hothouses where large grapes and tomatoes are raised for export form a truly unique feature. They illustrate how effectively Dutch energy masters such geographical disadvantages as those of a summer too cool for many of the finest fruits. This transition zone is the site of many flourishing towns and villages. These profit from the firm soil that is more suitable for building than are the polders, and is also good for trees and flowers, so that many parks and gardens add to the beauty of the scenery. The Hague, the residence of the queen and parliament (although Amsterdam is the actual capital), is the largest city of the transitional zone. It is comparable to Wash-

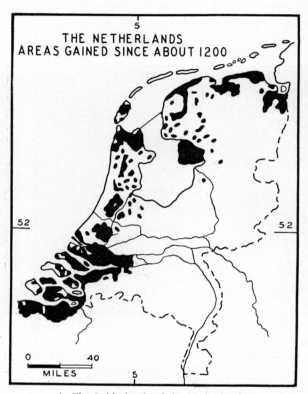

A. The Polderlands of the Netherlands.

ington in its dignity, in its large proportion of homes of officials, and as a retreat for pensioned colonials.

The Lowland and Its Cities. The Dutch lowland, or polderland, most of which is below sea level, represents Holland in its most typical form. Seen from the air or on a large-scale map, it shows an intricate pattern of polders with innumerable ditches separating the fields and providing drainage toward steam pumping stations. These stations ordinarily pump the excess water into the wide drainage canals, but in dry seasons they are used to pump water from the canals back to the land, thus making Holland doubly secure against crop failures. Windmills, which many people think of as the most typical feature of Dutch scenery, have lost a great deal of their importance. Extensive bodies of water represent parts of the former swamps where the underlying soil (peat or sand) was not worth reclaiming, although some of them were actually formed by man, who

THE NETHERLANDS

FUTURE RECLAMATIONS

A. Dutch Polders of the Future. The three main areas to be eventually reclaimed are the southern part of Lake IJssel, Zeeland, and the Wadden Zee.

dug out the peat as fuel and did not fill the depressions thus made. Dikes higher and broader than those of the canals protect the lowland from the waters of the inland marine basin of the IJsselmeer, and from the two branches of the Rhine River that flow across this polderland. Most interesting is the polder south of the island of Wieringen (A361), first to be completed among the four planned for the IJsselmeer. Until the early 1930's this area was part of the Zuider Zee, but now it is a perfectly flat, treeless plain on which the shelly soil and the remnants of shipwrecks lying on the meadows among grazing cattle join with the new and gaily colored brick houses to betray the recency with which the polder has been reclaimed. The much larger Northeast Polder shows the same characteristics.

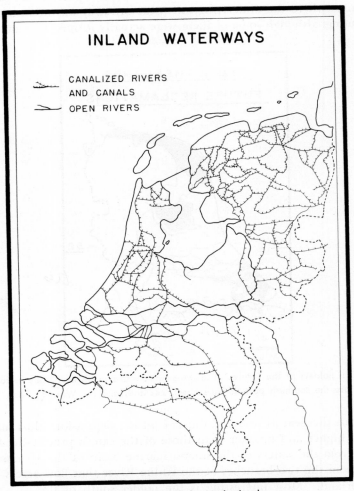

A. Waterways of the Netherlands.

In the polder region as a whole, grass is the dominant vegetation on the peat and on part of the clay. Green meadows studded with large farmsteads are surrounded by borders of trees. Roads, canals, tramways, and railroads provide transportation facilities to bring milk, butter, and cheese from the dairies to the towns.

On the higher clay soils grain does well; it is the dominant product in Zeeland at the southwest corner of Holland and also in Groningen at the northeast corner. In addition to wheat the major crops are sugar beets, fodder, and seed. The type of garden agriculture prevailing on the inner edge of the dune zone, with its sandy soils, extends into the polder region, where local areas are well known for

A. Frisian lake district with plots of grassland, scattered farms, and a compact village. Courtesy of KLM.

their vegetables, fruits, and tree nurseries. Moreover, especially between Rotterdam and The Hague, the hothouse type of agriculture has invaded the lowland and now covers 7,500 acres.

Two cities dominate the polder region—Amsterdam, the capital, and Rotterdam, Holland's greatest seaport. Amsterdam, originally a fishing settlement beside the Y, a gulf of the Zuider Zee at the mouth of the little Amstel River, became one of Europe's principal cities during the seventeenth century. Its colonial connections furnished one reason for its growth, and profits made in colonial trade were until recently the basis of its prosperity. With the decline of the power of the Dutch Republic, Amsterdam's glory was also for a time eclipsed, and its rise during the nineteenth century was restricted by harbor conditions unsuitable for modern trade. The Zuider Zee was too shallow for big seagoing vessels; a canal extend-

ing northward was too long to be successful; and it was not until
the straight, short North Sea Canal was built that the problem was
solved. At the seaward end of the canal, the great locks at Ymuiden,
the largest in the world, have a depth of 40 feet; and the Y, now
closed off from the former Zuider Zee, has become an excellent
harbor.

Amsterdam is Holland's economic center. The stock exchange
is one of the most important in Europe, and most of the banks and
many of the great business concerns have their headquarters in this
city. One of its specialties is the cutting and polishing of diamonds,
for which it has a world reputation. Most attractive as an example
of Dutch architecture and city planning, famous for its art collec-
tions, Amsterdam represents the best in Dutch culture. Unlike most
cities, it is surrounded by a broad expanse of grassland, and only
beyond this soft, damp area does one find the garden suburbs such
as Hilversum on the near-by sandy upland to the east and Haarlem
on the dunes to the west. Around Amsterdam, especially along the
Y, the North Sea Canal, and the little Zaan Canal, important manufacturing has developed under the combined advantages of ocean
transportation and the neighborhood of a comparatively large
market. Amsterdam also gets a share of the Rhine trade by way of a
canal connection, which was greatly improved after World War II.
However, in this respect it cannot compete with Rotterdam.

Rotterdam is quite different. Its position at the mouth of the
Rhine with its vast economic hinterland has made it an international
transit harbor rather than a purely Dutch terminus. The open canal
known as the New Waterway provides easy access from the sea to the
city, and all along both the canal and the river from the Hook of
Holland to Rotterdam stretch busy communities that share the city's
trade and industries. Shipbuilding is one of the city's primary industries. Prior to 1940, grain, ore, timber, oil seeds, cotton, and
petroleum were imported and reshipped on long barges that were
towed in strings up the Rhine River. Upon their return the barges
brought coal, iron, steel, and building stone, partly for export. The
Holland-American Line, with its fleet of ocean liners and freighters,
was one of the world's best-known shipping companies. It is not
surprising that Rotterdam became the first-ranking harbor of the
European continent. However, World War II altered the position
of Rotterdam as an industrial center and, especially, as a port.
Rotterdam suffered severely during the war, and, although it partly
recovered, it did not regain its former level. This is partly due to

the decline of the Rhine trade, but also to the competition of Antwerp. This Belgian port came through the war only slightly damaged and gained great advantage as a main port for Allied supplies during the last stages of the war; and later, as the principal harbor of booming Belgium, it continued its gain over Rotterdam. Geographically speaking, Rotterdam should regain more of its former

A. Old fortification of Naarden (southeast of Amsterdam), amid flat grassland and small horticultural plots. Courtesy of KLM.

importance, although loss of the great trade with Indonesia will continue to be a handicap.

There are many other cities in the lowland area of Holland often located on the edge of high land, dunes as well as the eastern sandy uplands. Also near the dunes are Leiden, a university city; Alkmaar, with its famous cheese market; and Haarlem, amid bulb and vegetable fields. On the eastern border are Nijmegen and Arnhem on either side of the beginning of the Rhine delta, both having a reputation as garden cities but also both having suffered greatly from war destruction, especially during the unsuccessful Allied airborne attack in September, 1944. Utrecht is the largest of these cities, well-known for its fair and, like Leiden, a university town. In the north is Groningen, market center for that part of Holland. The senior author of the book cannot omit his own town, Leeuwarden; at the time of his youth it was a quiet town, once the capital of the duchy of Friesland and then famous for its cattle market. Now it has more than doubled in size and shows the advantages of a central location in an expanding Frisian economy.

The Eastern Upland. Quite different is the picture on the east and south, where sands and high moors replace the lowland peat and clay. The elevation is still low, although it is above sea level; but in many cases north of the Rhine River, glacial ridges give a rolling aspect to the country, causing it to contrast strongly with the broad river valleys with their flat clays. In some places the landscape still includes some wasteland, which is wonderful in summer when the purple color of the heather stands out against the dark green patches of a forest of stately pines and majestic oaks and beeches. Aside from the timber, the present value of this wasteland is mainly that it serves as a recreation area for the surrounding dense population. Summer resorts and camps attract thousands during the vacation season, and on sunny days the tree-bordered roads, with bicycle paths on both sides are crowded with sight-seeing buses, cars, and bicycles.

A great shift has taken place in the use of the sandy uplands. Once they were the most backward part of Holland, a region of meager fields of rye, buckwheat, and potatoes and a place for wandering herds of sheep. But the need for arable land and the possibility of raising highly productive crops with the help of fertilizers changed the aspect of land utilization. Wheat, oats, and sugar beets, besides the still dominating rye, are now the chief crops. Emphasis is placed on dairying based on grassland as well as on the raising of fodder. Orchards and vegetable gardens do especially well on the river clays, and the raising of swine and chickens is now a major enterprise, with hams and eggs produced for export. Population, once sparse, increased rapidly with agricultural development of the area; and increased population, in turn, provided the needed labor for a growing manufacturing industry. One new development is the petroleum production in the southeast corner of the province of Drente, where oil derricks make it a miniature Texas.

Aside from the general industrial development, two regions gained special prominence—one in the eastern part of the province of Overijssel (the so-called Twente), east of the IJsselmeer, which specializes in textiles and machinery, and the other in the province of North Brabant that is more diversified, producing such goods as textiles, shoes, cigars, margarine, machines, and electrical supplies. Cities grew up as centers of industrial development. Those with a

population of more than 100,000 inhabitants are Enschede in Overijssel and Tilburg and Eindhoven in the south. Eindhoven, home of
the large Philips plant mentioned earlier, produces millions of incandescent lamps ("light bulbs") as well as radios and television sets.
    Limburg, Holland's southeastern province, extends far south along
the Maas (Meuse) River, touching a part of the fertile loess uplands

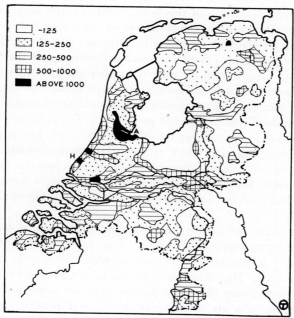

A. Density of Population per Square Mile in the Netherlands. The Northeast Polder
is not shown.

so typical of adjacent Belgium. Here the landscape is quite different. Elevations up to 1,000 feet are reached, whereas the glacial
ridges of the eastern upland scarcely exceed 300 feet and then only in
a few spots. Here are real valleys and hilly divides. Here are rock
quarries, although stone is unknown in the rest of Holland except
in the form of glacial boulders. Here also Holland has its share of
the coal zone extending from northern France through Belgium into
Germany. The production is sufficient to fulfill the national consumption; and canalization of part of the Maas, together with a new
canal connecting the Maas with the Rhine system, makes it possible
to ship the coal all over the nation. Here, also, was the place where

American troops prepared for their advance into Germany, and the large American cemetery of Margraten is an indication of the price paid by those troops to help free Europe from Nazi domination.

The Netherlands in Perspective

The beginning of this chapter examined the assets and liabilities of the Netherlands and drew a somewhat gloomy picture of the future. The first edition of this book, written many years before the war, forecast the eventual development of the present situation, but it came sooner than was expected. And yet the Netherlands has much to be proud of. Both the land utilization and the manufacturing attain a high level, in spite of—rather than because of—physical conditions, except for climate. Although certain factors, such as the central location of the country, have contributed to this progress, much is due to the energy of the population. This energy is helped by a climate that approaches the human optimum, but it also owes much to the stimulating effect of a constant and successful struggle against nature. Moreover, the inflow of refugees like the Huguenots and Portuguese Jews, from other countries, seeking a haven of protection in Holland, has increased the energy and ability of the people appreciably.

A glance into the future suggests that Holland will have to be content to be a center of commerce and trade and of specialized agrarian and industrial production—a second Denmark, but much more diversified. Dutch specialty products will go to all parts of the world, while at home there will be the need for imported food and raw materials. As an example of intensified production, it will stand as a unique case. But, if the present high birth rate continues, emigration will be necessary, and the Dutch, like the Swiss, will find new homes in various parts of the world where they will be welcome because of their ability.

·25·

Belgium (België or Belgique) and Luxembourg (Luxembourg or Luxemburg)

Belgium after World War II

Among the nations of Europe that were involved in the war, Belgium recovered most rapidly. Indeed, its recovery actually began during the war period, since it was liberated in the fall of 1944 and, well located as it was for the purpose, became a build-up area and supply area for the Allies. As was mentioned in the preceding chapter, Antwerp served as a very great supply port for the remaining Allied offensives against Germany. Such use of Belgium required that it be a "going concern" and, furthermore, brought American money into the country.

Before World War II, it was customary in a study of European geography to compare the two lowland countries, Holland and Belgium, and to bring out the difference between the dominance of manufacturing in Belgium and the more commercial and agrarian development in Holland. Such a comparison always reached the conclusion that, although Belgium was doing well, Holland was doing better, economically as well as culturally. The Dutchman even had a kind of superiority complex with regard to Belgium, a neighboring country that he considered as pretty good but certainly not Holland's equal. Those days are gone, because Belgium has surpassed the Netherlands. Belgium did not suffer so much from war damage, and it started producing at full speed while Holland was still German-occupied. Its colony, the Belgian Congo, although once regarded as insignificant if compared with the Dutch East Indies, greatly increased in economic value during the 1940's. Still more important is the fact that the Congo is still Belgium's. Antwerp, which formerly played second fiddle to Rotterdam, surpassed it after

1944, having been less involved in the decline of the Rhine traffic. While the Netherlands had to have a government-controlled, closed economy—and even so could not present a balanced budget—Belgium was open to the world market and did not have to protect the value of its money. In discussions of the execution of the Belgium-Nether-lands-Luxembourg economic union (Benelux), the Belgians tend to wield the most power because they are the strongest economically. Also, it is Holland that is the newcomer, since Belgium has had an economic union with Luxembourg since 1920. At that time Luxembourg, which had been part of the German Economic Union before World War I, had attempted to make such an arrangement with France, but was refused. Luxembourg then turned to Belgium, and the union has been quite successful. The little duchy does not come without a dowry: the large production of iron ore in southern Luxembourg has been a valuable asset to the Belgian heavy industries.

Natural Regions (A373)

Dunes and Polders. In Belgium, as in the Netherlands, a line of dunes borders the straight coast and affords sites for numerous beach resorts. One of them, Ostend, combines the catering to visitors with the work arising from its having a location facing the English coast at one of the best points for a fast crossing to Great Britain. At Zeebrugge is the outlet for the shipping canal connecting Bruges with the North Sea. The polderland behind the dunes forms only a narrow zone, in contrast to a much wider zone in Holland. Being especially good for grass, it is used mainly for dairy purposes, but also for crops and horticulture. The flooding of the southwestern part of the region, which is below the level of high tide, stopped the advance of the German army toward Calais in the fall of 1914, but the advance in 1940 was too rapid for flooding to be employed.

Sandy Region. In Belgium, just as in Holland, the next zone, the sandy region, shows a slightly rolling relief, with elevations up to 200 feet. It can be divided into two parts, Flanders in the west and the Campine in northeastern Belgium. Fertilization, already important during the Middle Ages, has here almost reached perfection; and this region, together with Holland, is probably the best-fertilized part of the world. Wheat, barley, rye, and potatoes, as well as sugar beets, hemp, chicory, and flax, are the chief crops; and horticulture, with tree nurseries, orchards, and truck gardens, ranks high. The density of the rural population in the Flanders part of the sandy region is exceptionally high, attaining as much as 800 per square mile. The consequent small size of the landholdings is a handicap, as is the fact that the little fields of any one farmer are often widely scattered and isolated.

In Flanders the old cities of Bruges (Flemish: Brugge) and Ghent

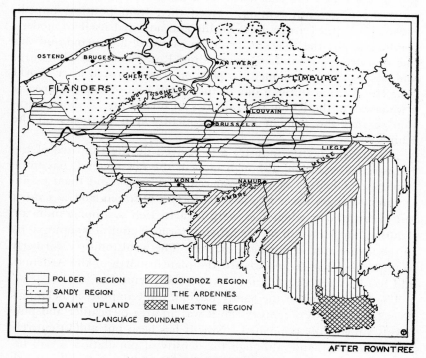

A. Agricultural Regions of Belgium.

(Flemish: Gent; French: Gand) were once harbors on southern distributaries in the Scheldt (or Schelde) delta. They owed their development in the later part of the Middle Ages to their marine location and to the availability of wool from the herds of sheep that wandered over the surrounding sandy plain with its cover of heather. Moreover, flax grows well in this climate, and it helped the Flemish textile industry to attain great fame. The increase of population arising from these conditions called for more intensive land utilization, and in recent centuries crops have supplanted pasturage in extensive areas.

The cities of Flanders have had a checkered history. The silting of their harbors caused Bruges and Ghent to lose their importance during the later Middle Ages, and thus Antwerp (Flemish: Antwerpen; French: Anvers) on the open stream of the main Scheldt became the leader. Foreign rule, however, and the closing of the way to the sea by the Dutch Republic broke the power of Antwerp until the nineteenth century. Freed then from political impediments, it obtained a new lease on life and adjusted itself to modern conditions. By the 1930's it served an extensive hinterland and was one of Europe's great harbors, rivaling Rotterdam and Hamburg; and, as has been mentioned, its position was improved after World War II. A canal through one of the Dutch isles of Zeeland gives it a waterway to the Rhine and provides an inland line of communication so that the Belgian flag is frequently seen on boats on the Rhine.

The ancient textile industry also revived during the time of the Industrial Revolution, although most of the raw material has to be imported. Ghent is again a great center of cotton and linen manufactures. Bruges never regained its former greatness and is a quiet but beautiful city, where lace work is carried on as a home industry. Tournai, farther south on the Scheldt, forms a kind of steppingstone to the textile area of northern France. The wool industry, formerly so important, has shifted toward the plateau north of the Ardennes and has Verviers, east of Liége, as the main center.

The eastern part of the Sandy Region, the Campine, is Belgium's "Newland." Only a century ago it was an area of heather and pine forests, only thinly populated. Now it has been put almost entirely into cultivation, and, although the density of population is still below that of Flanders, it is now dotted with small towns and villages. Fields of rye, oats, and potatoes, but primarily meadows and plots of root crops, have now replaced the former sheep pasture. Moreover, beneath the Campine is a large reserve of coal that was first exploited during World War I and now yields about one third of Belgium's coal production. Cheap land attracted modern industries, such as zinc refineries and glassworks that were formerly concentrated around Liége, as well as factories of explosives seeking the least populated areas. Crossed by canals—of which the Albert Canal, connecting the Meuse (at Liége) and the Scheldt (at Antwerp) is the most important—and having been provided with a good road and railroad system, the Campine is an excellent example of how a formerly poor sandy plain can change in less than a century into an area of intensive and varied production.

Loamy Upland. This next region occupies the center of Belgium and extends from the French border to the Meuse River. The term "upland" is applicable only in relation to the low sandy region to the north, since elevations in this region are only 150–300 feet. As in northern France, a widespread and fertile cover of loess (*limon*) makes this the best agricultural region of Belgium. The relief is rolling, and in the west there are small hills, relics of former escarpments. Some of these became famous during World War I as strategic points on the Flanders battlefield for the defense or capture of which thousands of men were killed, as at Kemmelberg near Ypres. Fields of wheat, barley, oats, and sugar beets, as well as orchards and vegetable gardens, surround the many villages. The population is very dense, and there are many towns that serve as centers of trade and culture—for example, the university city of Leuven (French: Louvain). But all roads on this upland lead to Belgium's great capital, Brussels (French: Bruxelles; Flemish: Brussel). Because of circumstances that were largely political, this chief city of the Province of Brabant chanced to become the seat of government during a period of foreign domination, and gradually overshadowed the Flemish cities. Having become the capital of Belgium in 1830, it continues to be the most important city, the very heart of Belgium. Essentially French in culture in spite of its location north of the language boundary (A373), it resembles Paris in many respects. Its delightful *Grand Place,* surrounded by tall, narrow medieval buildings and dominated by the spire of the Town Hall, is one of the most charming squares in Europe. Industrial development has followed on political importance, but there is little specialization. The Willebroeck Canal connects Brussels with the Scheldt, and small seagoing vessels can reach the city.

In the southern part of the upland along the Sambre-Meuse rivers, which follow the soft coal layers at the foot of the Ardennes, a great manufacturing development entirely overshadows agriculture, and from the French border eastward to Liége the landscape is dominated by factories (A377). The underlying coal has been the basic factor in this industrial development. The coal syncline crosses the country from France to Germany, forming the Sambre-Meuse depression. Exploitation is not always easy, for the coal seams are thin, the geological structure is in some places very complicated, the quality of the coal is not the best, and long, intensive exploitation has exhausted much of the better coal. Superior resources are found in the Campine, but at greater depth. For the iron industry, foreign coal of suitable quality has to be imported in large quantities, a disadvantage that is partly offset by the export of coal from Belgian mines.

The mining of iron ore, which was once important, is now insignificant in comparison with the large import of that commodity from French Lorraine. The southeastern corner of Belgium has a

A. Coalfield landscape: typical of the Belgium-Netherlands mining district. Courtesy of KLM.

very small share of the great Lorraine iron ore deposits (A429), but the neighboring mines of southern Luxembourg are of much greater importance. Their value is enhanced by the nearness of the German coal fields in the Aachen basin. Zinc, also, was formerly exploited in Belgium near the German border, but it is now imported as ore from foreign countries and smelted with coal from the Campine field.

The Sambre-Meuse industrial zone can be subdivided into three sections. The western section, the Borinage, around Mons is essentially a coal-mining region (A377). The next district, that of Charleroi, has developed—in connection with its coal output—metalworks, machine factories, chemical industries, and the manufacture of glass that is a Belgian specialty. In both sections, industries are more scattered and are carried on in smaller towns than in England. Even

Mons and Charleroi are comparatively small. This industrial development continues along the Meuse River to the third section, with the old town of Namur at the confluence of the Sambre and the Meuse as one of the centers. Only farther northeast, down the Meuse and around Liége, does it again take on great significance. During the nineteenth century, the ancient city of Liége became the center of a great industrial region, with the usual ironworks and machine factories as well as zinc smelters and glass plants, notably those

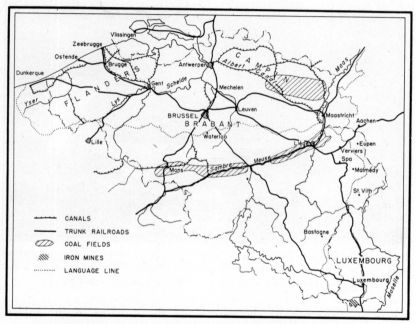

A. Rail Lines, Canals, and Minerals of Belgium and Luxembourg.

producing fine crystal. Long a fortress city, Liége was a key defense point in the line against Nazi attack in 1940, but the great fort turned out to be ineffective against the German onslaught.

Ardennes. The remaining three regions in A373 may be grouped together as the Ardennes and its foreland. This low mountain region, or old plateau, belongs to the ancient Hercynian system. After being eroded to a peneplain in the course of tens of millions of years, it was uplifted during the Alpine period. Its highest elevations, about 2,200 feet, are found in the east, and the plateau slopes down toward the northwest with a somewhat abrupt drop of 300 to 700 feet between the real Ardennes and the Ardennes foreland or Condroz region. The northward continuation of the Ardennes block lies buried under the young deposits and loamy soil of the central Belgian uplands. The rivers generally follow the inclination of the old peneplain, as does the Meuse River, which follows a narrow gorge northward until it reaches the soft coal layers outside the plateau,

A. The Ardennes in Belgium. Level upland surface dissected by the entrenched meanders of a small river. Sparse population. Forestry (notice clearings) is the main economic activity. Courtesy of Official Belgian Tourist Bureau.

where it turns toward the east along the outcrop of the folded soft rocks.

The Ardennes presents a strong contrast to the loamy upland in many respects. The Condroz foreland is, indeed, fairly productive, especially where it consists of limestone. In the limestone belts it supports rye, oats, and potatoes as the main crops, as well as numerous livestock, mostly dairy herds. But parts of it are covered with forest, and there the density of population is far less than that on the loamy upland. The high parts of the Ardennes, with their oak forests and moorlands, where sheep raising was formerly the chief rural industry, is still Belgium's least-developed region. Even here there has been an appreciable change. Forests still cover great areas (about a quarter of the region), but the number of sheep has declined and on every hand are meadows and fields of rye, oats, potatoes, and forage crops; cattle raising, too, is gaining in importance. Income from tourists who come to enjoy the rugged scenery or to climb the vertical cliffs is a major source of earnings.

The climate of the Ardennes, including the part in Luxembourg, shows the influence of high elevation as well as of increased distance from the sea. The higher parts have cold, raw winters; the depressions have fairly warm and rather dry summers. Snowfall is heavy. Timed with a period of snow, fog, and slush, it was here that the Germans in December, 1944, made their last offensive—the famous Battle of the Bulge. Names like Bastogne and St. Vith, once forgotten villages, are now inscribed on American battle rolls. It was also through the Ardennes that the Germans invaded France in May, 1940. In both cases the attack was unexpected because of the traditional difficulty with the Ardennes terrain. The first time the attack succeeded, but the second time it failed.

The small southeastern section of Belgium, belonging to the limestone region of the Lorraine cuesta landscape, is mainly devoted to rye and oats, but it does not show the intensive cultivation of the western regions. The same landscape extends eastward into the southern half of Luxembourg and constitutes the duchy's *Gutland,* which has fertile soils where oats, rye, and potatoes are grown in abundance, and where even grapes can ripen. The triangular northern part of Luxembourg lies in the Ardennes and is devoted mostly to forest. It comprises the duchy's *Oesling.* The rivers, subtributaries and tributaries of the Moselle, have eroded deep, winding valleys that are quite attractive and bring in many tourists. Luxembourg City, the capital, is located on the rock spur of an incised meander and practically surrounded by the gorge of the Alzette, and was through history regarded as one of the strongest fortifications of Europe. Along the French boundary are the mines of iron ore and the numerous small but bustling iron- and steel-producing centers of Differdange, Esch-sur-Alzette, Dudelange, and others. The small section of Lorraine iron ore possessed by the Duchy of Luxembourg gives it 56 million metric tons (iron content) of reserves. Its per capita wealth in iron ore is many times as great as that of any other country, as is its per capita production of pig iron and steel. Its annual steel production (2.4 million tons) is about the same as that of the Saar.

Belgian Economy

Belgium, in spite of small size (11,783 square miles) and a population of 8.6 million, is quite important. Although agriculturally it does not produce enough for the domestic consumption—despite the fact that the crop yields are among the highest in the world—it is a manufacturing concentration of great importance. Its coal output of about 28 million tons is quite respectable; and its steel production, together with that of Luxembourg, exceeds 6 million tons annually, which puts it in Europe only after the Soviet Union, Britain, France, and Germany. In smelter zinc, once based on local mines but now entirely based on imports, Belgium produces one tenth of the world's production, surpassed only by the United States and Canada. Export figures show high values for such manufactured products as iron and steel, machinery, glassware, and textiles. For many years it was the only nation that exported more of its industrial production than it consumed at home. Excellent transportation facilities to its neighbors, by railroad as well as by canals, and the growth of Antwerp into the largest European port, completes this picture of industrial efficiency and progress.

Thus Belgium, small though it is, has a remarkable balance between an efficient, highly developed agriculture and an equally efficient, highly developed, and diversified industry. Such a well-rounded economy in a small area is a rare phenomenon indeed. Coupled with economic balance is Belgium's physical balance, with the fertile plains in the north contrasting with the rugged Ardennes toward the south. So it is that a little country, only slightly larger than the state of Maryland, is especially well endowed geographically and well operated by its dense population.

Belgium as a State

The area now occupied by Belgium has always been a zone of transition between the Latin and Germanic worlds. The plains of Flanders and the hills of Brabant have been the scene of many battles. In the late Middle Ages, the citizens of the Flemish cities fought here against the French nobility; later, here were battles between the Dutch and the French during the reign of Louis XIV. It was at Waterloo, south of Brussels, that Napoleon met defeat. Again, during both world wars, Belgium was involved when German armies swept across its plains—the easiest route for armies—on their

way to France. The dividing line between the Flemish (Dutch) and
the Walloon (French) languages runs west-east (A377), dividing the
country in half ethnographically, with Brussels as a Walloon exclave
north of the line. The divide is quite a sharp one, with little over-
lapping. In some spots along the eastern boundary, German is
spoken. The German-speaking group increased in number when,
after World War I, the districts of Eupen and Malmédy were taken
from Germany. The Luxembourgers speak a German dialect, but in
the south they are practically bilingual. The present Belgium was
born in 1830, when it broke away from the Netherlands. At the
Congress of Vienna, the two countries had been united but it was an
unhappy marriage, which did not work out and ended in a divorce.
More than a century passed before the two attempted to come together again, in the Benelux union—an economic combination this
time rather than a political one.

After 1830, Belgium had as its chief problem the dual character
of the state—Flemish and Walloon. Whereas during the Middle
Ages Flanders had been the core unit and the Flemish cities had
dominated, in the newborn state of 1830 the Walloons prevailed.
This was partly the result of the influence of France, but it was also
due to the fact that the major industrial development took place
in southern Belgium. Although the state was theoretically bilingual,
the French culture nevertheless prevailed—and that in spite of the
fact that there were more Flemings than Walloons. Gradually there
developed a strong movement for Flemish recognition that increased
in strength and ended only when the equality between the two became reality. However, it was exactly 100 years before the Flemings
had their own university. Rivalry between the two parts at times
still leads to political weakness. During World War I, when the
Germans occupied almost all of Belgium, they sponsored a Flemish
movement of autonomy, which of course tumbled after the German
defeat but left some hard feelings. After World War II, when the
king was accused of German sympathies because of his surrender to
the Germans in 1940, the vote on his future status showed that the
ethnographic line became also a political line, with a majority of
the Flemish in favor of the king and most of the Walloons against
him. Religion does not enter into the picture; both groups are
solidly Catholic. If given time, Belgium will increase in unity
through the merging of ethnographic interests. However, such a
merger takes a long time, as is shown by the fact that even in Switzerland it is not yet perfect. Neither the Netherlands nor France shows

any desire to absorb the adjacent part of Belgium to which each is related.   As a zone of transition, Belgium seems to be a necessity, but it is difficult for its two peoples to forget their differences and accept their mutual role.   Perhaps it is even more remarkable that the country should do so well, despite the ethnographic cleavage that disrupts so many aspects of Belgian life.

·26·
France

The Maturity of France

To those who know the country, the expression "France" carries with it a very definite connotation of an intimate relationship between a land, a people, and a culture. Such a unity developed over a period of many centuries, and once the bond was achieved it demonstrated a remarkable stability. The vicissitudes of French development and the success the people have had in meeting persistent difficulties have given the French an unusual perspective, experience, and maturity. Despite the adversities of defeat in the Franco-German War of 1870–71, of destruction and manpower loss in both world wars, and of economic trials after those wars, France still stands as a cultural center and as a land and people always to be considered in world affairs. It is reborn after every apparent eclipse, and its influence remains great. True, the rapid changes in government are often perplexing, even to the French themselves, and they create administrative difficulties; however, even these changes reflect the individuality of the Frenchman and his determination to obtain precise results.

The maturity of France is demonstrated in a number of other respects. Territorially, it has altered little since 1500, with Alsace-Lorraine being the area of major change, although minor shifts have also occurred along the Belgian and Italian boundaries. Such territorial stability is partly traceable to the nature of the physical confines of sea and mountains that circumscribe France, and it will be noted that the main changes have taken place in the very areas where the physical frame is least pronounced. Maturity is evident in the French landscape itself because of the way in which man has so thoroughly utilized, adapted, and remade the natural features of the land through centuries of unbroken occupance. The especially strong French desire for security, which is an underlying motive for much of the political activity of the country, is another sign of maturity. Further evidence is the contentment the Frenchman finds in staying at home and continuing the comfortable round of daily duties which have become habitual. The early decline of the birth rate was apparently another sign of maturity, and the upward trend after World War II came somewhat as a surprise. Finally, there are the higher qualities of such a stage of development: France surpasses most countries in love of art and beauty; in clear, logical thinking and writing; and in practical, precise, and common-sense reasoning.

Geographical Assets

Location. Even observing the scientific caution that must be exercised in evaluating the significance of environment in a country's evolution, there is no doubt that the geographic location of France has been and is a primary asset. Occupying the extreme western part of Europe and lying on a wide isthmus, France fortunately faces the Atlantic, the English Channel, and the Mediterranean Sea. Its intimate contact with the continent, its facing on three seas, and its southern frontier along the Pyrenees barrier combine to give France rather than Spain and Portugal the function of Europe's western façade. By way of the Flanders plain in the north, the Lorraine Gateway and Burgundy Gate in the center, and Alpine passes in the south, eastern France communicates with the rest of Europe. Across the English Channel and North Sea, France communicates with Britain and Scandinavia; across the Atlantic, with the New World; and through the Mediterranean, with North Africa and the Middle and Far East. Closely related to France, the French lands of North Africa (with Algeria actually forming three *départements* of France) serve as steppingstones to other French territories in the Sudan and Equatorial Africa. The Atlantic Ocean invited France to exploitation of the New World in the sixteenth and seventeenth centuries, and, although most of the former possessions are now lost, commercial and cultural contacts remain.

Climate. Resulting partly from its location, a second geographical factor favoring France is its climate, which is almost a perfect blending of three different types: the western European, the Mediterranean, and the central European. Cyclonic control is dominant but is less vigorous than in countries farther north. Hence, the French climate is on the whole less stimulating than the climates of its northern neighbors, but it is generally more sunny and pleasant. Nearly everywhere it is conducive to a rather intensive and varied agriculture.

Relief. Landforms are another asset of France, since only locally and principally on the fringes is the country extremely rugged. Uplands and plateaus, mountain ranges, and wide, rolling plains conduce to diversity of agricultural production—especially in conjunction with the varied climates—to the great profit of the country as a whole. There are no mountain barriers to hinder deep penetration of marine influences from the west, as there are, for example, on the west coast of the United States. Moreover, the landforms are so arranged in relation to each other that, in spite of the existence of several uplands, there is easy access through gaps from lowland to lowland, permitting the construction of roads, canals, and railways to give unity to the country. French enterprise has taken advantage of such opportunity, and communications in France are excellent. Landforms are discussed in detail by regions in the next chapter.

Soils. The main characteristic of French soils is their great diversity, with a predominance of fertile types that are easily cultivated. Complexity of parent material, slope, and climate has produced many varieties of soil even in small areas; however, the great advantage is that so few soils are unproductive. Large areas, such as the *limon*-covered regions of northern France, include some of Europe's most fertile lands. It is to a favorable combination of climate, relief, and soil that the significance of agriculture in the French economy may be largely attributed.

Minerals. As will be seen later in this chapter, France is well provided with certain minerals, particularly iron; but, for a great industrial power, it is deficient in others, especially coal. Hydroelectric power is intensively developed to compensate partly for lack of coal for power, although coking coal is still in short supply.

French People. Last but not least of the assets of France are the people, who are not merely occupants of a space on the earth's surface but constitute a very great asset for the country and, indeed, for the world. Despite their frequent political disunity, the French are an energetic group with a strong sense of ethnographic unity who have for centuries withstood the shocks of national existence.

Climate

Mentioned as a chief geographical asset in the preceding section, the climate of France merits rather careful consideration. The maps of temperature (A-B386) and of precipitation (A36) show the average values of these two key climatic factors. Brittany and Normandy, in the northwest, have the typical western European type of climate

—frequently referred to as the marine west coast type—with mild winters, averaging 45° F (7° C) at Brest in January, and cool summers, averaging 61° F (16° C) at Brest in July. Northwestern France has about 30 inches of rain, which falls chiefly in autumn and winter. Typical also are strong and constant winds, a high degree of cloudiness, and numerous rainy days. Two of the three chief occupations of this region are largely influenced by climate: the dairy industry, based on the plentiful precipitation and cool temperatures, and the

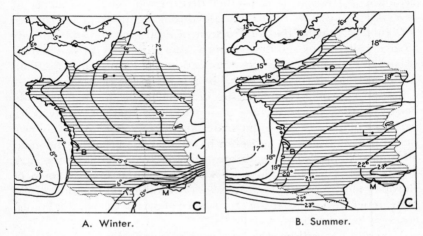

A. Winter.   B. Summer.

Isotherms in France (in degrees Centigrade).

cultivation of early vegetables (*primeurs*), based on the mildness of the winter and early spring.

A second type of climate is found in Alsace-Lorraine on the eastern border of France. It is more continental: the winters are much colder (Strasbourg: 32° F in January), the summers are warmer (Strasbourg: 66° in July), and the precipitation of about 27 inches shows a decided summer maximum.

A third climate type is that of the Mediterranean provinces as well as parts of the Garonne Basin and the coast of the Bay of Biscay. Winter temperatures are similar to those of northwestern France, but sunshine is much more prevalent in spite of rather heavy winter precipitation; summers are warm (Nice: 72° F in July) and relatively dry. Nevertheless, the fairly abundant rain in autumn and spring and the small amount of summer rain permit continuous use of the land in most sections without necessity of irrigation. Growth of grapes and olives, and even citrus fruits in protected spots, is one response to the climate; and, where summer rainfall is sufficient, corn is grown along with wheat and grapes. The French Riviera, protected on the north by the Alps, owes much of its reputation to its warm, sunny climate, although the beautiful coastal scenery is an additional asset.

Amid these three contrasting types of climate lies the most typical climate of France, a blending of all three, which Paris represents perfectly. Average temperatures of 36° F in winter and 65° in summer reflect both marine and continental conditions. Rainfall of approximately 24 inches, well distributed through the year, and an annual duration of sunshine of about 1,750 hours, in contrast with 1,500 hours in the Netherlands, make the Paris Basin almost ideal for agriculture and help to explain the dominant position of the farmer in the life of the French nation.

Minerals

Although France ranks near the top among the countries of the world in iron reserves and production, and although it contains some of the world's largest bauxite (aluminum ore) deposits, it is seriously deficient in a wide variety of other minerals that would place it on a par with the great industrial powers, such as the United States and the Soviet Union. France cannot even make up completely for her domestic deficiencies by importing ores from overseas, as does Britain, for example, since it lacks the great merchant marine of Britain; and its overseas territories—although very extensive and fairly well endowed with some minerals—are not so rich in raw materials as is the Commonwealth. Therefore, the mineral production and industries of France tend to be rather specialized and to take particular advantage of French creativeness, taste, and craftsmanship in their development. As a result, France has long been a power always to be considered both in peace and in war periods and yet has found itself at a disadvantage in many respects, especially in terms of mass production in time of war.

Sources of Energy. Coal supply is one of the most pressing problems that France faces. Although the resources are rather great, they are far less than those of Great Britain and Germany and are even matched by those of the little Saarland. Furthermore, they exist in such scattered localities and in such thin, broken, and tilted seams that extraction is difficult and expensive. The annual production of approximately 50 million tons is far less than half the

normal output of the German Rhine-Westphalian field, less than
one-fourth that of the United Kingdom, and about three-fourths that
of Poland. With such relatively limited production and great de-

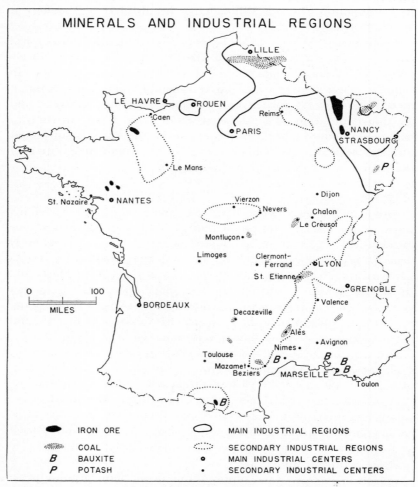

A. Principal Minerals and Industrial Regions of France.

mand, France is required to import nearly half as much again as it
produces. Part of the imported coal is coking coal for smelting iron,
since only a limited amount of the French coal is suitable for coke.
As a result, France is and has long been dependent upon the Ruhr

for its metallurgical coal and coke—a distressing fact to the French. As was discussed in Chapter 10, efforts are being made to ameliorate this dependency.

Among French coal fields the most productive by far is the field of the Nord and the Pas de Calais, which produces more than half the French output. The Lorraine basin along the Saar frontier produces approximately 15 per cent and is considered to be a large potential reserve from which future production may soon approach that of northern France. The relatively small and scattered Central Plateau basins, especially those of St. Étienne and Le Creusot, produce approximately one fourth of the French coal. Strangely enough, France, like several other countries, exports coal as well as importing it, since it is more economical to exchange products with border regions than to ship them far across country. The economic attachment of the Saarland to France in 1948 and the lease of Saar mines by the French in 1950 gave France access to a greater amount of coal from that region, but the amount added to the French total was relatively small.

In a concerted effort to overcome the shortage of coal for production of power, France has developed a large percentage of her potential water power. So important is hydroelectricity in France that it is frequently referred to as *houille blanche*—"white coal"—indicating its substitution for black coal. Approximately half the power generated in France is produced hydroelectrically and nearly all the remainder by steam from coal. Disregarding the unknown capacity of the Soviet Union, only Italy among European countries surpasses France in production of hydroelectricity, and only Norway and Italy exceed France in hydroelectric potential. One of the great difficulties with water power in France is the irregularity of stream flow resulting from freezing and low water seasons, which requires stand-by thermal power stations. Nowhere in France are there the dozens of large natural lakes typical of Norway and Sweden, and dams must be built to form reservoirs, thus adding extra expense to hydroelectric production. Nevertheless, coal shortage is driving France to install as many water power stations as possible, and her installed capacity is rising rapidly. The main regions for production of water power are, as might be expected, the Alps in the southeast (where one half of France's water power is generated), the Pyrenees in the southwest, the Vosges in the east, and the Central Plateau in the south-center. Availability of electric power in these regions is drawing industries to them.

Petroleum and natural gas are virtually negligible as sources of power in France, although there is a very small annual production of petroleum at Pechelbronn in northern Alsace, and natural gas is produced from fields discovered during World War II in the southern Aquitaine Basin.

Iron. The "minette" deposits of Lorraine, west of the Moselle River, are the chief mineral wealth of France and comprise one of the world's largest and most important deposits of iron ore. The ore is not rich, containing only about 32 per cent iron; and it is high in phosphorus, which accounts for the fact that it was not exploited on any considerable scale until development in 1878 of the Thomas-Gilchrist process for smelting high-phosphorus ore. However, the proved reserves are enormous—about 2,500 million metric tons (metallic content), exploitation is relatively easy in most of the basin, and the minette ores are conveniently located in the center of western Europe. Transportation is, however, relatively expensive, since lack of satisfactory waterways requires that much of the ore move out (to the Ruhr, for example) by rail and that much of the coking coal or coke be brought in by rail. Deficiency of iron ore in the rest of western Europe and of sufficient coking coal in France permits France to export great quantities of minette ore. Lorraine furnishes 90 per cent of French iron ore requirements, with most of the remainder coming from the Normandy ores south of Caen. The Normandy ores are richer in iron content and lower in phosphorus than the minette ores, but they are more difficult to mine, more eccentrically located with respect to coal and consuming centers, and are far less in total reserves than the minette ores. Iron ore is exploited occasionally north of Nantes in southeastern Brittany, and in the Pyrenees, north of Andorra; the Pyrenees ores may soon see greater use as expanded hydroelectric development in the region permits increased electric smelting.

Bauxite. The great bauxite deposits in the limestones of southern France permitted France to be the chief aluminum ore producer of the world prior to World War II. Production in 1949 exceeded that of the best prewar year, but the country's rank has dropped from first to fourth or fifth. Formerly, half the ore was exported to Germany and England, but the trend indicated by the fact that French aluminum production more than doubled from 1938 to 1948 suggests that France may soon absorb its entire bauxite output. Such a trend is largely traceable to the expansion of the hydroelectric capacity of southern France, since processing of bauxite to make aluminum requires enormous amounts of electric power.

Potash and Rock Salt. The potash deposits of southern Alsace were well-known but little exploited before 1919, since they were owned by Germany, which had plenty of potash in the great beds of the Stassfurt region. After World War I, return of Alsace to France permitted French exploitation of the potash, and production now exceeds 650,000 tons annually, making France the world's third-largest producer. The potash is used as fertilizer in all French agricultural regions and is exported to Italy, England, and the United States; in addition, it has given rise to large chemical industries in Alsace and Lorraine.

Rock salt, also important in the French chemical industry, is produced in the potash mines of Alsace, the salt mines of Lorraine (where it has been for centuries an important item of commerce), and the Jura salt mines. Large quantities of salt are also obtained by evaporation of water in basins along the Mediterranean coast.

French Industries

Metallurgy. The regional relationships of French manufacturing will be brought out in the next chapter, but it is pertinent here to examine briefly the nature of French industries from a topical viewpoint. The industry employing the greatest number of workers is metallurgy, which includes basic iron and steel production and all aspects of metalworking and machine manufacture—indeed a wide range of production. In iron and steel production, France stands fifth in the world, behind the United States, Soviet Union, United Kingdom, and (normally) Germany, with approximately 9 million tons of pig iron production annually and 10 million tons of crude steel. Thus, by 1950 France had regained the production it had in 1930, whereas Germany produced only half as much steel in 1950 as in 1939, albeit in a smaller area. In view of the great wartime destruction in the iron and steel industry and the difficulties attending reconstruction after World War II, France made a remarkable recovery. Manufactured metal products include automobiles (of which France is the world's fifth-largest producer), bicycles and motor-cycles, aircraft, railway locomotives and cars, electrical equipment, ships, and agricultural machinery. Great amounts of technical machinery are not characteristic of French industry as they are of that of Germany. Even in agricultural machinery, France is in sharp need of expansion, especially if the country is to achieve the mechanization of agriculture that it was attempting in the years after World War II. Like most French products, the metal goods often reflect good taste, artistic design, and colorfulness rather than extreme ruggedness. Metallurgy is found in many parts of France, but the great concentrations are in only a few main areas: the northeast, around the great minette iron ore deposits; the north, along the northern France coal deposits; the central-southeast, around the coal of the eastern Central Plateau and the water power plants of the northern Alps; around Paris; and in such scattered centers as Marseille, the lower Seine, and the lower Loire.

Textiles and Clothing. Manufacture of textiles and clothing, taken together, employs more workers than processing and manufacture of metals, a fact that is revealing of the nature of French industry. Again, the excellence of French taste and genius for imaginative creativeness is of prime significance. Also, textile-making had an early start in France under the stimulus of Flemish production of wool and linen based on local sheep and flax. All types of textiles are produced, including woolens, linen, cotton fabrics, silk, hemp fabrics, and rayon; and in amount of production France is a world leader, ranking after the United States and Great Britain, but comparing well with Germany and Japan. In general, nearly all raw materials must be imported, but the level of productivity is maintained by the skill and experience of the manpower, quality of the textile machinery, commercial advantages that France enjoys, and the skillful use made of the fabrics in the clothing industry. There are three main centers of textile production: northern France, particularly in the Lille district, where wool and linen are dominant; Alsace, where cotton is the leading fabric; and the Lyon district, where there is a great silk and rayon center. Cotton and wool are also produced in the lower Seine district. Clothing is made in all the textile areas, but, in addition, special mention should be made of the fashion salons of Paris, whence feminine styles for much of the western world were long dictated and are still greatly influenced.

Other Industries. Chemical plants are numerous in France, producing synthetic fibers, plastics, photographic chemicals, pharmaceuticals, insecticides, perfumes, fertilizers, and a wide range of other items. Centers are found near sources of raw materials, skilled labor, or power: northern France, where coke-oven by-products are important; northeastern France, where by-products, salt, and potash are raw materials; Lyon and vicinity, where power permits electrochemical production; and such scattered centers as Marseille, Toulouse,

Bordeaux, and the great Paris complex. Other significant French industries are those of leather-working and shoemaking, paper-making and printing, woodworking, and food preparation. Despite the great amount of destruction suffered from 1940 to 1944 by the main industrial areas, all branches of industry made remarkable recoveries after World War II, with appreciable credit due to economic aid France received in Economic Co-operation Administration (ECA) funds.

French People

In spite of certain marked diversities, the French people constitute one of the world's most homogeneous "nations," brought together by ties of a rich and dynamic language, common historical experience, and territorial integrity. The French have emerged from the biological synthesis of several different peoples—Iberians, Ligurians, Gauls, Romans, and several Germanic peoples, with Gauls and such Germanic groups as the Franks furnishing the dominant elements in the French mixture. Roman influence on French language and culture is incalculable, but the biological contribution of Romans to the general French synthesis was limited because of the relatively small number of Romans who were absorbed by the resident population. Around the periphery of France are fragmentary linguistic groups that in some cases include peoples who have not been absorbed into the general French "biological type": Basques, Bretons, Flemings, Germans, Italians, and Catalans. Alsace, with its German Alsatian dialect, is accorded special treatment by the French. Modern communications have further tended to unify the groups living within the boundaries of France, although regions of different languages and dialects, costumes, and traditions still remain. Nevertheless, nearly all these groups feel themselves intensely French, and these elements of diversity are of minor importance compared with the remarkable ethnographic unity that characterizes France as a whole.

Density of Population. The French population of 42 millions on an area of 213,010 square miles has a density of 197 persons per square mile—much lower than that of Germany, United Kingdom, and Italy, and far below the density of Belgium and the Netherlands. Considering the quality of French land, the country is, therefore, underpopulated in relation to comparable areas of the rest of Europe. Naturally, the figure varies greatly in different sections of France: the manufacturing region of the north and the Paris region

have densities exceeding 500 per square mile, and areas with more
than 250 per square mile are found in eastern Alsace, the Lorraine
industrial district, the Channel coast, the Lyon and Rhône Valley
areas, much of the Mediterranean coast, lower Garonne valley,
lower Loire Valley, and coastal Brittany. Lowest densities are in
the mountains, parts of the Central Plateau, and the poor soil areas
of Champagne and the western Aquitaine Basin.

Agriculture

Map A395 shows the general land use of France, and, although details of agriculture will be discussed in the regional treatment in the
following chapter, it is appropriate to examine the general significance of farming in the French economy. More than a third of the
20.5 million employed Frenchmen are farmers—nearly twice as many
as are industrial workers—and the farmer is the backbone of the
nation.

The farmer generally owns the small property on which he and
his family raise crops and livestock. He is often most happy when
he can use a garden type of cultivation, producing vegetables, grapes,
and tree fruits. His life is simple, as shown in the remarkable post-
World War II documentary film *Farrebique,* and changes have come
only very slowly to his way of life. His house is often centuries old
and represents one of the most stable elements in the French landscape, which the French farmer has done so much to mold. In most
cases his aim is simply to see his family well cared for at the traditional level, to have his eldest son follow in his footsteps, and to provide his daughter with a suitable *dot* or marriage portion. Although
simple in dress and mode of life, the ordinary French farmer is not
uncomfortably poor, and he often has money carefully invested, perhaps in government bonds.

Diversity of products in the highly varied environments of the
country is the outstanding characteristic of French agriculture.
Skill and creative ability have great importance in the justly famed
French cooking, but the infinite variety of fine foodstuffs available to
the French cook from the farms of France is also a key factor. Conditions for wheat raising are excellent, and, although average yields
are not so high as in Belgium and Holland, production is sufficiently
great to make France the leading wheat producer in Europe outside the Soviet Union. As a result, French bread is made from
wheat flour, whereas that of many European countries is made from
rye or mixed rye and wheat. Oats are also produced in great quan-

tity in the more humid sections, and French production comprises more than one fifth of Europe's total outside the Soviet Union.

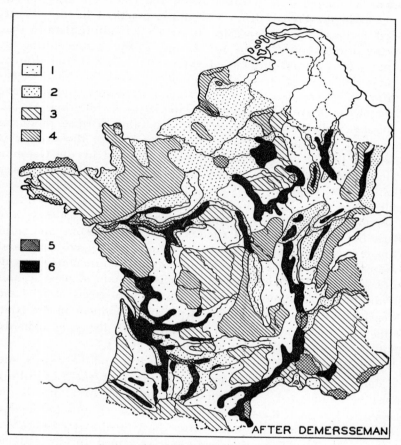

A. Agricultural Use of the Land in France.

Dominant Crop or Agricultural Activity

1	Rye	4	Intensive grazing (dairying)
2	Wheat	5	Horticulture (truck gardening)
3	Extensive grazing	6	Vineyards

Barley and rye are found on the poorer soils or in sections where cool temperatures prevail. Corn is grown for feed in the Aquitaine Basin and in the Rhine Plain. Sugar beet production supplies all of France's requirements for sugar and amounts to one fifth of all

European production outside Russia; sugar beets find a good position in rotation with wheat in northern France. Potatoes are also important in the country's agriculture and constitute a significant element in the French diet. Viticulture, practiced in several scattered sections, is more important in French agriculture than in that of any other country in the world; and, except in the northwest, wine is an essential element of every French lunch and dinner. Vineyard tending is one of the most highly specialized of the agricultural arts and has reached perfection in France and adjacent parts of Germany and Switzerland. Special local conditions of soil, exposure, and climate give especially high value to wines produced in specific small areas. The leading grape area of the country is southern France and the Rhône Valley, followed by the Garonne valley, especially around Bordeaux. Also significant are the lower Loire Valley, slopes in the Champagne region, the Moselle Valley, and Alsace.

Because of availability of large metropolitan markets—not only Paris but also London and Channel cities in England—and mild climate in southern and northwestern France, market gardening and raising of early spring vegetables are significant in French agriculture. A varied selection of vegetables is available in most seasons in the numerous stands and stores in the side streets of all large French cities. Orchards of many types are prominent in the landscape of some sections, such as Normandy with its apple orchards, and the Mediterranean coast with its olive groves.

The importance of livestock, both beef cattle and dairy cows, and of dairy products—milk, butter, and cheese—in French agriculture must be emphasized. The number of livestock in France is the largest in Europe if Russia is excluded, and French milk production is the third largest in the world (after the United States and Soviet Union). French cheeses of many types have gained world-wide fame and constitute an important export item. Furthermore, livestock on the farm is useful as a source of organic fertilizer, so important in the intensive agriculture characteristic of the regions in Europe A. Both beef and dairy cattle are found everywhere in France except along the Mediterranean coast, but they are especially numerous in the northwestern uplands and Central Plateau. Fodder crops are, therefore, significant in the agricultural pattern, as are grassland pastures in the uplands and mountains.

Transportation

Railways. The French railways radiate from Paris like spokes of a wheel, indicating the importance of the capital in the economy of the country. Like that of Western Germany, England, and the Benelux countries, the rail net of France is one of the densest in the world, and no point in France is more than 25 miles from a rail line. The lowest rail density is in the Central Plateau and the Alps, whereas the northern half of France has such a dense net that few points are more than 10 miles from a railway. International lines extend to all land frontiers of the country and connect with steamers at Channel ports. Connections with Germany are made via Metz, Strasbourg, and Mulhouse, and lines extend across the Swiss border to Basel, Neuchâtel, Lausanne, and Geneva. A direct line through the Mont Cenis tunnel connects France and Italy, as does also the coastal line along the Riviera. Railways to Spain skirt both ends of the Pyrenees, a main line from Toulouse to Barcelona crosses the mountains near Andorra, and a smaller line crosses the western Pyrenees. The several private rail systems were unified in 1938 into one state-operated system, the SNCF (*Société Nationale des Chemins de Fer*), and vigorous efforts have been made by the government agency to improve the railway system and make it more useful for freight conveyance and for tourist convenience. In spite of severe and widespread damage and destruction to tracks, bridges, marshaling yards, rolling stock, and control installations during World War II, when most of the damage was inflicted by Allied planes to upset German troop and freight movements in France, the French railways made a rapid comeback after 1945. By 1950 virtually all repairs were complete, control stations in the great junctions were equipped with the most modern devices, and French trains were once again transporting passengers and goods—in amounts, moreover, appreciably greater than those before the war. Such recovery is, of course, partly attributable to the vital economic assistance given by the United States, but it also reflects the French resiliency and determination to maintain the position of France as a leading world nation.

Highways. Roads were first developed on a systematic basis in France by the Romans, and many present-day routes follow those first laid out by them. After centuries of gradual extension, the road net was established by Napoleon on a scale unknown elsewhere in Europe, largely for military purposes. French highways are still, on the whole, some of the best in Europe; and great national routes, like railways, radiate in all directions from Paris and are interconnected by secondary ones. Motorcar traffic is considerable, and France, after Great Britain, has the greatest number of automobiles in Europe.

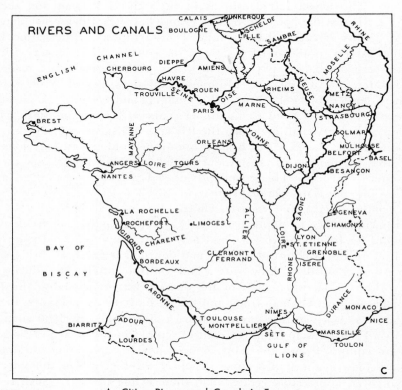

A. Cities, Rivers, and Canals in France.

Rivers and Canals (A398). The significance of waterway transportation in France is best understood if it is remembered that this is an old country in which transport was on a large scale prior to the coming of the railway and that the relief of the country permits development of an intricate canal system. As is the case with railways and roads, the gaps between upland areas in France are a very great asset for canal installations. However, different rainfall regimes and rock formations in the various parts of France create varying conditions for navigation, especially on natural waterways. Navigation is impossible in the more rugged regions, such as the Alps and the Central Plateau, and is difficult in regions of irregular river flow, such as southern France and western France. Rivers of the Paris Basin—Seine, Oise, Marne, and Yonne, for example—the Rhine, and the Saône, are the best rivers for navigation. The Loire and the Garonne have unreliable flow, frequently flooding in spring and turning into sand and gravel channels in late summer. The Rhône usually has a plentiful supply of water, more than any other river debouching into the Mediterranean; but the gradient is steep, and the stream is sometimes capricious because of the differing characteristics of streams that join it. Extensive and costly dams and locks will be necessary before the Rhône is tamed for reliable navigation.

A systematic network of canals was begun in the seventeenth century, gradually improved, and then greatly extended and made fairly uniform during the nineteenth century. By far the most important canals are those of the north and east, carrying the heavy products of coal, iron ore, limestone, chemicals, and construction materials between the northern industrial region and the Lorraine industrial region and connecting the navigable rivers of the area. The St. Quentin Canal, connecting the Oise and Scheldt, is one of the most important artificial waterways in the north, but there are many short canals connecting navigable rivers in the region: the Oise and Sambre, Oise and Aisne, Aisne and Meuse (Ardennes Canal), and Aisne and Marne. One of the principal French canals is the Rhine-Marne, extending from Épernay on the Marne via Toul and Nancy and through the Saverne Gap to Strasbourg on the Rhine; it is a vital link in the northeastern industrial traffic, but is cursed with 178 locks and must even pass through several tunnels, the longest of which is 5,330 yards in length. The long Canal de l'Est utilizes the Meuse for its more important northern half (as far south as the Rhine-Marne Canal), and the upper Moselle and Saône for its southern half, crossing the divide between the two rivers in a canal between Epinal and Corre. The middle Saône also receives four other important canals: (1) the Rhine-Rhône Canal, extending from Strasbourg through the Belfort Gap to the Doubs River; (2) the Burgundy Canal, extending from the middle Yonne past Dijon to enter the Saône nearly opposite the Rhine-Rhône Canal; (3) the Marne-Saône Canal, running parallel with the upper Marne to enter the Saône upstream from the junction of the two canals already named; and (4) the more important Canal du Centre, extending from

Digoin on the upper Loire Lateral Canal to Chalon on the Saône, downstream from the Doubs mouth. In southern France, the importance of canals diminishes, and even though a small canal joins the great port of Marseille with the Rhône, at Arles, nearly all land traffic moves in and out of Marseille by railway. Wine, coal, timber, petroleum, and some bauxite move along the Canal du Midi, extending from Toulouse through the Naurouze-Carcassonne gap and then via Sète to the Rhône; and Toulouse is also connected with Bordeaux by way of the Garonne Lateral Canal. Long-discussed plans to construct a "Canal of the Two Seas" from Bordeaux to the Mediterranean to obviate the trip around the Iberian Peninsula for small ocean-going ships seem to be doomed to remain on paper. In the northwest, a canal connects Nantes and Brest, using the central depression of the Brittany highlands.

The 6,500 miles of navigable waterways in France, of which almost half are canals, carry about one fourth of the French freight and furnish a cheap method of moving nonperishable goods. Wartime destruction of much of the French inland waterway fleet required extensive canalboat construction after World War II, and France is modernizing locks and motive power for moving boats through locks.

Airlines. Postwar France made a strong bid for a leading position in air traffic through the national airline, *Air France,* which flies the latest airliners between Paris and many chief cities in America, Eurasia, and Africa. Air connections are especially important between Paris and parts of the French Union in Africa. Distances within the country itself are generally too short and railway service too convenient to encourage much domestic flying; but the function of Paris, with its great Orly Field, as one of the principal air terminals of the world seems assured.

Problems of France in Their Geographic Setting

As has been shown in this chapter, and as will be further brought out in the regional discussion in the next chapter, France is blessed with a number of valuable geographic assets, but it also faces certain geographic and human limitations. Its position in western Europe has always forced it into active participation in all the main currents of European life, including wars. France is favorably situated to receive virtually every possible stimulus from the many cultures existing in Europe—and to exercise a reciprocal influence in turn; but such a position has, on the other hand, caused a terrible drain on French resources and manpower in wartime, whether the will to fight originated in France, as during the Napoleonic era, or elsewhere, as in 1939. The former *gloire de la France* is a matter of inordinate pride to the Frenchman, but he should know that it is gone forever in the old sense. He desires above all, then, security from a repetition of the destruction and debilitation that France has suffered in the last century, especially at the hands of the Germans. One attempt at achieving this security was construction of the Maginot Line fortification behind which France relaxed in 1938. More active efforts were made after both world wars when France first attempted to shackle Germany in every way possible and then attempted to achieve some sort of mutual understanding. Such contradictory efforts indicate that France is not so determined to destroy Germany as it is to remove the threat of German aggression against a France lacking the ability to resist that it had before 1850.

On the other hand, there is no doubt that France would like to replace Germany as the workshop of mainland Europe. However, the facts brought forth in this chapter, when considered with those in the chapters on Germany, demonstrate that France lacks the combination of resources, specialized skill, and transportation to displace Germany as mainland Europe's technological leader. Although France has the capacity to produce a little of almost any type of goods, it cannot produce in quantity certain vital products, particularly technical machinery and electronic equipment. France is making an effort to overcome this deficiency—particularly in the realm of machine tools—but traditional specialization primarily in luxury items will be difficult to alter.

In spite of the intensive efforts France made after World War II to develop increased hydroelectric capacity, shortage of power—resulting primarily from a deficiency of coal—continues to be an obstacle in French industrial development. The Schuman Plan for pooling French and German heavy industry and coal mining was one suggestion made by the French in 1950 that might lead not only to amelioration of the French coal shortage and German iron ore deficiency, but also to a Franco-German friendship unknown before in modern times.

One problem that has plagued France for 150 years is the declining birth rate and imminent decrease in population. Whereas during the eighteenth and early nineteenth centuries France had the largest population of all the European countries, the period of the Industrial Revolution stimulated Great Britain and Germany to outstrip France in population, and even Italy came to surpass it. Such a population decline naturally has for a consequence a decrease in the potential number of soldiers—a fact of vital concern to France, but it also has another serious result: inability of France to furnish needed labor to farms and factories. Ignoring military considerations, a population decrease might be an encouraging sign in an overcrowded country such as Italy or Japan; but France, on the contrary, sorely needs additional workers. The result is that foreign labor must be imported to supplement French labor, and such rapid immigration is a serious threat to the national unity of France. Before World War II workers were imported especially from Italy, Belgium, Spain, and Poland, and thousands of Russian refugees found homes in France. After World War II laborers were imported especially from Italy, Spain, and Germany. France has been encouraged since 1945 by an appreciably higher birth rate than that of prewar years: the rate rose from 14 per thousand in 1940 to 21 per thousand in 1949. How sustained that increase will be is of critical importance to the nation.

Another problem that France faces and that may be considered in conjunction with the matter of declining population is that of increased mechanization of agriculture and modernization of industry. Economic assistance rendered by the United States after World War II offered some stimulus in this direction, particularly in industrial modernization in those areas where destruction of old factories was greatest. Mechanization of agriculture is made somewhat difficult by the small size of most French farms, since small holdings make large investment in machinery impossible for the average farmer. Co-operative action would help in farm mechanization, but the French farmer is a highly individualistic person who has shown himself reluctant to engage in co-operative activity in other phases of farming, although co-operatives market southern wines and Vendée butter. Also, despite the existence of a number of very large industrial enterprises in France, French manufacturing tends to work on a small scale—again largely because of French individualism—and introduction of American methods of production on an appreciably greater scale would be difficult.

The geographical and ideological position of France between "East" and "West" during the "Cold War" forced the nation into a very delicate political position. Because of its completely western culture, conviction of personal liberty, conservative elements in government, and especially its location in western Europe, France generally adhered to a position opposing that of the Soviet Union;

it continued to show its desire for security and yet evinced unusual vigor by becoming an active participant and even a leader in attempts at security for western Europe. Typical is its leadership in the Council of Europe and the North Atlantic Treaty Organization, both of whose headquarters were set up in France. The large communist party—800,000 in 1950, smaller by one third than in 1947—is in a way contradictory to French individualism; however, it is largely traceable to vigorous communist exploitation of the uncertainty and unrest prevalent during the period of postwar recovery, when both state and private industries were intent on re-establishment of basic operations rather than improvement of housing, working conditions, and wages. The great losses sustained by the country imposed sacrifices on the people as a whole, but labor suffered especially after 1945 from the high cost of living and the low wage scale for workers. At the end of 1951, equilibrium had not been achieved, and an unstable situation existed in the government, with right, left, and center elements almost equally balanced in the National Assembly. In general, however, France was strongly united with the west in opposition to Soviet communism, and its people, resources, and industries constitute a vital factor in world affairs.

· 27 ·
The Regions
of France

Regional Relationships

The land that is included in the political frontiers of France may be rather easily divided into a number of well-defined geographical regions. The physiographic basis for the division is shown in A405, and this map, as well as Chapters 4 and 5, should be referred to in a study of this chapter. In the discussion that follows, the many facets of the strong geographic personality of France will be shown through a consideration of the definite and diverse landscapes that together make up the country. This analytical approach should not obscure the fact that France is the classical example of a land in which the individual regions blend into a harmonious whole. Yet this blending does not erase the individuality of the parts, which retain their own characteristic personalities—physical and human, economic and historical. It is no wonder that the French school of geography has become known for its excellent and brilliantly written regional studies.

Before examining each region separately, it is instructive to look at the general arrangement of the regions so that the relationships between them can be seen in a broad perspective. Located in the functional heart of France, although well to the north of the geographical center of the country, is the Paris Basin (1 in A405). Surrounding this focal center is a discontinuous ring of old, hard rocks forming a series of four disconnected uplands or highlands: first, the Northwestern Uplands (2 in A405); second, the Central Plateau (3), which is not actually in the center of France but south of it, just as the Paris Basin is north of center; third, the Vosges (4), forming a small upland east of the Paris Basin; and fourth, the Ardennes (5) in the northeast, of which only a small section extends into France. The northern part of the ring of uplands appears to be missing, but in reality the Pennine Chain and the highlands of Cornwall and Devon in England are part of this same system, albeit separated from the French elements by the English Channel. All the

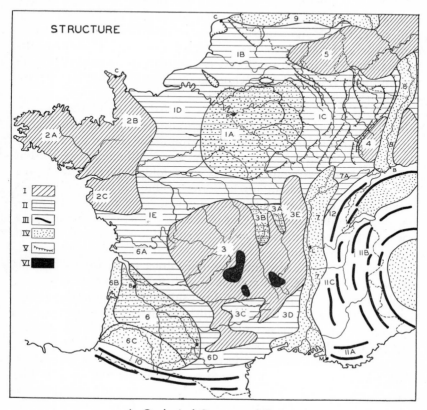

A. Geological Structure of France.

   I   Stable blocks of old geologic age
  II   Slightly tilted Mesozoic layers
 III   Alpine ranges
 IV   Nearly level young deposits in lowlands
  V   Escarpments (cuestas or *côtes*)
 VI   Recent volcanic formations
       Capital letters beside dots are the initials of main cities (see A398).

upland blocks in France, like their English counterparts, display clear evidence of an old peneplain—the Hercynian—which was warped and uplifted into the present uplands during the period of Alpine mountain building. In general, all four are also rather similar in their agricultural response to an upland climate with relatively heavy rain and poor, leached soil.

The four uplands are separated by broad lowland passages, through which the rock structure or plains relief of the Paris Basin projects outward and connects more or less closely with another concentric although incomplete ring of four lowlands: first, the Aquitaine Basin in the southwest (6); second, the Rhône Valley in the southeast (7); third, the Rhine graben or rift valley in the east (8); and the lowlands of Belgium (9).

Still farther out from the center is a partial ring of high mountains of the Alpine type: the Pyrenees (10) in the south and the French Alps (11) in the southeast. The Jura Mountains (12) in the east may also be included in this mountain rim, since, although they are not the Alpine type of mountains, they were folded during the Alpine period of Tertiary mountain building. Thus, in spite of various irregularities, the schematic arrangement of relief regions of France may be said to be essentially that of the Paris Basin surrounded by a ring of disconnected uplands, an outer ring of lowlands, and a partial ring of high mountains.

Accessibility of one lowland region of France to the others through passages between highland areas is of such significance in integrating France that the gaps justify brief discussion. Two gateways between the Paris Basin and the Rhine Plain have already been mentioned: the Saverne Gap at the northern end of the Vosges and the Belfort Gap or Burgundy Gate between the Vosges and the Jura. The Rhône-Saône Depression connects the Paris Basin and the Rhine Plain with the Mediterranean coast by way of the low Langres Plateau (as well as other passageways) and the Burgundy Gate, respectively. The Paris Basin gains access to the Aquitaine Basin through the Gate of Poitou, guarded by the town of Poitiers. In turn, the Aquitaine Basin connects with the Mediterranean coast through the depression that separates the Pyrenees from the Central Plateau and that is generally referred to as the Gap of Carcassonne, although it is sometimes called the Gap of Naurouze. The Loire Valley affords easy access between the Paris Basin and Brittany.

Paris Basin

In population, agriculture, industry, transportation, and mineral wealth the Paris Basin is the leading region of France and one of the most productive regions of Europe and the world. Its northward displacement from the mathematical center of France is more than compensated by its increased nearness to the center of great development around the Rhine mouth—the heart of Europe A. Because of the significance of the area and the excellent geographical study that it makes, it is presented in appreciable detail as a type region.

In general, the Paris Basin forms a very shallow bowl-shaped depression with its approximate center around Paris. Broadly speaking, it is a plain, but the surface is not to be thought of as flat except in local areas; there are hills, valleys, plateaus, and escarpments, with some locally steep slopes and some sharp relief of 500 to 600 feet. The general structure of the basin may be likened to a stack of saucers, each one smaller than the one below it. However, the present relief is traceable not only to the original formation of the layers of Mesozoic and Tertiary sedimentary rocks, but also to the fact that, after the entire region was uplifted, earth forces from the southeast during the time of Alpine mountain building pushed up the outer edges—especially in the east—more than the center. Subsequently, differential erosion lowered the areas of softer rocks and caused the harder layers to stand out in prominent relief as escarpments or plateaus. During the erosional process, the drainage pattern was somewhat altered, as headward erosion of some rivers caused stream capture and diverted such rivers as the Moselle and the Loire from their former courses (into the Seine drainage basin) to their present basins. Finally, it might be mentioned that the Paris Basin, unlike the North German Plain or the East Anglian Plain of England, was never glaciated.

The Paris Basin is the chief agricultural region of France. As in Belgium, much of the surface of the region—frequently underlain by limestones—is covered with rich loam called *limon*. Originally, the material comprising the *limon* was loess brought by dry winds during the glacial period when the northern ice sheet lay not far away, but most of it appears to have been reworked by water. The rolling hills and plateaus near Paris and to the north are almost entirely used for wheat, oats, and sugar beets, except for a local development of truck gardens along some of the valleys and around Paris (A395). Wheat is the most abundant crop, since relief, soil, and climate make this region well suited for that crop. Here are the best yields of France, and from here comes the greater part of the large French wheat production. The sugar beet area of France forms a wedge, wider at the north, extending from the Loire through Paris to the Channel coast and corresponding well to the choicest agricultural area of the country.

The heart of the Paris Basin is the Île-de-France, surrounding the location of Paris. It is essentially a subregion of plateaus of Upper Tertiary limestones, marls, and sandstones cut by valleys and separated from one another by the main rivers that focus on Paris. It terminates on the east in an escarpment, the Falaise de l'Île-de-France, at the foot of which lie Reims and Épernay. The markedly different geographical personalities that characterize the several plateaus and other parts of the Île-de-France are typical of the diverse landscapes that occur in even small areas in France.

Southeast of Paris between the Seine and Marne rivers is the Plateau of Brie, underlain by limey Tertiary deposits and mostly covered with thick *limon*, forming an excellent wheat region. The Beauce Plateau, extending southward from Paris to the Loire, is underlain with a hard limestone and presents a dry, flat, treeless surface; however, a thin covering of *limon* makes this barren region another great wheat country. Northwest of Beauce is the old cathedral town of Chartres, and at the foot of its eastern escarpment is Fontainebleau with its former royal palaces and magnificent parks. On the northernmost bend of the Loire is the historic city of Orléans, important as a market center for the agricultural region in which it lies and as a manufacturing center for agricultural equipment; it was in this city that Joan of Arc lead the French to victory over the English and earned the name "Maid of Orléans." Located south of the Loire bend is the Sologne, a formerly swampy area that was transformed in the mid-nineteenth century by drainage of lakes and swamps; however, it is still sparsely settled and largely wooded, permitting an appreciable amount of hunting. West of Sologne is Tours, the former capital of old Touraine Province, which, like Orléans, formerly had a greater importance when the Loire was a waterway of prime significance.

The dominating city not only of the Île-de-France and the Paris Basin but of all France is Paris, in which are centralized most national functions, a fact also true of Copenhagen and Vienna for their respective countries. The ideal location of Paris can be deduced from what has already been said of the regions in which it is centered. Orléans is perhaps more centrally located mathematically in France, but it lacks the focal position in the Paris Basin, the magnificent waterways of Paris, and the surrounding fertile soil. Through the centuries Paris has come to be not only the chief city of France but also one of the greatest cities of Europe and the world, if the term "greatest" is interpreted to apply not so much to the number of inhabitants as to cultural influence. In this respect, no other city is the equal of Paris, and, excepting perhaps New York, no other city attracts so many visitors, who come from all over the world to breathe the cultural atmosphere that is unique to Paris.

The attraction that Paris exerts on Europe and the rest of the world is almost mystical, and once Paris is seen it is never to be forgotten. Whatever drawbacks the city may have are overlooked in favor of the wide and tree-bordered boulevards with their sidewalk cafes, the crooked streets of the Montmartre and the Latin Quarter where little shops offer all sorts of products from paintings to bad-smelling cheese, the quiet border of the Seine River where open-air bookstalls invite the literary enthusiast, the public gardens and parks where children under the watchful eyes of uniformed nurses sail toy boats on the grass-bordered ponds, and similar charms. Nevertheless, the educational, social, and political attraction of Paris has been a tremendous drain on the rest of France. Today, as for many centuries, Paris is the focus of all ambitions, the magnet attracting the country's brains and energy. Metropolitan Paris, with a population of about 5 million, far outranks all other French cities in size and contains one fourth of the urban population of France.

The immediate site of the city was selected because of the existence of a small island—now called the Île de la Cité—in the Seine that facilitated crossing of the river and defense of the settlement. As it successively became a Roman fortress and cultural center, then the capital of French kings and emperors, and finally a great economic center, the city expanded from its tiny island to the higher ground on the left (south) bank, then to the marshy land on the right bank (an abandoned meander), and finally up the slopes of the limestone plateau into which the Seine valley is cut. Successively larger protective walls were found to enclose insufficient areas, and new walls were built to enclose the expanding city. The lines of demolished walls became the sites of the broad boulevards. The nineteenth century was a time of the systematic planning of Paris, the razing of hundreds of old buildings and construction of broad, straight streets that gradually came to be lined with massive blocks of solidly constructed buildings. The center is still the commercial heart, with great department stores and *ateliers* or dressmaking "studios" that mark it as the fountainhead of world fashion. The eastern part contains most of the industrial establishments that make Paris a first-rank center of diversified manufacturing. The western section and suburbs provide residential quarters, with wide avenues and extensive parks. With the decline of Berlin after World War II, Paris became without question the greatest metropolitan center on the continent of Europe. Several of the suburbs of Paris possess an interest and significance that are an integral part of those of Paris itself. Such is Versailles, with its magnificent Grand Palace, smaller palaces, parks, and fountains.

East of the Falaise de l'Île-de-France is the Champagne region. The western half of the region comprises the Champagne Pouilleuse (literally meaning lousy or wretched country), a flat, sterile, sparsely populated area underlain by a chalk yielding a soil that is stony and hard when dry and a sticky mass when wet. On the southeast-facing slopes of the Falaise de l'Île-de-France are the famous vineyards of Champagne, which are individually very small and are cultivated only under difficulty because of early frosts. However, as is often the case with fruit produced near the northern limit of growth, the quality of the Champagne grapes is high. The sparkling wine that has gained fame as champagne is produced by careful processing of the wine in immense caves hollowed out in the limestone of the escarpment; moreover, the amount of champagne is augmented by local processing of wine imported from other parts of France. Reims and Épernay are famous wine centers, with Reims the more important of the two and significant also for its woolen textiles. Reims Cathedral is one of the best-known of the French cathedrals because of both its charm and the damage that it suffered in World War I. Châlons-sur-Marne, located out on the plain, is also a wine center and transportation center.

East of the Champagne Pouilleuse a new rock layer comes to the surface from beneath the chalk, and the Champagne Humide is formed on the sands and clays. Population is again sparse, not because of dryness of the surface but because of lakes, swamps, and forests. The alluvial valleys, however, are more densely populated and give rise to such market centers as Troyes on the Seine.

The landscape eastward from the Champagne witnesses the best development of the alternating escarpment-and-plains topography formed by successive outcrops of hard and soft layers of rock as each emerges eastward from under the outcrop to the west of it. The outcropping hard ridges form cuestas and are called *côtes* by the French; the two most prominent and famous are the Côtes de Meuse, lying just east of the Meuse River, and the Côtes de Moselle, lying just west of the Moselle. These forested cuestas of Jurassic limestone have gentle back slopes toward the west and steep front slopes toward the east, thus presenting difficult terrain for an army attacking from the east and relatively easy terrain for defenders from the west. Thus, many of the main towns of Lorraine are fortress cities located in gaps or other strategic places and have gained fame as sites of historic battles. Such are Metz, Toul, Verdun, Sedan, and St. Mihiel. Agriculture on the lowlands between the cuestas of Lorraine is not so intensive as that of the northern part of the Paris Basin, and much of it is based largely on dairying in response to the demand for milk in the industrial centers of the region. The agricultural village of Lorraine is a classic type, with its farmhouses aligned along the street and combining dwelling, barn, and stable under one roof. The affluence of the farmer is measured by the size of the pile of fertilizer that stands reeking before the house.

The great significance of Lorraine is not so much its agricultural productivity or even its strategic value as a bulwark against invasion, but its great wealth in the limonitic iron ore found in the oölitic Jurassic limestone of the Côtes de Moselle. In spite of the fact that large-scale exploitation of the iron was delayed until development of the Thomas-Gilchrist method of smelting high-phosphorus ores, one of the world's greatest iron and steel industries developed along the Moselle by the outbreak of World War I. Significant in the industrialization of the region is the fact that much of the iron ore was included in Germany after the annexation of Alsace-Lorraine in 1871 after the Franco-German War; thus, the great Ruhr coal deposits and much of the Lorraine iron were on the same side of the political and tariff boundary. The region is still largely dependent on the Ruhr for coke and coking coal, although both are also brought in from northern France and from the Saar. The iron lies in three main basins, those of Longwy, Briey, and Nancy; and numerous great mining and metallurgical enterprises are found in the towns surrounding these centers.

A general situation similar to that of Lorraine exists in northern France, where industrialization and strategic defense are also important. However, there are very great differences: the basis of the industry is coal and not iron; the textile industry has long been highly developed and is more important than metallurgy; the coastal location is an advantage to the region; and, finally, agriculture is of very great significance in this densely populated region. The coal seams extend in a roughly east-west direction on a line through Lens,

Douai, and Valenciennes, and continue eastward into Belgium along
the line of the Sambre-Meuse valley. The deposits are in seams
only 3 to 6 feet thick and are greatly fractured so that exploitation
is difficult and costly. The mines are also deep, with some pits ex-

A. Historical Regions of France.

ceeding 3,000 feet. The mines and the mining industry suffered
during the fighting of both world wars, with destruction particularly
great after World War I. It was in return for the great damage sustained by the coal mines of the region that France demanded con-
cessions in the Saar in 1919.

Textiles have dominated manufacturing activity in the region
since the Middle Ages, but increased development of coal mining and
agriculture has diversified the industries to a large extent. The distribution and nature of the industry can perhaps best be shown by

consideration of the cities of Flanders and adjoining regions. The chief city of the region is Lille, which specializes in cotton and linen thread but produces also chemicals, textile machinery, and heavy equipment like railway rolling stock. Roubaix and Tourcoing specialize in woolens, and near-by Armentières in linens. Coal mining dominates in a number of towns, especially such centers as Lens, Douai, and Valenciennes, with a number of steel mills around Valenciennes and in such surrounding towns as Denain. Charleville is the principal center of a number of industrial towns in the Meuse valley that manufacture agricultural machinery, hardware, and tools; iron or steel is brought from Lorraine as raw material for the industries. Raw materials for the industries of Flanders are imported through the port of Dunkerque, the importance of which has increased with the evolution of the industries of Flanders and with the silting up of formerly important ports. It was from the beaches of Dunkerque that scores of thousands of British soldiers were rescued by English boats of all types in 1940. Calais serves a slightly different function in that it is much more dependent on passenger traffic across the Channel, especially to and from Dover, from which it is separated by only 18 miles of channel water.

Southwest of Flanders is the low anticline that is a southeastward continuation of the breached Weald anticline of southeastern England. Erosion similar to that that breached the Weald has created the Boulonnais, an amphitheatre-shaped depression open to the Channel and backed into the hills of Artois. In the southwestern corner of the depression is Boulogne, important as a cross-channel port for both freight and passengers and also as a manufacturing center, producing large quantities of cement. Heavily damaged in World War II, Boulogne slowly recovered and rebuilt after 1945. Not the least importance of the port is its fishing activity, since the Boulogne fishing fleet has access to the North Sea, the Channel, and the Atlantic; the city is thus the main fishing center of France.

Southeast of the region just described is the lower Seine region, with centers at Rouen and Le Havre. This densely populated and active region has a number of economic stimuli, including its agricultural productivity, its river artery, its location between Paris and the important coast, and the availability of raw materials easily obtained from imports. Le Havre is especially important for the Atlantic trade both in steamship passengers from North America and in freight items such as cotton, coffee, and tropical produce. The extreme damage suffered by Cherbourg during World War II, especially at the time of the Allied invasion of Normandy, worked to the advantage of Le Havre, in spite of the damage inflicted on Le Havre itself. Rouen, located on the Seine where it is still under tidal influence, is the port of Paris, and along with Marseille and Le Havre is one of the three chief ports of France. Rouen has been important for centuries as a bridge town and developed important woolen and linen textile industries in the Middle Ages, to which that of cotton was added in the eighteenth century. South of Le Havre along the Channel coast are pleasant seaside resort towns such as Trouville and Deauville.

Armorica

The region of Armorica is the first of the upland areas ringing the Paris Basin to be considered and is shown as 2 in A405. The three hilly sections of the region have no great elevations, rarely exceeding 1,000 feet, and accordant summits reveal the former peneplain on the old Hercynian stumps. The heart of Armorica is the Brittany Peninsula or Bretagne (2A), projecting westward into the Atlantic. Hundreds of small fishing villages are sheltered in the bays and coves of the highly irregular Brittany coast, and many have more recently become resorts for vacationists attempting to escape the warmth of Paris in summer. Four coastal locations have become ports of appreciable importance: Brest as an Atlantic naval base, Lorient as a Welsh coal importing port, St. Nazaire as an outport for Nantes and as a shipbuilding center, and Nantes as port for the lower Loire region. All these ports were important German naval bases during World War II, especially for submarines attacking Allied shipping on the Atlantic. The coasts of Brittany are covered with a rather fertile soil, on which *primeurs* are produced in great quantities, and are relatively level; both sides are referred to as Armor as distinguished from the hilly interior, the Arcoat. The Arcoat, with its hilly relief, hard rocks trending east-west parallel with the structure, and sterile soils shelters the Bretons, a Celtic-speaking people who fled hence from Britain and to some extent retain their old language and traditions, although modern communications are gradually reducing their isolation in the poor hill lands. Dairying is supreme in the economy of the Arcoat, but in the better soils and milder climate of the Armor early vegetables and grains are intensively cultivated. The Armor is one of the most densely populated parts of France.

Normandy (2B) is less intimately related with the sea and more diversified in landscape and activity. The port of Cherbourg, on the tip of the Cotentin Peninsula, was, it is true, a principal port of France before it was virtually destroyed during World War II, but the many fishing villages of Brittany are lacking. Famed for its

A. Uplands of Brittany: windswept—bush vegetation. Courtesy of French Government Tourist Office.

unusual character is the *bocage* landscape of the Normandy hills, in which the fields are enclosed by hedgerows, and wooded areas are scattered throughout. The hedgerows were significant in the fighting in mid-1944 when the Allies broke out of St. Lô; tanks attempting to move cross-country found the hedgerows almost impossible to penetrate in many sections, and German infantry used the hedges as screens for their ground operations. The economic activities of dairying in the hills and raising of *primeurs* on the coast are diversified with those of textile manufacturing, iron mining, and metallurgy. Apple orchards are numerous, and the Norman regional beverage is cider, as contrasted with the wine of France outside the

northwest. The beaches of Normandy, part of which belong to the
Paris Basin rather than to Armorica, have been turned into a virtual
national shrine because of their significance in the Allied landings

A. A castle in the Loire region. Small village in the valley dominated by the
castle. In the background, well-tilled fields. Courtesy of French Government
Tourist Office.

in June, 1944. Wreckage of ships and parts of the breakwater
formed by sunken ships may be seen on the beaches and offshore.
The quaint old towns of Normandy, such as Caen, St. Lô, and
Avranches, are among the towns most completely destroyed in
World War II fighting and will retain prominent places in military
annals.

South of the Loire, the Vendée (2C) is a continuation of the structure of Brittany, and the granitic hills of the Bocage Gâtine are likewise devoted to dairying. The surrounding lowlands are devoted to wheat and cattle, and butter co-operatives play an active role in the region's economy.

Lying between the Normandy hills and the Vendée upland is Anjou, with its capital of Angers, gateway of the Loire Valley from the west to the Paris Basin. This is the center of a productive region and one of the most charming landscapes of France. Fields, orchards, and peasant houses form a harmonious landscape of great charm, but the crowning touch is added by the large number of imposing châteaus, which were built up and down the Loire Valley during the Renaissance. Northwest of Anjou, lying in a basin between the uplands of Brittany and the Norman hills, is Rennes, which struggles to be the regional capital of Armorica.

Central Plateau

Sometimes referred to as the Auvergne Plateau or the *Massif Centrale,* the Central Plateau (3 in A405) is more complex than any other part of France in its structure, relief, and land utilization. Evidence of the pressure and disturbance that uplifted the eastern edge of the plateau and fractured the entire block is seen in the numerous volcanic necks (*puys*) and cones, rift valleys such as those used by the Loire (3A) and the Allier (3B), and other signs of volcanic action such as dikes and hot springs. The surface of the Central Plateau is, therefore, far from level. In the south-central part of the plateau, horizontal Jurassic limestones almost encircled by older rocks constitute some of the wildest and most unexpected landscapes of France, the Causses (3C). Comprising a group of barren karst plateaus, the largest of which is the Causse de Larzac, the Causses are deeply trenched by meandering streams, whose valleys are the main sites of settlement, agriculture, and routes of travel. The gorges of the Lot and Tarn rivers are especially good examples of such entrenched streams. The rugged Cévennes (3D) in the southeast, carved by torrential rains in limestone, form the edge of the plateau. The physiographically interesting massif of the Morvan (3E) forms an offshoot of the Central Plateau toward the northeast.

The region has been largely denuded of its forests (compare A418), and use of the land is generally for grazing and hardy cereals. Raising of sheep in areas of scanty fodder is typical, and the Roquefort area in the south is renowned for its cheese produced from sheep

milk and stored in limestone caves in the Causses. An area on the
lower slopes in which rye is dominant forms an irregular band
around the plateau. Weathering of lava has produced excellent
soils in regions affected by vulcanism, where, even at 3,000–4,000
feet, intensive agriculture is practiced and gives rise to a population

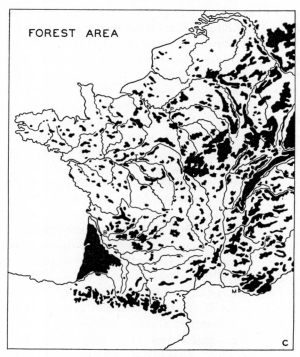

FOREST AREA

A. Forests in France.

appreciably denser than that characteristic of the rest of the plateau.
Dense population also characterizes the Limagne (Allier rift valley,
3B), a fertile former lake bottom producing wheat and sugar beets.
Clermont-Ferrand, at the western edge of the Limagne, is the economic center of the area and one of the main centers of the whole
Central Plateau region. It owed its original importance to its position as a route junction and to the fertility of the plain; but the unusual energy of the inhabitants has led to its further development
as the automobile tire center of France, and it has in addition a wide
range of industrial products such as chemicals, machinery, and tex-

tiles. The famous resort town of Vichy is located on the Allier in the center of the plain and attracts thousands of visitors each year to its mineral springs; Vichy served for a time during World War II as the capital of unoccupied France. At the southern end of the near-by Forez (rift valley of the Loire, 3A) is the coal-mining and industrial city of St. Étienne which is more closely linked economically with the Rhône Valley region. Iron deposits formerly exploited at Le Creusot, near the northeastern corner of the region, are now exhausted; but the great armament works are maintained by iron brought from Lorraine and by local coal. On the northwestern slopes of the Central Plateau is the Limousin with its center of Limoges, where use of kaolin resulting from the weathering of local granite has given rise to a world-famed porcelain industry.

Vosges

The next unit in the ring of old uplands is the Vosges Mountains (4 in A405) in the east. The large amount of forest gives rise to an active lumbering activity; and, high above the conifers, luscious meadows supply the basis for a highly developed dairy industry. Pleistocene glaciation widened many of the valleys, facilitating penetration into the mountains and dense settlement in the valleys. The heavy precipitation on the west and the steep gradient of the streams has given rise to a large number of small water power installations, and industries of woodworking, paper making, and textile manufacturing have developed in a number of the valleys. The Ardennes region (5) is discussed in Chapter 25.

Aquitaine Basin

The first region in the outer lowland ring is that of the Aquitaine Basin (6 in A405), sometimes referred to as the Garonne Basin after the principal river of the region. Toward the north it includes the Charente area (6A), to the northeast it extends up the lower slopes of the Central Plateau, to the southeast it communicates with the Mediterranean coast through the Gap of Carcassonne (6D), on the south it joins the Pyrenees, and to the west it is completely open to the Atlantic. The floor of the basin is composed of Tertiary rocks—soft limestones and marly sandstones with a thin clay cover. In the south the region of Armagnac is a vast area of alluvial fan deposits radiating from the Plateau of Lannemezan and deposited by swift-flowing streams tributary to the Adour or the Garonne. Jurassic and Cretaceous limestones in the northeast form semi-karst landscapes, with the Causse de Quercy the largest and most representative. In the limestone bluffs overlooking the Vézère River are solution caverns on whose walls Stone Age man left fascinating paintings of contemporary animals that he hunted, and implements left in the caverns constitute a fine record of the culture of such peoples as the Cro-Magnon. This same region of the Périgord is famed for its truffles, which are fungoid growths that develop on the roots of oak trees and are gathered by peasants who use trained pigs to root out the truffles. Finely minced truffles are mixed with goose liver to make *pâté de foie gras,* for which the Périgord, like the Strasbourg region of Alsace, is famous.

The western part of the Aquitaine Basin comprises a low, sandy area that borders the Bay of Biscay with a straight coast along which extends a line of sand dunes. Behind the dunes are a number of lagoons. The flat area back of the lagoons was formerly a marshy plain that was unhealthy for human habitation and was sparsely settled. However, drainage of the swamps and afforestation of the area with pine has transformed it into the largest forest section of France, which, however, was partly destroyed by the great fire of 1950. Far to the south, the winter resort of Biarritz has developed as a result of—relative to northern France—greater sunniness and warmth from the lower latitudes and warm ocean.

The great value of the Aquitaine Basin lies in its agricultural productivity. The rolling lowlands and river valleys, profiting from the generally fertile soil and warm sunny climate, are under intensive cultivation. Summer precipitation permits extensive growth of corn, and it and wheat are the main cereals; early vegetables and fruits such as peaches, apricots, apples, plums, and cherries are abundant. However, the vine is the principal element in the agriculture of Aquitaine and is seen everywhere—on the slopes, in the valleys, and on the plains. Wine from most of the vineyards is characteristically ordinary or everyday red wine, but the limestone slopes produce sauternes, the Charente region is famed for the fine brandy produced at Cognac, and the Médoc Peninsula west of the Gironde (the estuary of the combined Garonne and Dordogne rivers) is famed for its cordials.

In spite of the great diversity and intensity of agriculture in the basin, it is unfortunately true that the yield of crops (as indicated by that of wheat, A103) in this region is appreciably lower than that of the Paris Basin. Furthermore, tenant farming and even share-cropping are widespread and conduce to poor farm management, and emigration of rural population is persistent. The population of the area is not so energetic as in other parts of France, possibly as a result of the less stimulating climate, the less reliable precipitation in regard to crop return, the plentiful supply of wine, or the social organization. Hence, it is classified in Europe B.

Bordeaux is the main city of the Aquitaine Basin, and its function as the principal outlet for the products of the region—especially wine —has led to its development as the fourth port of France in foreign commerce. Connections are especially close with England and Spain, as well as with tropical Africa and the West Indies. As the center of the Bordelais wine region, it is especially active in preparation, bottling, and shipping of wine. In the Charente region north of the Gironde, Rochefort, near the mouth of the Charente River, and La Rochelle, to the north, are small ports especially engaged in fishing. The city of Toulouse is the largest center of the interior of the region. It occupies a good nodal position for routes from the Atlantic to the Mediterranean and from the Pyrenees passes to the north, with its river port furnishing appreciable stimulus to its trade.

Midi

The Mediterranean coast of France, the Midi, is in marked contrast to the remainder of France, primarily as a result of the Mediterranean climate of the region. Vegetation, landform details, agriculture, and architecture all differ markedly from the rest of France and are similar to those of Mediterranean Spain and peninsular Italy. Its integration with the Mediterranean environment is reflected in the historical association it has had with other Mediterranean countries: Phoenician, Greek, and Roman colonies were established in Mediterranean France, and numerous Roman ruins in many parts of the Midi attest to the ancient association. The region may be divided into two parts: Languedoc west of the Rhône and curving around the southeastern edge of the Central Plateau, and Provence east of the Rhône and south of the French Alps.

Mediterranean scrub or maquis covers the lower slopes of the coastal ranges, whereas on the higher slopes chestnut trees form an almost continuous zone along the side of the greatly dissected Cévennes. In the valleys and on the plains olive groves are conspicuous, but, as in the Bordelais area, vineyards dominate the use of the land, making Languedoc the principal wine-producing region of France. Vegetables and wheat also abound. Along the coast a series of lagoons (*étangs*) has been formed as the result of the building of broad sand bars by the waves and currents of the Mediterranean Sea, and evaporation of sea water for salt is a thriving industry in Languedoc.

Bauxite is mined both in Languedoc (in Hérault *département*) and in Provence (Var *département*). The valley of the Argens River in Var, around the towns of Brignoles and Le Luc, is the principal center of extraction, and the reddish ore is shipped north to the Alpine valleys for reduction by hydroelectricity or exported from Toulon and other near-by ports. The ore is named from the village of Baux, northeast of Arles, where it is also mined.

East of the main branch of the Rhône is the low, gravelly region of La Crau, formed as an alluvial fan by the Durance when its course brought it directly into the Mediterranean during the last glacial period. During the first half of the twentieth century the dry plain of Crau was changed from largely a wasteland into a productive agricultural region by using water from the Durance for irrigation. *Primeurs* for the metropolitan areas are produced in great quantities, giving the ancient city of Avignon a new stimulus as an agricultural and canning center. Containing a number of ruins from the period of Roman occupation, Avignon was selected as the Papal Seat in the fourteenth century when the Pope fled Rome temporarily, and the old Papal Palace constitutes another attraction of an already interesting city. Also receiving a stimulus from the new use of the Crau is Arles, whose heyday ended in the sixteenth century with continued silting of its port. However, it had been a main regional center from the days of Julius Caesar and because of its well-preserved ruins ranks with Nîmes as one of the finest Roman cities in France.

East of the Crau plain and over the Estaque ridge is Marseille, located on higher ground well west of the marshy mouth of the Rhône so as to avoid the silt with which the Rhône is laden and which over the centuries submerged a number of smaller ports in the region. Marseille is not only the great port that would certainly be expected to develop at the outlet of the very significant Rhône corridor; it also vies with Le Havre as first port of France and is the second city of the country after Paris. It has been a vital center since Greek trading days, but has faced varying fortunes as trade routes have shifted from the Rhône Valley to the Alpine railway tunnels. Although necessarily located well east of the Rhône delta deposits, the site of Marseille makes connections with the hinterland difficult. The limestone mountain spur of the Estaque requires that both rail and canal connections between the port and the Rhône go through tunnels; and the Rove Canal tunnel, opened in 1926, is 4.5 miles long. Marseille functions primarily as an import and passenger port, especially for North Africa, the Levant, and the lands beyond the Suez Canal. Unlike the other French ports, Marseille is even more industrial than commercial, and its many imports are more for its own industries than for consumption by the hinterland. This bustling manufacturing city produces a wide range of products ranging from foods and fats to chemicals and ceramics.

To the east of Marseille is the naval base of Toulon, where much of the French fleet was scuttled during World War II to prevent its falling into German hands. Farther east still, along the southeast-facing coast so well protected from the cold northern winds—especially the bone-chilling *mistral*—is the famed and delightful *Côte d'Azure* or Riviera. Resort towns such as Nice and Cannes attract thousands of visitors annually, especially in winter when the warmth and bright sunshine make the Riviera greatly preferable to the chilly, damp northern regions of Europe. In Grasse, northwest of Cannes, is the center of the perfume industry, where scores of species of flowers are grown and processed into the highly prized scents for which France is so famous. Monaco, east of Nice, with its famous city of Monte Carlo and its renowned gambling casino, is an independent state of miniature size that is closely affiliated with France.

West of the main Rhône outlet is the deltaic plain of the Camargue, a marshy area devoted to livestock pasture and, in the more northern parts away from the salt of the delta edge, rice and grapes under irrigation. To the northeast of Camargue is Nîmes, displaying evidence of its importance as a Roman city in its numerous ancient ruins. In the coastal plain of Languedoc are several cities that have preserved their Roman ruins along with their importance as trade centers and wine-handling centers: such is Montpellier. Sète, with an artificial harbor, serves as a wine-exporting center for the region. Narbonne, at the Mediterranean end of the Canal du Midi, was a port as late as the Middle Ages, but Rhône silt carried westward by currents has sealed it miles inland. Also an important Roman center and preserving many Roman ruins, Narbonne is a great wine center, thriving on its transportation advantages.

Rhône-Saône Corridor (7)

The profound depression between the Central Plateau and the Alps has been of great human significance since the first appearance of man in western Europe in late glacial times. The Rhône-Saône corridor is the easiest and most direct route between northwestern Europe and the Mediterranean. The use of the corridor by Allied armies in 1944 for the southern invasion is a recent illustration of its function. Mediterranean influences, cultural as well as climatic and vegetational, extend far up the valley, and the gradual transition from the environment of northern France to that of the Mediterranean along the valley is fascinating to trace on a trip through the depression. Vineyards clothe both sides of the valley, and fields of early vegetables reaching well up the valley attest to the mild climate. Among the cultivated trees walnuts are prominent. North of Lyon, the depression widens and increases in agricultural importance in the Bresse region, an old lake bottom, around Chalon on the Saône. West of the Bresse, on the slopes of the Côte d'Or, are the famed Burgundy vineyards. Dijon, at the northern end of the Côte d'Or, is a wine center but owes much of its development also to its nodal position on transport lines and to its manufacture of food articles, such as mustard.

The French attempts to increase hydroelectric output are evidenced by the work that was in progress in 1951 on the giant Donzère-Mondragon power plant on the lower Rhône south of Montelimar. This plant, only one in a series of such projects, will be one of the largest in Europe and will help France achieve its goal of producing twice the hydroelectric power it did before World War II.

Lyon is challenged by no other city as the center of the region. Located at the confluence of the Rhône and Saône rivers, it has been for centuries an important east-west and north-south crossing, and it serves as a transshipment point for goods moving southward on the swift Rhône. The silk industry, initiated by Italian immigrants in the Middle Ages, transformed Lyon from an old commercial center into one of the great industrial cities of France. Drawing on coal deposits from a rich surrounding industrial region that includes St. Étienne to the southwest, Lyon manufactures besides silk and other textiles such products as chemicals, leather goods, and food products. It is the only city of France that even challenges Paris as a cultural center, and it is also one of the chief banking centers of western Europe.

Rhine Plain of Alsace (part of 8 in A405)

The structural character of the Upper Rhine Valley, as described in Chapter 4, is that of a graben, or rift valley, let down between the blocks of the Vosges on the west and the Black Forest on the east. That part of the plain included in Alsace should also be thought of as being intimately connected with the eastern slopes of the Vosges, already discussed in this chapter. The zones of soil parallel with the Rhine are similar to those on the German side of the river and are characterized by different types of land use. That part of the plain well back from the Rhine and west of the Ill River has been drained and made productive, with cereals (especially wheat), tobacco, vegetables, and—along the Vosges foothills—grapes as the principal crops. The intensive agriculture on the *limon* soils supports a dense population of the individualistic Alsatians, whereas the zone along the river is either in forest or marsh and is sparsely populated.

Mining and industry, in addition to active agriculture, are important in the Alsatian economy. The great potash deposits of southern Alsace, exploited north of Mulhouse, are second in the world only to the almost unlimited beds in the Stassfurt region of Germany. Large amounts of potash are shipped to other parts of France and even overseas for use as fertilizer, and the mineral is also employed locally in chemical plants in Mulhouse and Strasbourg. The principal industry of Alsace is textile manufacturing—especially of cottons, but also woolens and to some extent silk and rayon. Mulhouse is the principal textile center, but Colmar is of appreciable significance; and, characteristic of Alsace, many small home industries are still found in the region.

The plain has served as a great thoroughfare since the earliest movements of men through the area. Railway, highway, and canal transportation all utilize the terrain for north-south shipping. The Rhine-Rhône Canal extends southward from Strasbourg through Mulhouse and then southwestward to join the Doubs River south of Belfort. A branch canal leaves the Rhine-Rhône waterway above Mulhouse and reaches Basel. It is indicative of the character of both the Rhine and the Ill rivers that the Rhine-Rhône connection follows neither stream but has been artificially constructed in the soft alluvial deposits of the plain.

The great nodal point not only of Alsace but also of the entire middle Rhine region is Strasbourg: the very name means "fortress of roads." A Gallic settlement even before Roman times, the city owes much of its significance to its location at the crossing point of north-south routes following the Rhine plain and of east-west routes joining the Paris Basin with central Europe. Its junction of roads was reinforced after the construction of its canals made it the junction of three great waterways: the Rhine-Marne Canal, the Rhine-Rhône Canal, and the lower Rhine; and transshipment of goods is one of its chief functions. Because of the availability of almost the gamut of raw materials moving through the transport routes, Strasbourg has developed an industry of bewildering variety. As a meeting ground of Germanic and Gallic culture, the city itself is of great interest and considerable charm. In 1950 it became the seat of the Council of Europe, both because of its generally convenient location in western Europe and also because the city's own history as a shuttlecock between France and Germany reflects the tragic consequences of antagonism and disunity.

Pyrenees (10)

The high, continuous chain of the Pyrenees Mountains, with their rugged alpine forms, constitutes an effective barrier between France and the Iberian Peninsula. Although the upper valleys were glaciated during Pleistocene times and show U-shaped valleys below the jagged forms typical of upper elevations in alpine glaciation, the valleys are not extensive; and settlement is sparse throughout the region. Since the Pyrenees are rich in mineral waters, there are dozens of mineral water resorts, and winter sports attract visitors from southwestern France. Lourdes, on the upper Gave de Pau, is sought out by thousands of pilgrims and infirm persons each year in hope of a miraculous sign or cure at the Grotto of Bernadette. The high mountain meadows are used for cattle in summer by dairymen of the Aquitaine Basin who practice transhumance between their lowland valley homes and the alpine meadows of the mountains. Hydroelectric power has been developed in a number of the valleys, including the upper Ariège above Foix, the Neste in the headwaters of the Garonne, the Gave de Pau, and the Gave d'Oloron. Small electrochemical and electrometal industries have developed near the power sites; and electric smelting of the iron ores mined in small quantities in the Ariège valley is increasing.

French Alps (11)

The French Alps form the second (after the Pyrenees) link in the partial outer highland rim of France. Occupying the southwestern portion of the main Alpine arc of Europe, they display the characteristics of young, rugged mountains and carry glaciers on the higher parts. The massif of the Maures (11A) is geologically part of the east-west structure of the Pyrenees and belongs regionally to Provence, already discussed in the section on the Midi. The Alpine chains proper can be divided, as in Switzerland, into the High Alps (11B) and the Pre-Alps (11C), separated by the longitudinal upper valleys of the Isère and Durance rivers. Mont Blanc, whose very name indicates its perpetual cover of snow and ice, is the highest mountain of Europe (15,782 feet) except for peaks in the Caucasus, and the great massif that the peak surmounts marks the junction of the French, Swiss, and Italian frontiers.

As in Alpine regions in general, dairying is the dominant agricultural activity; and milk, butter, and cheese are produced in great quantity, Gruyère (or "Swiss" cheese) being a regional specialty. Transhumance is practiced on a great scale, animals being brought even by railway from the Rhône Valley to feed in the rich *alpages* or high pastures.

Use of local resources, such as wood from the forests for woodcarving and paper making and hides for leather working, has for centuries occupied the population during the winter months. However, the twentieth century has seen a marked increase in industrialization of the region, largely as a result of the increasing supply of water power. Hydroelectricity is generated at scores of stations and is not only used locally by industries developed in the broad valleys but is also "exported" by high-tension lines to cities of the Rhône Valley and the Mediterranean coast. Electrochemical and electrometal plants are numerous in the northern Alps, especially in the valleys of the Are and upper Isère. The vast resources of bauxite in the Midi feed the aluminum plants of the Savoy Alps. The small boundary changes, made official in 1947, gave France increased hydroelectric supply as a result of the transfer to France of water power plants erected by the Italians. However, France sends part of the power back to Italy—an agreement that was made part of the treaty.

The economic and cultural center of the region is Grenoble, on the Isère, which is not only the regional rail junction (a function that it shares with Chambéry farther north) but also the location of the chief French glove industries and of a leading university. Among the numerous resort towns the most favored is Chamonix, magnificently situated in the Chamonix valley at the foot of towering Mont Blanc.

Jura (12)

The small Jura region is of interest both in its physical and in its human geographical aspects. Since the Jura folding was accomplished at the time of Alpine mountain building and can be better understood when related to the general structure of Switzerland, the physical aspects are described in Chapter 33. In the French Jura, the traditional economic activities have been dairying and timber cutting. However, during the latter nineteenth century and first half of the twentieth century, more varied activities came to diversify the economy of the region, especially as a result of a modest hydro-electric development. Production of pulp and paper utilized the forest resources to a greater extent, various kinds of woodworking were expanded from the long-practiced home industries, and watch-making increased in importance. Center of the French Jura watch-making is Pontarlier, near the source of the Doubs, most of whose output is sent over the frontier to the Swiss factories. On the warmer and sunnier western slopes of the Jura are extensive vineyards, with a number of small towns having developed as wine centers at the foot of the slopes. Besançon, dramatically situated on a "peninsula" formed by a meander on the Doubs, acts as a modest commercial center. Although it dates from the days of pre-Roman Gaul, its significance dimmed after the sixteenth century.

Despite the increasing importance of other activities, dairying remains the most important aspect of the Jura economy. Most of the milk is turned into cheese, which, like that produced in the French Alps and especially in Switzerland, is primarily Gruyère—or Swiss cheese. As in the Vendée, co-operative organizations have been formed among the Jura dairy farmers, and the cheese is produced in "co-op" plants.

THE SAARLAND (DAS SAARLAND) *

Although legally the Saarland is part of Germany, as it has been for centuries except for brief periods, it became so closely identified economically with France after World War II that it is discussed in this chapter. Its status is more fully explained below.

The primary handicap of the Saarland is its geographical location (A429) in a political marchland—by reason of which it has been repeatedly involved in conflicting territorial claims—and on an ethnic front, the line of contact between the Germanic and Gallic cultures. Such a location would not, of course, alone be potentially explosive,

* This short description is taken partly from the junior author's dissertation, "The Political Geography of the Saarland," and partly from his article, "The New Saarland," *Geographical Review,* XLI, 4 (October, 1951), pp. 590–605.

A. Political- and Economic-Geographical Aspects of the Saarland in Western Europe.

but to it must be added the strategic gateway function of the Saar, with part of the Lorraine Gateway extending through the Palatinate Depression in the northeastern Saar, and its wealth in coal—about 6,000 million metric tons or about that possessed by all of France.

France's deficiency in coal, particularly coking coal, mentioned in the preceding chapter, and its large Lorraine iron ore supplies lying only 50 miles west of the Saar coal make the two areas of Saar and Lorraine an economic-geographical unit: a kind of "symbiosis." Unfortunately, however, Saar coal alone is not good for making coke for large modern blast furnaces, and it must be mixed with small amounts of coal that is good for coking—that from the Ruhr or Aachen basins, for example. The mixture is then used both in the numerous large iron plants of Lorraine and in the several Saar plants.

Minette ore moves eastward to the Saar from Lorraine, and Saar coal and coke move westward to Lorraine from the Saar. Naturally, this exchange thrives best when least interfered with by a political or customs boundary, and it first developed on a large scale during German possession of both the Saar and much of Lorraine between 1871 and 1920. It continued from 1920 until 1935 while the League of Nations administered the Saar. During these fifteen years, France and the Saar as constituted by the Treaty of Versailles were in a customs union that ended after the 1935 plebiscite showed Saar desire for reunion with Germany. Only five years later they were together again after the Nazi conquest of northeastern France. Another five years later, agreements following the Potsdam conference assigned the Saar to France as part of its zone of occupation. During the next few years the Saar was administratively detached from Germany, became closely integrated economically with France, and entered into economic union with France in 1948, by which time it had its own governmental organization. In early 1951 the Saar was an autonomous unit and France had a fifty-year lease on the coal mines. This autonomous *de facto* status was recognized as temporary by France and the other western Allies, by the Saar, and especially by Germany. Only the peace treaty with Germany was to decide the final disposition of the Saar.

In addition to being a coal-mining region—a fact that is not unusually obvious in the landscape, since the mines are frequently nestled in the forests—the Saar is a center of heavy industries and diversified metal-goods manufacturing. Coal yield in 1951 was at the rate of 17 million tons annually, and the twenty-one blast furnaces were producing 2.4 million tons of steel each year. With a population of nearly 1 million persons on 991 square miles, the Saar has the very high density of nearly 1,000 persons per square mile. The capital, Saarbrücken, is the largest city and the main manufacturing center, with the great Arbed iron and steel works on the banks of the Saar River. Völklingen, Neunkirchen, and Dillingen are also iron and steel centers. Merzig and Mettlach, also along the river, are famed for their pottery, tile, and mosaic works; and St. Ingbert produces millions of square feet of plate glass annually. All these large industries are dependent upon the plentiful supply of coal or of gas produced as a by-product of coke ovens.

· 28 ·

Spain (España) and Portugal

Unity and General Character of Mediterranean Lands

The south of Europe, more markedly than the west, displays a certain geographic unity, even though it includes such zones of transition as northern Spain and the Po Basin. The climate is a strong factor in this unity, for the mild, rainy winter and the hot, dry summer are not only characteristic of all Mediterranean countries, but also are responsible for very distinctive types of vegetation and agriculture. The typical forest is the maquis, which covers the slopes of hills and mountains and is composed of scrubby trees and bushes with small, hard, thick, and often shiny leaves. The typical crops are wheat and grapes with more subtropical products like olives, citrus fruits, and even rice. The relief of the Mediterranean countries is also similar—a structural coincidence, but a fact nevertheless. Mountains abound; plains are the exception and are mostly small. Nevertheless, most of the people are concentrated in the regions of low relief and better soil, with the result that there are numerous small areas of dense population surrounded by regions of very low density. Moreover, within these areas of low relief, and also in the more rugged areas, there is a very strong tendency for the people to be concentrated in villages that are like miniature cities. Since the Mediterranean is an area of long human occupance, most of the towns are quite old, with streets that are narrow, crooked, and paved with stone—often cobblestones—and have no sidewalks. They are completely bounded by the mud or stone walls of houses or of small courtyards. Scarcity of timber together with abundance of stone has resulted in the use of stone almost exclusively in Mediterranean buildings, which are also usually stuccoed and then whitewashed. In the brilliant summer sun, towns are dazzling because of the white stucco exteriors, although at close range the appearance in many cases is one of age and deterioration. Usually no verdure is visible until one gets inside one of the better courtyards or suddenly emerges from the village into the vineyards, olive orchards, and wheat fields. Only in rare cases do people live outside the villages or cities.

The people of all the Mediterranean countries also have many characteristics in common. Originally of Mediterranean stock, their one-time racial unity was eventually modified by successive invasions, but new blood did not change their ethnographic characteristics. Greek, Roman, and other cultures, which had become closely adapted to the geographical environment, were strong enough to absorb the foreign elements and remold them into Mediterranean forms. The languages of today are merely modified relics of those used in the time of classical glory. The sociability and love of crowds and gaiety, which are fostered by the city-like mode of life, are even more pronounced than in the past.

The development of these countries in recent centuries has been influenced by a variety of complex factors. One of these has been overpopulation. This is not so evident when the total number of persons per square mile is considered, but it becomes very clear when the amount of cultivated land per person is considered. It falls to a minimum of 1 acre in Greece, and is only 0.91 in Italy and 1.64 in Spain. With this must be coupled the fact that because of the dry summers the yield of crops per acre is small. This reduces the income per family to so low a level that in no Mediterranean country does it average much above half as high as immediately around the North Sea (B16).

Another factor common to the Mediterranean countries is shortage of coal, which has been a great handicap in their attempts to take part in modern industry. Again, the discovery of America tended to put the Mediterranean countries at a disadvantage compared with those farther to the northwest. The center of the world's activity in trade passed from the Mediterranean Sea to the North Atlantic Ocean. From the very start this was a disadvantage to Italy and Greece. Spain and Portugal profited by it for a time, but other conditions, such as those described in the chapters on Great Britain, gave the northern countries an advantage, while their own poverty and other handicaps made the Iberian countries unable to maintain their position. In addition to all this the general progress of inventions made it more and more feasible for civilization to advance into cooler regions, but did not help the Mediterranean countries so much. Thus, although these countries did not actually retrogress, they did not go ahead so fast as northern and western Europe. This

fact has often made people suppose that countries like Greece and
Spain have gone backward in recent centuries, but what they have
really done is merely to make progress more slowly than countries
like Germany or France.

Cultural as well as geographic and economic conditions enter
into the problem of the advance made by the Mediterranean countries in comparison with those of other parts of Europe. Here more
than anywhere else in Europe a strong consciousness of their own
cultural and historical unity and former greatness has greatly influenced national development. This feeling of pride in ancient culture has often been a handicap because it has retarded the impulse to
join in the progressive enterprises of the rest of Europe. It appears
to be related to the fact that the countries of southern Europe are
relatively unstable politically. The same kind of pride that em-
phasizes the importance of past achievements often causes individuals of more than the average force of character to be unwilling
to submit to the rule of the majority. On the other hand, the pride
of people of less ability makes them prone to hero worship. The
achievements of the hero are adopted as their own and thus minister
to each man's personal pride.

This state of mind, as well as chronic discontent resulting from
poverty and misfortune, probably has much to do with the fact that
the Mediterranean countries are comparatively unstable politically.
Every one of them has had far more revolutions than have the countries of western and northwestern Europe. A country like Sweden
makes progress by a series of small but steady steps with no great
crises or revolutions. The two countries with which this chapter is
concerned—Spain and Portugal—are examples of the Mediterranean
variability.

Whereas Portugal has profited during the period of twentieth-century European wars by staying neutral or being involved to only a
small extent, Spain suffered terribly from the Civil War (1936–39)
that put an end to the republic and resulted in dictatorship. For
Portugal, World War II was to some extent a boom period. Portugal's otherwise rather insignificant tungsten production suddenly
jumped to first place in the value of exports because of abnormally
high prices caused by competition between the nations at war.
Lisbon at the time was crowded with refugees, mostly Jews, who
had escaped the horrors of Nazi persecution and were attempting to
find a haven beyond the Atlantic. Temporarily, Portugal was rich,
but after the war the boom stopped, and again the problem of how

to pay for the needed imports of food and manufactured products confronts the Portuguese government.

Spain, which by devious dealings also managed to stay out of the war—although officially favoring the Nazis—profited to some extent during the war by selling her minerals and citrus fruit. However, it was too exhausted from the Civil War to use that opportunity fully. Towns and villages had been destroyed, land cultivation had been neglected, families had been divided in their political interests, and hatred and distrust prevailed. But above all this was the poverty of the ordinary man, who lived miserably in contrast to the life of luxury of a few. Spain since then has made steps forward, but it still gives the general impression that it is an unhappy country.

Effect of Location

The Iberian Peninsula not only juts southward until it almost touches Africa at Gibraltar, but also is cut off from the rest of Europe by the mountain barrier of the Pyrenees. Hence it has always been more open to influences from the sea and from Africa than from Europe. From the Mediterranean side it was conquered two thousand years ago by Carthage and then by Rome. Later from North Africa came the Mohammedan Moors who were responsible for much of the cultural and economic achievement of the Middle Ages. In Portugal the influence of the proximity of Africa is still seen in the presence of many people with a large infiltration of African blood. Because the Iberian Peninsula lies thus between Europe and Africa it was long the battleground between Mohammedanism and Christianity, and between the Nordic and Moorish types of people. The Nordic Visigoths, Vandals, and others pressed down through Spain with its old population of typical Mediterranean stock and even passed over into Africa. The Moors, on the other hand, who were Mediterranean people of the Arab type, pressed northward and even spilled into France before they were turned back in the battle of Tours in A.D. 732. After that the European and African types of civilization seesawed back and forth for many centuries, with cities like Granada, Córdoba, and Seville to represent the Moorish or African civilization, and the provinces of Castile and Aragon to represent the Christian or European type.

Structure and Relief

The geological structure and physiographic form of the Iberian Peninsula have much to do not only with the minerals that brought the Phoenicians thither but also with the climate, the poverty, and the cultural status of the peninsula. They likewise help to explain the separation between Spain and Portugal. The greater part of the peninsula is composed of a mighty block of ancient formation—the old massif and tableland of A436—uplifted during the Alpine period. The elevation was more pronounced in the east than in the west, the general westward slope of the block being indicated by the fact that

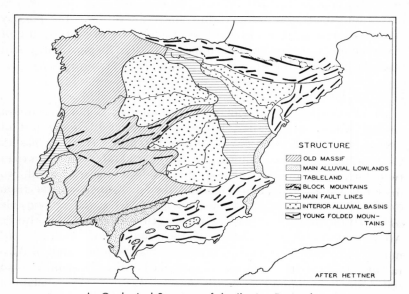

STRUCTURE

⟋⟋⟍ OLD MASSIF
▭ MAIN ALLUVIAL LOWLANDS
▭ TABLELAND
▰▰ BLOCK MOUNTAINS
⌒⌒ MAIN FAULT LINES
⋯ INTERIOR ALLUVIAL BASINS
▱ YOUNG FOLDED MOUN-
TAINS

AFTER HETTNER

A. Geological Structure of the Iberian Peninsula.

the Douro (Spanish: Duero), Tagus (Spanish: Tajo; Portuguese: Tejo), and Guadalquivir rivers rise far to the east of the center of the peninsula and flow westward. Numerous horsts, or blocks of the earth's crust, were hoisted above the general level of the plateau. The greatest of these, the great central massif that culminates in the lofty Guadarrama Mountains north of Madrid, separates the plateau into two sections—Old Castile to the north, and New Castile to the south. The tableland of Estremadura, an extension of this horst, swings southwest toward Lisbon and forms a sharp division between northern and southern Portugal.

The western edge of the Iberian Plateau is formed by a number of faults whose steep slopes, cut by narrow and precipitous canyons, make intercourse difficult between the west coast and the main plateau. The boundary between Spain and Portugal lies near the point where it becomes easier to go downhill to the west coast rather than uphill and across the plateau to the Spanish centers. On the plateau, young alluvial deposits cover extensive sections and make the regions between the horsts fairly level, as in the region of New Castile southeast of Toledo, and Old Castile to the north—the alluvial basins of A436. There great areas are extremely flat. Although the plateau is more than 2,000 feet above sea level, one rides for miles over a smooth plain from which at long intervals rise steep steps a few hundred feet high leading to other flat areas, called *mesas*, or tables. In winter and spring these plateau-plains are beautifully green with wheat, then they turn golden with the harvest, but in summer they are dry, dreary, and dusty.

Against the northeastern and southern edges of the great resistant block of the plateau young mountains were upfolded during the Alpine period. In the south these rise to 11,660 feet in the Sierra Nevada; in the north are the almost equally high Pyrenees and the Cantabrian Mountains; the latter are geologically a transition between the Alpine and the older types of structure. Between the folded mountains and the plateau are wedge-shaped depressions. One of these is the plain of Andalusia (Spanish: Andalucía) in the south, which contains the Río Guadalquivir and opens toward the Atlantic in the Gulf of Cádiz. Another is the Ebro Valley in the north, separated from the coast by the young Catalonian coastal ranges. Narrow plains border the Portuguese shore and much of the opposite Mediterranean coast of Spain.

Minerals

The mineral resources of the Iberian Plateau are numerous and important, but they belong chiefly to Spain. In ancient days they were one of the main attractions for the Phoenicians, Carthaginians, and Romans. Today the scarcity of coal, the most important mineral except iron, is a handicap. Portugal has virtually no coal, whereas Spain's resources are about equal to those of the Saar or of Czechoslovakia. Production, however, is not great, amounting to about 10 million tons annually. It comes mostly from Asturias, near the port of Gijón, whence it is shipped to other parts of the country. Spain's iron ore resources, on the other hand, rival those of Germany, although Spanish production is lower than Germany's and equals that of Luxembourg. Most of this is produced along the north coast around Bilbao and Santander and is largely exported from these two

ports. However, about a tenth is smelted in Spain. Good deposits
of copper, lead, and zinc, as well as silver and mercury, give Spain a
real economic advantage. The Río Tinto copper mines, northwest
of Seville, are world famous, and Huelva, not far away on the south
coast near the Portuguese frontier, is the main export harbor. The
Almaden mines, roughly halfway between Madrid and Seville, are
credited with nearly one half of the world's mercury production, but
output varies. Among European countries Spain's standing as a
silver producer has gradually declined, although its production is
still appreciable. Like Portugal, Spain sold tungsten ore during
World War II, although its wolfram resources are smaller than those
of Portugal, whose deposits near Fundão (on the edge of the plateau
and north of the Tagus) are the largest in Europe. One evidence
of the retarded industrial development of Spain is the country's
practice of exporting its ores rather than processing more of them
itself. The coal shortage is a factor to be considered, but production
of coal could be increased with proper management. With such
diversified mineral wealth, Spain could raise its present level of development of metal industries especially. Many of the Spanish
mines are operated by foreign capital, and the country even loses
part of the income to be derived from export of raw materials.

Climate

The climate of the Iberian Peninsula (see general climatic maps
in Chapter 2) varies widely in response to the latitude, the relief of
the land, and the position in respect to the ocean. To begin with,
the best but unfortunately most limited type—that of the mountainous north and northwest—is a typically marine climate with
winter temperatures averaging no lower than 45° F at sea level, and
summer temperatures averaging not above 70°. Cyclonic storms are
frequent, and rainfall is plentiful (A439), ranging from 35 to more
than 60 inches, and being highest on the Galician or northwest coast
and in the western Pyrenees. It is well distributed throughout the
year. The result is seen not only in prosperous agriculture with
varied crops of fruit and grain, but also in forests, and especially in
the health, activity, and progressiveness of the people. Except for
the rugged relief, this is the best part of Spain.

Southward, along the Atlantic coast, comes a gradual change to a
more Mediterranean type of climate, although the influence of the
sea is still felt. Rainfall decreases toward the south, being less than
30 inches at Lisbon, but increases slightly again along the Spanish

Atlantic coast south of the mouth of the Guadalquivir and is about 30 inches at Cádiz and 36 at Gibraltar. Thus Portugal is a well-watered land—dry to be sure in summer, but not hot. Lisbon averages only 72° F in July, or about the same as New York, and 50° in January, or about like Charleston, South Carolina. For some reason, however, the yield of crops and the degree of progress are lower than one would expect from the climate alone.

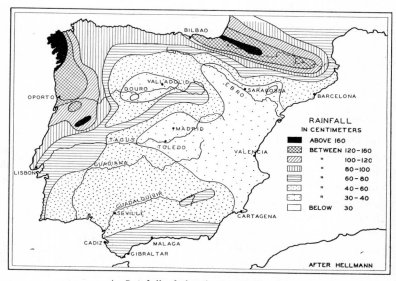

A. Rainfall of the Iberian Peninsula.

In the south of Spain the true Mediterranean type of climate prevails, most of the rain falling in the winter season and the summers being dry. East of Gibraltar along the Mediterranean coast, the temperature averages 50° F or more in winter and about 80° in summer. The rainfall diminishes toward the northeast, being only 14 inches at Murcia, just north of Cartagena; and June, July, and August are almost rainless. The result is seen in bare mountain slopes, planted sometimes with drought-resistant almond groves and broken by the little green irrigated fans of rivers on which sugar cane and rice are grown.

The plateau, surrounded by mountain walls, is a miniature continent in itself, with relatively cold, rainy winters; hot, dry summers; and low rainfall. Thus, in spite of being a relatively small peninsula surrounded by water except along the Pyrenees, the Iberian Plateau has unexpectedly severe climatic conditions. At Madrid, over 2,000 feet above sea level, January averages 40° F. July 77°, and the rainfall is only 17 inches. The northern part of the plateau may be considered a transition zone between the western European and Mediterranean climatic types, with rainfall up to 20 inches. But great sections (A439), a third of Spain, are so cut off from the west winds by mountains that they have a steppe climate, with a rainfall of 12 to 16 inches, and sometimes even less in the southeast and in the Ebro Basin. In summer the plain of La Mancha in New Castile, for instance, is extremely hot and dry, and vast dust clouds blow over the scorched country. The Andalusian Plain has a better climate because it opens toward the west, and hence receives more rain.

Use of the Land

The vegetation of the Iberian Peninsula reflects the climate, particularly the rainfall. The forests that prevail in the north are of the western European type, but farther south, on the plateau, the cork and stone oaks are almost the only large trees, and in the drier sections there is only grass. The Mediterranean coast has the typical scrub vegetation. On the mountains, where the rainfall is heavier, the forests are denser. In Spain alone the area of cork oak amounts to about 750,000 acres, largely in Estremadura in the southwest where the Guadiana River flows south, and in Catalonia in the northeast (A441). The red trunks of the oaks, where the cork or bark has been stripped off, present a unique appearance as they stand scattered about on the grassy plateau. In autumn, herds of pigs greedily eat the acorns that the swineherds lash from the trees with long whips. The cork is of great value, the annual exports sometimes being worth nearly 30 million dollars.

A far more valuable tree, well suited to the limestone slopes in the drier climate, is the olive. The area of olive trees in Spain is estimated at 4.4 million acres, with about 300 million trees. In A441 note how altitude and rainfall combine to prevent this tree from growing in the northwest. In all parts of the Mediterranean basin with a true Mediterranean climate, lack of dairy cattle causes a shortage of butter, and olive oil replaces not only butter but also virtually all other fats and oils. Olive oil is one of the chief elements in the Spanish diet; in the southern sections the commonest

meal of the peasants is olive oil and bread.   The upper part of
Andalusia is one great olive grove, but the trees are found everywhere
in the south, and less abundantly in the center.   The view from the
higher elevations in Andalusia often shows little except gray olive
trees, and an occasional whitewashed *hacienda,* belonging to some
landowner.   The export value of olives and olive oil is about twice

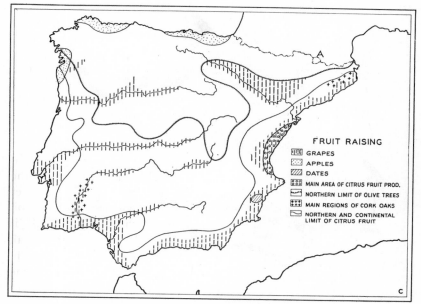

A. Fruit and Tree Crops in the Iberian Peninsula.

that of cork, but this represents only a small fraction of the full
value of the crop.   In 1949, Spain and Portugal together produced
390,000 metric tons of olive oil, three fourths of which came from
Spain.

Land utilization (A442) largely reflects climatic conditions.   In the
northern mountains, where the heavy rainfall (A439) is favorable for
meadows and grasslands, stock raising is the main rural industry.   To
the south, on the plateau of Old Castile, lies the chief agricultural
region of Spain, with wheat as the leading crop; still farther south
and east, barley has increasing importance.   On the western slopes
rye is prominent, and on the lowlands of northern Portugal corn
prevails.   But a dry summer limits grain production in the south,

and a large part of New Castile, south and east of Madrid, is of value chiefly for raising the famous Merino sheep.

Most of the region with a rainfall of less than 40 cm. (16 inches) in A439, together with the warmer, drier valleys to the southwest of it, forms the Campo Regadio, or the part of Spain where agriculture is feasible only with irrigation, in contrast to the Campo Secano, or

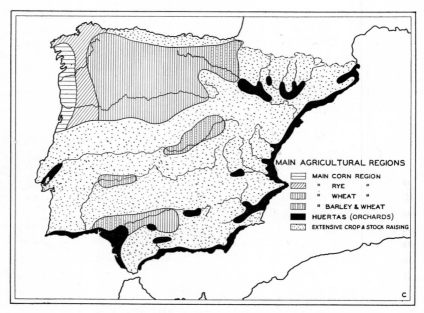

A. Agricultural Regions in the Iberian Peninsula.

dry fields to the north and west where the rainfall suffices. Irrigation is limited to a few sections along the rivers, such as the irrigated Ebro plain around Zaragoza, which is like an oasis in a dry, barren landscape; and the fertile Vega of Granada, the old Moorish capital.

The coastal plains, where water for irrigation is available, support the splendid Mediterranean fruit gardens or *huertas* (A442). By their high productiveness these make possible a dense population (A454), just as does the high rainfall of the northwest (A439). The huertas of Valencia and Murcia are famous for their luxuriant vegetation and subtropical crops. Practically anything can be raised, even cotton, sugar cane, and dates, but the main emphasis falls on citrus fruits and grapes (A441). The plain of Andalusia and the lowlands of southern Portugal are not so dependent on irrigation as are the eastern coastal plain and the Ebro Valley, for the rainfall is heavier here. Citrus fruits are important, although their importance cannot compare with that of olives.

Agricultural Products

Field Crops. Wheat, raised on more than 10 million acres in Spain and more than 1 million in Portugal, is the leading Iberian crop. This acreage almost equals that of France and exceeds that of Italy, the two most important wheat-producers of Europe outside Russia. However, the yield per acre is so small that the production is less than half the French crop and about half the Italian. Spanish wheat production by 1951 had not recovered from the effects of the Civil War and was averaging one third to one half less than in prewar years. In addition, a series of disastrous droughts contributed to the lowering of production. The low yields and the droughts help to explain the deplorable fact that in most years importation of wheat is necessary to meet the high consumption typical of most Latin countries. On the light alluvial soil of the Old Castile Basin and also in the south in Andalusia, where wheat is often raised between young olive trees, wheat fields dominate the landscape. Green in winter, they ripen in spring and lay a golden color over the rolling country. One of the familiar sights in the late spring and early summer is long lines of high, creaking, two-wheeled oxcarts, loaded with sheaves. Another is teams of horses and mules threshing the grain by walking around a central pole amid clouds of dust. In the late summer the fields lie bare and dusty, baked by the hot sun, until the autumn rains arrive and the farmer brings his oxen out for plowing.

Corn stands next to wheat as a grain crop for human food, but occupies only one-sixth the acreage devoted to wheat. It is characteristic of sections with relatively abundant summer rains, as in northern Spain and Portugal, but is also found in the south. There small patches are seen in many places, chiefly in the gardens around the villages where some water is available for irrigation. In northern Portugal corn is actually the main food crop. A combination of corn and olive oil, with the occasional addition of fish or meat, is the mainstay of the great mass of the population. Although corn is typical of the wet, northern border of the Iberian zone of wheat, barley replaces it where the rainfall is especially scanty. This is principally the case in the inner basins and in the Ebro Valley of

Aragon. Barley is used mainly as feed for horses and mules. Rye and oats, as in France, are upland crops where the rainfall is fairly abundant. On the Iberian Peninsula this limits them to the northwestern and northern mountain rim. Finally, rice is raised on the irrigated fields of the Mediterranean coastal plains. It is of very

A. Olive grove with old trees that combine trunks gnarled through centuries of existence with young, olive-bearing branches. Photograph by Ivan Dmitri for American Export Lines.

high quality and forms the basis of many specialties of the Spanish kitchen. In spite of the northern latitude, the yield per acre is almost twice as high as in Japan, the world's most intensive rice producer. Rice is a highly specialized crop and is restricted to only 120,-000 acres, with the production amounting to less than half that of Italy.

Horticulture. More than 5 million acres of olive trees and almost 4.5 million acres of grapevines are certainly astonishing figures. The products of both have been essential to Mediterranean life from the days of Greece and Rome and will probably long continue to be so. The olive tree seems never to be old enough to die. From the time when a little pyramid of earth protects the young plant until the time when the gnarled old stem sends out its last fruit-bearing branches, the plant looks old, but still it is as vital as Mediterranean culture itself. Most of the olives are used by the people for oil, but a great number are pickled when ripe. Green pickled olives comprise one eighth of the total value of the exports.

Grapes are widely distributed. They are found on the terraced slopes of deeply eroded river valleys, such as the Douro, the Tagus, and the Guadiana. They also abound on many of the Mediterranean coastal slopes. Fragrant wines varying in color from amber to a deep red have made the names of many localities famous all over the world. The port wine of Pôrto, the sherry named after Jérez in Andalusia, and the wines of Málaga and Alicante are exported in large quantities. Wine is the largest single item of export from both Spain and Portugal. Fresh grapes are also greatly appreciated and are exported in large quantities, Almería being the center of this trade.

In addition to olives and grapes, citrus fruits are a third type of horticultural product. Oranges attain special importance around Valencia on the east coast. The orange is not native; it was introduced by the Moors, who brought it from Arabia and originally from southeastern Asia. In the patios and gardens of old Moorish homes and mosques, rows of orange trees with their dark green foliage contrast pleasantly with the white walls round about. Extensive orange groves now produce fruit for both the home and foreign markets. Loaded ships carry them to less-favored climates as a gift from the Mediterranean when the grasp of rude winter is felt most keenly.

Almonds, which are increasing in importance as an export article, are characteristic of warm, sunny slopes in southern Spain and in the Balearic Islands. In Majorca the roads that radiate from Palma, the capital, toward the western mountains with their coastal resorts, cross large areas of well-planned almond groves. These are located on the alluvial lowland and are replaced by olive groves on the dry limestone slopes of the foothills. The importance of all these fruits not only as food for the people, but also as exports, may be realized from the fact that olives, grapes, oranges, and almonds supply half of the total Spanish exports. No such percentage of fruits and nuts is reached in any other European country except Greece, where the geographic conditions are very similar to those of the Iberian Peninsula. Other Spanish or Portuguese fruits include dates from the famous Elche date forest near Murcia, pineapples from the Portuguese Azores, and bananas from the Canary Islands. Early vegetables as well as special kinds like the artichokes of the Azores have some commercial value.

Livestock. In Spain and Portugal, as in all Mediterranean countries, domestic animals play an important role in human activities. Oxen, horses, and mules are used for work in the fields: they do the plowing; they pull the carts that bring in the crops; they thresh the grain. Donkeys burdened with amazing loads are a familiar sight in the villages, or may be seen blindfolded turning large water wheels. These pump the water from canals onto the fields. Six million goats browse in the bushy growth of maquis on the slopes. On the extensive inland plateau large herds of sheep are grazed, migrating in summer to higher elevations in search of grass. The swine fattened on the acorns in the oak forests form an important source of meat.

Among all the animals, however, only sheep have more than local importance. The name Merino is widely known for a superior kind of wool. Although cropland has invaded the steppes and limited the grazing grounds, there are still 22 million sheep in Spain (2 million in Portugal), and wool is an important export. In the northern mountains with their rainy climate, the western type of stock raising prevails, with most of Spain's dairy cattle and swine raised on the farms. Very typical is the breeding of bulls for bullfights. Every town of any significance has an arena where bullfights frequently take place. The constant demand for bulls, which are doomed to die, sponsors a widespread and prosperous industry.

Fishing. The animals of the sea support extensive sardine fisheries in Galicia along the Atlantic coast of Spain, and in Portugal. Tuna fish are caught along the Mediterranean shores, including the coast of Morocco, and even farther south off the Río de Oro of Africa. Sardines and tuna fish are exported in large quantities, but the total value of all exports from Spain and Portugal together by no means equals that of cork, and is a small matter compared with olives and wines. Moreover, the exports of fish are largely offset by imports of dried cod from Norway. In view of the fact that they are Roman Catholic countries, Spain and Portugal consume surprisingly little fish compared with northwestern Europe.

The Agricultural Situation. In both Spain and Portugal, agrarian conditions are bad. This is serious because in both countries more than half of the people depend directly upon agriculture. Except on the huertas, which were originally the work of the Moors, little has been done to make the land really productive, and the yields per acre are exceptionally low (A102). One of the chief reasons for this is the dry climate, which is comparable to that of Turkey. Not only does the paucity of the rainfall lead to small crops, but also its irregularity and frequent crop failures discourage improvements. The farmer never knows whether extra effort will prove fruitless because of scanty rain. On the irrigated land of the huertas no such difficulty arises, for the yield is not only large per acre but regular. This is one reason why the ancient Moors were able to rise so high in civilization and build structures like the famous Alhambra at Granada. The severity of the difficulty arising from scanty rainfall may be judged from the fact that from 1867 to 1875 Madrid had an annual average precipitation of only 13.6 inches (334 mm.), which is inadequate to produce good crops unless very favorably distributed throughout the year. From 1880 to 1888, on the other hand, the average was 20.6 inches (511 mm.), or 53 per cent more, which is enough to give good crops of winter wheat. In some years Madrid receives only a little more than one third as much rain as it does in others.

The difficulties due to climate are aggravated by the prevailing system of landholding. In the south the estates are enormous. The landowner may have a house on his land, although he generally spends most of his time in Madrid, but the laborers live in city-like villages, many of which are of astonishing size, up to 10,000 inhabitants or more. Every morning during the working season long lines of laborers with their high two-wheeled carts drawn by mules or oxen wend their way slowly for a mile or even five miles out to the fields. With their primitive equipment, the laborers accomplish little, even though they work rather long hours. When there is no work in the fields, the laborers stay in the villages and enjoy the talking, music, dancing, and other recreations that make Spanish life so attractive. But such a system, joined with the small yield of crops per acre, inevitably means great poverty, small capital with which to make improvements, and chronic political and social discontent.

In the north the peasants to a large extent own their land, but the holdings are so small that they produce barely enough to support their owners, leaving nothing with which to make improvements, buy better seed and stock, or lay by money for modern tools and machines. In both the north and the south pressure of population is a great curse. In the north, and wherever the peasants own the land, it means that each family has less land then it could easily and profitably cultivate. In the south, or wherever there are great estates, it means that laborers are so abundant that wages are very low and periods of idleness long. This has led to great emigration from the north where the people are especially alert and enterprising. It is probable that such emigration, dating back to the period immediately after the discovery of America, has done more harm to Spain than to most countries. It has taken away millions of the most able young men and in the final analysis has given nothing in return except temporary wealth that was soon squandered. Spain has lost practically all its colonial empire except a few bits in northwestern Africa. Moreover, although no exact data are available, there is reason to think that in Spain, taking the last four centuries or more as a whole, the emigrants have come from the higher levels of the population more commonly than in most of the European countries.

Geographically, the contrast between north and south is best shown in Portugal. Northern Portugal is primarily a country of valleys and mountains except for a fairly wide coastal plain, which, however, suffers from the fact that the immediate coastal section is not of much economic value because of its infertile sands and lagoon swamps. Comparatively mild winters (except for the high elevations), the high rainfall, and the shortness of the dry season in summer has made it an area of intensive production. Corn, which is generally irrigated, is the chief crop, but vineyards cover the valley terraces, especially in the Douro district. Cattle graze in the lowland meadows, and sheep are herded up the mountains in summer in a system of transhumance. Northern Portugal is still a well-forested area, with broad-leaved trees in the majority. Density of population is high (A454), except in the mountains. The farmers have small individual plots that are well cared for, and small towns and villages dot the landscape.

How different is southern Portugal! The low valley plateau south of the Tagus is almost treeless, and only on the slopes do such Mediterranean trees as the olive and cork oak break the feeling of complete monotony. It is the region of large holdings mainly devoted to wheat, the yield of which is low, and of sparse population living in a small number of little towns and villages. Walled cities and castles reflect the period of war against the Moors. Only where water is available for irrigation are there signs of higher productivity in rice fields and fruit gardens. On the southern coast, sheltered by the hills of the Serra de Monchique, one gets the impression of already being in North Africa; and it is as if the Moors had just left, although they actually left five centuries ago. Cities with white-painted, flat-roofed houses are surrounded by subtropical fruit trees. But, otherwise, the general impression is one of monotony—and of poverty.

The conditions among a large part of the people of the Iberian Peninsula who depend on the farms are almost medieval, and only a radical change is likely to work any improvement of consequence. Most Spaniards agree that something should be done, but, as so often happens there, adequate appropriate action does not follow. Attempts to improve Spanish agriculture have, indeed, been made since 1930, but they have been far short of what is necessary. Land expropriated from the Church in the early 1930's was returned to it after Franco became dictator. Some estates have been broken up, so that by 1948 one half of the Spanish farmers owned their land; but this figure indicates that much remains to be done, considering the agrarian situation in the country. The low level of mechanization is indicated by the fact that in 1949 Spain, along with Yugoslavia, had the highest number of acres of arable land per tractor in Europe (2,841 acres), although Poland was about the same. The figure for Spain might be compared with 247 for Ireland and Norway, 988 for Hungary, and 62 for the United Kingdom and Switzerland. The fact that a land like the Iberian Peninsula, which is still mainly agricultural and which was one of the granaries of the Roman Empire, imports part of its cereal, shows how faulty is the adjustment between the land and the people.

Manufacturing Industries

From the point of view of manufactures, the Iberian Peninsula is not well developed. Two regions in Spain, however, are exceptions: the northern industrial area around Bilbao, Santander, and Oviedo in Asturias; and the eastern industrial area of Catalonia with Barcelona as its leading city. Note how conspicuous these are in the map of population (A454). Both have the advantages of water power: the first, that of the Cantabrian Mountains; the other, that of the southeastern section of the Pyrenees.

Barcelona and the neighboring cities are the center of the Spanish textile industry, for here, as in most of the less-advanced countries, textiles come next to food as the first type of manufactures to be extensively developed. Imported cotton is all-important, for the Spanish domestic production is insignificant. In Portugal, the cities of Pôrto and Lisbon are textile centers. In both countries, the production is primarily for home use, but Barcelona exports a little, mainly to Latin America. The woolen industry is a very old one, based on the abundance of home-grown wool; of this Catalonia is also the center. Silk manufacture is little developed, although it has some local significance in Murcia.

Metalworks are mainly concentrated in the northern industrial center, and there is some shipbuilding at Bilbao and Barcelona, and also in the south at the Atlantic port of Cádiz. Leather industries are widespread but primitive. They are based on domestic materials, chiefly the skins of goats and sheep, and are particularly well developed in Barcelona and Pôrto. Sugar factories are operated in the sugar beet area of Old Castile and in the small sugar cane districts of the south coast; beets account for the greater part of the sugar production. Other industrial undertakings include tobacco factories (especially in Seville), fruit canneries, and fish-packing plants, as well as dairies in the northwestern corner. All industries and mines together, however, employ only one third as many men as do the farms, whereas in France the industrial and mining workers are two thirds as numerous as the farmers, and in the United Kingdom they are three times as numerous.

The possibility of expansion of Spanish manufacturing is shown by the fact that Spain has a water power potential, 5.7 million horsepower at minimum flow, greater than that of Switzerland (3.6) and even of Sweden (4) and almost as great as that of France (6) and Italy (6). Yet the developed capacity is only half that of Sweden, Norway, and Switzerland, and less than a third that of France and Italy. In billions of kilowatt-hours of hydroelectricity produced in 1950, several European countries ranked as follows:

TABLE A

Italy	22.2	Switzerland	10.3
Sweden	17.5	Western Germany	8.2
Norway	17.3	Austria	5.0
France	15.6	Spain	5.0
European Russia	12.0	Finland	3.6

No other country in Europe produced more than 1.5 billion kilowatt-hours. Thus, with sufficient capital and proper management, Spanish electric power from water could be increased to rank Spain along with Switzerland and France. Indeed, Spain was planning at mid-century to double its output of hydroelectricity and to electrify much of its railway system, but progress was slow. Severe droughts in the late 1940's curtailed hydroelectric production to one-third the normal level, indicating one of the hazards Spain faces not only in hydroelectric production but also in agriculture—including irrigated agriculture to some extent.

Historical Aspects

The population of Spain and Portugal, amounting in all to 37.2 millions, is of essentially one stock. This fact, together with the similarity of physical and economic conditions, makes it legitimate to treat the two countries as a unit for geographical study. Only the Basques at the western end of the Pyrenees form a distinct ethnographic remnant with their own unique language, customs, and characteristics, as is explained in Chapter 12. Spanish caves have revealed traces of the old population that, like that of the Central Plateau of France, was probably of the Cro-Magnon type. When the peninsula first became important as a part of the civilized world, it was already occupied by a rather homogeneous population, probably with some Celtic elements, in the form of a people called Iberians.

The Phoenicians, the traders of the ancient Mediterranean, came early to the Spanish peninsula, and the present city of Cádiz was originally one of their settlements. Later, Carthage established colonies along the eastern coast, among them the present Cartagena. These were subsequently taken over by the Romans, who occupied the entire peninsula. Only in the northern mountains did the native population remain independent, secure in the protection afforded by the rough and forested terrain. After the downfall of the Roman Empire, the Nordic Goths and Vandals invaded Spain from the Garonne Basin by way of Catalonia, but their biological influence has been relatively unimportant, although for some time they formed the ruling class.

The invasion of Iberia by Moors from North Africa was of the greatest influence on later development. They occupied most of the peninsula and even tried to follow the route of the Nordic tribes northward into France. Again the northern mountains provided a retreat, this time for the Christian population; and, during long centuries of struggle, central Spain and Portugal oscillated between Cross and Crescent.

In the south, especially along the coastal plain, which is in many respects like northern Africa, the Arab economic influence was great. The Moors introduced many of the present fruits and other crops—such as the orange, fig, and almond—and constructed aqueducts and irrigation works that are still in use and are the wonder of tourists. A period of high cultural development made southern Spain a prosperous country with numerous important and architecturally beautiful cities such as Seville, Córdoba, and Granada.

Then discord among themselves, and the degeneracy that often seems to ensue after an ethnographic group ceases to be strengthened by new and vigorous migrants and ideas, brought about the downfall of the Moors. Christian tribes from the north, aided by foreign knights, conquered one region after another, and at length the last Moorish stronghold, Granada, fell into their hands in 1492. With this, the economic picture changed profoundly. The proud Christian conquerors from the plateau looked down upon the soil-tillers of the coast, and lacked insight to realize the importance of their marvelous agriculture.

The location of Portugal away from the main lines of migration of both the Nordics and the Moors in the center and east of Spain may be one of the reasons for the general backwardness of that country in most respects. Almost the only numerically important migrants into that country for many centuries have been African Negroes. Being brought as slaves, they missed the selective action that is so important in free immigrants. Thus Portugal has been at a disadvantage compared with Spain not only in the biological quality of its immigrants, but also in the culture that they brought with them.

The great decline of Spain and Portugal had begun before the discovery of America, but mighty achievements abroad, and the discovery of new worlds, overshadowed the economic retrogression at home. Gold and silver poured into both countries, but the density of population in rural districts decreased and in Portugal, Negroes, whose biological influence is still perceptible, were imported to work in the fields. Spain and Portugal no longer possessed the power to maintain themselves as world empires, and gradually lost their sources of income. They became stagnant countries that, even during the nineteenth century, failed to share in the economic revival that touched most of the rest of Europe. But the people at home did not recognize this. In their own eyes they were still the conquerors, the cultural representatives of Europe, and they scorned the foreigners who began to develop their mines or to construct railroads for them. The Pyrenees were a real wall between modern Europe and Old Spain.

Change came, but slowly. The governing classes of noblemen and clergy at length professed to realize that the working population was the backbone of the country and not something to be despised. Measures were taken to increase production, improve transportation, and encourage trade. The last king, who was deposed in 1931, secured the construction of a splendid series of trunk highways. Motorcars today in Spain are largely confined to rich people in the cities. Accordingly, one may drive 20 or 30 miles over a fine road out in the country without meeting a car, but scores of springless mule carts or ox carts that use the soft shoulders of the road may be passed. Meanwhile the minor roads are as bad as ever—stony or muddy, steep, and often without bridges. In practically everything a similar trouble appears—that is, magnificence, charm, and beauty stand side by side with sordid poverty and backwardness. The trouble is that in most regions there is no strong middle class that wants solid, useful improvements and is able to pay for them.

The apparent beginnings of an awakening in Spain in the mid-1930's were counteracted by a conservative revolt, resulting in the Spanish Civil War. Nearly three years of fighting set the country back physically through the destruction of roads, bridges, and buildings that were difficult to replace in the retarded Spanish economy. But perhaps more damaging was the loss of forward momentum as a result of the war. Some forward steps have been made, but the full energy of the Spanish people has been repressed. A release of that energy—even operating as it must in a limited environment—would do much toward helping Spain join the march of modern development.

Political Sectionalism

The southward movement to thrust out the Arabs came from three separate sections that still retain their identity. One of these is now the independent republic of Portugal. The other two, centering in Castile and Aragon, are now united as Spain, but tend to pull apart. There are no important physical distinctions among the people of these three sections, and the differences in language are only enough to be annoying without making the three sections unintelligible. Portuguese independence arose partly from that country's physiographic aloofness on the coastal margin of the plateau, separated from Spain by rough mountain country and subjected to foreign influences, principally English.

The two sections that united to form Spain were, first, the rather secluded plateau of Old Castile, and, second, the Ebro Basin of Aragon with its irrigation and the Catalonian Coast, both of which were more open than other parts of Spain to the influence of France. These two sections were united by the marriage of their rulers, Ferdinand and Isabella, but this did not give them unity of interest. Un-

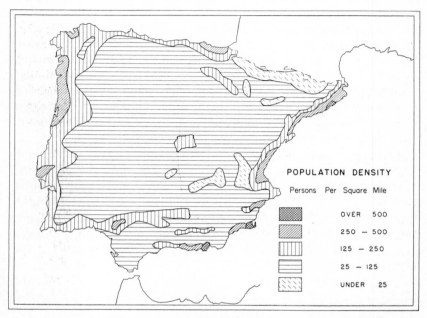

A. Density of Population in the Iberian Peninsula (persons per square mile).

affected by this union, the Catalonians conserved their own traditions and, as in so many other parts of Europe, a national revival occurred in the last century. This Catalonian movement is not really one for separation, even if it is sometimes called so; the industrial development there depends too closely on the Spanish hinterland to make absolute independence desirable. But the energetic, progressive Catalonian people hate the autocratic spirit of Castile and feel that they are making a disproportionately large contribution of taxes without getting much in return. Catalonia was the center of strongest resistance against the insurgent Nationalists during the Civil War, and Barcelona suffered rather severely from bombing. The Basques in the north, at the western end of the Pyrenees, have resisted not only the cultural influence of the Spanish but also excessive political interference. These independent people have been especially cool toward attempts of the Madrid government to dislocate their local educational system and customs.

The density of population varies widely in the different regions. The average density in Spain, on an area of 195,000 square miles, is 142 per square mile; and of Portugal, with an area of 34,400 square miles, 240 per square mile. In the coastal regions, the density rises to above 500 per square mile; in small northern industrial sections it even attains 850. In contrast, the density on the southern plateau is as low as 40 per square mile. The number of emigrants to South America from both countries is very high.

A typical example of the low cultural standard is the great proportion of illiterates: in Spain about 25 per cent, and in Portugal as many as 50 per cent. The northern part of each country contrasts favorably in this respect with the southern.

Cities

Madrid, the capital of Spain, with nearly 1.5 million inhabitants, is situated in the mathematical center of the peninsula, where it was located at the behest of Philip, king of Spain during the sixteenth century. Its environs have no great economic importance, and its buildings rise suddenly from the midst of wheat fields and sheep pastures. It is essentially a beautiful and aristocratic city, the cultural and financial center, and the focus of transportation, especially of the railroads that radiate to the coastal regions of Spain (A159). Valladolid is the only other important plateau city, and it has less than 131,000 inhabitants. It is the center of the agricultural region of Old Castile. All the other large cities lie either along the coast or in the main river valleys.

In the extreme northeast stands Barcelona, with a population somewhat smaller than that of Madrid, and not only the greatest industrial and commercial city of Spain, but also the principal port for foreign trade. Surrounded by busy, smaller industrial towns, it presents a sharp contrast to official Madrid. Zaragoza, an isolated industrial center, is the main city of the irrigated Ebro Basin, and stands amid extensive huertas watered by both the Ebro and Gallego rivers.

The densely populated coastal plain of the Mediterranean supports a succession of important cities, all of them except inland Murcia being located on harbors. Valencia, the largest of these, has considerable variety of local industries. Alicante, Cartagena (the naval base), Almería, and Málaga are all export harbors for the fruits of the coastal plain. The promontory of Gibraltar, guardian

A. Eastern slope of the Rock of Gibraltar. Smoothed slope to catch rainwater. Small fishing village on the shore of the Mediterranean. Courtesy of American Export Lines.

of the entrance to the Mediterranean, is an English stronghold. Cádiz, the southern Spanish port on the Atlantic, has international steamship connections, in particular with South America. Seville (Spanish: Sevilla) is the great inland center of the Andalusian Basin and can be reached by small steamers up the Guadalquivir. Palma on Majorca is the capital of the Balearic Isles.

Portugal has only two cities of importance: Lisbon (Portuguese: Lisboa) and Pôrto. Lisbon, with over 800,000 inhabitants, lies at the mouth of the Tagus River, and is the capital of the country as well as its principal port. Although it has lost much of its one-time international importance as a transfer point where Mediterranean and South Atlantic commerce once met that of the north, it is still a port of call for many lines from northern Europe to South America, Africa, and even Asia and Australia. Located on the estuary of the Tagus at the junction between northern and southern Portugal, it has all the attributes to make it a large city. To this can be added the beauty of its location, its many points of historic interest, and even its attraction to visitors who enjoy the very mild winters. The sheltered coast west of Lisbon is a veritable Riviera lined with resort towns. Pôrto on the Douro River is the principal harbor of northern Portugal and an industrial center.

The drowned coastline of Galicia offers excellent harbor facilities, but the connections with the hinterland are difficult on account of the severe mountain relief. In addition to being fishing ports the leading harbors, La Coruña and Vigo, have some importance as intermediate ports of call for certain steamship lines.

On the northern coast are mineral-exporting towns like Gijón and Santander, while inland Oviedo is the center of ironworks; but Bilbao is the leading port. It carries on important manufacturing by means of coal brought from England in ships that come for iron ore. Like Barcelona, it is a modern, energetic town, rapidly progressing. San Sebastián, near the French border, is well-known as a shore resort, the rival of Biarritz in France. The small independent principality of Andorra high up in the Pyrenees between France and Spain also deserves mention (A in A182). Although it has an area of only 191 square miles and a population of about 5,400, its independence of both France and Spain gives proof of the protective influences of the mountain fastnesses.

Transportation

Like so many other things in Spain and Portugal, transportation is not yet up to modern standards. One reason is the great expense of construction imposed by the difficulties of relief. A few international railway lines connecting Lisbon, Madrid, and Barcelona with France maintain good schedules, but traffic along the other lines is generally light and slow. The main line from France to Madrid climbs from San Sebastián up to the plateau and continues via Burgos, the old capital of Spain, and Valladolid to Medina. There a branch turns southwest to Lisbon, and the main line crosses the high central divide. The existing system of railways radiating from Madrid can do little to satisfy the modern requirements of commerce. New lines are under construction and will help to develop remote corners and bring the various regions into closer relation with one another. It should be mentioned, however, that in 1949 a Basque military engineer invented an "articulated train," with each coach having wheels only on the rear end—one of the most radical and interesting changes in passenger rail transportation in decades.

The rivers of the Iberian Peninsula have little value as means of transportation, for their beds are rocky and dry in summer. The highways, even the good ones between the main cities, need far more care than they get, and most of the others are scarcely better than they were a hundred years ago.

The traditional importance of the Spanish and Portuguese merchant fleets waned with the other glories of these countries. The Castilian conquerors of Spain lacked any aptitude for sea trade, and with few exceptions the coasts offered little opportunity for modern harbor developments. Recently, however, especially in Spain, there has been a revival in this respect, and new lines once more connect Spain with lands across the seas. The Spanish merchant fleet amounts to not quite 1.5 per cent of the world's total; that of Portugal is negligible except for sailing vessels.

Trade

Nearly a third of the fruits, wines, olive oil, minerals, cork, and other exports of Spain has, since World War II, been taken by the United Kingdom, and about one tenth by France. The United States has taken only 6 per cent, principally in cork and olives. The Spanish imports come primarily from Argentina (wheat and corn), United Kingdom (fish, iron and steel, machinery, and coal), the Netherlands, and the United States. Portuguese exports amount to a little more than a tenth of those of Spain, and of these only 6 or 7 per cent usually come to the United States. The main exports are wine, sardines, and cork. The imports are two or three times as valuable as the exports, and one seventh or one eighth comes from the United States—mainly cotton, iron and steel, and coal. The extremely unfavorable trade balance, especially in Portugal, is an ill omen. It reflects the unfavorable agrarian situation, which in turn is primarily a matter of poor rainfall, overpopulation, and consequent lack of capital and of the opportunity and incentive for new methods. How far the supposedly volatile but really conservative and, on the whole, industrious but unprogressive character of the main mass of the Spaniards is a result or a cause of the economic and political difficulties is a matter of great dispute.

Overseas Territories

The relative unimportance of most of the Spanish and Portuguese overseas territories and the non-entry of Spain and Portugal in most

A. Northwest coast of Majorca (Balearic Islands). Terrace agriculture, vineyards, forested limestone mountains dropping steeply to the sea. Photograph by Ivan Dmitri for American Export Lines.

world disputes often hides the fact that both countries have a number of overseas holdings. Indeed, the Portuguese Empire is the fourth largest in the world, ranking after those of Britain, France, and Belgium. These colonial holdings do not include the Azores (Portuguese: Açores) and Madeira Islands, which are administered as an integral part of Portugal; nor, for Spain, do they include the Balearic Islands (Spanish: Islas Baleares) and the Canary Islands, both groups of which are likewise administered as integral parts of

Spain. All these island groups are principally significant as producers of various subtropical and tropical fruits such as citrus fruits and bananas.

Portugal's two largest possessions are Angola (Portuguese West Africa) and Mozambique (Portuguese East Africa), which produce sugar, coffee, sisal, fish, cotton, and copra. Island possessions include the Cape Verde group off west Africa, São Tomé and Principe in the Gulf of Guinea, and Timor (only half of which Portugal owns) in the East Indies. Finally, Portugal controls Macao on the China coast west of Hong Kong, Portuguese Guinea on the west African coast, and three small areas on the west coast of India: Goa (the largest), Diu, and Damão. All these territories together cover 803,-835 square miles and have a population of nearly 13 million. They are the remnants of the once great empire that in the sixteenth and seventeenth centuries covered many times the present extent.

Spain's colonial holdings are not only much more modest in extent (135,000 square miles) and population (1.5 millions) than those of her small western neighbor, but they are much less valuable. Scattered from the Strait of Gibraltar around the western bulge of Africa to the Gulf of Guinea, they include Spanish Morocco (a protectorate), the tiny enclave of Ifni (administered as part of Spain), Spanish Sahara (combining Río de Oro and Sekia el Hamra), and Spanish Guinea (including Río Muni on the coast and Fernando Po and four other small islands). Three fourths of these holdings are included in Spanish Sahara, which actually has a smaller population and less trade than Ifni!

The Outlook

Both Spain and Portugal need a great deal of help to overcome accumulated handicaps of inertia and mismanagement. In spite of certain physical handicaps and limitations, both countries could be fairly productive if the production were well planned. What is needed is an overhaul of existing agricultural practices, introduction of a certain amount of mechanization, and a rejuvenation and expansion of manufacturing. Such a program requires capital and know-how. Both countries need at present the profits of their exports to pay for the food imports that continue to be required. Portugal, for instance, sells wine, cork, and sardines, and buys primarily food—dried cod, wheat, and sugar. Spain exports similar products—citrus fruit, wine, cork, and cotton fabrics of the Barcelona area, and in return imports primarily food products and raw cotton.

Only foreign capital could furnish sufficient funds, but much money is needed and both countries are poor risks. Portugal has certain advantages over Spain, which faces a partly antagonistic world. The results are visible. In Portugal, which received millions of dollars in ERP funds, one sees some progress even away from the cities. Spain does not give that impression, and many of the reasons for that are political and not geographic. Still the future is not a hopeless one. The people themselves still have the qualities that once made these nations leaders in the world. Political stability, capital, and an appreciation of human values would go a long way toward securing a better future.

· 29 ·

Italy (Italia)
and Its Regions

The Uniqueness of Italy

Italy is unique in many ways. It is the only country of southern Europe that became a great power in the modern sense, although the development was short lived and was incomplete. It is the only one of the great powers that has risen repeatedly to greatness—in antiquity, in medieval times if the great northern cities are considered as Italy, and during the twentieth century. Again, in proportion to its size it has an extremely long coastline, but the lack of good harbors has caused its development as a sea power to be very sporadic, and there have been long intervals when the sea has almost been forgotten. Then, too, Italy's capital, Rome, has been a world center in more ways and for a longer time than any other city. Also unique is the way in which the shifting of the center of power in Italy has epitomized the corresponding but greater shift in Europe. Sicily and the south of the mainland were the first parts of the country to emerge into civilization. Then Rome and the central part of the peninsula occupied the main place on the stage of history. In medieval times the northern part of the peninsula, with Florence as its most famous center, came close to being the most enlightened and progressive part of the world. And now the Po Basin, especially its western end where Milan and Turin are located, probably does more than even Rome itself to maintain the position of Italy as a great power. Its significance is further examined below.

Evolution of Modern Italy

With the decline of the Italian states during the period from the sixteenth to the nineteenth century, other parts of Europe surpassed Italy, and it became the scene of the interplay of foreign powers, such as France, Spain, and Austria. Politically fragmented, it lacked unity, and only the location of the seat of the Pope gave it a certain prestige. For 300 years a substantial part of the peninsula was under the domination of one or more foreign powers. Modern Italy was born only in the middle of the nineteenth century; and, for the first time since the Romans, Italy within its northern mountain frame, which made it a perfect geographic unit, was an independent state. Its economic and political growth was rapid. The Po Basin, an area of high productivity, became one of the outstanding areas of Europe's industrial development.

Perhaps exaggerating its importance, Italy at times dreamed of political greatness and started down the road to expansion and conquest. Playing a rather tragic role in World War I, it gained some territory in the northeast (see A178 and A180). The Italian role in World War II was even more tragic than that it played in World War I. After its ordeal of suffering and destruction, physical as well as moral, Italy is now trying to reconstruct its economy and find its proper place among the nations of Europe. Politically still rather unstable, with a strong communist party that evolved in economic misery and that sabotages many of the efforts for improvement, Italy has a difficult road ahead. One of its chief problems is the unhealthy contrast between north and south—a problem important enough to put it ahead of the regional discussion.

A Contrast

On the map of the economic-cultural divisions of Europe (A15), Italy is the only country that contains extensive areas of all three zones: A in the north, C in the south, and B as a transitional belt. Obviously, then, a great contrast exists between northern and southern Italy, a contrast that merits analysis. However, the obvious fact should be kept in mind that, in what is said about southern Italy, there are some exceptions to the general conditions of backwardness and that, for instance, certain areas in Sicily, such as those around Palermo and Mount Etna, vie in production with any other part of the country. What is said below concerns the averages.

To begin with agriculture, a first fact is that northern Italy has a great variety of crops. It is true that among the grains wheat prevails, but the value of rice or corn is as great as that of wheat. Furthermore, there is a great variety of fruit and also industrial crops such as hemp. Yields are high, even for Europe, although not reaching those of the North Sea countries. In contrast, southern Italy has primarily a wheat economy. Olives and citrus fruit are locally important, and grapes are typical in virtually all Italian landscapes.

The yield per acre between north and south is, however, significantly different. The southern average of wheat yield per acre is only two-fifths that of the Po Basin—a tremendous difference. Moreover, the north is the center of Italy's dairy production, whereas in the south cattle are few, and sheep prevail. Industrially, the contrast is even more striking. Northern Italy is one of Europe's chief areas of manufacturing, possessing great modern factories and producing high-grade goods. The south has practically no industries except for small local plants and home industries. From the human point of view, the south shows a high rate of increase of population, despite a high death rate. The average worker makes only about 70 per cent the average income of Italy, which means about one-half the income of the northern worker. The average number of persons per room is 1.5 for northern Italy and 2.9 for the southern part, where 40 per cent of the population lives in overcrowded, congested, and inadequate dwellings. Only one half of the houses have electricity, and only one in 25 a bath. Illiteracy is high—39 per cent in contrast to 12 per cent for the rest of Italy. Although the population density is low compared with that of the north, the land is actually quite overpopulated for the present economy, and up to 400,000 people yearly emigrate. Shortage of arable land and prevalence of large landholdings, often with absentee landlords—in contrast to the much smaller properties in the north generally owned by the farmer—cause unrest and spread of communism.

The reasons for this contrast are only partly geographic, and they will be discussed in this chapter. They include such factors as less favorable climate and relief and lack of irrigation possibilities in the south. But the poor showing of the south is also the outcome of a long period of mismanagement and neglect: Italy's major interest has long been centered in northern Italy, and the south was left to itself. It was only rather recently that Italy awoke to the fact that the south was like a spreading cancer and that something had to be done in order to avoid misery and chaos. What is being done will be discussed later.

The Importance of the Po Basin

In view of the contrast described in the preceding section, the advantages possessed by the Po Basin will be given special attention. These advantages are as complex as they are numerous, and it is difficult to separate one from another. It would seem, however, that the importance of the north reflects not only its economic development but also the quality of its people. Regardless of whether one "race" or another displays innate superiority, it seems to be true, as has been mentioned again and again, that migrants of any group who have traveled far, endured much hardship, and overcome many difficulties tend to have more than the usual ability and to pass on to their descendants a kind of energy, originality, and determination that leads to high achievement. The Po Basin affords an example of this. In Italy itself, and wherever the country as a whole is well known, it is generally recognized that the northern Italians are on the average much more forceful and energetic than those of the south. Mazzini, Garibaldi, Cavour, Marconi, and Mussolini are examples of the kind of men who have arisen there. The fact that northern Italy has a genuinely cyclonic climate has been a help in giving the northerners energy, but the selection due to migration appears also to be important. In the north for two thousand years or more there has been a repeated influx of virile immigrants derived from the survivors of long periods of struggle, hardship, and migration. In the south the same human stock has persisted for hundreds or even thousands of years. Phoenicians, Greeks, Arabs, and Normans have all come to Sicily but have mostly disappeared. Thus there seems to have been only slight admixture of strong new elements, and little to weed out the less adaptable, less original, and more conservative types that were established long ago.

The migrations into the Po Basin have been largely stimulated by the economic attractions of that fertile and beautiful region. Time and again in European history the plain of the Po has aroused the avarice of neighboring countries, notably France and Austria, as its numerous battlefields bear evidence. Enclosed though it is by one of the strongest natural boundaries in the world, foreign armies from Hannibal's to Napoleon's have surmounted enormous difficulties to invade its fertile cropland and meadows. The proud, ancient names of towns along its borders and on higher spots, secure from floods, within the plain itself, are reminders that this region, like Belgium, is one of the important older sources of Europe's political and cultural progress. Then in the nineteenth century, when Italy gradually freed itself from foreign domination and struck out on a course of self-determination, the northern plain was the center of the new economic development, adding manufacturing industries to its former cultural contributions and to the produce of its soil.

The advantage enjoyed by the northern Italians in having greater cultural contacts with the main body of Europe has also contributed to its greater development. The proximity has had the detraction of inviting invaders, it is true, but these invaders and the travelers of peacetime have brought ideas that were not taken into southern Italy, where only a much smaller number of visitors came by sea.

Although they have perhaps been given too much attention by Italy, the manufacturing industries of the Po Basin are one of Italy's chief advantages when the country is compared with others in the Mediterranean. Denied resources of coal and iron, Italy has based its modern industrial development upon water power, particularly from Alpine sources, and upon cheap but skillful labor, thus demonstrating the superior importance of power and skill over raw materials.

This development is still in full swing. It involved serious difficulties, but the growth of population and the consequent mounting imports of food evoke urgent efforts. The depression after World War I was perhaps more severely felt in Italy than elsewhere, for the country was still relatively young in its new industrial role and had not yet become economically stabilized. The development during the Mussolini regime was not offset by destruction during World War II, but the disruption was very severe.

Structure and Landforms

Knowledge of the landforms of Italy is basic to any understanding of the geography of the country. A glance at a physical map shows that mountains predominate and that, except for the Po Basin, lowlands are relatively few and limited in size. For this discussion, four major regions are recognized: the Alpine Border, the Apennines, the Sub-Apennines, and the Lowlands.

The Alpine Border. Italy is cut off from central and western Europe by the highest mountain system of the continent. The entire land boundary of the country from the Riviera to the Adriatic Sea follows more or less closely the central divide of the Alps until in northeastern Italy it turns south and descends the slopes of the Julian Alps to the Adriatic. Most of the slopes of the Alps within this great arc are too rugged for human habitation, and the valleys are very steep-sided because during the Ice Age the glaciers scooped out their bottoms into a U-shape and converted the sides into cliffs. Almost the only habitable portions are the valley bottoms and the numerous terraces that indicate successive phases of valley development. Heavy precipitation and great elevation cause snow to accumulate deeply at the higher levels. Meltwater descending the

and consequently are forced to give up practically all their moisture before descending the Italian side, where they are drier and warmer than they were originally. This föhn effect is better developed on the Swiss side of the Alps. The relatively mild winter climate and subtropical vegetation that characterize the lake region combine with the superb beauty of the lakes to make them famous as winter resorts, as well as great favorites of tourists all the year round. The contrast between the open, rolling morainic scenery at their southern ends and the grim, majestic, precipitous scenery where they penetrate deep into the mountains at their northern ends is superb.

The Apennines. In northwestern Italy, the Maritime Alps, curving southward and even southeastward from the main chain, merge gradually into the much lower Apennines. The Apennines differ in structure and relief from the Alps, and are not themselves uniform throughout. Starting from the main chain in the Ligurian Alps, they branch off in a succession of ranges that overlap *en echelon.* The best-known of these are the Apuanian range, with its famous marble quarries near Carrara northwest of Florence, and the Etruscan Apennines, which form the main chain. Tucked away on a mountain top in the eastern part of these mountains is <u>San Marino</u>, an independent republic that claims to be the oldest state in Europe. With an area of 38 square miles and a population of 12,000, it is important chiefly because of political uniqueness and the postage stamps that it issues, mostly for collectors. It causes Italy some difficulty in that Italian businessmen often register their firms in San Marino to avoid Italian taxation. In 1950 the tiny republic had more business firms registered than it had inhabitants! The Apennines tower highest in their central section in the two ranges of Abruzzi east of Rome, where the Gran Sasso reaches 9,584 feet. Farther south in Basilicata (the instep of the foot of Italy), Calabria (the ball of the foot), and Sicily, this Apennine mountain chain is marked by more widely separated uplifted blocks between which lie lower sections. Thus, the Apennines fall into a threefold division: Northern, Central, and Southern.

The various portions of the Apennines differ materially in geological composition and hence in appearance. In the north, clay and sand formations generally prevail, giving rise to well-rounded summits and slopes, and exhibiting remnants of an older peneplain that has been uplifted and eroded. The Central chain consists mainly of limestone that forms many bold cliffs, whereas in the Southern blocks this is combined with outcrops of older granites and

gneisses that stand out because of their hardness. The divide between the Adriatic and Tyrrhenian seas follows the eastern side of
the Apennines quite closely until the spur near Foggia is reached.
There it swerves westward toward the Tyrrhenian coast, to which it
approaches especially close in Sicily. Because of the location of the
mountains, the rivers on the east side of the Italian Peninsula lie
close together and flow swiftly in short parallel courses into the
Adriatic. Their alluvial deposits form broad, flat fans that merge
into a narrow plain along the east coast and that have joined the
former island of the soft limestone Gargano Plateau (the spur) to the
mainland. At a few places the Apennines include volcanoes like
Vultura, halfway between Naples and Bari (A468). Another such volcano is high Etna (10,740 feet) in eastern Sicily. Extending northwestward from the heel of Italy is the dry limestone plateau of le
Murge.

   Sub-Apennine Italy. The irregular courses of the rivers that drain
the southwestern side of the Apennines illustrate the fact that most
of the region from Florence to Rome and Naples is an irregular mass
of low mountains, many of which are volcanic. The curious right-
angled course of the Tiber is caused by a depression arising from the
geological structure. Lake Trasimeno, famous from the time of
Hannibal, falls in this same structural depression and is surrounded
by lava. On the southwest the depression is bounded by a complicated but low range of mountains called the Sub-Apennines. Their
chief distinguishing characteristic is their recent volcanic nature.
Southern Tuscany is entirely of volcanic origin with lakes like Bol-
sena marking former craters. Here cities such as Perugia, with its
stone houses, look out from lofty hilltops over rolling, well-cultivated
slopes that resemble the stiff background of the paintings of the
older Italian masters. It is a charming country no matter whether
the wheat is green in early spring or the grapes and olives are being
harvested in the fall.

   South of the so-called Campagna Romana, or Tiber lowland in
which lies Rome, the volcanic structure continues in the Alban Hills
and others southeast of Rome. It is exemplified still more fully
around Naples, with the famous Vesuvius as the outstanding feature.
This crater attracts thousands of tourists who find there an opportunity to see a constantly active volcano with the pleasantly modern
facilities of a cable railroad. The Lipari Islands north of Sicily are
also volcanic. There Stromboli, the chief active volcano, emits frequent little puffs of incandescent ashes and serves as a natural light-

house for passing vessels at night. These volcanic regions, in proportion to their size, are the most productive parts of Italy. Around Naples, for instance, the soil has been intensively cultivated for centuries. The combination of warm climate, adequate moisture, and fertile, volcanic soil makes possible a density of population unknown in other agricultural sections of Europe, and even approaching the great density of certain sections of the Far East.

In concluding this sketch of the Italian highlands, Corsica (French) and Sardinia (Italian) may be mentioned. They belong for the greater part to the resistant rocks that form the central parts of Spain and Germany. The east coast of Corsica, however, is a continuation of the Alpine region, whereas western Sardinia presents in the south a landscape of more typically Apennine forms, and farther north an extensive young volcanic section where lava covers great areas.

The Lowlands of the Peninsula. Aside from the Po Basin, the lowlands of Italy are few in number, limited in extent, and scattered. The most important of the peninsular plains are: the Pisan Plain, extending up the Arno to Florence, where it continues northwestward to Pistoia and southeastward to the Val di Chiana, and combining old lake beds with recent marine deposits; the Grosseto Plain along the Maremma Coast east of Elba; the Campagna Romana, including the Pontine Plain; the fertile Campania around Naples; the Campidano in southern Sardinia; the Catanian Plain in east-central Sicily; and, largest of all, the Tavoliere, south of the Gargano Peninsula. The Tavoliere played a major role in the air aspect of World War II by furnishing vast flat areas for aircraft landing fields, first for the Nazis and then, to a much greater extent, for the American and British bombers.

Most of these lowlands are centers of peninsular Italy's agricultural development and are densely populated. Some of them, however, have come into considerable production only during the third and fourth decades of the twentieth century, and population is not densely settled on them. However, rolling hill areas—such as those of Tuscany, of the dissected slopes of Marche and Abruzzi-Molise on the eastern side of the peninsula, and of Sicily—produce large crops, but their yield per acre tends to be low.

Imperfect drainage and the resultant swamps and malaria have always been a serious obstacle to the development of these lowlands. Often the lowlands have been cultivated by people who did not dare live there, but located their villages on higher land some distance away.   Much of the marshiness is inherent in the origin of the plains, many of which began as deltas, lake bottoms, or filled-in coasts. Nearly all of them have expanded appreciably in historical times with addition of alluvial material.   Centuries of neglect, chaos, and weak government caused many of the plains to be poorly utilized, and the marshes became highly malarial.   The debilitating effect of malaria further weakened the energy of the people who could most easily have drained the marshes, and by the early twentieth century malaria was a serious problem in many parts of Italy.   One sensible program of the Italian government under Mussolini was extensive drainage and reclamation of marshy areas, work that was carried on not only in every one of the lowlands listed above but also in vast sections of the eastern Po Basin.   By the outbreak of World War II, hundreds of square miles were changed from disease-ridden, swampy grazing lands to productive grain-producing areas with new towns and roads.   Malaria was decreased greatly.   When the American forces moved up the Italian Peninsula especially during 1944, their systematic use of DDT did more to wipe out the malarial mosquito than most previous efforts—a fact in which the Italians can take some comfort when they contemplate the damage inflicted by the war. Reclamation continues in the Italian lowlands, partly with the help of ERP funds, but much remains to be done.

The Po Basin.   The plain of the Po, comprising about one fifth of Italy, supports nearly two fifths of the population.   Alluvial material, brought .from the Alps by rivers and glaciers, and from the Apennines by rivers, has converted this one-time extension of the Adriatic Sea into a vast, fertile lowland sloping gently toward the Adriatic coast.   The eastern part is still swampy, although much less so than it was before extensive drainage work during the 1930's, and has sand bars along the shore enclosing salt-water lagoons.   Taken as a whole, however, the north Italian plain with its young soil presents the best example of Italian rural as well as industrial development.

The present inland location of former harbors, like Ravenna and Adria, indicates a rapid growth of the land into the shallow Adriatic.   As in Holland, the rivers are often bordered by dikes, because sedimentation has raised their beds above the surface of the plain, and high water causes serious floods.   The course of the Po, well over toward the southern side of the plain, indicates that more alluvial material has come from the high, well-watered Alps with their glaciers than from the lower and drier Apennines.   Where there are no lakes, as in Venezia, the Alpine rivers are often real torrents, wide and swift, and during the period of heavy rainfall a serious hindrance to transportation. Their effectiveness was demonstrated during the advance of the German and Austrian armies in 1917, when the rushing Piave and Brenta were perhaps an even more formidable obstacle to the invasion of northern Italy than were the Italian armies.

Mineral Resources and Water Power

As is natural in a geologically young country, Italy is poor in mineral resources. Coal, the great source of power in western Europe, is almost entirely absent except for small deposits on Sardinia; hence, coal is one of Italy's principal imports. Fortunately, however, water power is plentiful, chiefly around the Po Basin, where the mountain valleys, especially those of the Alps with their more constant water supply, are dotted with power stations. As a producer of hydroelectricity, Italy ranks first in Europe, although the per capita production is higher in Switzerland and Scandinavia. Nearly 90 per cent of Italian electric power is generated by water power. The western Po Basin is crisscrossed by high-tension electric lines transmitting power from the Alpine valleys to the great industrial centers of Turin and Milan. Between 1938 and 1950, Italy increased its hydroelectric capacity well over one third and hopes to increase it still more. Capacity of installed plants already amounts to more than 100 per cent of the potential at minimum flow. Thus, further increase will become more and more difficult, unlike the situation in Norway, which can easily double or triple its present installed capacity. Iron ore is mined on the Isle of Elba and the adjacent mainland of Tuscany, but the amount is small; and large amounts of iron and steel have to be imported in addition to imports of iron ore and scrap. Sardinia and Tuscany produce approximately 2 per cent of the world's lead and 3.5 per cent of the zinc.

Italy's loss of Istria deprived the country of most of the bauxite resources (although some remain in the heel and in the region south of the Gran Sasso) and some of the mercury (in Idria), but Italy is still a major world producer of mercury, from deposits in Tuscany. Sicily adds to Italy's mineral resources by producing some asphalt, but its chief contribution is sulphur from deposits of gypsum; however, American competition has decreased Sicily's share of world sulphur production to 4 per cent. A petroleum pool was discovered in 1949 southeast of Piacenza in the Po Valley, but production was negligible by 1951.

Altogether, this short survey reveals that only in water power and mercury is Italy well off and that any development of industries, especially heavy industries, must be based only on such factors as electric power, labor, and market.

Climate

Temperature. With the exception of the Po Basin, the climate of Italy is truly Mediterranean; hot, dry summers alternate with mild, rainy winters. But, even in winter, blue skies generally prevail, and dull, cloudy days are comparatively rare. The summer temperature differs little between Sicily in the south, with a July average of 80° F, and the plain of the Po in the north with a July average of 76°, but of course the mountains are cooler. In winter the differences are more marked, the average January temperature ranging from close to the freezing point at Turin and Milan to 53° F at Messina in Sicily. In the interior the peaks are covered with snow, and among the mountains the cold air coming from above often causes even the low basins to have temperatures below the freezing point. Nevertheless, outside the Po Basin snow is rare in the parts of Italy where most of the people live. The most curious feature of Italy's temperature is the belt of relatively high winter temperature around the lakes at the foot of the Alps, and especially on the Riviera coast south of the western or Ligurian Apennines, and on the peninsulas and islands at the head of the Adriatic Sea. For reasons already explained, such a place as Locarno (in Switzerland) at the head of Lake Maggiore is 2° F warmer in January than is one like Milan, which lies 300 feet lower and two thirds of a degree farther south. The other two cases are far more impressive, because the proximity of the warm Mediterranean Sea is added to the effects of southward-facing slopes and protection by high mountains against cold winds. The Riviera is represented by Genoa, where the January temperature, 46° F, is nearly the same as at Naples four degrees of latitude farther south. The Dalmatian islands at the northern end of the Adriatic are equally warm, although Skopje, less than 1,000 feet above sea level in the interior of Yugoslavia and as far south as Rome, averages 29°.

The Warm Mediterranean. The winter warmth of the Mediterranean Sea may be traced to the fact that the heat stored up during the long, sunny summers has no chance to escape by means of ocean currents. The Strait of Gibraltar, the only opening to the main ocean, is not only relatively narrow (11.5 miles), but shallow (1,300 feet). Therefore not much of the warm Mediterranean water flows out on the surface there, and the cold deeper water of the Atlantic has no chance to come in. Consequently the lower parts of the Mediterranean Sea remain stagnant and have an almost uniform temperature of approximately 56° F (13° C). This helps to explain not only the mild winters of places like the Riviera and the Dalmatian coast, but also two other less favorable conditions. One of these is the relatively poor quality of the Mediterranean fisheries. Practically all the best fisheries elsewhere are associated with cool currents and especially with places where cold and warm currents meet. The Mediterranean water has an almost tropical character, and so have its fisheries. The other unfavorable effect resulting from the enclosed character of the Mediterranean is the hot summers. San Francisco in California and Messina in Italy lie at almost the same latitude and have about the same January temperature (50° and 53°). San Francisco, however, is exposed to an open ocean where cold water comes down from the north and wells up from below. Hence its July temperature averages only 57° F (September 59°) in contrast to 79° at Messina. Even at Genoa the July average is 75°, which is 10° or 12° above the ideal for human health.

Advantages of the North. Although northern Italy has no such cool, bracing summers as has the narrow coastal strip of California, it enjoys two real advantages compared with the south. One is winters that have a temperature (38°) not far from what appears to be the mental optimum, and the other is frequent cyclonic storms. Some of the storms sweep in from the Atlantic across southern France; others originate in the stormy Gulf of Lions south of Marseille, or even in the Po Basin itself. This fact, combined with the fairly equable seasonal distribution of rain and to a lesser degree of atmospheric moisture, increases the healthfulness and invigorating qualities of the northern climate in contrast to that of the south.

Rainfall. The economic value of the more abundant and steadier rain of the north is also considerable. The total annual rainfall of Italy (A476) varies according to two main factors. One is latitude, for there is a decrease from north to south. The other is the mountains and their relation to the prevailing west winds that cause the western slopes of the mountains to have much more rain than have the areas in the rain shadows to the east of them. On the whole the total annual rainfall is high for a country with the Mediterranean type

of climate. The rain comes usually in heavy showers that cause
numerous landslides, or *frane,* on the soft formations of the Apennines.

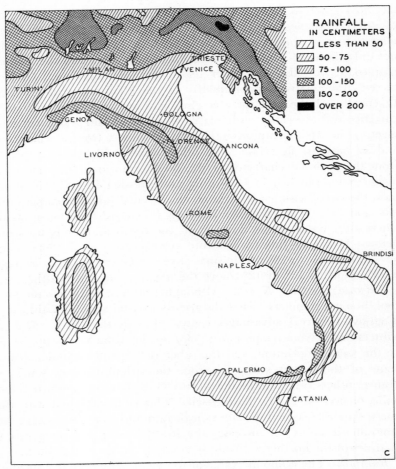

A. Precipitation in Italy.

In addition to the contrast in the amount of rainfall from north
to south there is also an important difference in seasonal distribution. A477 shows the average seasonal rainfall at four northern cities
in the Po Basin (Turin, Milan, Bologna, and Venice) compared
with four southern cities (Naples, Bari, Gallipoli, Messina). The

double maximum of the north in spring and fall contrasts strongly with the single maximum of the south in winter. The occurrence of a good rainfall in the spring and of a moderate rainfall in the summer means a tremendous advantage to the north not only in the yield of crops per acre, but likewise in the reliability of the crops from year to year. These conditions also enable the north to raise good grass and forage for dairy cattle, whereas the south with its dry, brown summer hillsides has to keep the far less profitable sheep and

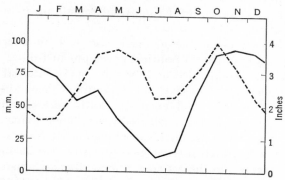

A. Comparison of Rainfall Regimes of Northern and Southern Italy. Dashed line is average of rainfall in four cities of northern Italy; solid line represents four cities in southern Italy.

goat. Moreover, the great height of the northern mountains causes them to supply far more water for irrigation than is possible in the south, and the spring and summer precipitation maintains this throughout the growing season. The great advantages of northern over southern Italy become clear when to all these climatic advantages are added those arising from the broad fertile plains, the immigration of active people, and the nearness of this region to other parts of Europe from which stimulating ideas are received.

Land Utilization

Italy's warm climate, good winter rainfall, and fertile soil have from the earliest times made the country attractive. When Greece was in its prime and when Rome was first developing, Sicily was the most valuable island of the Mediterranean world, and many wars were fought for its possession. The Italian peninsula, too, offered numerous advantages. Greek colonists occupied the toe of Italy in such numbers that it was called "Magna Græcia" (Great Greece).

The sunny hills of Tuscany brought forth the Etruscan civilization as a precursor of the later Roman development. Centuries passed, but the land continued to produce in spite of the ravages of deforestation and war and in spite of neglect and erosion of the soil. Nevertheless, as time went on, various disadvantages of southern Italy have become more apparent, especially with the huge increase of population in recent years. The long dry season halts nearly all productivity of summer crops in the south except where irrigation is possible; landslides caused by the heavy winter rains destroy fertile sections; and the unhealthful conditions remaining in some of the swampy lowlands limit their use for crops.

Seemingly extraneous factors have also had an effect on land utilization. Italy's modern political development from a number of separate states, accompanied as it was by many internal wars, had an unfavorable effect, especially in the south. There the big landholdings or *latifundia* of absentee landlords were characterized by very low yields per acre as well as by very poor living conditions among the peasantry. In the former kingdom of Naples and Sicily, for instance, a very high percentage of the area still belongs to landlords and is rented to the actual farmers. But a change has come: modern Italy desires high productivity in order to feed its large population and thus decrease the large food imports. In fruits and early vegetables, Italy has also a valuable source of income by selling to northern Europe. Mussolini started the so-called "Battle of Grains" as an effort to increase production by combating malaria and by draining marshes. The present government has increased that effort with the help of American funds, as was mentioned earlier. The plan now in operation includes improving animal husbandry, increasing the use of farm machinery, increasing the land under irrigation, and training as well as organizing agricultural producers. Experimental stations show the farmers what can be done.

Types of Agriculture *

Four different types of agriculture can be recognized in Italy on a regional basis (A479): the Po Basin type, the Northern Mountain type, the Mediterranean type (nonhorticultural), and the horticultural Mediterranean type. The political units shown in A479 are those of the time the statistics were compiled (beginning of World

* This section is based on the senior author's article, "The Structure of Italian Agriculture," *Economic Geography*, XVIII, 2 (April, 1942), pp. 109–124.

War II), and differ slightly from names and boundaries created by the new constitution of 1947: Lucania is now officially called Basili-

A. Types of Agriculture in Italy by Political Units of 1942.

cata, Emilia is now Emilia-Romagna, Venezia Tridentina is Trentino-Alto Adige, Veneto was enlarged to take in what was left to Italy of Venezia-Giulia (not shown in A479) and was redesignated

Friuli-Venezia Giulia, and the Valle d'Aosta was created as a new Region out of Piemonte. These changes have perforce been ignored so that the map would correctly reflect the discussion of agricultural types and regions, which uses statistics based on the older boundaries of the political units, and they have no influence on the agricultural regions themselves.

Po Basin Type. As one of the prominent regional types of European agriculture, the Po Basin merits rather full description. Percentage of land in food crops varies between 30 and 40, which seems rather low, but, if fodder and improved grassland are included, the percentage rises perceptibly and ranges from 55 to 64 per cent. Though the whole flat plain itself is productive and, when seen from the air, displays a striking picture of parceling (cities, villages, and roads occupy a certain nonproductive share), the enveloping mountains included within statistics for the provincial area account for the fact that the cultivated percentages are not higher, since forests and mountain pastures are not included as cultivated land and the higher mountain zone is entirely unproductive. Crop value indexes are consistently high—highest in Emilia, where the rolling slopes of the Apennines can be partly put in cultivation, and lowest in Piemonte, where hills and mountains occupy a considerable area. Yields are high, as is indicated by the wheat yield map, and other crop yields are similarly high. Cereals dominate the agricultural structure and in Lombardia attain 80 per cent of the total food and industrial crop value. Piemonte and Lombardia are the two rice provinces of Italy, where water from the Alps can be used for irrigation on the flat plains. Corn, also comparatively a wet ground crop, reaches its peak in Lombardia and Veneto, in the northern part of the Po Basin, where summer rainfall is heavier and irrigation also is possible. In Emilia, the "bread basket" of Italy, wheat reaches its highest importance: almost half the total agricultural value is represented by wheat. Wine is prominent, especially in the Piemonte, where the Asti region, southeast of Turin, has a high reputation. Vegetables play a minor role, and of the fruits peaches thrive well in Piemonte and Emilia. Two industrial crops become primary: sugar beets for Veneto and Emilia (Po Delta) and hemp (Emilia). The cold winter of the region prohibits the growth of olives, the great Mediterranean crop, and citrus fruits are limited to some well-protected gardens along the Italian lakes.

Stock raising, based on fodder crops and irrigated meadows, is well-developed here and constitutes the center of distribution of

Italian cows, from which come the famous Parmesan and Gorgon-zola cheeses, as well as milk, butter, and meat. Altogether, the con-clusion is justified that land utilization reaches not only the highest level in Italy but also a high ranking position in the whole of Europe.

Northern Mountain Type. Venezia Tridentina represents the northern mountain type. As might be expected, the area in food crops is limited as a direct result of rugged terrain and high eleva-tion. The standard of agriculture is comparatively high, but the actual production figures are low. Wheat drops to almost one fourth of its importance in Lombardia, as does corn; and rye comes to the foreground, replacing wheat on mountain fields. Grapes are still important, and the wines of the Merano Basin, northwest of Bolzano, are well-known. However, the most interesting aspect is the im-portant role of potatoes, by far the major crop in value of this type. Cabbage is the common vegetable, and conspicuous in this type are such fruits as pears and apples. Improved pasture occupies more acreage than food crops, and dairying is well-developed. Altogether, Italian northern mountain agriculture is typical for most of the Alpine area and closely resembles that of Switzerland.

Horticultural Mediterranean Type. The highest grade of land use of the Mediterranean climate—fields of vegetables, orchards of peaches, groves of lemons and oranges with grapevines swinging from tree to tree or hanging from trellises—forms this type. How-ever, its eminence is not possible without water running through nar-row ditches to offset the scorching desiccation of the summer, al-though in certain places soils are sufficiently moisture-retentive to keep them productive through the summer heat.

Liguria is the best example. The southern slope of the Apennines overlooking the Ligurian Sea—a climatic oasis in winter as the re-sult of protection against inflow of cold northern air—is a garden of fruits and vegetables, not only for Italy but also for the general European market, where such subtropical fruits and early vegetables are in great demand. Agricultural intensity is the highest in Italy, but cultivated land is restricted to the immediate coast and to some short valleys; the actual value is small. Very little land is in fodder or improved pasture. Even wheat, the crop that leads in all other Italian Mediterranean provinces, achieves only sixth rank. Extraor-dinarily high value indexes are obtained for olives, peaches, and grapes, although 90 per cent of the value is in fruits and vegetables, a unique case for the world. Of the vegetables, potatoes (especially early varieties), fresh peas, beans, artichokes, tomatoes, and cauliflower are most important. The Mediterranean region here attains its most perfect development, with nature exhausting itself in beauty.

Two other provinces in Italy show similar development. However, the type is less distinctive because of the extension of the area far beyond the horticultural zone, resulting in a mixed type in which the horticultural factor carries total value far above that of the surrounding nonhorticultural provinces.

From the horticultural point of view, Campania differs from Liguria rather obviously. They have in common a general crop structure; though potatoes rank high and all kinds of fruits and vegetables are well represented, Campania's lower latitude is reflected by the appearance of oranges and lemons, and nuts also become important. Two industrial crops also should be noted: tobacco and hemp. Campania is the second-largest (after Emilia) hemp-producing region of Italy, and the plains north of Naples become pervaded by the stench of retting hemp in summer. Parts of the Campania also show the simultaneous three-crop system of agriculture. Grapevines are suspended along lines of widely spaced fruit trees that are, in turn, surrounded by crops on the ground.

Sicilia Region differs from the other two. Its structure would even be typically nonhorticultural Mediterranean, with wheat, wine grapes, olives, nuts, and dried beans, but for the fact that it forms the center of citrus fruit production, particularly of lemons. Citrus groves dot the northern coastal zone of the island and are chiefly responsible for the high value index.

Nonhorticultural Mediterranean Type. Pre-empting the largest territory of Italy, this type is probably most characteristically developed in Lucania, where five crops comprise more than 80 per cent of the total value: wheat (with only slightly less than 50 per cent), oats (often planted after wheat), dried beans, olives, and grapes. In Lucania, grapes do not rank very high; they fall below the general Mediterranean average, but otherwise represent the type.

Generally speaking, the percentage of land in crops is rather high, reaching 67 per cent in Puglie, with an exception in the toe province, Calabria, where mountains prevail. Very little of the land is in fodder or improved pasture, and sheep replace cattle as typical stock; the valley of the Tiber in Lazio, and the island of Sardinia (Sardegna Region) as a whole, represent the peak of sheep density. Vegetables and fruits, with the exception of olives and grapes, are generally of minor importance, although in Lazio, where market demands of a large city (Rome) encourage truck gardens, vegetables and fruits are abundant. Potatoes of Abruzzi reflect the mountain character of the interior.

Puglie should be differentiated as a subdivision, where natural conditions favor olives, which here reach the world's greatest concentration, whereas almonds and one industrial crop (tobacco) form deviations from the average. The extensive Tavoliere Plain has extensive wheat fields where marshes formerly existed. Irrigated vineyards are tenderly cared for on the limestone slopes surrounding the plain and extending into the heel.

Although both Toscana and Umbria show influences of the neighboring division to the north and northwest without disturbing the general aspect of this type, Marche is definitely a transition in character. In many ways it resembles Emilia, but value of corn decreases appreciably, and the appearance of olives gives it a Mediterranean touch.

Summary of Italian Agriculture

Of approximately 40 million acres of land in crop and food-bearing trees, more than one fourth is in wheat, whose average yield is 22 bushels per acre. The average is, of course, much higher for the north than it is for the south. Corn, occupying the second-largest acreage of all crops—but only one-fourth the acreage of wheat—yields only 26.5 bushels per acre, compared with 32 bushels per acre in the United States. Rye, oats, and barley, all of which are significant in the agriculture of northwestern Europe, play a role in Italian agriculture also, reflecting the great diversity of the Italian climate. The tonnage of olives produced is about half that of corn. The tonnage of grapes is five sixths as great as the tonnage of wheat. Indicative of the level of the recovery of Italian agriculture is the fact that agricultural production in 1949 was 90 per cent of that of 1938, with cereals having the lowest percentage of recovery of all crops.

· 30 ·
Italy:
Population and Industry

Population and Its Distribution

Historical Aspects. From the earliest historical times Italy appears to have been well populated. It is interesting to note, however, that the Po Basin, now accommodating nearly two fifths of the population and providing most of the food supply, was outside the area of the earliest development. The fertile coastal zone of Apulia, which faced Greece in the Italian heel; Sicily, with its wheat and its excellent central Mediterranean location near Carthage; the hilly sections of Tuscany and Albani north and south of the site of Rome—these were the earlier centers of human occupation. Rome was built in a central location on the Campagna where small hills protected it against floods of the Tiber, and the center of the Roman Empire became the world's most famous city.

The Po Basin, which the Romans called Gallia Cisalpina, was at that time outside the civilized Mediterranean world. This was probably because of a difference in climate, for the more severe winters made it less attractive to people who were accustomed to the climate of Greece and southern Italy, and among whom the technical arts were not sufficiently advanced to provide good protection from low temperature and cold rains. Even then, however, the Po Basin was known for its fertility—its large production of grain, fruit, flax, and wine, and its herds of cattle. Later the center of Italian influence shifted northward. Then the basins of the Arno with Florence, and of the Po with Venice dominated medieval Italy. Rome remained the religious and historical focus, but the economic center had changed. Towns like Genoa, Venice, Milan, and Verona became leading European cities, and the trade from Asia and the Mediterranean region passed through them on its way across the Alps to northern Europe. Still another change came later. The decline of the Mediterranean region and the rise of western Europe made northern Italy relatively less important than before, although it still remained the key to Rome.

Density. (Compare A468 and A486.) Standing out on the population density map (A486) as areas of population concentration are the Po Basin with the core around Milan, horticultural Liguria and the

A. Ruins of Roman aqueduct near Rome, indicating the efforts made in ancient times to bring water from the Alban Hills to the city of Rome. Photographed by Ivan Dmitri for American Export Lines.

Arno Basin, the east coast except for the dry Tavoliere and the Gargano Peninsula, the Campania around Naples, and the Catanian Plain and some northern sections of Sicily. Very sparsely populated are the mountains—Alps as well as Apennines, the marshes and former marshes of southern Toscana, the Pontine Marsh region, most of Lucania (the Basilicata), and most of Sardinia, except the southern lowland depression of the Campidano and the northwestern corner around Sassari.

The concentration of the population in urban settlements and villages is probably due in part to the greater economic opportunity

that town life affords, in part to the scarcity of permanent sources
of water, in part to the need of mutual protection, and in part to
the social inclination of the Italians. During times of peace and

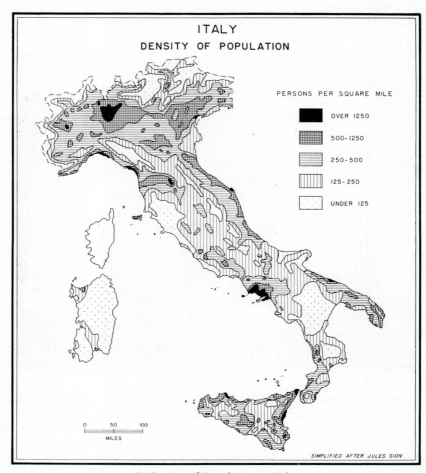

A. Density of Population in Italy.

progress the population of Italy has tended to disperse over the cultivated area, but it has retreated into fortified towns and villages in
times of war and political disorder. As peace was rare in ancient
Italy, the form of settlement was almost exclusively urban. Hilltop
villages, especially in picturesque Tuscany, enhance to this day the
attractiveness of that charming country.

The social factor seems to enter too, however, for every evening and often at other times the main streets and squares in Italian villages are crowded with talking, debating citizens. Even in southern Switzerland, where wars were not a common experience, the tendency for everyone to live in villages with the typical square-built stone dwellings is so strong that from the high summits one looks down upon the slopes of the southern Alps dotted with little settlements that are urban in quality even though inhabited by only a few hundred people.

Emigration and Postwar Policies. The favorable political and hence economic conditions of the last half-century or more have brought to Italy a great increase of population, beyond the power of the country to support. Part of this excess population has left Italy and migrated to other European countries, especially to France, and still more to the two Americas. From 1876 to 1905, 8 million Italians left their country. This national loss was balanced not only by a declining death rate, but also by a corresponding increase in the birth rate, so that Italy's increase in population went on almost unchecked. Moreover, many of the emigrants came back, often with enough money to pass their old age in comparative affluence in Italy. Then, too, large sums of money are sent home each year by emigrants to their relatives in Italy. Nevertheless Italy's loss of strong, young citizens appears to be serious.

After World War I the situation changed. The American immigration law and the attitude of some European countries—especially France, which feared to receive too many foreigners—left South America as the only freely accessible outlet. The government was not in favor of emigration, and it stressed the desirability of an increase in population, with the result that the population increased yearly by about 400,000. This, of course, raised a serious problem of employment. The solution was sought in a more intensive land utilization and the development of additional manufacturing industries.

After World War II, Italy again faced the problem of too many Italians for the existing Italian economy. The number of unemployed was in 1950 still more than 2 million, and emigration started again, chiefly to South America (especially Argentina) and the United States, and exceeded 70,000 in 1947, compensated by a return of about 30,000. The problem of population pressure will remain a serious one, and no real solution is in sight, since improvements in the economy will not even take care of the regular population in-

crease. The somewhat lower birth rate after 1940 was offset by a
decreasing death rate, so that after World War II the Italian population was still showing a net gain of nearly 0.5 million each year.

The Southern Tirol and Istria. After World War I, Italy had
brought all land occupied by Italians into Italy, with the exception
of the Italian-speaking Swiss canton of Ticino and the area around
Nice. But Italy also included foreign groups that had the character
of antinational minorities. One of these groups lived in the former
Austrian Southern Tirol, added by Italy to Venezia Tridentino.
The 300,000 Austrians transferred to Italy with the territory presented a harassing problem until Mussolini and Hitler came to a
compromise in 1939. The compromise permitted all Austrians who
wished to do so to leave the area and settle in Austria or elsewhere.
Although thousands of Tiroleans emigrated, the outcome of World
War II stopped the emigration, and at present the Southern Tirol
(or Alto Adige, as the region is called by the Italians) has autonomy
within the Italian state, and the German-speaking population appears to be receiving equitable treatment.

A second area occupied by antinational peoples was the Istrian
Plateau, where Slovenes and Croats formed the bulk of the rural
population and greatly objected to Italian rule. After World War
II, Yugoslavia was awarded most of the Istrian Peninsula, including
also the coastal zone formerly occupied by Italians but then evacuated by them. The city of Trieste, focus of political and economic
interest and coveted by both Yugoslavia and Italy, was made a Free
Territory under the United Nations. Breakdown of the administrative plan created two zones of military occupation, one in the south
under Yugoslav control, and one in the north—including Trieste
itself—under American and British control exercised in the name of
the United Nations. Essentially an Italian city wanting to return
to Italy, Trieste, once the harbor of Austria, had a certain postwar
boom because of the use of its harbor for the occupation forces in
Austria, but, so long as Yugoslavia and Italy are unable to agree on
the Istrian boundary, the fate of the Free Territory of Trieste remains
a question mark.

Manufacturing

It has already been mentioned that Italy is seriously deficient in
both mineral and vegetable raw materials and has only water power
as an industrial asset. Yet Italy has been quite successful in developing manufacturing, a very great deal more so than Spain, for ex-

ample, which has many more raw materials and almost as much potential water power. Italy has, of course, a large home market and abundant labor, but another important factor is the ingenuity of the Italian worker and scientist, especially in the field of mechanics, producing such items as motorcars and power motorboats. The Po Basin, especially around Milan and Turin, and also the Arno valley around Florence contain the great majority of the Italian industry. Although, for the country as a whole, food processing, including packing and canning, ranks as the major industry, the outstanding manufacturing industries are concerned with textiles and mechanical products. Milan is the main European silk center using locally produced raw silk, but the silk industry has shifted to a large extent to rayon, in which Italy excels. Cotton manufactures rank high among the Italian exports. Raw cotton must be imported, although a small amount is raised in Sicily. Concentrated in Piemonte and in Lombardia, the cotton textile industry has few large establishments. Wool textiles, once based on the home supply but now primarily based on imports, are also important; they are chiefly produced in the area between Turin and Milan but also in Tuscany, at Prato near Florence. Italy has always been known for its motorcars and shipbuilding. Turin is the home of the famous Fiat plant, which manufactures one of the popular cars in Europe. A number of varied metalworking industries diversify the manufactures of northern Italy and produce such items as sewing machines and typewriters. Around Milan and Turin are industrial towns, such as Monza, Biella, Bergamo, and Brescia, all teeming with industrial life.

Conspicuously lacking in the Italian industrial scene is a highly developed and highly concentrated iron and steel industry. Previous discussions explain this lack: severe shortage of iron ore and of coking coal. The complete inability of Italy ever to have an appreciable heavy industry will always be a serious deterrent to Italian manufacturing, and the only way the handicap can be compensated is for Italy to increase exports of the goods it can produce in order to be able to pay for imports of ore, coal, pig iron, steel, and scrap. There is no reason why Italy should not have a small, efficient iron and steel industry; and, indeed, both prior to World War II and again by 1950, Italian steel production was comparable with that of the Saar. However, the Italian population is forty-five times greater than the Saar population! Furthermore, Italian steel is much more expensive to produce than is Saar steel. Iron ore is available in quite adequate quantities in North Africa, but it must be paid for; and the problem of coking coal supply remains a thorny one. Perhaps Italy would do well to consider extensive use of electric smelting, as practiced on a modest scale in Norway, Sweden, and France.

In the years immediately after 1945, Italy was penalized by the fact that the Germans had, in 1943, removed thousands of tons of heavy industries equipment. The country had to pay much higher prices for the coal it imported—much of which had to come from the United States, whereas before 1943 it had come from the Ruhr. Italy at mid-century was awaiting re-establishment of trade with Germany so that it could send fruits and vegetables and receive coal in return. However, a similar exchange with Britain was in operation on a healthy scale, although British coal supplies for export to Italy were limited.

Cities and the Transportation System

The location of towns in northern Italy is very systematic, their original growth being due to the zone of contact between mountains and plains, the crossings of trade routes, the entrances to Alpine passes, or the nearness of useful waterways, and often to such strategic factors as defense by swamps, which made difficult any rapid advance upon the town by hostile forces.

One type of cities forms a line at the base of the Alps. It starts with Turin (Italian: Torino), the Italian focal point for traffic coming via the Mont Cenis tunnel from Paris. The focal character of Turin is emphasized by the Alpine line from the French Riviera via Cuneo. Located at the northwestern foot of the vine-clad Monferrato and at the confluence of the Dora Riparia and the Po, Turin is one of the largest (730,000) and most modern of Italian cities, and the center of iron and textile manufactures. Other cities of about 50,000 to 150,000 inhabitants in this line at the base of the Alps include Como, Bergamo, Brescia, Verona (where the Brenner Pass route enters the plain), and Udine. All these towns have appreciable historical interest but have also developed—in addition to lively trade because of the agricultural productivity of the regions in which they lie—modest industries using the hydroelectric power available.

A second line of cities lies between the Alpine base and the Po River. Its location is partly due to the *fontanili,* a line of springs that issue forth along the contact between the glacial cover and the river plain. These springs furnish not only adequate supplies of drinking water but also large amounts of water for irrigation. Milan (Italian: Milano), the only large city in this line, occupies first place among the cities of northern Italy and, with a population of 1.3 millions, is second only to Rome. Centrally located at the crossing of the north-south trade route from the Simplon and St. Gotthard passes to Genoa, and the east-west road from Turin to Venice, this old capital of the Visconti is once more the center of life—Italy's industrial capital, surrounded by spreading factory suburbs.

A third line of cities consists of small urban centers, with less than 100,000 people, on the edge of the swampy lowland along both sides of the Po. It includes Pavia, Piacenza, Cremona, Mantua (Italian: Mantova), and Ferrara—places that survive mainly on account of their original location at the crossings of trade routes, and participate only modestly in the industrial life of today.

A fourth line is located at the foot of the Apennines along the so-called Via Emilia. Here Parma, Reggio nell'Emilia, Modena (all exceeding 100,000), and Bologna (350,000) have names of historical fame. Bologna, whence the main route of travel crosses the Apennines to Florence, has developed an active industrial life. It was especially heavily damaged during fighting in World War II when the Allied attack from the southwest was stalled in the Apennine passes. Other cities mentioned were also damaged to some extent, but Bologna was more severely hit.

Transportation for the most part still follows the ancient routes, shortened now by tunnels. Schemes of modern river and canal navigation connecting the Adriatic Sea with Turin, Milan, and the Italian lakes are only partly completed.

In spite of its location south of the Apennines and not on the Adriatic coast, where the natural outlet of the Po Basin might be expected, Genoa (Italian: Genova) is the main export harbor of northern Italy. Proximity to the Atlantic and a minimum of trouble with silting now that the new harbor has been completed, are important factors in its success. Railroad lines cross the Apennines to Milan and Turin. Surpassed only by Marseille, Genoa is the second harbor of the Mediterranean, not merely serving northern Italy, but handling also a great deal of the trade of Switzerland and southern Germany. East and west from Genoa may be seen the extension of the French Riviera with its steep, olive-clad hills, winding roads, lovely views of mountain and sea, and its intimate mixture of closely packed Italian villages, big hotels, boardinghouses, and lovely villas bowered in trees where people from cooler climates love to spend the winter. Where France and Italy come together, the little independent principality of Monaco, with its famous gambling resort, adds to the attraction for tourists. Early vegetables, flowers, and the tourist business are great sources of revenue. Bordighera

A. Waterfront of Venice, the island city, once the seat of a city-state. To the left, the San Marco Cathedral and the famous Campanile. Photograph by Ivan Dmitri for American Export Lines.

and San Remo on the Riviera di Ponente, and Rapallo on the Riviera di Levante, are the best-known resorts. To the southeast is the Italian naval base of La Spezia, which was severely damaged during the latter months of World War II and now has little in the way of a navy to harbor.

Venice (Italian: Venezia), well to the north of the mouth of the Po, was once the main outlet of the Po Valley and the capital of a great medieval Mediterranean state. Despite the disadvantage of its greater distance from the Atlantic in comparison with Genoa, it is again progressing rapidly. Built on islands between lagoons and the sea where it could not easily be reached by enemies, it profited for centuries from its strategic position, and suffered less than other Italian cities from the many wars. Today its famous canals, its old churches, its treasures of art, its glassworks, and its bathing beach of the Lido make it one of the most satisfying of tourist resorts. Fortunately, it was little touched by the fighting of World War II.

The Arno Basin repeats in a smaller way the story of the Po Basin. The charming old town of Florence (Italian: Firenze), medieval capital of the Medici, now as of old is the center of industrial life, although the industries are small and do not detract from the delightful landscape around the city. The famous Ponte Vecchio over the Arno was the only bridge over that river that escaped demolition by the retreating Nazis in 1944. Leghorn (Italian: Livorno), south of the Arno where the mountains approach the coast, is the harbor of this basin, and Pisa and Lucca preserve wonderful mementoes of medieval glory. Farther south the Tuscan Apennines never developed towns of importance, and the city of Siena is still a beautiful but quiet community. Because of its hills the great trade routes keep away from it, the one from Florence to Rome passing farther east along the Arno-Trasimeno-Tiber line and the one from Genoa and Milan to Rome running along the coast via Pisa.

Rome (Italian: Roma), as the capital of the Italian state and the center of the Roman Catholic Church, has lived on into yet another period of prosperity. Three towns in one it is: the old Roman capital with the ruins—especially those of the Forum—that tell of its ancient glory; medieval Rome with its famous churches and palaces; and modern Rome (with a population of 1.7 millions), the busy capital of a young and energetic nation. No industrial development yet mars it, but Rome, the Eternal City, has again become one of the great centers of political and intellectual life. Like Venice and Florence, Rome escaped virtually unscathed from the fighting during World War II. The tiny Vatican City state, where the Pope once more has a small section of Rome under his personal sovereignty, has provided the solution of a long quarrel between the Roman Catholic Church and the Italian state.

Naples, the third-largest Italian city, with slightly more than a million inhabitants, is very different from either Rome or Milan. It is the only great city and harbor of southern Italy. Wonderfully located at the foot of Vesuvius, surrounded by traces of volcanic action, it has less practical sanitation but a more picturesque city life than might be expected. Vibrant with carefree gaiety, but in many ways still primitive, it has about it some flavor of the East. Naples suffered terribly from bombing during World War II, and the misery that has cursed the Neapolitan slums for decades was intensified after 1943. It is the terminus of many transatlantic lines, but the tonnage of the vessels entering the port is higher than the value of the trade would indicate. The beauties of the Gulf of Naples, Capri, and Sorrento, the excavations of the Roman cities of Pompei and Herculaneum, and the famous Vesuvius are inducements that bring thousands of tourists.

A. The city of Naples along the bay of the same name, with Vesuvius in the background. Photograph by Ivan Dmitri for American Export Lines.

The railroad from Rome, having followed the Liri depression to Naples, continues via Salerno along the Calabrian coast to Reggio on the Strait of Messina. Along the other side of the peninsula the Via Emilia line continues from Bologna along the Adriatic coast to Ancona, cuts off the peninsula of Gargano, crosses the fertile and densely populated plain of Apulia with Bari as its center, and ends at Brindisi whence the European mail is sent by fast boats to Egypt and India. Apart from the cities just mentioned, only Taranto on the gulf of that name has more than local importance in the entire foot of Italy.

Sardinia

This rugged island has always been more or less remote from the general Mediterranean life, but it is a genuine part of Italy. Essentially a mountain country, like Corsica, with only one important plain (the Campidano) crossing the island in the southwest, it suffers certain disadvantages in common with other rugged sections of Italy. Among these are a heavy winter rainfall with consequent floods and landslides, dry and hot summers, destructive deforestation, and a serious loss of precipitation through rapid runoff or through absorption by the permeable soil. Malaria in the lowlands has also been a terrible handicap. Nevertheless, there is progress and activity. The famous mines of earlier days have been reopened. The plains are being drained, and dams, like that on the Riso River, provide a water supply for irrigation in summer. Cagliari, the principal city and port, reflects the fact that Sardinia is almost purely an agricultural and relatively undeveloped section of Europe.

Sicily

A comparison between Sicily and the Po Basin sums up many essential features of Italy and brings out the contrast between north and south. The steep northern coast of Sicily with its citrus fruit groves and vineyards; the rugged southern plateau with its wheat fields, sulphur mines, and dense population; and finally the great Etna, with its high, cultivated slopes and the fertile Catanian plain at its southern base—all these are the direct opposite of the level plain of the Po. The long, hot, dry, dusty summers, when everything turns brown even in the best-watered parts of the island, and the warm winters with their freedom from frost and snow, afford another marked contrast to the north. The human contrasts are equally strong. For century after century Sicily has presented an almost unchanging picture, little modified even by maladministration, war, and deforestation. Its people have preserved and accentuated their innate traits through almost complete isolation for several thousand years. Phoenicians, Greeks, Carthaginians, Saracens, and Normans, as well as people from the mainland of Italy, have indeed invaded Sicily and settled in parts of it. In spite of all this, however, the fundamental biological quality of the Sicilians has not become diverse as has that of the Italians of the Po Basin. The invaders in Sicily either died out or were so completely absorbed that there is today an extraordinary degree of uniformity among the peasants from whom is derived practically the whole population of Sicily. In the Po Basin there is far more diversity not only of physical type, but also, apparently, of ability. The late date at which there began to be adequate regulation of the landholding system, protection against brigandage, suppression of the terrorism of the *Mafia,* compulsory education, and other measures to elevate the standards of economic and cultural life is another witness to the contrast between Sicily and the Po Basin. So, too, are the rough mountain trails of Sicily and the scarcity of modern roads in contrast to the many fine oiled roads and even speedways of the north. The cities also show the same sort of contrast. Palermo on the northern coast is the main Sicilian export harbor and a really great city. Messina, in an earthquake zone, is also a seaport and owes its location and growth to the Strait of Messina; and Catania is the center of one of the few small level parts of Sicily, the intensively cultivated plain south of Etna. Syracuse, an old Greek colony, has regained some of its former eminence as the point of contact with North Africa. But all these cities are commercial in nature, and practically all their industries have to do only with the ordinary business of living, like bakeries, printing shops, and shoemaking shops, or with the simple preparation of agricultural products such as wine and olive oil.

The latitude of Italy is the same as that of the region from Richmond, Virginia, to Quebec in Canada. The difference in latitude between Syracuse in Sicily and Milan in the Po Basin is about the same as that between Portsmouth in southern England and Aberdeen in Scotland. But the cultural difference is enormously greater than is seen with a corresponding difference of latitude in the United States and Canada or in Great Britain. Only a small part of this great difference can be due to cultural conditions, for all of Italy has the same government, the same language (albeit several dialects), the same religion, and the same general culture. Part of the difference must be due to physical differences in the people and part to the way in which historic development and modern life have been influenced by the geographic environment. If all of Italy were like Sicily, the country would rank scarcely higher than Turkey; if all were like the Po Basin, Italy would rival any of the other great powers in level of economic-cultural development.

Territory and Colonies after 1945

Mention has already been made of the fact that, in the treaty of 1947 signed in Paris, Italy surrendered the Istrian Peninsula (nearly all of the Region of Venezia Giulia) to Yugoslavia. In addition, Italy also gave up to Yugoslavia its Dalmatian coastal islands of

Cherso, Lussino, and Lagosta, and the mainland city of Zara; to Albania the little island of Saseno; to Greece the Dodecanese Islands off the coast of Turkey; to France four tiny frontier passes (with hydroelectric plants); and to China its concession at Tientsin. However, Italy lost far more extensive areas when it renounced all claim over its African colonies: Libya, Eritrea, Italian Somaliland, and the Ethiopia that it conquered with such noise in 1936–37. Actually, these colonies were of little value to Italy except as points of prestige, which the country desired after entering the race for colonies late because of its delayed unification. Thus, Italy is now restricted to its peninsula and the two large islands of Sicily and Sardinia, although in 1949 it was given a ten-year United Nations trusteeship over Somalia.

A Summary and Evaluation

Italy's unfortunate role in World War II cost her dearly: she was first humiliated and then robbed by the Nazis, and then she suffered terribly in the Allied invasion and struggle up the peninsula. Physical damage was very great to many cities and towns, harbors, railways, bridges (which are of vital significance in the mountainous terrain), irrigation works, and fields. But in Italy probably more than anywhere else the human degradation was great. After hopes and dreams of having a place in the sun under Mussolini, the people were whipped into the Nazi mechanism and then found themselves surrounded by a varied army—Americans, British, Poles, Brazilians, Indians, and other national groups—of the Allies. Few people knew where to put their trust or allegiance, especially when front lines wavered back and forth. The urge for self-preservation at almost any sacrifice was great. Life became extremely primitive in many areas for many months, and food was very scarce. Poverty-ridden southern Italians pilfered from the Allied armies by whom they were employed as stevedores, cooks, waiters, and handymen. Nevertheless, many were scrupulously honest and perfectly aware of the issues at stake. In the north the Partisans—chiefly communist-led—carried on a strong resistance and harried the Germans behind the lines. Life in the north was never as disrupted as it was in the south, although dislocations were severe enough.

These facts are significant in any attempt to understand the difficulty Italy has experienced in trying to resume its place in the European family of nations. Less than a century old as a unified state, Italy still has many improvements to make before it becomes

a "going concern." The disorganized manner in which many procedures are carried out in Italy—tax-collecting, for example, in which
the government expects the declarer to falsify his tax and automatically doubles or triples the declaration—are sometimes exasper-
ating. Corruptibility of government officials reflects the pitifully inadequate pay they receive. But Italy is trying—more desperately
than might be realized in view of the apparently slow progress.

Postwar recovery was slow because of the complex factors analyzed in this and the preceding chapter. Not until 1950 was the
Italian level of production equal to that of 1938, whereas every
other country of Europe except Germany had a level appreciably
higher than that of prewar years. Spain was 44 per cent higher,
Britain 50 per cent higher, Bulgaria 180 per cent higher. Italian
merchant shipping tonnage at mid-century was still one third below
that of the Netherlands, with its population only one-fifth that of
Italy.

The hundreds of millions of dollars of ERP funds allotted to
Italy were the lifesaving economic element for the country, and
the money has had tremendous benefits in many aspects of Italian
life. Hundreds of bridges restored or erected after 1948 bore the
familiar shield of the ERP. Dams for irrigation and water power
development were built and were especially valuable to the neglected southern part of Italy. Many of these improvements should
have been made long ago, but the capital has hitherto been insufficient. Even so, much more could have been done, especially by the
small group of very wealthy Italians who live as luxuriously as
medieval princes. One of the severest attacks leveled at Italian
businessmen after 1945 was that they failed to reinvest their wartime profits in their plants. The customs union between France
and Italy that was arranged in 1948 had no appreciable effect on
Italy's recovery, since the Franco-Italian exchange is limited by
similarity of the two countries' products.

The lack of mechanization on Italian farms is perhaps not so
serious as might be thought. True enough, there are 620 acres to
every tractor, but the small size and slope location of many fields
prohibit extensive use of tractors: many Italian farms are more
like carefully tended gardens. Nevertheless, co-operative use of machinery would definitely lift the level of agriculture in many sections.

One of the most serious problems capable of practicable remedy in
Italy is that of land tenure, a problem that has harassed Italy all
during the twentieth century. Mussolini spoke of land reforms, but

the results were disappointing. The post-1945 efforts have, on the whole, also been disappointing, but appreciable steps have been taken. The retardation of such reform is, of course, largely traceable to government fear of alienating the influential landowners. The large communist party—second in Europe only after that of the Soviet Union itself—has won many adherents among the peasants of southern Italy by insistently demanding sweeping land reforms. During 1950 progressive steps were actually taken, and, by 1951, 2 million acres were purchased from large landholders who had failed to utilize their land effectively. Another 2 million acres were scheduled for government purchase and redistribution to landless peasants during the 1950's.

Such steps are necessary in the general program to provide more of the food consumed in the country. Prospects of striking any reasonable balance between exports and food imports are rather dim, but progress can be made. The most serious over-all problem facing Italy, then, is the pressure of population and the agonizing poverty in which a large segment of the Italian people live. Such poverty is marked in the Naples area, for example, where thousands of adolescent children wear rags of patches that in turn have had to be patched and repatched. Emigration is a temporary palliative, but it is no solution to the ever-increasing population that long ago passed the maximum that the economy could support at even a reasonable level of life. Sustained unemployment of 5 to 10 per cent of the population leads to discontent and then to spread of communism.

One of the most important sources of "invisible income" for Italy —besides that of money sent back by emigrants to the family members left behind—is money spent by the thousands of tourists who visit Italy. The country has four great assets for tourists: thrilling scenery, ranging from the rugged Alps in the north to Etna cone on Sicily; a fascinating record in ruins and well-preserved buildings of a glorious past and an intriguing present; a delightful climate for vacationists, with a brilliant sun bathing the landscapes most of the time; and finally the attraction of the Vatican as the seat of the Pope—an attraction that demonstrated its significance in the Holy Year of 1950.

Not the least factor to be considered in this discussion of Italy is the postwar change (1946) of the country from a monarchy to a republic. Although the change was not a great one outwardly, it was one more sign of the evolution that the country has been experiencing, and it was another occasion for demonstration of the political instability of the country.   During the referendum feelings ran high, as many signs for and against the king were painted on the sides of buildings or on walls along streets and roads.   The hammer and sickle, crudely painted thousands of times in both north and south, was a sign of antimonarchial feeling.

Thus, at mid-century Italy stood as a very old yet very young state attempting to solve a large number of serious problems so that it could assume a place of dignity among the nations of Europe and the world.   The country's geographical structure gave it both assets and liabilities, and the goal is an effective relationship between the land and the people.

· 31 ·
Albania (Shqípní)
and Turkey
(Türkíye Cümhuríyetí)-
ín-Europe

Albania

The republic of Albania (A510) is probably Europe's most back-ward country. The explanation of this, as of the stage of progress in other countries, is not to be found in any one fact. The situation of the country in a region of high and inaccessible mountains certainly has a great deal to do with its economic-cultural retardation. So has the Mediterranean climate, in so far as it is less stimulating to man and less favorable for crops than is a more steadily rainy climate with cooler summers. Physical character of the people and religion may play some part, although it is difficult to evaluate these factors. The long-continued rule of the Turks, especially during the decadent last decades of the Ottoman Empire, imposed further handicaps on the country while it tried to escape from its unhappy economic and social conditions. In the past Albania has not always been thus, for in the ancient Illyrian period it was comparatively prosperous. How much of the change is due to human conduct and how much to such matters as change of climate, deforestation, soil erosion, or alteration of the ethnic composition of the population, it is impossible to say.

The inaccessibility of Albania is conspicuous. High mountain ranges representing the continuation of the Dinaric Mountains toward Greece, and sometimes rising above 9,000 feet, quite effectively isolate the country by land. The low-lying coast with its lagoons not only hinders the development of good harbors, but also hampers contact with the interior because it is so malarial. An increase in the amount of malaria and other diseases may have helped to make Albania relatively more backward in modern times than it was in the past. Only the southern part has a firm coast, but here it becomes rocky, rising steeply out of the sea, and this again impedes access to the interior. Vlonë (Valona), where the rocky section joins the low coastal plain, has the only harbor of any significance.

Whatever economic strength the country has is based on agriculture and sheep raising. Between the mountain ranges lie basins of great agricultural value, and it is in these, as well as on the once densely populated plain along the Adriatic coast, that future development may be expected to focus. The prevailing Mediterranean climate causes the products of the coastal plain, which extends a considerable distance inland, to be essentially the same as those of southern Italy. The westward exposure of the country, however, causes the rainfall to increase inland and to be abundant on the western slope of the high mountains, even in summer. Accordingly dense forests of the central European type, comprising beeches, oaks, and conifers, cover much of the mountains and promise a valuable source of future income. Corn is the principal crop of the plain, whereas wheat, oats, and barley thrive better in the mountain basins. Olive trees cover the slopes near the Adriatic Sea, along with citrus fruits and grapes. However, only 11 per cent of the land is cultivated, and the yields are very low. Sixty per cent of Albania is in forest or waste land, indicating the relatively small amount of suitable land available for crop agriculture.

An important source of livelihood is stock raising, the herds and flocks being driven to the mountain meadows during the summer and returned to the plain in winter. Cattle, and in particular sheep, do well; and cheese, wool, and pelts are export products of importance. Even so, numbers of livestock are small. The basin of Korçë (Koritza) in the southeast has been considerably influenced by emigrants who have returned from America, and its prosperity during the 1930's illustrates what can be done when peace prevails and modern methods are employed. Mineral resources that once were famous now lie unused but hold promise for the future. However, petroleum production is sufficient for the small consumption, and a pipeline extends to Vlonë from the oil field northeast of the town.

The population of only 1.2 millions on an area of 10,629 square miles is of one physical stock, but the rugged relief and lack of easy communication cause the people to be grouped into a number of tribes, most of whom follow many customs reminiscent of feudalism. Political dissension among the various tribes, the lack of a common language, and the confusion of antagonistic religions would hamper progress even if the geographic conditions were more favorable. About 68 per cent of the people are Moslems, 11 per cent Roman Catholics, and 20 per cent members of the Albanian Orthodox Church. Modern highways are rare, and there is only one short railroad, built during the 1940's, between Tiranë (Tirana), the capital, and the harbor of Durrës (Durazzo). Except for the air routes, narrow trails suitable only for pack animals provide the only means of communication among small interior towns, although the larger towns are connected by passable roads.

The chief problem of Albania is that it has always been influenced by outside powers. After it was born as an independent state after the Balkan Wars—reluctantly at that, since the Albanian Moslems had been quite friendly with the Turks—Albania, with the help of the Great Powers, became a kingdom; but Italy soon regarded it as belonging to the Italian sphere of influence. After World War I, Albania, having got rid of the imported king, tried a home product for that position; but again Italy, having already occupied the isle of Saseno (Albanian: Sazan) in front of Vlonë Bay, could not leave Albania alone and soon controlled it financially. In the spring of 1939, the Italians took the country over entirely, and the king of Italy became also king of Albania. It was from this bastion that Italy started her war with Greece and suffered heavy defeats, with the Albanians standing by and waiting for the outcome.

After World War II, Albania, for some unknown reason, voted communist and became a Soviet-controlled peoples republic. It is unrealistic to regard Albanians as communists: in their environment of isolation, Albanians became strong individualists, and it would seem that the communist doctrine is the last philosophy they would adhere to. However, reports indicate that Albania has increased its physical equipment under the Soviet program, although to what extent and at what sacrifices are unknown. Surrounded by unfriendly nations, Greece and Yugoslavia, Albania is even more isolated than ever before; and reports indicate constant unrest. People who know Albania like it very much not only because of the beauty of the landscape and the picturesque rural life, but also because of the sturdy quality of the people. Albania deserves better; perhaps for it also the day of liberation will come.

Turkey-in-Europe

Remnant of large southeastern European holdings of a great oriental empire, once reaching to the very walls of Vienna, Turkey-in-Europe (A510) now covers only 9,000 square miles. Most of the area is comparatively unproductive. Outside of the Maritsa Valley the monotonous upland with its dry steppe climate, cold and often snowy in winter, is sparsely inhabited, and sheep raising is the principal occupation. Even the coastal region along the Aegean, the Sea of Marmara, and the Black Sea is dreary and unproductive. The mountainous peninsula of Gallipoli along the Dardanelles is the strategic key to the Bosporus, as World War I again proved, but it is a region of little economic value. The really good part of European Turkey is a narrow strip close to the Bosporus, which is more rainy, more beautiful, more accessible, and far more populous than any other part of the country.

Outside of Istanbul, the former Constantinople, the only city of any size is Edirne (Adrianople). This small, ancient community of oriental aspect was left after 1920 in an impossible situation, virtually surrounded by Greek and Bulgarian territory, and its dwindling population evinces its economic decline.

All interests are focused in Istanbul, which has one of the most economically advantageous locations in the world. The narrow Bosporus, a drowned former river valley, down which a strong current still flows from the Black Sea, divides Asia from Europe. Its shores are protected by the rising upland against cold winds, and they receive more rain than the surrounding uplands. Accordingly these exhibit a different kind of vegetation from that of the steppes, typically Mediterranean but with more trees than elsewhere. The dark cones of cypress trees, the pink of Judas trees, and the yellow of locusts, together with the blossoms of fruit trees, join with an exuberant display of flowering herbage and with the songs of innumerable nightingales to make the shores of the Bosporus truly entrancing in the spring. Olive trees are excluded by the winter frosts, but snow never lies more than a few days.

Istanbul is located where a small drowned tributary valley enters the southern end of the Bosporus and offers a safe harbor called the Golden Horn. Founded originally as the Greek settlement of Byzantium, this city, which was once the greatest in the world, became the capital of the Eastern Roman Empire. Then for centuries it was the stronghold of southern European culture against the forces of Asia. Capturing it in 1453 after previous unsuccessful sieges, the invading Turks held it as their capital and made it the center of their empire. World War I, which was catastrophic to the old Ottoman Empire, brought about the city's temporary decline; but, despite the loss of its European hinterland, and despite the removal of the capital to the more centrally located city of Ankara, Istanbul recovered and is a bustling crossroads city. It could hardly be otherwise. Dominating the trade routes between the Black Sea and the Mediterranean, where the old Danube roads cross over into Asia, the location has advantages that can never be taken away. The population is on the increase again, and by 1950 it had reached the million mark. In Istanbul, unlike the rest of Turkey, both Greeks and Armenians still live in large numbers, although they are not so numerous as formerly.

The tonnage of vessels clearing and in transit is generally greater at Istanbul than at any other Mediterranean port. The city is still the great commercial port of Turkey and has dealings with a large part of western Asia. Imports from the United States include leather, cereals, motorcars, and agricultural machinery. Exports comprise mainly tobacco, silk, pelts, wool, furs, and opium. The United States purchases little except tobacco and chrome ore.

Today Istanbul is in a curious state of transition. This is typified by the fact that automobiles have to go very slowly over the Galata Bridge across the Golden Horn in order not to run down *hamals* or men who make a business of carrying loads on their backs. Equally typical are the rowboats that ply for hire on the Bosporus, and the old-fashioned ferryboats that carry passengers to suburban homes along the Bosporus and the Sea of Marmara. Everywhere one sees such contradictions as a superb museum on the one hand, and many valuable monuments of antiquity lying unprotected in the grass on the other hand. The old, narrow, crowded, noisy bazaars with their curious smells and their craftsmen clanging away at copper kettles, cutting out shoes from odoriferous leather, or setting out all sorts of curious dishes in the open air to tempt the palate, are in strong contrast to excellent stores and fine hotels run in the most modern fashion. Old Greek and Roman walls and pillars, early Christian churches—among which St. Sophia is the most outstanding —and medieval mosques with their great domes bring to mind the ancient greatness of the city. Huge palaces, used now as government buildings, join with the roughly paved streets, the slow electric cars, and the leisurely Bosporus steamers to suggest the conflict between the old and the new in the last century. And a modern university, the American colleges on the Bosporus, the offices of business firms from western Europe and America, great tourist steamers, and an eager, forward-looking spirit among the Turks show what is happening today.

After World War II the Bosporus became strategically even more important than it had ever been before. Refusing the demand by Russia of joint Russian-Turkish control of the Bosporus and the Dardanelles, the Turks had to prepare for potential attack. The nearness of the boundary with Bulgaria, Russia's ally, and the flatness of the terrain make such a land defense very difficult. Nevertheless the mobilized Turkish army, courageous and well trained but lacking modern equipment, such as tanks and planes, has been standing ready for any emergency, while looking to the United States for assistance, which was forthcoming at a steady rate. The narrow peninsula with Istanbul at the apex is still the bolt that locks the Black Sea and prevents the Soviet Union's reaching the Mediterranean.

· 32 ·
Greece (Hellas)

At mid-century, the scars of war on the landscape of Greece were slowly being healed after a long period of fighting. The country suffered not only from invasion by Italy and Germany in the early years of World War II, when it made a heroic if futile defense, but also from an even more destructive civil war after V-E Day. The fighting left Greece with burned-down villages, destroyed lines of communication, and all the demoralization of internal struggle in which Greek fought Greek.

When at the end of World War II Britain—which had been the guardian of Greece since Lord Byron fought at Mesolóngion in the Greek war of independence—declared itself no longer financially capable of fulfilling its obligations to Greece, the United States agreed to step into Britain's place. The belief at that time was— and subsequent events seem to have justified the belief—that the strategic peninsula that had been the fountainhead of western civilization would fall into oblivion without western assistance. Revolution, encouraged and supported from the northern neighboring states, and economic chaos plagued this last bastion of democratic thought in southeastern Europe. If Greece had also disappeared behind the Iron Curtain that was being lowered at that time, Soviet control would certainly have been further extended to embrace the eastern Mediterranean.

Through military assistance to the Greek government, but especially through more tangible help in the form of food and other supplies for the people, the United States helped keep the country alive during the dark days of civil war. Uneasy peace returned to the troubled land of Greece, and the enormous task of restoring the economy and spirit of the country began—again, with help from the United States. Reconstruction and rehabilitation are difficult in view of the inability of the Greeks to agree politically or even to compromise. An almost fierce individuality of thought, interregional antagonisms, and a pervading poverty greatly hamper progress, but slow advances are being made. With one of the most niggardly environments in Europe—certainly in relation to the population—Greece cannot expect the prosperity of Belgium, with its geographical assets and African possession of the Congo. But Greece can expect to have the opportunity to take advantage of such assets as it has.

The Problem of Modern Greece

Greece is a small country with a very famous name—a name that to the modern mind connotes the birthplace of an ancient civilization, calls up pictures of ruined temples, and stirs memories of the time when this little land was the cultural and political leader of the world. In a sense the glory of its history has been a disadvantage to modern Greece, for travelers from other lands have been primarily interested in that aspect of the country, and the Greeks themselves have more often boasted about their origin than justified it. But the name also calls up another picture—that of a poor and struggling country that belongs to the zone that we have called Europe C. In map after map this country is extreme. Its per capita income (B16) is one of the lowest in Europe; the yield of wheat per acre (A103) is almost the minimum; railroads, automobiles, manufactures, and other evidences of wealth and progress are scarce.

This unsatisfactory showing is not the fault of the people only. Political and geographic causes have combined against the country. Reborn more than a century ago after a war of independence against Turkey, the new country has never quite become stabilized. One war followed another, with gradual acquisitions of territory, until World War I brought a fateful defeat in Asia Minor. It compelled about 1.85 million Greeks to withdraw from there and from Istanbul and to settle in Greece itself; thus, the country had suddenly to assimilate numbers of penniless immigrants that are truly astonishing in comparison with the previous population. Only 350,000 Turks left Greece in the population exchange, so that 1.5 million new people had to be absorbed by a country with a population of only about 3 millions. Internal troubles and political upheavals after both world wars have been still more disruptive. One government has succeeded another, with frequent changes in policy, but there was little effective action to improve the state of the nation until after 1948, when the guerrillas began to be pushed northward and American funds flowed in to help in rehabilitation.

In Greece, as in Spain and Sicily, there arises the perennial question of the degree to which the political difficulties are of economic origin, and the degree to which the economic difficulties arise from geographic causes, or from the innate character of the people. Authorities differ on this point according to their training and interests. This much, however, seems clear: political, economic, and geographic factors are inextricably mixed. A geographic condition, such as rugged relief, may lead to economic distress. This may foster political confusion and war and may prevent the maintenance of roads and other facilities, thus increasing the geographic isolation, making the people still poorer, and adding greater complications to the political situation. Since this book deals primarily with geography, it is geography that will receive the main attention. However, the reader must recognize that, although geographic factors are fundamental, their effect is often diminished, and perhaps even neutralized, where people have sufficient innate ability, training, or outside help so that they can create the proper economic and political situation.

Applying all this to Greece, the student of political history may say that what the country needs is a long period of peace. The educator holds that it needs schools and good teachers; the engineer calls for good roads, better irrigation works, and better harbors; the businessman says that the greatest need is capital, new factories, and a higher plane of business ethics; and the agricultural expert recommends better methods of farming. The geographer says that all these needs exist, and that every one of them must be satisfied in order to raise Greece to a high level of prosperity and progress. He adds, however, that it is doubtful whether any or all of them can accomplish the desired results unless the environmental handicaps are recognized and overcome, and unless the environmental assets are likewise recognized and effectively exploited.

Greece Compared with Norway

A good way to understand the true situation in Greece is to compare that country with Norway. Aside from climate, the geographic conditions of the two countries are much alike. Both occupy peninsulas and lie on the margin of Europe on the way to enclosed arms of the sea that lead past other countries to Russia. Greece has the additional advantage of lying close to the main trade route through the Mediterranean to Suez and the Orient. Both countries have extremely long and deeply indented coasts with many deep bays and offshore islands. In both the beautiful coasts are very attractive to tourists, but Greece has also the great advantage of historical asso-

ciations and marvelous ruins that almost every informed person is
eager to see.

Another important resemblance is found in the mountainous relief and the scarcity and small size of level plains.   Moreover, in
both countries most of the level and easily habitable sections are iso-

A. General Map of Greece and Albania.

lated from one another, but open freely to the sea.   In this respect,
also, Greece has a certain advantage, for it has some habitable interior basins that are benefited by their altitude, whereas the interior of Norway is so high that the limited parts that are level
enough to support a considerable population are too cold.   Because
of the mountains and the peninsular form of the land the rivers in
both countries are short, steep, and useless for navigation, but good
for water power.   In this respect, however, Norway has by far the
advantage because of glaciation, a more steadily rainy climate, and
cooler temperatures that reduce evaporation.   In each country, again,
a little iron is mined, although again Norway has a great advan-

tage. Other minerals are present in moderate quantities, but they have not been of great importance and are not likely to be in the future. Greece has a greater variety of minerals than does Norway, and it could probably produce more if they were fully exploited, but Norway's actual production is greater. Moreover, Greece exports most of its minerals, whereas Norway uses most of its ores. After a survey of the landforms of Greece, more will be said about the similarities of Greece and Norway.

Landform Regions of Greece

The Northwest. The central part of Greece north of the Gulf of Corinth is occupied by the massive system of the Pindus, a continuation of the Dinaric ranges of Yugoslavia and Albania. Its main axis lies west of the center of the country, and projecting spurs reach the west coast. This western Pindaric slope forms Ípiros (Epirus), one of the five natural regions of Greece. It includes several small plains along the Adriatic coast, and a few fertile interior basins like that of Ioánnina (Yannina), but most of it is very rugged and sparsely populated except by shepherds who bring their flocks up from the lowlands in summer. The western plains look toward the sea and are cut off from one another in the characteristic fashion by rough tracts where the mountains end in a precipitous coast. They are cut off from eastern Greece by lofty Pindus itself, which is nowhere crossed by a railroad—indeed, no railways exist west of the range—or even a good motor road; routes are little more than rough cart tracks that degenerate into trails where the mountains are steep. Seaward the plains look out upon, and are tempted toward, the beautiful, densely populated, and yet rugged Ionian Islands: Corfu (Greek: Kérkira), Levkas, and others. All this is typically Greek; the land repels man, the sea attracts him. A good colored relief map brings this out clearly.

Thessaly, Boeotia, and Attica. In the section east of Pindus, a number of subparallel mountain ranges extend eastward or southeastward to the sea and are separated by fertile basins. One range rises south of Bitola (Monastir) in Yugoslavia, culminates in lofty Olympus (the fabled home of the Greek gods), and then skirts the Greek coast as the peninsula of Vólos. Just south of Olympus, in latitude 40°, this range has been cut through by the Piniós to produce the Vale of Tempe and drain the fertile plain that is the heart of Thessaly. The range continues seaward in the Northern Sporades Islands, and even in Chios on the Asiatic side of the Aegean Sea.

Óthris, the next of the ranges jutting out from Pindus, lies south of Lárisa and the plain of Thessaly. Its seaward prolongation includes the great elongated island of Euboea and its structural extension in Andros and other Aegean islands. A third and smaller range rises south of the small plain of Lamia and extends along the coast south- west of Euboea. In one place the cliff along its northern margin once lay within about 40 feet of the sea and provided the setting for the famous battle of Thermopylae, where Leonidas with 300 Spartans held at bay the huge army of Xerxes. Since then the deposits of a neighboring mountain river, aided perhaps by a slight change in the relative levels of land and sea, have formed an alluvial plain 1.5 to 3 miles wide between the cliff and the sea. Farther east the mainland and Euboea approach one another so closely that a swinging bridge only 180 feet long connects them. Through the narrow strait a curious current runs like a river with a speed of 4 or 5 miles per hour, but unlike a river it reverses itself ten or twelve times a day and is a hazard to mariners.

Between this mountain range and the next one to the south lies the basin of Boeotia. A small lake (Copaïs) in this basin was long the source of countless mosquitoes that afflicted the Boeotians with malaria. It is sometimes supposed that the universal prevalence of this disease among the Boeotians while Athens was still free from it gave the Boeotians the reputation for stupidity that has come down in history. Certain it is that the constant recurrence of malaria saps human vitality and that it has played an important part in retarding the progress of Greece, Sicily, and large sections of Italy and Spain. Moreover, there is evidence that in ancient times the disease did not prevail to anything like the great extent it did in the nineteenth and early twentieth centuries and that its increase during the centuries before the Christian era coincided with a pronounced decline in the alertness and achievements of the Greeks. In modern times a large part of Lake Copaïs has been drained; this has diminished but not eliminated the malaria and added more than 50,000 acres of good level land to the scanty supply of Greece.

The Boeotian basin in its turn is bounded on the south by the famous range that includes Mount Parnassós, home of the Greek Muses, and Delphi, just north of the Gulf of Corinth, where the famous oracle uttered its solemn warnings. This range, which to- ward the south includes Mount Hymettus, famous for its honey, swings around north of Athens and ends in a promontory where the white columns of the ruins at Sunium gleam against the brown mountain side and the blue sky. Seaward it forms part of the Cyclades Islands, especially Naxos. Where a low pass crosses it, south of the little plain of Marathon, the Greeks made a famous stand against the Persians in a battle that is forever associated with the runners who heralded the victory in Athens. South of the mountains lies the Attic Basin with Athens, the most famous of Greek cities, and perhaps the most prolific of all sources of great men in proportion to the population. The way in which the mountains at Thermopylae and Marathon helped to check invaders on their way to Athens illustrates how greatly Greece has been influenced by the barriers that isolate one little section of the country from another. The relief map makes it clear that here on the east side of Pindus, even more than on the west, Greece consists of a series of small, fertile basins, open to the sea as a rule, but separated from one another by rough mountains. Here, however, railways in modern times have connected them by land.

Macedonia and Thrace. North and east of Mount Olympus lies a third section of Greece, comprising Macedonia and part of ancient Thrace. Here, too, is a series of basins, beginning on the west with that of Thessaloníki near the mouth of the great Vardar River, and going on through others to the Maritsa River at the Turkish border. These are neither so small nor so separate as those farther south, but they are cut off from one another by mountains and, especially because of the Rhodope Mountains and other highlands north of them, look seaward more than landward. One-half million of the immigrant Greeks from Turkey settled on the land here after World War I. Mount Athos, the easternmost of the three rugged promontories of the peninsula of Chalcidice, is noted for its autonomous Greek Catholic monasteries. Greece formerly had many famous monasteries, such as Megaspelion (or Great Cave), which clings to the face of a precipice, south of the Gulf of Corinth; but the government has now taken over most of their property.

Peloponnesus. The fourth section of Greece is the Peloponnesus, sometimes called Morea, south of the deep Gulf of Corinth, whose western part is called the Gulf of Pátrai. The Isthmus of Corinth joins the Peloponnesus to the mainland, but it is only 3.5 miles long and 240 feet high. Even in antiquity small ships were dragged across it. Now the Corinth (Greek: Korinthos) Canal makes the Peloponnesus an island, but it is narrow and has so strong a current that large ships rarely use it. The Peloponnesus is like a hand with a thumb and three fingers. The main part of the hand is the moun-

tain knot of Arcadia, a continuation of Pindus. There, as in all the
Greek mountains, small, primitive stone villages are scattered among
the valleys. Often they are reached only by bridle paths. Many
have very little level land except land that has been laboriously obtained by building terraces. Arcadia is synonymous with a region of
rural simplicity and innocence because in old days, as now, this
region lay apart from the active life of the basins near the sea.

Here, as in many other parts of Greece, the presence of soluble
limestone has caused the development of a karst topography. A few
little lakes, like Stymphalos, have underground outlets, and some of
them vary greatly in size according to whether these outlets are
clogged or not. The Lado River, a tributary of the Alfiós, is frequently subject to flood resulting from the bursting of underground
barriers, even though the lake from which it is popularly supposed
to come by an underground outlet does not change in size. Large
quantities of water must, therefore, be dammed back within subter-
ranean caverns. The burial of Olympia beneath many feet of gravel
is often ascribed to such floods in the early Christian era. This is a
mistake, for corresponding gravel deposits form terraces on innumerable other streams where floods of this karst type are not
experienced.

The burial of Olympia is probably due to an irregular but momentous decline in rainfall during a long climatic cycle, the dry
phase of which culminated in the seventh century after Christ. During this period the increasing prevalence of dry years appears to have
prevented the forests on the mountains from reproducing themselves, and also to have diminished the cover of vegetation as well
as the amount of cultivated land in most of Greece. As a result the
torrential rains were able to carry away the soil from thousands of
square miles of sloping land, and to deposit part of it on the valley
bottoms, thus ruining many of the best agricultural sections. At the
same time the crops presumably declined in yield per acre, and it is
well known that the population became very sparse and poor and
was much disturbed by migrations and wars. Today the climatic
cycles have reached a point at which the rainfall appears to be
greater than in the seventh century, although less than in the best
periods of antiquity, but the lost soil has not been restored, nor
have forests again spread over the mountains to anything like the
former extent. But Arcadia, being high and exposed to the west
winds, has more than its share of forests. Part consists of the typ-

ical maquis and such trees as the laurel; but oak, chestnut, and sometimes beech, pine, and spruce also occur.

From Arcadia minor ranges project out into four rocky peninsulas. Between them lie small plains, first Argolís, between the thumb and the forefinger, then Laconia with ancient Sparta (Greek: Spárti) as its main town, and next Messinía with its orange groves. Where the little finger has been cut off lies still another plain, that of Olympia, with the ruins of its famous temples almost buried in gravel. These projecting ranges, like those farther northwest, are continued seaward in islands, the forefinger especially being curved around through mountainous Crete (Greek: Críti) to the equally mountainous island of Rhodes. The plains, too, are separated from one another and from the interior basins as in northern Greece. Railways extend around most of the Peloponnesus but do not, for example, reach Sparta.

Islands. The fifth section of Greece is the Aegean Islands, tops of drowned mountain ranges that rise again in Asia Minor. Like so many other parts of Greece, they contain great areas of bare, pale gray limestone and of less precipitous brown slopes whose thin soil is tinged with the green of grass for only a short time in the spring. Higher up, where the air is cooler, most of the loftier islands are clothed with thin forests of beech, oak, and even pine at the highest levels. All these islands, like Greece itself, are full of vestiges of ancient civilizations that showed an originality and vigor greater than that of the present. In the northwestward march of civilization Crete was one of the most important stations long before the mainland of Greece had risen to any high position.

Effect of Rugged Lands and Tempting Seas

This résumé of the physical divisions and relief of Greece permits a continuation of the comparison of Greece with Norway. Two human responses to the geographic environment stand out especially. The first is that in both countries the division into many isolated little sections fostered the growth of a great many small, independent states and delayed the coming of political unity. All through the main period of ancient Greek history each basin with its little city preserved its own independence and even its own special type of culture. Athens, Corinth, Sparta, and Boeotia all stand for distinct and sometimes antagonistic types of culture. Often these little neighbors were at war with one another. They fell eventually because they could not unite against Philip of Macedon, who came not only from a more northern home, but also from one where the basins are built on a larger and less isolated scale so that his power had a broader basis than that of the little city-states of Greece.

Norway displays a similar response to isolated basins. That country was later than almost any other part of Europe in having a real king. Until the ninth century each of its little plains or valleys was ruled by its own lord who paid no allegiance to anyone else. Mountains everywhere tend to keep people divided, and in Greece this sort of division bore its finest fruit.

The second similarity in the human responses of Greece and Norway to their geographic environment is that the inhospitable character of the land and the difficulty of traveling from one basin to another join forces with the deep bays and many islands in inducing men to sail out over the water. In Greece this is easier than in Norway, for during the long summer no storms arise, the air is clear, and the winds are steady. Moreover, the great number of islands, visible one from another, made it safe for primitive voyagers to sail far from home. Thus the Greeks have become the most thoroughly seafaring people in Europe aside from the Norwegians. In both countries the overwhelming majority of the people live close to the shore. In Greece practically no one lives more than 50 miles from the sea, and since the interior is highly mountainous fully 90 per cent must live within about 25 miles of it. This is why the Greeks are the fishermen and merchantmen of southeastern Europe, just as the Norwegians are of the northwest. The fishing around Greece is not so good as around Norway because of the warm, stagnant quality of the Mediterranean water. It forms an important industry, to be sure, but the country nevertheless imports part of its fish supply.

In former times when ships were small, the opportunities for trading were far greater around Greece than around Norway. Nevertheless, from both countries the inhabitants pushed far out along the coasts as traders and colonists. The little island of Siros in the midst of the Cyclades repeatedly rose to eminence as a center to which trading ships came from all directions. Great markets or fairs were held there. Greek colonies were established on many parts of the shores of the Black and Mediterranean seas. The Vikings from Norway did the same thing except that they established themselves violently on the coasts of Britain, France, Spain, and even Sicily, instead of in the quieter way of the Greeks. Almost invariably the Greek colonists, like the Vikings, stayed near the sea and left the interior to its old ways. They did not seek political expansion but merely places in which to live and carry on trade. Until World War I the west coast of Asia Minor had been largely inhabited by Greeks for two or three millenniums. This coast gave to the world many of the greatest ancient Greeks, such as Thales, Sappho, and Herodotus. After World War I the Turks were able to expel the Greeks with comparative ease because most of them still lived near the seacoast.

In our day the maritime quality of the Greeks is evident in the high percentage of persons engaged in trade and transportation, two or three times as great as in other parts of Europe C. It is also evident in the fact that, whereas Spain has only one ton of shipping for every 23 inhabitants, and Italy one for every 19, Greece has one for every 6 or less.

Character of the Greeks

Both the mountains and the sea appear to have had a deep influence upon the character of the Greeks. These people are sometimes described as having the love of country, vigor, and courage that are usually found among highlanders, together with the spirit of adventure, the versatility, and the passion for freedom that are characteristic of seafarers. They are also described as having the faults that belong especially to traders and sailors. These include avarice, undue sharpness in driving bargains, a tendency to tell boastful stories, and none too keen a sense of honesty. Such traits spring in part from long centuries of political oppression by the Turks, but they appear to have been relatively common even in antiquity when the Greeks ruled themselves. They do not apply to the villagers so much as to the townspeople. The villagers are friendly, reasonably honest, and moderately industrious, although physical work is nowhere in great favor. In all the towns, and even in the villages, the influence of the sea seems to be evident in a rather high degree of mental activity and of interest in affairs beyond their own locality. The mere fact that men from almost every village go to sea or migrate across the water gives a general alertness that is not found in inland countries.

Another interesting feature of Greek character is the great abundance of professional men. Keenness of mind, joined with knowledge of the world and aversion to manual work, leads to a great desire for an education that will assure the young men of what they consider easy jobs. A large part of the men who are thus trained do not practice their professions, but go into mercantile pursuits, strive for political office, or eke out a scanty living in all sorts of odd ways. This is one reason why political disputes are so warm and so common in Greece.

Climatic Environment

The differences between Greece and Norway show a close connection with the climate, just as the resemblances do with the relief and the sea. A518 shows that at all seasons Greece is not far from

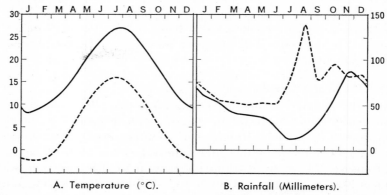

A. Temperature (°C).   B. Rainfall (Millimeters).

A–B. Comparative Climatic Curves for Greece (Solid Lines) and Norway (Dashed Lines).

20° F warmer than Norway. A518 shows that both countries have about the same rainfall in winter, but that in summer Greece becomes very dry, while the rainfall in Norway increases notably. As a result Greece seems comparatively dry even in the winter, whereas Norway seems moist all the time. The spring in Greece is not a long period of verdure as in regions with the cyclonic type of climate. It comes with a sudden rush—there is almost an explosion of gay flowers and green grass and of blossoming trees on the hillsides. Few sights are lovelier than a Greek olive orchard where the ground is scarlet with poppies. Every species of plant seems to know that it must blossom and get its fruit and seed well matured before the dryness and heat of summer make further growth impossible. Thus the spring has a truly marvelous beauty, but a disappointing brevity. This rapid onset of heat and dryness, together with the frequent absence of rain at both the beginning and end of what is normally the dry season, is the bane of Greece. To it, more than to any other cause, is due not only the low yield of most crops per acre, but also the great variability of yield from year to year. No contrast between Greece and Norway is greater than this, for Norway, like most cyclonic regions, has high crop yields per acre, and shows relatively little variability from one year to another in spite of the danger from frost.

Western Greece, being exposed to the west winds from the ocean, does not suffer from drought and heat so much as eastern Greece. At Corfu, for instance, the temperature averages 50° F in January and 77° in July, while Athens registers 47° and 80°. The western rainfall is also heavy, for the mountains act as a barrier. Thus Corfu, one of the rainiest parts of Greece, gets 54 inches per year, whereas Athens, which lies more fully in the rain shadow than almost any other part, gets only 14. This contrast explains why the population in western Peloponnesus is much denser than in the east. From Athens northward the population is denser in the east because there are the harbors and the plains.

The scarcity of cyclonic storms in Greece during the winter and their absence in summer is another point concerning which Greece is at a disadvantage compared with Norway. The lack of storms and consequently of atmospheric variability as well as humidity join with the high summer temperature and dustiness to make the death rate in Greece higher than in Norway. The energy of the people shows a corresponding difference. This accentuates such matters as the tendency of the Greeks to talk politics while the Norwegians are developing power plants. It is doubtless one reason—but not the only one—why Greece, in proportion to its population, has only one of each of the following mechanical contrivances whereas Norway has the number indicated: miles of railway 2, passenger automobiles 9, and telephones about 6.

Low Agricultural Intensity

The greatest influence of the Greek climate and other geographical conditions is exerted through the crops. The reason is that 54 per cent of the Greeks are engaged directly in agriculture, and perhaps 15 per cent more are engaged in supplying their wants. Hence the agricultural production per man is the most important of all economic facts in Greece. The first fact to note is the small amount of cropped land, only 7 acres per agricultural family of 5 persons in comparison with 12 in Belgium. This contrast arises not wholly from lack of land in Greece, but because the average Greek farmer leaves about 3 acres lying fallow each year in order to allow the land to recover its fertility. The trouble is not, as some people suppose, that the land has been used so long that its fertility is exhausted. The Belgian land has been used far more intensively for many centuries. Moreover, most of the soil now in use in Greece is not very old, for the topsoil is carried off by rain and wind at an alarming rate. In fact that is one of the great troubles; the Greek soil is more often too young than too old. Moreover, much of it is derived from limestone and is therefore deficient in phosphorus. Nitrogen is also scarce because of lack of humus.

No soil can be devoted continuously to the same crop without fertilization and still retain its fertility. The Belgains can cultivate the same land every year because their climate permits a great variety of crops, and also because it favors the growth of abundant, juicy grass and other forage at practically all seasons so that large numbers of cattle can be kept, and fertilizer is abundant. Most of the unirrigated land in Greece is not moist enough for crops like corn and summer vegetables, or even for good clover. So its use is more or less limited to winter grains. If the Greeks could find enough capital to pay for better seed and plows, more fertilizer, and the stronger draft animals needed to haul the heavier plows, probably most of their fallow land could be cultivated, and the crops on all the land could be increased. The difficulty of getting the required capital, however, is perhaps even greater than that of arousing the Greek peasant to alter his traditional methods. American aid after 1948 helped somewhat, but much remained to be done.

Consider the Greek farmer's income. About a third of his land is devoted to wheat, another third to other cereals, and the rest to olives, grapes, and tobacco, with a few small scraps for other products. From each acre the Greek farmer gets only about one quarter as much wheat and one third as much of other cereals as does the Belgian farmer. His other crops are more profitable, especially his tobacco and the small grapes sold as dried currants, but even from the 2 or 2.5 acres devoted to these his return per acre is probably less than the Belgian farmer's return from each of the 6 acres of land that he devotes to the more profitable kinds of non-cereal crops. When it comes to animals there is the same sort of difference. Then, too, the Greek farmers are rarely able to earn much additional income by working in factories as do many Belgians. Nor do they have the chance to work in forests, for their dry climate limits them to only a fraction of the forest area possessed by the Norwegians in proportion to the population. Moreover, the Greek forests are mostly high in the mountains and inaccessible to the ordinary farmer.

All this explains why the income per farmer in Greece is less than a quarter as much as in Belgium. The smallness of this figure is not due to the faults of the Greeks to anything like so great a degree as to the dryness of the summers, the badly eroded condition and poor quality of the soil, and the difficulty of getting more water for irrigation. The smallness of the income also indicates why it is so hard for the Greeks to use improved methods. It would take the average Greek farmer years to save money enough to buy the cheapest American car even if he and his family could live without food and without buying anything whatever. It would take most of a year's income to buy a mowing machine, and even if he got a machine his fields are so small and in many cases so steep and so terraced that it would be of no use to him.

The foregoing discussion of farming in Greece is not applicable to northern Greece, where conditions differ appreciably. This difference is partly the result of climate—especially the fact that summers are less dry and the annual rainfall heavier—but it is also partly the result of the fact that particularly in Macedonia there are fairly extensive plains, formerly swamps but now for the greater part drained and cultivated. Here, as in northern Italy and in the Danube basin, corn becomes a leading crop, and even cotton does well. Tobacco is still the important cash crop, ranking first as a Greek export and followed by products from the south—currants and olive oil. The broad Macedonian Plain of ancient fame is now dotted with new modern villages, often occupied by the farmer refugees from Turkey; and the broad plans of the plains villages are in marked contrast to the concentrated settlements in the hills overlooking the lowlands.

All the difficulties of the Greek farmer were greatly intensified by World War II and its terrible aftermath. Even by 1950 the level of Greek agricultural production was 13 per cent below the prewar average. Population had meanwhile increased by 15 per cent!

Manufactures

Manufacturing industries do not attain great rank in Greece, with about 8 per cent of the economically active population being thus employed compared with 20 per cent in Norway. In spite of the lack of coal, the development of water power has not yet gone far, partly because of the great seasonal variation in rainfall, the scarcity of forests to hold back the water, and the scarcity of lakes. Such conditions cause the rivers to vary enormously in volume from winter to summer and to be very muddy and hence difficult to control by dams. Another reason is that here, as elsewhere in Europe C, there is great scarcity both of capital to establish factories and of income with which to buy the manufactured goods. And finally the long, hot summers are very uncomfortable for people who are shut up in factories. Because of all this, practically all the industries are of a simple kind based on agricultural commodities. They include especially tobacco factories, soap factories, and flour mills. The only real industrial development is around Athens and Thessaloníki. Textiles—including cotton (with nearly all raw cotton imported), wool, and silk—along with leather goods, are of principal importance. Edhessa, west of the Macedonian Plain, is the chief textile center.

Population and Its Distribution

The present population of 8 millions on an area the size of New York State or Louisiana makes Greece a very densely populated country, with 156 per square mile. Of course this sounds small compared with 731 in Belgium, but the real density can be appreciated only when one considers that 54 per cent of the Greeks depend directly on the land and that the mountains leave only about 30 per cent of the area available for utilization. Reckoning on this basis and considering only the farmers, the density of the agricultural population is more than 15 per cent greater than in Belgium. For so small and densely populated a country to assimilate nearly 2 million refugees after World War I was extremely difficult. Nevertheless the feat was successfully accomplished, partly through the growth of the cities, partly by using some land hitherto neglected, and partly by exchanging the Greeks of Asia Minor for the former Turkish inhabitants of Macedonia. About 300,000 settled in Athens and Piraeus, another 350,000 took the places of Turkish farmers who moved out of Macedonia, and the remaining 1.25 millions found places, mostly on previously unoccupied land or in the northern towns such as Thessaloníki. After their arrival the land under cultivation increased more than 40 per cent, and in Macedonia it nearly doubled. Another change is that more valuable crops are now being raised, the acreage of tobacco being threefold what it was. Cotton shows a similar increase and is now raised on 140,000 acres or more.

In this way the old Macedonian problem, so far as it concerned Greek against Turk, has been solved, for few except Greeks remain in Macedonia. Many people think that the Greek nation has been strengthened by these new people. The weaklings among them, both mentally and physically, were eliminated by persecution and migration; their trials have taught them to be more adaptable and industrious; those who have settled on the land appear to be of rather high grade. In spite of this, however, about 40 per cent of the population above 10 years of age is still illiterate, but schools are rapidly increasing, and the percentage of literacy increased 10 per cent between 1930 and 1950.

The events of history have not continuously favored the maintenance of the cultural apex Greece achieved in the centuries before Christ. Political changes, the dying out of certain minor but very important elements in the population, the introduction of slaves, the spread of malaria, and the migration of many of the best Greek minds to Rome in later days have all diminished the impulse toward learning and the arts. Physical changes due to long climatic cycles have probably worked to the same effect, and the washing away of the soil from vast areas has certainly impoverished the country. Thus Greece has surrendered its claim to being the heart of the civilized world. Nevertheless there seems to be no insuperable obstacle to new and important contributions to human progress from Greece.

As in Italy, the most distressing problem is pressure of population. Furthermore, in Greece the poverty almost everywhere is like that in the worst parts of southern Italy. As has been indicated, the Macedonian basins are normally somewhat better off than the more southerly parts of Greece, but they certainly are not the equivalent of the Po Basin. And the mountains of Macedonia suffered intensely during the civil war after 1945. The miracle is that the Greeks—like the Italians—are capable of being cheerful and of enjoying life in the midst of such utter penury. In this respect, Greece is even more remarkable than southern Italy.

Even though overpopulation is such a problem, the birth rate remains one of the highest in Europe, and, since modern measures have decreased the death rate so that it is equivalent to that of France, population increase is very great.

Cities

Only two Greek cities, Athens and Thessaloníki, are outstanding. Athens (Greek: Athínai) and the port of Piraeus (Greek: Piraiévs) now form in reality a single great city with a population of more than a million. The city took on new life in the last century and has expanded from a small country town to become the great capital of the new Greek state. With its splendid historical shrines, Athens has renewed its standing as the cultural and political center of the country and has become at the same time the center of manufacturing industries, such as they are. The influx of refugees who settled there increased the potential industrial power. Piraeus is the main harbor of Greece, particularly in imports. Thessaloníki (Salonika), about a third the size of the metropolitan district of Athens, lies at the terminus of the old Morava-Vardar trade route from the Danube to the Aegean Sea. As a railroad junction, port, and center of an important tobacco district, it slowly regained its former importance after having suffered severely during the war period of the 1940's.

Pátrai and Vólos are two smaller ports, the first of which is a great center for the export of currants, and the second for the shipment of the wheat of Thessaly to Athens. Sparta of ancient fame is now a small inland town of little importance. Ermoúpolis on Siros is still the main trade center of the Aegean Islands. Alexandroúpolis, the former Dedeagach, would be the natural outlet of the fertile Maritsa Basin if it were Bulgarian instead of Greek. Corfu is becoming a well-known winter resort. Italy's return of the Dodecanese, with its main island of Rhodes, had more national than economic value, although Rhodes under normal conditions attracts quite a number of tourists.

Summary and Evaluation

Greece, on the way back after the trials and destruction of a decade of fighting, has a long way to go. Its merchant marine, once its pride, is recovering only slowly from the serious wartime depletion. The continuing unfavorable balance of trade is especially traceable to the food deficit, which is certain to remain a problem for many years to come. To achieve even a moderately successful relationship between land and people, the Greeks will be forced to work even harder than they have in the past.

As is true, of course, of every country, the fascination of Greece must be experienced to be appreciated. The senior author feels that this is particularly true of Greece as he recalls the privilege he had of seeing it in spring when the land looked fresh after the winter rains. The fields of wheat covered the plains with a golden mantle broken only by the orange of the poppies. The hills were alive with the flowering scrub of the maquis, and even the olive trees looked less drab. The mountain profiles were etched against a blue sky by the brilliant Mediterranean sunshine. Ancient ruins —classical, medieval, and the later Renaissance—dotted the landscape. Centuries of occupance were reflected on every hand.

Perhaps Greece will always be a kind of cultural luxury for the rest of the world to help support in partial payment for what Greece gave the world: a bequest whose value cannot be measured in money. For it was here that western civilization was brought to flower and from here that it was dispersed—a gift that can never be repaid.

· 33 ·

Central Europe: Switzerland
(Schweiz, Suisse, Svizzera)

Central Europe

Surrounded by other geographic regions of strong, uniform characteristics, central Europe stands apart as a zone of transition. Nordic Scandinavia, marine western Europe, Mediterranean southern Europe, and topographically uniform eastern Europe surround a great section reaching from the North and Baltic seas to the Black Sea. The transitional character of this zone is evident not only in its climate, vegetation, and crops, but also in the industry, commerce, and political and social organization of its people. Since most of it has no ready access to the sea, the ocean does not play so important a role as elsewhere.

The diversity between the eastern and western parts of central Europe is extreme. Western Germany has the typical qualities of western Europe, as does Switzerland in many respects. Rumania east of the Carpathians belongs to the eastern European world, and some sections of Yugoslavia and Bulgaria are distinctly Mediterranean. Good reasons can be given for including Poland in central Europe, especially because of its former many western cultural ties, but, like Rumania, it also shows strong eastern European tendencies.

Within this great section of Europe two groups of countries are clearly recognizable. In the north and west, Germany, Switzerland, Austria, and the Bohemian Plateau of Czechoslovakia are highly industrialized lands unable to feed themselves despite intensive farming, although they possess high standards of efficiency and culture. Mostly of German stock, aside from the Czechs, they look to the North Sea as the outlet of their ocean trade as well as of their main rivers.

The south and southeast are different. Agriculture of the extensive type is there dominant, and except in some local centers the cultural standard is relatively low. The Danube River, once the backbone of the Austro-Hungarian Empire, remains the great potential trade artery that gives to this section the name of the Danube states. Hungary, Czechoslovakia, Yugoslavia, Rumania, and Bulgaria are the political units of this section, with Austria and western Czechoslovakia as their zone of contact with the industrial half of central Europe. Poland forms a transition toward Russia, which is the real eastern Europe.

Both world wars left their marks upon central Europe more than anywhere else. After 1920, old states were reborn and new ones created with economic results that sometimes challenged the practical wisdom of the new political alignment, and there was a manifest tendency to create new economic ties between nation and nation. Political conditions were in many sections still unsettled, and dissatisfied minorities increased the difficulties of economic adjustment. After World War II, it was central Europe that became the focal point of the struggle between East and West in Europe. The entire eastern half disappeared behind the Iron Curtain after extensive rearrangements of political frontiers. Switzerland suffered least from these conditions, for its boundaries remained unchanged after both world wars, and the country itself was not involved as a belligerent in either conflict.

Introduction to Switzerland

Switzerland feels that it is on top of the world, although it may worry at times about European political tensions. Believing in complete neutrality except when attacked, it only occasionally joins international agreements and has not even joined the United Nations, although it is co-operating in some of its functions. To a certain extent it is still Europe as it was before the world wars, somewhat conservative—one might say rather solid but not interested in drastic changes.

Switzerland was always one of the more prosperous countries of Europe. Deprived of most raw materials, with a climate not conducive to grain agriculture, and, of course, with all the handicaps of a mountain topography in the greater part of the country, the Swiss—as an intensely patriotic and democratic nation—have accepted the challenge that nature gave them and have made good. Switzerland has made its reputation through the quality of its products, agricultural (dairy) and industrial (textile machinery, chemicals, and watches). Its tourist industry is a model of planning and execution;

its *hoteliers* are found all over the world. Two other factors have
added to its high standard. One of them is the fact that Switzerland became—and remains—a haven for refugees, who in many cases
prove to be valuable additions to the cultural life. The other factor
is that Switzerland is a keystone in European transportation (see
A528). The existence of this international transportation system was

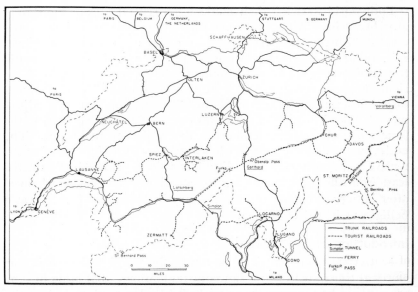

A. Trunk Lines and Tourist Railroads of Switzerland.

one of the reasons for Switzerland's staying out of the war, because
any attacker knew that the Swiss could and would destroy that system, most vulnerable because of its tunnels and viaducts, immediately
and beyond hope of repair with any dispatch.

At present Switzerland ranks first in Europe from the point of
view of standard of living. Financially very strong with its well-
organized banking systems, and proud of its small but well-equipped
army, it feels it can weather the storms that threaten on its horizons.
One wonders sometimes whether Switzerland does not put too much
faith in its security and whether it overestimates its economic position. However, meanwhile, Switzerland is prosperous: a happy
country in a troubled world.

Ethnographic Diversity and Political Unity

In spite of its small size, Switzerland is one of the best-known countries of Europe, and its influence is far greater than its size would indicate. The contrast between the country's unity of national sentiment and its lack of real national boundaries, as well as its diversity of language, culture, and religion, is astonishing. Switzerland is not a unit from the physiographic point of view, for its boundaries do not in general follow the mountain crests, but swerve in and out irregularly. Among the 4 million Swiss there is a sharp difference between the German Swiss (72 per cent), speaking a German dialect and having a culture largely the result of German influences, and the French and Italian Swiss, occupying the western and southern parts (A530). Even between these two Latin sections there is a great difference in culture as well as in language. The French or "Romand" Swiss (21 per cent) have been much influenced by France, especially in recent generations; the Italian Swiss (5 per cent) are typically Italian, a bit backward in culture, but developing rapidly. In the eastern part there is still another language, the Rhaeto-Roman or Romansch (1 per cent). This relic of very old times is decreasing in importance. Nevertheless, it is another genuine element in the Swiss ethnographic composition.

The distribution of religions is even more complicated than that of languages, and it can be understood only by studying the regional history. With a compact Catholic population south of the Alps, the rest of the country is divided, although the Protestants form the majority with 58 per cent of the population. Geneva in the west and Zürich in the northeast (A532), with Calvin and Zwingli, played an important part in the history of Protestantism, but the nucleus of the Swiss state, the old lake cantons (Lucerne, Zug, Schwyz, Uri, and Unterwalden in the center of A530), has always remained Catholic.

Despite all this, Switzerland presents a unit of great strength. Born about A.D. 1300 of a rebellion against Austrian domination, it began as a combination of a few small states or cantons (Schwyz, Uri, and Unterwalden) in the mountains around the Lake of Lucerne (Vierwaldstätter See) and grew gradually as other districts joined the movement for freedom. Aided by its mountainous environment, Switzerland as a combination of small states continued through the intervening centuries. Its field of influence waxed and waned, but its heart—the mountains and the central plateau—remained always united.

The present Swiss Republic is an extremely democratic federation of twenty-two cantons, every one of which retains large rights. Nevertheless, the federation is strong, not alone because of common interests and a common historical development, but also because of

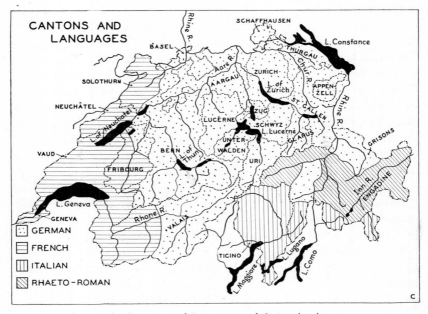

A. Cantons and Languages of Switzerland.

the country's very high standing in education and in general culture. Switzerland has sustained in Europe the idea of democracy for a longer time and more steadily than any other country. It has been imitated by other states, but the extreme Swiss form of democracy has never been equaled. Any law of importance is brought directly before the people, who are free to make their own decision. It was appropriate that this country should become the seat of the old League of Nations, secure from foreign political influences and under the protection of the Swiss democracy. The Swiss respect for individuality and personal freedom seems to be in part a product of the stern environment that demands personal initiative and constant struggle as the price of survival. This same quality has made Switzerland a haven for refugees, who wait there till better times enable them to return home, or else definitely settle there, bringing new ideas and new energy to a new fatherland.

The basic factor in the geography of Switzerland is the struggle of the population, helped by an energizing climate, to make the best of the great handicaps of relief and poor soil. In recent generations they have used the beauties of the rugged relief as the basis of a highly developed tourist industry, and the available water power has been utilized for a highly specialized type of manufacturing, which provides exports that partly offset the great deficit of grain and raw materials. But the country's fundamental character was established long before these resources came into play.

The Alps

Structure and Relief. The three chief natural regions of Switzerland, as was outlined in Chapter 4, are the Alps in the south, the Jura in the north, and the much lower Swiss Plateau between them (A532).

The Alps, which occupy almost two thirds of the Swiss area, are the central part of the great Alpine mountain arc that begins in southern France and continues into Austria. As is clear in A532, they can easily be subdivided into long east-west zones of different topography and economic value. The backbone is the High Alps (3, ruled vertically in A532), mostly above 10,000 feet in altitude, and covered in part by glaciers and snow fields. A central depression, the so-called Rhône-Rhine depression, divides them into a northern zone of which the Bernese Alps (A in A532) are the best-known section and a southern zone composed of the Alps of Valais (B) west of the St. Gotthard nucleus where the Italian boundary makes the more westerly of its swings to the north, and the Grison Alps (C) on the east. Farther east another depression, the Engadin, occupied by the Inn River, separates the Grisons from the Bernina Alps (D) in the southeastern corner of Switzerland.

Both north and south of these High Alps a lower section of mountains (the heavily dotted area, 2 in A532) forms a kind of transition to the foreland. Less majestic, but with broad valleys dotted sometimes with lakes, this section with its more rounded ranges, broader valleys, and milder climate is equally attractive to tourists. On both sides of the High Alps the land is also more productive and more densely populated than the central chain. Here, as in France, both sections may be called the Pre-Alps. The southern section covers most of the canton of Ticino, where the Swiss border swings far to the south. The northern Pre-Alps form an unbroken band from Lake Geneva to the Boden See (Lake of Constance).

For an explanation of the present relief of Switzerland, one must go back to the time when the Alps were folded between the African and Nordic blocks as explained in Chapter 3. They were bordered then by seas on both sides (the present Po Basin and the Swiss Pla-

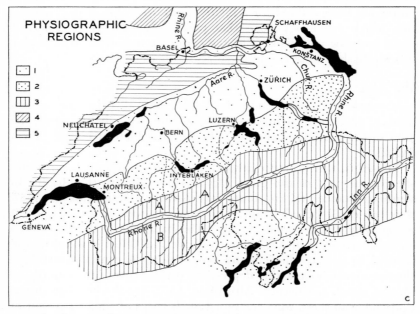

A. Physiographic Regions of Switzerland. The black areas are lakes.

teau, which forms the main lightly dotted area, 1 in A532). Into these seas flowed rivers that gradually reduced the complicated mountain system to a mature surface with broad valleys, low relief, and a central divide not much higher than 5,000 feet. The sea at the north gradually disappeared in consequence of the uplift of the land, and the erosion surface probably extended across what is now not only the Swiss Plateau but also the Jura. This ancient surface was next uplifted and warped into its present form of a huge anticline, sloping down on both sides, but more steeply toward the south than toward the north. Along the crest of this anticline occurred a slight longitudinal hollow, the beginning of the present central depression. Both running water and the glaciers of the Ice Age—

especially the latter—remodeled the uplifted surface into its present shape. Glaciers from the high mountains followed the rivers into the surrounding lowlands, polishing, widening, and deepening the valleys. Everywhere in the Alps broad straight valleys, numerous terraces, polished rocks, and many hanging valleys still afford clear evidence of this period, and river erosion since the Ice Age has affected the glacial topography but slightly. In some places the high mountain section still exhibits remnants of the old preglacial surface, for on some nearly level areas the ice cover was almost motionless and even protected the underlying rocks from erosion.

The central depression of the High Alps was much widened and deepened by glaciation. It thus became a longitudinal passage of great economic importance, with two main outlets, that of the Rhône near Martigny on the west and that of the Rhine near Chur on the east. A third minor outlet follows the Reuss River where it escapes northward from the central depression through the narrow gorge of Göschenen in Uri to Lake Lucerne. The central depression continues into France between the French High Alps and the Pre-Alps as indicated in the description of that country, and in it one finds such famous places as Chamonix at the foot of Mont Blanc.

Although in the High Alps the moving ice was largely confined to the valleys, in the Pre-Alps such ice covered practically everything. Thus it was responsible for the rounded forms and blocked drainage of these sections. Where the valley glaciers flowed onto the soft materials of the Alpine Foreland, long basins were gouged out and later occupied by the famous Alpine lakes that stand out so clearly in A532. Terminal moraines at the ends of these lakes often indicate their glacial origin, although a postglacial sinking of the Alps and consequent warping of the valleys was probably another factor in damming back the water.

Land Utilization in the Alps. The mountain climate with its long, severe winters makes crops unprofitable in the Alps except in some of the lower valleys. Hence stock raising on the Alpine slopes has always been the principal occupation. But valuable as this mode of earning a livelihood is among the mountains, it is only a small factor in the total economic life of Switzerland. Except in some sections of the Pre-Alps, like the southern part of Ticino where grains and grapes can be raised, the population of the Alps is sparse and is confined to the valleys. For security against floods, the small villages are often located on the protected parts of the valley bottoms, such as alluvial fans, or the lower of the many fluvioglacial terraces that are a feature of most of the valleys. Springtime can often bring sudden destruction and death to Alpine villages when avalanches of wet snow initiated by the seasonal thaw thunder down the valley sides. Even in winter, dry snow avalanches roar down the mountains after heavy snowfalls. Forests are retained in the known avalanche tracks to inhibit these terrifying intruders of the Alps.

Another phenomenon of the Alpine valleys—although it also affects part of the plateau—is the föhn, already mentioned in the description of the Italian lakes. In Switzerland, the föhn arises when an atmospheric low-pressure system lies over northwestern or northern Europe and draws air from the Mediterranean. As the wind rises over the southern Alpine slopes it is cooled and loses its moisture, its temperature falling at the approximate rate of one degree Fahrenheit for every 325 feet that it rises ("wet adiabatic rate"). In descending the northern slopes of the Alps, however, it is warmed at the approximate rate of almost two degrees Fahrenheit for every 325 feet that it descends ("dry adiabatic rate"), and so reaches Switzerland as a dry, warm wind. The föhn is akin to the well-known "chinook" winds of eastern Colorado and, like them, evaporates moisture and snow and raises the temperature 20 and 25 degrees in only a few hours. Sometimes it ruins tender crops and at times causes avalanches.

In the winter there is a long period of rest because of the heavy snowfall. In spring the Swiss mountain dwellers take up a variety of activities. Some, usually women, remain at home, or, if they live high up, descend into the valleys to look after the crops and hay that must be made ready in order to feed the cows in winter. The men take the cattle up into the mountains, slowly following the retreat of the melting snow from one terrace to the next until in August the highest Alpine meadows are reached. Forests cover the steep slopes between the terraces, and firewood is gathered there. In the fall the process of migration—transhumance—is reversed.

In recent years the significance of the "alps," or high mountain pastures, for the production of milk and cheese has decreased, and these Alpine meadows are more and more used to pasture young cattle before they are sent down to the plateau where the dairy herds are mainly kept.

The central depression, especially the Rhône section, has unusual economic value on account of its warm climate and light rainfall. Sion in the Rhône Valley has the lowest rainfall of Switzerland, 16 inches. Fruits are common here—grapes for wine and all kinds of small fruit for canning and export.

Tourist Industry. The greatest economic value of the Swiss mountains lies in their attraction for tourists. The love of mountain scenery is rather recent; not so long ago the Alps were avoided and the Swiss Plateau was more favored. In time, however, the discovery of the Alps by mountain climbers (in the beginning mostly English), and the combination of love of sport and love of nature, resulted in the opening of the mountains to tourists.

The present Swiss tourist industry is wonderfully well organized. From the main railway lines, scenic railroads (see A528) and good highways with motorbus services invade the mountains in all directions. Hotels of all kinds from the most elaborate to the simplest are ready to care for the tourists. Even the high mountains are no longer forbidding. Steep cable railroads make it possible to reach with ease high elevations, such as the Rigi, which in former times necessitated hours of strenuous, dangerous climbing.

At the beginning of the twentieth century came the discovery of the winter beauty of the Alps, and winter sports have given new life to the quiet Swiss villages. Places like Zermatt in the Valais, Gstaad, Adelboden, and Grindelwald in the Bernese Oberland, and St. Moritz in the Engadin, once small, little-known villages, have now become famous the world over. In addition, the climate of the mountains has given rise to various health resorts like Leysin in Vaud and Davos and Arosa in the Grisons.

In spite of this modern penetration, the Alps are so vast that they still offer plenty of sport for the mountain climber or lover of scenery who wishes to escape from every sign of modern civilization. Much of the Alpine world with its wonderful peaks and glaciers, its high meadows covered with brilliant flowers, its great coniferous forests, and its picturesque valleys with their clear-running rivers is still remote from modern luxury and affectation. This is true on the steep southern slope of the Alps as well as on the north, but around Lake Lugano and Lake Maggiore the scenery is different. These places face the sun and are protected against northern winds so that they have a milder climate and partly subtropical vegetation. In winter, snow falls occasionally, but in early spring and fall Lugano and Locarno are centers for people seeking to escape the inhospitable climate of northern Europe.

Transportation. Even in very early times travelers between central Europe and Italy crossed the Alpine passes. Amber from the

Baltic region was brought across them to the ancient Mediterranean lands; here Roman warriors and merchants once crossed the heights and passed the trade caravans of Venice and Genoa during the Middle Ages. Names of passes like the Great St. Bernard, the Simplon, the St. Gotthard, the Splügen, and the Bernardino are still well known, although motorcars now speed across them on modern roads and only the old-fashioned hospices where dwelt the kindly monks on the highest points recall the ancient times.

Today railroads have taken the place of the old caravans and the later stagecoaches, and various tunnels penetrate the Alps, connecting the Swiss Plateau with the Italian plain (A528). The most important of these is the Gotthard line from Lucerne, which climbs up the Reuss Valley, crosses the main chain between Göschenen and Airolo at an elevation of 4,000 feet through the St. Gotthard Tunnel (9.3 miles long), and then winds down toward the Swiss part of the Italian lakes and Milan. One may come back from Italy by a second line, the Simplon, crossing from Italy to Brig at an elevation of about 2,000 feet through the Simplon Tunnel (12.3 miles long). In Switzerland this line has two branches: one along the Rhône Valley to Lausanne and Paris, the other crossing the Bernese Alps at an elevation of 3,500 feet by way of the Lötschberg Tunnel to Bern and northern Europe. A third way of crossing the Alps is important only to tourists. It leads from the Rhine at Chur south of the Boden See to the Engadin by way of the Albula Tunnel, and then over the Bernina Pass at 7,000 feet to the Adda Valley and Lake Como. On the northeastern edge of Switzerland the Arlberg line connects Switzerland with Austria and forms part of the line from Paris to Vienna via Zürich and Innsbruck.

The Swiss Plateau

Structure and Relief. The Swiss Plateau, which comprises 30 per cent of the area of Switzerland, is the uplifted depression between the Alps and the Jura. Before the uplift, enormous amounts of material from the eroded mountains were deposited here. The uplift raised the region so that the present elevation varies between 400 and 700 meters in the valleys and 700 to 1,000 meters on the divides. Then the mighty Alpine streams eroded the plateau; and finally the glaciers of the Ice Age poured down over it, sometimes achieving erosion but mostly covering the plateau with glacial drift. Terminal moraines that form the dams of lakes are numerous, and enormous glacial boulders of material from the High Alps indicate the extension of the ice during that period. At present, here as in the Alps, erosion by streams is readjusting the glacial forms to the shapes demanded by water, and broad valleys with rounded hills between them dominate the landscape.

The lakes along the northern base of the Alps and also at the southern edge of the Jura bring to the plateau a considerable share of the tourist trade. The lake shores are dotted with summer resorts that attract people who care for a less majestic but more romantic environment, and towns with such well-known names as Zürich, Lucerne, Interlaken, Montreux, Lausanne, and Geneva afford contact with the High Alps.

Land Utilization in the Swiss Plateau. It is well to realize that the Swiss Plateau is the nucleus of Switzerland. Here are the fields and gardens; here are found the greater part of the cattle; and here, also, are the manufacturing industries, and finally the bulk of the population in towns, villages, and individual farmhouses. The Alps have made Switzerland famous all over the world, but without the plateau the country could not exist. As soon as Switzerland began its independent existence, the three mountain cantons (Schwyz, Uri, Unterwalden), where strong mountain folk defied the power of Austria, looked toward the plateau for the extension of their new country.

Most of the plateau is under cultivation; orchards and vegetable gardens surround the villages, and fields of wheat, rye, oats, and potatoes cover many valley terraces and lower hill slopes. Most of the land, however, is in grass, providing hay for cattle that are kept in barns and are stall fed. Forests of oak and pine cover the upper parts of the hilly divides. The dairy and its associated industries—chocolate, condensed milk, and leather—are the chief Swiss agricultural developments. Although Switzerland is not self-supporting in dairy products and has to import butter in considerable quantities, it has become a leader in the export of cheese (Gruyère and Emmenthal) and of milk-chocolate, both of which have an almost world-wide distribution. The shoes made of Swiss leather are likewise of very high quality, and the Bally shoe factory is famous.

Switzerland also ranks high as a producer of fruits and vegetables. Grapes ripen on the south-facing slope of the lakes and are used for wine. In some places large canning plants have developed, producing a high-class product based on several types of berries and vegetables. Apples are the most common fruit all over the plateau, and the apple blossoms rank with the narcissus of the western Pre-Alps and the bulbs of Holland as one of Europe's most colorful spectacles. Swiss cereals, in spite of a high yield per acre, by no means equal the home consumption, and large quantities have to be imported. The difficulty of obtaining grain during World War II forced the government to encourage the production

A. South-facing slope along Lake Geneva between Lausanne and Montreux. Terraced vineyards. Above, forests leading to the Swiss Plateau. Along the shore, main road and railroad (part of the Paris-Istanbul line) and shore village.

of cereals and potatoes, with the result that the general increase during the period 1943–47 was more than 75 per cent in acreage, with wheat gradually replacing rye. By 1950, the subsidies paid to Swiss farmers, who make up only 20 per cent of the economically engaged population, aroused appreciable resentment among the Swiss employed in factories. The subsidies were believed necessary in order to keep the food-producing capacity of the country at a peak in view of the general European political situation.

Manufacturing. Long before the modern development of manufacturing the Swiss had achieved great technical skill in their home industries. The long, raw winters encouraged homework in woodcarving and embroidering. In modern times this industry, encouraged by the buying power of the numerous tourists, still holds an important place. Fine laces, clocks, and woodcarvings bring profits to many homes and provide an income for an otherwise unproductive season.

During the twentieth century hydroelectric power has come to dominate Swiss life to a degree equaled nowhere except perhaps in Norway. It permits the manufacturing of a great number of specialized products. These are partly the outcome of former home industries, but part are new and are made possible by the keenness of the population to exploit their resources. The country's standing among European countries in production of hydroelectricity is shown on page 450.

Textiles dominate among the manufactured products, and among these silk is pre-eminent. Located in and around Zürich and based on imported raw materials, this industry, including spinning, printing, and dyeing, and the weaving of silk ribbon, produces some of Switzerland's main exports. Cotton spinning and weaving are centered in the northeast of the plateau around St. Gallen. The making of embroidery, a special branch of this industry, illustrates how the Swiss apply great skill to their work instead of being content with cheap goods like those of such countries as Egypt. The wool industry, including knitting and hosiery, does not attain the importance of silk and cotton; in recent years the rayon industry has made its appearance.

Although Switzerland has no raw materials for machinery, electrotechnical supplies, and other metal goods, the making of these is an important Swiss industry. By specializing in products of superior quality, the Swiss have been able to command a special place in the world market, with Zürich and neighboring towns like Baden and Winterthur holding rank as centers. Turbines, electric engines, and textile and agricultural machinery are the chief products and are sent to all parts of the world.

The chemical industry, relatively young, is gaining rapidly in importance. It is concentrated near the sources of power, where a wide range of chemical products is made. The manufacture of dyes is carried on mainly at Basel. In the production of aluminum, Switzerland formerly ranked third in the world, but developments after 1935 have moved it far down the list—after Russia, Britain, France, Germany, Norway, and Italy in Europe, and far after the United States and Canada.

Cities. Most of the Swiss towns have been mentioned in the discussion of the plateau and its economic development. Zürich and

Geneva are outstanding. The capital is Bern, centrally located in the zone of contact between the German Swiss and the Romand Swiss. It has retained many of its ancient characteristics. A number of towns are also academic centers, for Swiss universities have long attracted students from all parts of the world; and such communities as Geneva, Lausanne, Neuchâtel, and Zürich are famous for their schools.

Zürich is by far the largest city (386,500) and combines the advantage of a beautiful lake location attractive to tourists, and educational centers with manufacturing, which extends into neighboring towns such as Oerlikon and Baden. Geneva, also in a very attractive location, feels the loss of the seat of the League of Nations —the United Nations has its headquarters in New York—although it kept the labor office of that organization, and the former Palace of the League is used for many conferences. Although both Geneva and Zürich have an international character, Bern, the capital, is typically Swiss with its old buildings and gallery sidewalks.

Transportation. Besides the north-south lines that cross the Jura and continue toward Italy, the main railroads, all electrified, follow the east-west direction of the plateau, with Geneva, Lausanne, Bern, and Zürich as main junction points. They extend to the Boden See, where boats provide a connection with the railroad systems of southern Germany.

The Jura

The Jura region covers the western and northwestern parts of Switzerland between Geneva and Schaffhausen, with an offshoot extending nearly to Zürich (A532). The western part is a plateau of horizontal structure, most of which is not in Switzerland but in France. The eastern zone consists of folded ranges following the direction of the main chain and separated by longitudinal valleys. The landscape resembles the folded Appalachians of the United States. In both places it is possible to reconstruct an old warped erosion surface below which the present valleys have been cut. Here, as in the Appalachians, river gaps provide access to the more remote valleys of the interior. The higher sections are wooded, and the meadows are used for cattle.

Life in the Jura does not differ much from that in the Pre-Alps. Rain falls plentifully, and the winters, with their heavy snowfall, are long and severe. In the broad valleys there is more room than in the Alps, and the population is naturally far denser. Water power sufficient to operate small mills has co-operated with the aversion of the people to idleness during the long winters. The result is a home industry that specializes in the making of watches. Although this is still in part carried on in homes, it has also given rise to the greatest modern watchmaking industry of Europe. The products range from cheap dollar watches to the most perfect instruments of precision. Sometimes in a single year the value of watches and clocks exported amounts to more than 190 million dollars. Many watches and clocks, but by far more watch movements, are exported to the United States, in spite of the large American watch production. La Chaux-de-Fonds is the present center, but the clock and watch industry has also grown up along the southern foot of the mountains in towns like Biel, Neuchâtel, and Geneva, where living conditions are more attractive.

The importance of the Jura as a climatic barrier has already been indicated. It is also a barrier to transportation. Only in three places do rivers break entirely through it: the Rhine near Schaffhausen at the falls of the Rhine, the Aare more to the west, and the Rhône below Geneva. As most of the principal trade routes have always been at right angles to the direction of the ranges, numerous railroads cross them, some using the gaps, others using direct tunnels like that between Basel and Olten on the line to Zürich and Bern.

Basel, at the northern foot of the Jura and the southern entrance of the rift valley of the Rhine, lies at the junction of three countries. It is almost an independent geographical region, as it does not belong to either the Jura, the Swiss Plateau, or the Alps, the three Swiss natural regions. Its chief importance, in addition to being an industrial city in which dyeworks are a specialty, is as a railroad center. Most of the Swiss railroad connections with northern France, Great Britain, western Germany, and northwestern France focus here, making Basel the entrance to Switzerland. Basel is also Switzerland's only harbor, for river boats from Rotterdam can come up the Rhine to this point.

· 34 ·

Germany (Deutschland):
The Country

The difficulty of analyzing the geography of Germany is intensified by the fact that Germany at mid-century is vastly different from the Germany of 1914 or 1920 or 1939 or 1943. This constant shifting of the territorial base of the country means that Germany's capabilities also experience marked changes and that German performance at any one period must be considered against the background of the German territorial base of that period. And, finally, such shifting indicates a deep-seated maladjustment or malfunctioning of the land-and-man combination. The psycho-social factors that are partly responsible for German national behavior are beyond the scope of this discussion, but the geographical factors on which many of the broader aspects of such behavior are based, and the geographical consequences of that behavior, will be examined in these three chapters on Germany.

Not only is Germany at mid-century different from Germany at other periods during the twentieth century, but it is also split into two unequal parts that are as distinctively separate politically as are any two states in Europe. Since the Iron Curtain extends along the dividing line, the separation is even much greater than that between Italy and Austria, for example. Therefore, in this treatment of the country, reference must necessarily be made to the two parts of Germany: the German Federal Republic in the west and the German "Democratic" Republic in the east.

Territorial Evolution

It is even more important in a study of Germany than in a study of most European countries to examine the territorial evolution. In such a study one comes to understand not only the simple expansion and contraction of the state of Germany but also many aspects of the geographical forces that influence affairs in the heart of Europe.

Slow Growth of Coherence. The checkered history of Germany persistently shows the effect of geographic environment. For many centuries the most conspicuous fact in the history of the country was the extraordinary lack of coherence of its various sections, a condition that seems to be related to the irregular character of the Central Uplands that have long been the geographical heart of the country. Up to 1870, Germany consisted of a large number of small and more or less independent principalities. These were an inheritance from earlier times when not only Germany but also every other country consisted of relatively small units. The essential point in Germany is that the political consolidation of the units came late in European history and, furthermore, was delayed long after their cultural unification. However, between 1878 and 1945, the political unity was greater than the cultural unity, for the old principalities were completely swept away (although the persistence of peculiar administrative boundaries until 1945 reflected their former existence), whereas there is still a pronounced contrast between the culture of the north and the culture of the south. Less marked contrasts exist among scores of smaller areas.

Rome and the Holy Roman Empire. Both the political and cultural evolutions of Germany bear traces of events at least as ancient as the days of the Roman Empire. Most of what is now Germany was not included in the Roman Empire and remained practically untouched by Roman culture except through occasional traders. The upper Rhine plain and the Danube valley were, however, conquered and occupied by the Romans. Thus at that early date there was a distinct cultural contrast between the wild Teutonic or Germanic tribes (the "barbarians") of the north and the more cultured people of the south. With the collapse of the Roman Empire, the Teutons, especially the Franks, advanced westward, and thus their territory became politically connected with what is now France. The empire of Charlemagne represents the fullest development of this tendency. Charlemagne's capital was at Aachen (Aix-la-Chapelle) in the northwest where Germany now adjoins Holland and Belgium, but much of his time was spent in the cultural centers farther south. His empire lay mainly south of his capital and included much of France, Germany, and even Italy. A generation after Charlemagne's death, the Treaty of Verdun (843) placed the part of his former empire east of the

Rhine under a separate ruler, for the first time putting Germany
on the map as a country of civilized Europe. The following centuries saw the development of the Holy Roman Empire, with its
cultural center in what is now southern Germany (chiefly Bavaria)
and Austria. At a later date, Austria under the Hapsburgs claimed
the leadership, and Vienna was long the capital of the Holy Roman
Empire, which included much of what is now Germany, Austria,
France, and even Italy.

Divided Allegiance. Meanwhile, the rest of present Germany
was only loosely connected with the south. It consisted of a confusion of small political units under counts, dukes, and bishops,
or of autonomous cities. This was especially true of central Germany, very largely because of the great complexity of the relief as
illustrated in A569. There the division of the country into small
natural units approaches conditions in the Balkan Peninsula, where
numerous basins and valleys are separated by uplands or low mountain ranges. The separations in central Germany are, however,
far less complete than those in the Balkans, and a certain uniformity of culture and economic development prevailed in spite
of political complexity. The conditions in central Germany may
well be compared with those in ancient Greece.

In the north, two other factors entered into the historical development of Germany. One was the fact that the seacoast, the navigable rivers, and the easily traversed plain facilitated organization
of the Hanseatic League, which claimed many coastal and river
cities as members, especially those west of the Elbe. This helped
greatly in raising the northwest to a cultural level equal to that
of the south. Meanwhile, a second powerful influence was developing in the northeast. There Prussia was developing in territory
that had been abandoned by Germanic tribes during a westward
migration but that Prussia was gradually reconquering from the
Slavic tribes that had occupied it. Pushing across the northern
plain, the Prussians gradually extended their influence from their
relatively poor northeastern home until they dominated first the far
wealthier commercial and agricultural northwest and then the
more highly cultured regions farther south. Always, however,
there has been tension between their militaristic culture and the
more peaceful but no less vigorous culture of Bavaria and Austria.
The little principalities between the two groups swung first one way
and then the other.

The Power of Prussia. The Prussians furnish an interesting illustration of the origin and preservation of national traits. Their colonization of northeastern Germany was almost exclusively a military movement. This was true in Brandenburg, the center of Prussian power where Berlin has now grown up. It was even truer of Pomerania and former East Prussia farther to the northeast. Although other types of German colonists came into these regions, the dominant type consisted of military leaders and their war-like retainers. Prussian military families thus became established as proprietors of large estates. At first only people with the adventurous military spirit were willing to face the struggles and dangers of the new environment. Later the military spirit was necessary in order to protect the new homes. This necessity helped to establish the custom whereby the Prussian Junkers, as the upper class was called, held themselves aloof from the rest of the population; they usually married only within the group.

These strong people naturally extended their power westward into the richer region of the old Hanseatic League where the open lowland, undisturbed by natural barriers, facilitated their acquisition of parts of the Rhine valley soon after 1600 and the whole of it north of Frankfurt by the mid-nineteenth century. Southeastward they early extended their power up the open Oder valley to Silesia, whereas southward the irregular topography of central Germany was a vital factor in making their advance curiously irregular and spotted. In 1870, when the German Empire became a fact, Prussia as the strongest state assumed the lead, and its Hohenzollern king became emperor. The great development of Germany after 1870 was to an appreciable extent a Prussian achievement, and the perfectly organized German army reflected the old Prussian idea of constant military preparedness. It is worthy of note that one of the foremost objectives of the occupation of Germany after mid-1945 was the eradication of Prussia from the political map and the eradication of Prussian militarism from its traditional position of influence in Germany.

The Rise to Power after 1870. The sensational economic development of Germany after 1870 was one of the great phenomena of Europe. Here was proof that national progress rests on human qualities as well as on such physical factors as relief, soil, climate, and minerals. The successful war with France in 1870–71 helped to consolidate Germany as an economic unit under the leadership of Prussia, excluding its formal rival, Austria. That event ended

a century of war and economic troubles that had affected not only
the two greater German units, Prussia and Bavaria, but many of
the numerous smaller ones as well.   Then suddenly Germany,
which had been considered a country of poets and philosophers,
sprang into prominence industrially.   The industrial development was reinforced by self-consciousness and national pride that
had been stimulated through unification and the victorious war of
1870.   It was also intensified by the disposition of the people as a
whole to obey and co-operate, which is a strongly marked German
characteristic and which does much to enable determined leaders
of well-organized political groups to maintain a strong and often
autocratic government.   Equally important was the fact that the
Germans were an energetic, inventive, and numerous people, speaking one language, possessing essentially uniform ethnographic characteristics despite biological differences, and possessing an increasingly great consciousness of their potentiality as a group.

This modern development of Germany had agricultural and
commercial as well as industrial and political phases.   In agriculture the methods of land utilization were modernized, and crop
production was enlarged.   Nevertheless, the food supply became
insufficient for the rapidly increasing population.   The most signal developments were in manufacturing.   It was indeed fortunate for the developing Germany that just as it achieved unification a number of technological changes made many of its resources of great value.   In the middle of the nineteenth century
coke began to replace charcoal in iron smelting, and Germany possessed enormous deposits of coal admirably suited for coking purposes.   Furthermore, increasing use came to be made of by-products from coke manufacture.   And, probably most important in
the evolution of German heavy industry, the development in
1878 of the Thomas-Gilchrist process for smelting iron ore high in
phosphorus permitted Germany to utilize its great supplies of coking coal to smelt the enormous amounts of minette iron ore that
Germany took from France when it annexed part of Lorraine in
1871.   However, raw materials for the great textile industry had
to be imported.   In the completeness of their industrialization, the
Ruhr district, Saxony, and Upper Silesia came to be second to
none in the world.   As a result of the industrial progress Germany's
trade progressed with tremendous strides.   Hamburg became the
leading harbor of the continent, and the Rhine River was converted into a commercial artery with an enormous flow of traffic.

German ships carried German manufactured products all over the world and brought back in exchange the food and raw materials that the homeland lacked.

Meanwhile, the political development that crystallized in the formation of the German Empire in 1871 advanced still further by means of colonies. Not much of Africa remained unclaimed by Europeans then, but after 1884 Germany acquired more than 1 million square miles of African territory with a population exceeding 10 millions. This whole process of development, aside from its agricultural features, inevitably aroused some alarm, envy, and an active spirit of competition in neighboring countries. Germany's diplomatic methods toward these economic rivals did not always improve political relations, the more so as German national pride sometimes took the form of arrogance.

Changes Resulting from World War I. Defeat at the hands of the Allies obliged Germany to accept losses of territory totaling 27,083 square miles, about 14 per cent of the 1914 area. More than half of this land went to Poland; the rest went to France (Alsace-Lorraine, which had been taken in 1871), Denmark (Schleswig), Lithuania (the Memelland), Free City of Danzig, Belgium (Eupen-Malmédy), and Czechoslovakia (a small part of Upper Silesia).

During World War I, Germany's economic system changed greatly under the necessity of relying on home production to feed the population and supply war materials. Remarkable new inventions were used. But, under the handicaps of insufficient labor and worn-out machinery, the farms declined in productivity. Germany's defeat increased the economic difficulties. Transition from empire to republic, deflation of money, loss of economically valuable territory, loss of the merchant marine, scarcity of capital to improve the soil and provide new machinery, and foreign occupation of some of the most important industrial regions all bore heavily upon Germany and threatened to ruin it. But, when the brink of economic destruction was reached, Germany once more astonished the world by its adjustment to new conditions. Crop production increased, and livestock reached its prewar figures. Ships were built, factories were remodeled, and in 1928 for the first time the total trade surpassed the prewar figures. Germany's industrial energy had once more conquered all but insurmountable difficulties and had almost restored the country's old position among the nations of the world.

However, still indignant—rightly or wrongly—at the harshness of the Treaty of Versailles, Germany looked for leaders who would be able to wipe out the disgrace of defeat; but the democratic parties did not supply such a leader. The policy of co-operating with former enemies, saying little for a time about Germany's own grievances, and thus trying to obtain better international understanding and enduring peace was not popular. This spirit of discontent was intensified by the generally low standard of living, the unequal distribution of wealth, the effects of the Great Depression, and the heavy burden of taxes, debts, and war reparations. In such an atmosphere the Nazis under Hitler came to power.

The Nazi Tragedy. The story of the Hitler period and its immediate consequences not only for Germany but also for all Europe does not need to be told here. It is sufficient to say that, after a short period during which Nazi power was exerted over all continental Europe except Portugal, Spain, Sweden, and part of the Soviet Union, Germany collapsed under Allied attacks. The country was occupied by the Allies, and it was obliged to surrender more than 44,000 square miles of territory on a *de facto* basis until a peace treaty could be written and signed. Nearly all the territory went to Poland, although the Saar was also separated from western Germany (see Chapter 27). Thus, in 1950, Germany was only 65 per cent as large as it was in 1914. Two aggressive wars had cost it dearly in territory, resources, industries, and manpower instead of extending German sway over greater lands. These territorial changes may be followed in A178, A180, and A182.

Germany after 1945

Having brought upon itself the most catastrophic defeat ever suffered by a country in modern history, Germany surveyed the results of World War II. Unlike Germany in World War I, the country experienced both heavy air bombardment and actual invasion in World War II. In 1918 no fighting had taken place on German soil. In 1945 much of Germany lay in ruins. Although no German city suffered as much as Warsaw (see Chapter 43), many great cities of Germany were largely or partly destroyed: Berlin, Dresden, Frankfurt, Essen, Nürnberg, Munich, Cologne, Kassel, and scores of others. Transportation facilities were severely crippled, and great numbers of railway and highway bridges in the Central Uplands and over the many rivers were wrecked—often blown up by retreating SS forces. Industries were piles of steel and mortar—and the larger the industrial establishment, the more likely it was to be heavily damaged. On every hand the physical destruction underlined the cost of attempted aggression against larger, better-endowed countries with the will to resist imposition of Nazi totalitarianism.

The human wreckage was equally appalling. Disillusionment over the reality of things after the promise of a mighty German empire, bitterness over loss of the war, occasional feelings of guilt over the enormity of many Nazi acts—along with a tortured refusal to recognize that many of them could possibly have occurred, anxiety over the millions of missing men, most of them held by the Soviets, uncertainty as to which way the political wind would blow, indignation over foreign occupation, fear of the Russians and a smoldering dislike of all other foreign forces—all these subjective feelings played havoc with the German emotions during the years immediately after 1945. However, there were more tangible aspects to the human phase of postwar chaos. Whereas Germany for decades had pointed to the millions of *Volksdeutsche* (Germans living in other countries) with a certain amount of pride and with a certain hint that the lands they occupied should rightly belong to Germany, the country was shocked to have between 11 and 12 millions of these *Volksdeutsche,* along with the *Reichsdeutsche* from former eastern Germany, dumped into postwar Germany. They came from nearly every country in central and eastern Europe: Poland (7.5 millions), Czechoslovakia (2.4 millions), Austria, Hungary, Rumania, and others.

Thus, despite the loss of millions of lives in fighting and through bombing, the population of Germany in 1950 was actually greater than in 1938. And worse still—from the German point of view— was the fact that this slightly greater population (nearly 70 millions) had to live in and subsist on an area 25 per cent smaller than that of 1938. As a result, the density of population in Germany soared from 381 in 1938 to 505 in 1950, by which time the problem of housing, feeding, and employing the added millions was a grave one. Such a blow is certain to make a German think twice before engaging in aggression again, although the German mind thinks also of every reason why none of the territory should have been severed from the Fatherland in the first place. However, the final peace treaty legalizing the territorial shifts had not been signed in early 1952, and it was difficult to foresee what ultimate decisions would be made.

Through a long series of events that need not be recounted here, the zones of occupation established in 1945—which were never intended to be more than general, temporary zones preliminary to restoration of Germany—eventually gained great significance in one aspect: the Soviet zone, in the east, was operated independently by the Russians, whereas the Western Allies found it necessary to combine their zones first into Trizonia and then, in 1949, into the German Federal Republic (area: 94,634 square miles; population: about 48 millions), with its capital at Bonn. Soon thereafter, the Soviets formed a rival state of their zone—the German Democratic Republic (area: 42,392 square miles; population: about 19 millions). Thus, despite the essential geographic unity of Germany, and despite the very great desire of all Germans for political unity, there were two political Germanies after 1949, and prospects for consolidation appeared dim. Only positive assurance that country-wide free elections—with none of the single-list communist techniques employed—would be held could extract Western German and Western Allied agreement to unification; and in early 1952 it did not appear that the Soviets were prepared to risk such a free expression of political opinion in their satellite state of Eastern Germany. Thus the East-West antagonisms in the Cold War were of enormous significance in Germany.

This significance demonstrated itself in another way: the East and the West each wanted to have Germany—with its strategic position, its industrial capacities, its manpower, its trained soldiery, and its technical skill—on its side in the Cold War and, if the worst happened, in actual hostilities. This tug-of-war for German support is a dramatic illustration of the geographical importance of this country in central Europe.

The effect on postwar Germany of the severance of the trans-Oder-Neisse lands and of the split between eastern and western Germany is shown, in terms of agricultural production, in Table A551.

With a population slightly greater than that of the prewar period, Germany as a whole has not only lost a large share of its cropland, but the 48 million people of Western Germany have a relatively small share of what is left compared with the 19 millions of Eastern Germany—not counting the 3.2 millions of Berlin. Thus, a tremendous burden falls on Western Germany. For instance, the per capita acreage of the two bread grains, wheat and rye, was before 1939 one quarter of a hectare per capita, whereas it is now,

TABLE A

CROPLAND (1934–38 AVERAGES) IN THOUSANDS OF HECTARES

	West Germany	East Germany	Lost Provinces
Wheat	858	490	323
Rye	1,398	1,130	1,470
Barley	500	300	373
Oats	1,202	785	657
Potatoes	1,119	800	890
Sugar beets	160	206	123

(Note: One hectare is 2.47 acres.)

for Western Germany, only little more than one eighth of a hectare, exactly one half what it was. Here lies the chief food problem of Western Germany, especially since the surplus from the eastern part may not be available because of political conditions. The figures for livestock show the same situation, except that the statistics cover only 1948, and the situation improved after that time. These totals might be compared with the national pre-

	West Germany	East Germany	Lost Provinces
Cattle	10,573	3,045	4,105
Hogs	6,758	2,672	5,603

war totals of 21 million cattle and 24 million hogs, both of which show a very great drop.

The Geographical Sources of German Strength

Geographically, Germany has great advantages. Among Europe's four main physiographic zones it has no part in the most unfavorable one, the Northwestern Uplands. It includes just enough of the Alpine section to provide a delightful summer playground, but not enough to hamper communications within the country. Considerable parts belong to the Central Uplands—the Mesozoic area and old blocks of A568—but these do not have great elevations and are greatly interrupted by broad valleys and depressions such as the Rhine graben. A large part of the country— the North German Plain—belongs to the Central Lowlands, where the chief handicap is the poor sandy soil of the north. However, the area of the North European Plain included in Germany decreased appreciably after 1945, when Silesia and eastern Pomerania were transferred to Poland.

Another great advantage Germany enjoys is the nature of its rivers. Germany may almost be said to be a country of four rivers: Rhine, Weser, Elbe, and Oder. The upper parts of the Rhine and Elbe, to be sure, are in foreign territory, and the outlet of the Rhine is in the Netherlands. It was only after World War II that the Oder was practically lost to Germany, since most of the upper part and the outlet are in Poland, and the rest is used as the German-Polish boundary. Nevertheless, each of the four rivers has long been essentially German. The most valuable feature of these rivers is that they flow in a favorable direction through a highly developed lowland, level enough to make navigation easy and to permit many interconnecting canals, and yet not so flat as to cause a great deal of meandering or of development of very extensive swamps, except in a few regions. The upper Danube also traverses Germany, but the Danube assumes great economic significance only beyond German boundaries. Still another German asset is its portion of the North Sea coast, whereby Germany not only shares the marine climate of western Europe, but also has free access to the world in general and western Europe in particular. The Baltic coast and the Kiel Canal also give Germany a peculiar advantage in relation to Scandinavia and Russia, although the length of Germany's Baltic coast was greatly reduced after 1945.

One of the greatest German advantages is a climate that is good for highly developed and varied agriculture and that comes close to the human optimum. The frequency of cyclonic storms and the lack of extreme temperatures in the northwest do indeed present a contrast to the less cyclonic but more continental climate of the south and east, with greater differences between summer and winter. Even in the east, however, the precipitation and temperature nowhere approach the danger point for human occupancy and economic activity, and the most continental part of the east was surrendered to Poland. Consequently the crops, although differing in yield from year to year, never fail entirely, and the energizing effect of the climate on man is undoubtedly an important factor in the great industrial development.

In addition, Germany has long been blessed—and, even after losses of coal resources after both wars, is still blessed—with great sources of power and fair supplies of raw materials. The sources of power are coal, lignite, and water. The raw materials take the form of numerous ores, together with nonmetallic minerals, among which extensive potash deposits have been a great factor in improving agriculture.

The practical use of these basic geographic advantages and the consequent high level of industrial productivity could never have occurred except among a people of unusual ability and energy. Despite the rather obvious fact that the Germans have frequently prostituted their abilities and energy to aggressive ends, the people have shown that they are extremely capable in many lines of endeavor. Although many Germans rank among the finest artists—especially musicians—the particular forte of the German appears to be science and technology. Consequently, German technical products such as precision optical goods and machine tools are among the world's best and are produced in great quantities.

Thus one can begin to understand why a country no larger than the two states of Colorado and Nebraska combined could support a population of nearly 70 million—largest in Europe outside the Soviet Union—and could become such a power on the European continent. After 1945, the area shrank to only half that of the state of Texas, yet the population and significance of Germany remained.

Agriculture and Agricultural Regions

The utilization of the land in Germany has reached a very high pitch. In fact, it may fairly be said that no other large European country has done so much to increase the productivity of its soil. About 29 per cent of the economically engaged population of Western Germany depends upon agriculture, forestry, and fishing for a livelihood; and the percentage for Eastern Germany is much higher. The high percentage of productive land (90 per cent) shows how completely the land contributes to the national economy, especially when one considers that of the remaining 10 per cent almost two thirds is occupied by roads, buildings, and the like. Despite untold difficulties, agricultural production in Western Germany was in 1950 only 16 per cent below that of the average for the period 1934–38, although the level in Eastern Germany was 29 per cent below the 1934–38 average. Undoubtedly the redistribution of land retarded recovery in the Soviet zone.

Germany's attitude toward the land has been different from Great Britain's. During and after the Industrial Revolution, Great Britain ceased to strive for agricultural self-sufficiency and depended on imports for most of its food. Germany, however, attempted to expand agricultural production in order to feed the rapidly increasing population. Clever scientific crop rotation and the increased use of fertilizers have done much to make this effort successful, but success would never have been achieved if the climate and soil had not been sufficiently favorable.

In general, the climate of Germany is a happy medium between that of the marine Atlantic border and that of the continental interior of eastern Europe. Southern Germany has the advantage of warmer summers and a longer growing season, except where elevation offsets latitude. Rainfall everywhere is sufficient for farming, although it varies in amount.

German soils are of great variety. In general, residual soils have a leached appearance, the result of a relatively cool, moist climate. The map of European soils (A95) bears this out by showing two divisions for Germany, namely the gray leached Podzols and the darker leached Brown Forest soils. However, many German soils are not residual but have been transported by sea, river, wind, or glacier, and as a result may have a much greater value for agriculture. Here are some examples: the heavy marine clays of the North Sea marshes, the loams of the Baltic ground moraine, the alluvial soils of many river valleys, and the dark loessal soils along the northern foot of the upland brought by cold, dry winds blowing off the Scandinavian glacier.

The main crops of Germany are indicated in Table A551. However, among special crops should be mentioned the grapes, which can be found on the sunny slopes of the Rhine valley and many of its tributaries. Their northern boundary lies where the Rhine gorge opens to the lowlands. Although German wines are far from sufficient for home consumption, their high quality gives them special fame and a relatively high price for exports. Forests occupy 23 per cent of the land of Germany, and forestry was very well organized in prewar Germany. Forests suffered severely from overcutting during and especially after World War II, when fuel was scarce; it was then a familiar sight to see groups of people go into the woods and return with handcarts loaded with twigs, branches, and chopped wood. Fishing is a fairly productive enterprise along the North Sea coast and to a minor extent in the Baltic, but the total catch in 1949 was less than twice the amount landed in Denmark, which has only 4 million inhabitants. Fish accordingly is quite an item for import, especially since meat is scarce.

A555 shows that in a simplified form the main agricultural zones follow the general arrangement of the natural regions of Germany (A569), which are discussed in detail in the following two chapters.

The Mountains (I in A555). A mountain type of land utilization prevails in the German section of the Alps and some of the higher

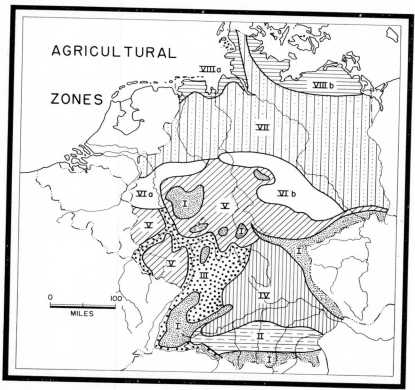

A. Agricultural Zones of Germany.

central and southern uplands, such as the Schwarzwald (Black Forest) and Oden-Wald, the high western part of the Jura Escarpment, parts of the Rhine Uplands, the Harz, the Thuringian Forest, and the Bohemian mountain border. In all these regions forests are important, and in many cases a valuable forest industry has grown up. In the Alps and in the higher parts of the Schwarzwald the type of land economy closely resembles that of the Swiss Alps. In summer the cattle graze on high mountain meadows, but in winter they are stall fed in the valleys.

The Southern Dairy Zone (II in A555). The dairy region of the south corresponds fairly well to the natural region of the Alpine Foreland and lies chiefly in Bavaria. The more fertile part of Bavaria near the Danube, however, must be excluded, for there crops are more important than stock raising. Crops have a greater importance on the warm southward-facing slopes north of the Boden See. As will be shown later, glacial deposits cover the Alpine Foreland, and vast high moors are common. Hence it is not surprising that grassland prevails over cropland and that dairying is the chief economic activity. The main crops are rye, oats, and barley, a response to rather poor soils and a raw climate. Butter and cheese, as well as meat, give a surplus that is transported to other parts of Germany.

The Upper Rhine Mixed Crop and Fruit Zone (III in A555). Zone III extends well beyond the natural region of the Upper Rhine Valley into the surrounding lower hills. It also includes the narrow gorges of the Rhine and Moselle and the western part of the Triassic Depression in Württemberg. All these areas have in common a warm climate due to low elevation and protection by mountains. Except in the narrow central Rhine and Moselle valleys, abundant fertile soil makes this a zone of high-priced farmland. The crops are of great variety. Wheat is grown for human food, and rye, barley, and even corn for fodder. Crops that yield more per acre are also grown: tobacco, for example, is an industrial crop, and the growing of fruit and nuts is typical of the whole section. Peaches, apricots, and almonds find here their most northern limit. The most characteristic fruit is the grape, which grows on terraced southward-facing slopes where stoniness often increases the effect of the sun's heat. Along the southern foot of the Schwarzwald this zone of mixed crops and fruits extends eastward to include the northern slopes of the Boden See.

The Southern and Central Zone of Rye (IV and V in A555). The largest agricultural zone of southern Germany, that of rye, covers a great number of natural regions. Nevertheless the central agricultural zone is identical with central Germany aside from the higher mountains. The southern zone (IV) is limited to the Jura Uplands, the eastern and higher part of the Triassic Depression, and the Danube valley. Although these areas vary in relief, they are alike in usually having rye, accompanied by oats, as the major crop, and in depending on crops more than upon livestock. Forested divides, meadows along the river courses, and croplands on the higher valley bottoms and lower slopes give an appearance of agricultural variety. In some of the basins, for example in Thüringen and Hessen, a warmer climate and deeper soils favor wheat over rye as the main crop. Cattle and swine are important locally, and sheep raising is still a prominent enterprise on the rather barren limestone uplands of northern Bavaria.

This zone of rye is separated into a southern and a central portion because in the southern portion barley comes strongly to the foreground and is the base for the large beer production. Locally, hops are also typical.

The Zone of Wheat and Sugar Beets (VI in A555). Along the foot of the Central German Uplands, the soils contain much loess, some of them resembling the Russian black soils (Chernozems). The greater fertility of these loessal soils, as well as the somewhat warmer climate (a result of low altitude as well as of relative nearness to the ocean), is responsible for a shift in the crops. Rye, oats, and potatoes give way in part to larger acreages of wheat and sugar beets, and in the eastern part to barley. Comparison with the map of natural divisions shows that this zone is almost identical with the Foreland zone. In some cases, however, the importance of rye limits this zone of wheat and sugar beets on the north. Moreover, the zone invades the eastern part of the Thuringian Basin and the lower part of the Saxonian Uplands.

Two units are recognizable in the zone of wheat and sugar beets. In the more marine western section (VIa), including part of the lower Rhine valley and Münsterland, pastures and dairying are still important. The eastern section (VIb) includes the area north of the Harz, the western part of Saxony, and a portion of the Thuringian Basin. Here sugar beets reach their peak, especially in the Magdeburg region. The cattle industry profits from the utilization of beet waste. The average value of farmland in this zone is almost three times as high as in the adjacent zone of rye.

The Northern Zone of Rye and Potatoes (VII in A555). Except for the North Sea marshes and the ground moraines along the Baltic coast, this large zone covers all the rest of the German Lowlands. The dominance of cropland over pasture and a major emphasis on the raising of rye and potatoes make it possible to include this great area under one heading. Only in the western part does the climate show the marine characteristics of mild, moist winters and cool, moist summers. Eastward, however, the continental influence increases, and the sequence of cold winters and warm summers favors crop raising above pasture. Except in the present river valleys and old glacial valleys, the soils are sandy in nature and need heavy fertilization. Large herds of sheep once wandered over the vast moors such as those of Lüneburger Heide between the Elbe and Weser south of Hamburg. These are now reduced to small numbers, because most of the moorland has been brought under cultivation. Next to rye, oats are the chief grain; buckwheat has lost most of its former importance. On the alluvial clays laid down by the rivers, rye loses its dominance; and wheat, sugar beets, and garden crops can be raised to advantage. In the west, dairying is still important, a response to the moist climate; but toward the east, it is limited to concentrations around the cities. Large numbers of swine are found throughout the region and profit from the surplus of potatoes and the skimmed milk of the dairies.

Northern Dairy Zone (VIII in A555). In this zone the dominance of dairying makes it advisable to combine the North Sea marshes and the Baltic Ground Moraine, although the two are different in land economy. Each of these sections is a unit in the description of natural regions: the North Sea marshes are identical with the natural regions of the same name, and the Baltic Ground Moraine zone appears as a subdivision of the Baltic Moraine Zone.

A. North Sea Marshes. The coastal marshes with their clay soils, equivalent to the "polder region" of the Netherlands, are used mostly for pasture. The cattle here are kept chiefly for dairy products, but also for fattening. The mild winters and cool summers are ideal for dairying, and the cattle can be kept outside most of the year. Only on the higher clay soils, found immediately behind the dikes, does cropland surpass pasture in area; and wheat, barley, and oats are raised.

B. The Baltic Ground Moraine Zone. In land utilization, the Baltic Ground Moraine Zone strongly resembles the Danish islands, of which it is a logical extension. A marine climate and rather heavy, loamy soils favor pasture and the raising of fodder crops such as clover and oats. Dairy cattle are the most typical economic response. Wheat, barley, and—in the eastern part—rye are the principal grain crops.

Mining and Manufacturing

Despite the significance and high development of German agriculture, it is in the field of mining and manufacturing that Germany must seek its economic salvation—as, indeed, the country long ago realized. The very significant role of manufacturing in Germany will be brought out in detail in the next two chapters, but some general survey of the nature of German industries and their recovery from the effects of World War II is appropriate.

Power. Possession of the greatest reserve of coal in Europe—and a reserve with a very high percentage of excellent coking coal—gives Germany a prime basis for an industrial development. The country has exploited its coal resources well, although not to the extent that Britain has. Even with severance of the Saar and Silesian fields from German production, Germany possesses more coal than any other country of Europe, if the Asiatic fields of the Soviet Union are not counted in the Russian total. However, German production before 1938 was not as great as that of Britain. With a total hard coal production of 175 million tons for all Germany in prewar years, Western Germany alone produced in 1951 about 120 million tons, a figure almost equal to that of prewar years for the same fields (Ruhr-Aachen). Coal production from the Saxonian fields in the Soviet zone is about 3 million tons yearly.

It is precisely in regard to Germany's great coal production that the vital significance of Germany in the European economy must be considered. Prior to 1938, Germany supplied approximately half the coal required by all the coal-deficient countries of Europe. After 1945, as has been mentioned elsewhere and as will be brought out in Chapter 43, decreased German coal production was reflected in decreased exports, and Poland became the chief coal exporter, although it had ranked a poor third to Britain and Germany in 1938. By 1950, however, Germany was rapidly regaining its prewar level and was exporting at a rate twice as great as that of Britain—but still somewhat behind Poland. Eventually its exports will stabilize at approximately 40–45 million tons annually, which will place it ahead of Poland, who is attempting to achieve a level of 35–40 million tons annually. Both will greatly surpass Britain, which will probably range between 20 and 30 million tons annually.

Germany also possesses the largest lignite ("brown coal") reserves in Europe, and during World War II production reached 250 million tons in a year. Lignite furnishes a large amount of fuel for domestic heating and thermal electricity production and also furnishes a very important raw material for synthetic petroleum products and chemicals. However, most of the lignite is produced in that part of Germany under Soviet control, so that at mid-century Western Germany produced 80 million tons and Eastern Germany 113 million tons annually. Since 9 tons of lignite are required to furnish the equivalent heat of 2 tons of coal, Western Germany produces, in coal and lignite, the hard coal equivalent of 192 million tons against Eastern Germany's 28 million tons —a ratio of almost 7 to 1.

Although Germany does not possess a great potential in water power, the country has developed every possible natural site until its installed capacity is far above its potential at ordinary minimum flow. Western Germany's rank among the countries of Europe in production of hydroelectricity may be seen on page 450. Incredible though it may seem, Germany at mid-century—despite the wartime destruction—generated more electric power (with both thermal and hydroelectric stations) than did either France or Britain, but not as much as did the Soviet Union as a whole.

Finally, a small petroleum pool near Celle, northeast of Hannover (A563), produces approximately 850,000 metric tons of oil yearly. This figure is slightly more than that for the Netherlands and supplies only a fraction of the normal German consumption of petroleum.

Raw Materials. Except for potash and coal, which through the highly developed German chemical techniques supply the basis for a tremendous number of products, Germany is not well supplied with raw materials. The great potash deposits surrounding the Harz, centering especially on Stassfurt, are, indeed, a great asset; they supply not only great amounts of fertilizer but also raw materials for the chemical industry. Unfortunately, most of the deposits are in Eastern Germany. Having lost 75 per cent of its iron ore after World War I with the return of Lorraine to France, Germany lost most of its zinc and lead deposits to Poland in 1945, thus further decreasing the modest supply of ores. Iron ore long mined in the Sieg and Lahn valleys south of the Ruhr is gradually being exhausted, although the large low-grade ores of Peine, west of Braunschweig, hold promise of supplying ore in the future. Only 3 million tons (iron content) of iron is mined annually within Germany, and millions of tons of ore must be imported, chiefly from Sweden and Lorraine. The numerous varied ores of the Harz and of Saxony (mostly in the Erzgebirge) are almost exhausted, although the Soviets are working uranium deposits in the Erzgebirge with slave labor.

Such raw materials as cotton, wool, and silk for the textile industries must be imported, although synthetic fabrics, using yarns chemically produced from coal, have become more and more important in the textile areas. Even wood and wood pulp, despite the relatively large areas of Germany under forest, must be almost entirely imported.

Manufacturing. Manufacturing is one of the main manifestations of German energy and intellect. The rapid increase of the German population, the many large towns, the intricate system of railroads and canals, the heavy boat traffic along the main rivers, the intense exploitation of natural resources, the busy ocean harbors, and finally the high standing of science—all these are connected with the greatest industrial development the European continent (as distinguished from the islands) has ever known. Energy and native ability were doubtless primary factors in this growth, but the direction that it took was strongly influenced by sources of power, raw materials, and transportation. This combination of circumstances has brought the trademark, "Made in Germany," into general favor throughout the world—at least so far as quality is concerned.

One of the most outstanding features of German industry is the extraordinary combination of favorable conditions in a single limited section. A similar association of diverse types of advantages is found in other European countries—for instance, in northern France, the Po Basin, and Belgium, but rarely or never is it so perfect as in Germany. Belgium, to be sure, shows practically the same advantages as Germany, but lacks a forested hinterland and a vast home market. Moreover, it is a comparatively small region, whereas the German industrial area spreads over a large area of unusual agricultural prosperity. In Great Britain, the other great western European industrial power, advantages like those of Germany are found, but in no one place are advantages of every kind so closely brought together as in the lower Rhine region. Scotland, to be sure, is almost equally favored, for coal and easy transportation by water are found in the Scottish Lowland just where agriculture is most profitable, but the area is very small. The great circum-Pennine industrial development of England does not coincide with the best agricultural district, which is located in the southeast. The home textile industries that were once developed under the stimulus of rich agricultural returns, especially in Norfolk, have moved northwestward toward the source of power.

Neither can the United States boast an agreement between agricultural prosperity, transportation, and sources of power so perfect as in Germany and hence so favorable to manufacturing. The main American industrial regions are indeed located in a climate that is admirable for both man and crops, but from Boston to Philadelphia, where the climate is best and ocean transportation most feasible, there is neither coal nor iron, and the combined effects of relief and glaciation in many places limit the extent of good soil. Around the Great Lakes, although raw materials, fuel, waterways, and agricultural possibilities rank very high, the distance from the sea and the extremes of temperature in both summer and winter are more disadvantageous than in Germany. Outside of Germany it is difficult to find any large section that equals the main German industrial region and especially the Rhine region in its well-nigh perfect combination of all the factors that promote manufacturing.

Despite the appalling destruction of German industries by air bombing, ground fighting, and reparations removals during and after World War II, recovery was amazingly rapid after 1948, and by 1950 Western Germany was producing at a level almost equal to that of 1938. Even in Eastern Germany, despite wholesale removals of industries by the Soviets as reparations for destruction inflicted by the Nazis in Russia, the level of production in 1950 was only 10 per cent below that of 1938. It was in the great Berlin industrial concentration that recovery was slowest.

The necessity for a healthy, producing Germany for an economically healthy Europe gradually forced the Allies—including the Soviet Union—to permit a restoration of German industries. The original plan had been to cut German industry sharply in order to decrease its war potential, and removal of industrial plants to countries that had suffered destruction by Nazi armies was an ideal method of effecting the decrease. However, it was quickly seen that such a plan was completely impracticable: Europe—including Germany itself—needed the products of German industry, and furthermore the country would have become a great charity ward without employment for its millions of people. Thus, defeated Germany by 1950 was operating at a high rate of production.

The variety of German manufactured products is infinite. There is virtually nothing that is not produced in one of the many industrial areas shown in A563, each of which will be described in its proper regional setting in the next two chapters. In general,

German industry is marked by a contrast between several very
large concerns—which were, before 1945, united in some of the

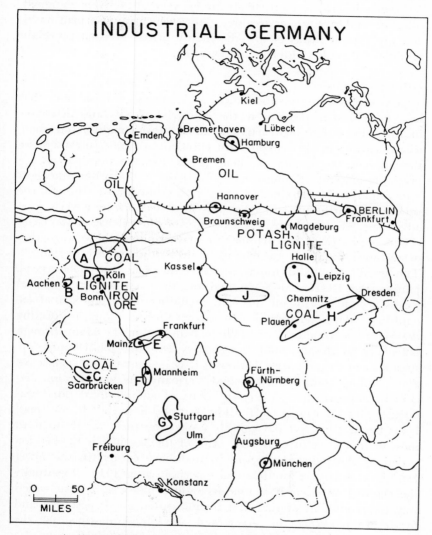

A. Main Industrial Regions and Principal Minerals of Germany.

world's largest cartels—and a vast number of small concerns, some
of which are no more than home industries. The range of German products demonstrates more of an efficient, functional char-

acter than great beauty and fine taste. A German bicycle, for example, is likely to be sturdy and heavy with a coat of black paint.
A French bicycle is more likely to be very attractively designed,
colorful, and not so serviceable. However, many German products are superb works of art—the highly prized Meissen porcelain
products ("Dresden china"), for example.

Transportation

Germany possesses a superb network of transportation lines that
have developed in response to the industrial activity and that have
in turn stimulated such activity. Most of the main rivers mentioned earlier in this chapter are excellent natural waterways, although even the greatest of them, the Rhine, has required an appreciable amount of improvement to make it the prime transport
artery that it is. Drainage of the rivers northward through the
productive northern plain is, as was suggested before, a very great
advantage. Furthermore, the existence of ancient east-west glacial
channels (described in Chapter 36) has permitted the construction
of east-west canals in the channels already pregraded by nature.
The great Mittelland Canal connects the Ems and Elbe rivers,
joining the Dortmund-Ems Canal on the west and the several
canals around Berlin on the east, including the Finow Canal extending to the lower Oder. The narrow Ludwig Canal, connecting
the Main and Danube, extends from Bamberg on the Main through
Nürnberg to the Altmühl, a tributary entering the Danube upstream from Regensburg. However, it is inadequate for such a potentially important waterway, and Germany has planned for decades to improve this connection. Part of an improved canal was
opened after World War II. The Danube is navigable for small
boats below Ulm, but navigability is poor on the river throughout
most of its course in Germany. Use of the Danube is further impeded by the political disruptions that have existed in the lower
Danube countries since 1920 and especially after 1945. Eventually
the Danube must surely assume its rightful place as a great waterway for movement of coal and manufactured goods eastward and
for return movement of cereals and other foods destined for the
densely populated industrial sections of northwestern Europe.

However, the greatest of all the waterways not only of Germany
but of all Europe is the Rhine, the mighty "flowing highway" that
joins the ocean with the heart of western Europe. No brief consideration of even the economic significance of the Rhine could

reveal its complex importance, but some suggestion of its advantages as a waterway are in order: despite some irregularity, the Rhine flow is remarkably even, receiving as it does rain runoff in nearly all seasons from its many tributaries and snow and glacier meltwater in summer; the Boden See acts as a regulating reservoir for the flow; the gradient is relatively uniform and approaches the maximum for easy navigation only between Basel and Strasbourg; the few rapids it originally possessed have been either bypassed or blasted out; some of the richest mineral regions and greatest industrial areas of Europe lie on or near the Rhine and have access to it via tributary rivers or canals; and, finally, its mouth lies in the North Sea, with easy access to the busy North Atlantic. Above all, the Rhine is a coal river: coal from the Ruhr moves both downstream to Rotterdam for export overseas, and upstream for southern Germany and as export to Switzerland and, from Basel by rail, to Italy. Duisburg-Hamborn, located at the mouth of the Ruhr River in the Rhine and at the Rhine end of the Rhine-Herne Canal, is the great coal export port and is normally the greatest inland port of Europe.

The North Sea-Baltic Canal (or Kiel Canal, formerly called the Kaiser Wilhelm Canal) across the base of the Jutland Peninsula is 61 miles long and cuts off the 470-mile trip around the Jutland Peninsula. It was built chiefly for strategic reasons to facilitate transfer of the German fleet between the Baltic and North seas, but it proved to be of great commercial benefit and normally passes 10 times as many vessels annually as either the Suez Canal or the Panama Canal, but the total tonnage through the Kiel Canal is appreciably less.

The rather large merchant marine possessed by Germany prior to World War II was either sunk during the war or seized by the Allies after V-E Day. Thus, whereas Germany had the fifth-largest fleet of the world in 1939, by 1945 it had lost more than 4.5 million tons of shipping, and not until 1950 did it recover enough to have 1 per cent of the world's merchant shipping. German shipyards were, however, very active at mid-century. Germany's main port of Hamburg, at the outlet of the Elbe, is normally the greatest port on the continent of Europe, and it made rapid recovery after 1946. Handling nearly 20,000 ships of 20 million tons annually before 1939, Hamburg was handling only half as much traffic in 1950. Other important German ports include Bremen, Bremerhaven, Kiel, Lübeck, Emden, and Rostock.

The German rail net, as may be seen in A159, is very dense. As in France, virtually no spot in the country is more than 25 miles from a rail line. Before 1939, the German State Railways, highly organized by Bismarck, were a model of operation; after 1945, the system operated under great difficulty, although it had recovered well by 1950. The highway system of the country is also excellent. As was mentioned in Chapter 11, the magnificent system of parkways, the *Autobahnen,* is the finest uniform national road net in the world. These superb concrete parkways, similar to the Pennsylvania Turnpike or Merritt-Wilbur Cross Parkway, extend only across country and connect the main cities of Germany; they are not toll roads like many similar highways in the United States.

The following two chapters discuss the geographical regions of Germany, relating the general points brought out in this discussion to the specific regional settings.

· 35 ·

The Regions of Southern and Central Germany

Patterns of Structure and Landforms

The exceedingly varied landforms of central Germany are the result of an extremely complex physiographic structure and history. Germany is the meeting ground of the mighty physical forces that through millions of years have shaped the relief features of Europe. A brief outline of some of these forces was given in the note to Chapter 3. Because of the focal character of many aspects of the structure of Germany, the landforms of the country must be considered in relation to those of all of central Europe and part of western Europe. Thus, it is advisable to correlate with this discussion the description of landforms as given in the chapters on France, Czechoslovakia, Poland, Switzerland, Austria, and—so far as glaciation is concerned—Fennoscandia (general treatment).

From a general viewpoint, Germany is easily divisible into three great physiographic regions: the Alpine region, including the Alpine Foreland south of the Danube; the Central Mountain and Basin region, including the basin and cuesta section between the Main and the Danube, as well as the Rhine graben; and the North German Plain. This threefold division is clearly visible in the map of the structure of central Europe (A568) and may be traced also on the map of natural regions of central Europe (A569). Within each of these three broad physiographic regions—especially in the Central Mountain and Basin region—are numerous smaller geographical regions with their correlated human activities. In this chapter the first two broad regions will be described, and in the following chapter the northern plain and its peripheral sections will be analyzed.

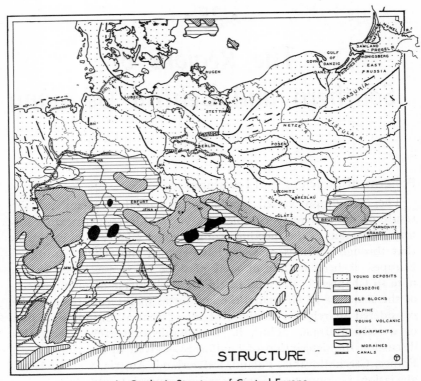

A. Geologic Structure of Central Europe.

Alpine Region

The Alps proper and the Alpine Foreland or Bavarian Plateau combine to form the Alpine region; thus, on a larger scale the same relationship between Alpine ranges and plateau described in the chapter on Switzerland continues from Lake Geneva northeastward across the Boden See and eastward into Austria beyond Linz.

German Alps. Extreme southern Germany just reaches into the northern ranges of the Alps and embraces enough of the rugged Alpine terrain to afford a share of the mountain economy. As important as the dairying is the tourist industry, which was great before 1939 and which slowly regained its importance after World War II. Nestled in the foothills is the charming village of Oberammergau, world-famed for its locally produced Passion Play, presented decennially, and for its woodcarvings. Farther into the mountains are the twin towns of Garmisch-Partenkirchen, ideally situated as winter sports resorts. Deep in extreme southeastern

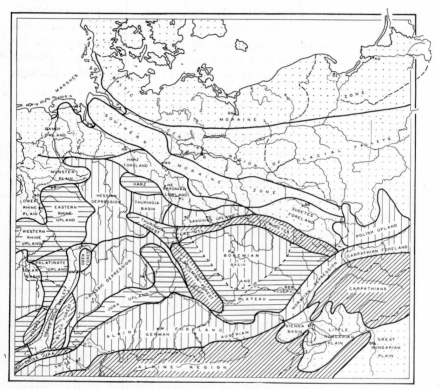

A. Natural Regions of Central Europe. (The Oden Forest is the Oden-Wald of the text, and the Erz Mts. are the Erzgebirge.)

Germany is the old salt-mining and resort town of Berchtesgaden, located in a rugged region whose wild scenery attracted Hitler to build his "retreat" here. All along the frontier, deep valleys lead well into the mountains, many of which are perennially snow covered and one of which—the Zugspitze, 9,738 feet—is the highest point in Germany. Scenic Alpine lakes add to the charm of the mountain atmosphere. Despite the limited extent of the Alpine region in Germany, numerous modest hydroelectric stations have been installed to furnish power to Munich and other cities of Bavaria and Swabia (southwestern Germany). However, large amounts of power are "imported" from Austria and are wired far into central Germany (see Chapter 38). The upper Isar valley facilitates communication with the Inn valley and, via Innsbruck, leads to the Brenner Pass connection with Italy. This pass still affords the best connection between central Europe and the Po Basin, and rapid trains now make the trip in a few hours. During the Middle Ages, when the route was a primary connection through Venice with the Levant, the trip consumed many days.

Alpine Foreland. The squatty-triangular-shaped area between the Alps and the Danube comprises the Alpine Foreland, a rolling area—much less hilly than the Swiss Plateau—sloping gently northward. Underlain by folded and faulted Mesozoic and Tertiary marine deposits, the Foreland surface is formed chiefly of glacial materials, although some Tertiary hills are found just south of the Danube, in the east. Valley glaciers descending the northern slopes of the Alps during the Pleistocene Ice Age—during the same time that the Scandinavian ice sheets expanded southward, as described in Chapter 15—spread out over the southern part of the Foreland as piedmont glaciers. The farthest extension of the ice tongues in the last advance is clearly marked by prominent moraines, inside the curves of which lie numerous moors and the charming lakes of the area: Ammer See, Würm See, and Chiem See, to name the three largest. With the thawing of the glaciers, meltwater streams poured northward and distributed fluvioglacial sands and gravels over much of the Foreland, and these "outwash" deposits, combined with moraine deposits from earlier glacial advances, have pushed the Danube far northward to the base of the Swabian Jura.

It was in this remarkably interesting region that much of the history of glaciation was unraveled by German physiographers studying the succession of moraines that mark various advances and retreats of the ice. The last stage of European glaciation was, in fact, named after the Würm See, southwest of Munich. Fine material blown by winds accumulated as loess in several areas south of the Danube—especially in the angle between the Danube and the Inn—and created fertile agricultural land. The four main rivers flowing toward the Danube—Iller, Lech, Isar, and Inn—follow meandering, braided courses and have swampy sections such as that north of Munich. Although the latitude of the Foreland is more southerly than that of Paris, the relatively high elevation (1,300 to 2,000 feet) compensates for latitude and gives the Foreland a somewhat raw climate.

The Alpine Foreland was well occupied in the Roman period, many of the cities having been Roman settlements, and it was during the first centuries of the Christian era that the region came to be divided along the Lech River between Swabia on the west and Bavaria on the east. In the Middle Ages, when northern Italy was in its glory, the most important city of the Foreland was Augsburg, from which roads continued to Ulm and the Rhine or crossed the Danube at Regensburg (the old Ratisbon) or farther west to reach Nürnberg. Numerous little towns flourished in that period, and their medieval character is a great attraction for tourists, but only Augsburg and Munich survived as centers of prominence until the present time. The highly developed aircraft industry of Augsburg caused the city to be heavily bombed during World War II.

Despite its later development, Munich (German: München) has become the principal center of the Foreland. Its original settlement arose from its position on the crossing of the Isar River by the medieval salt route from Salzburg to Augsburg, and it was also well located in relation to the Brenner Pass route up the Inn valley. Thus, like Milan in the Po Valley, it has an excellent piedmont location for both east-west and north-south traffic. Such advantages led to Munich's being chosen as the residence of Bavarian princes and kings, who endowed the city with palaces, museums, art galleries, educational institutions, monuments, and parks that made Munich a cultural center of world-wide fame. In the twentieth century Munich became the third largest city of Germany, and, despite the very heavy bombing it suffered during World War II, by 1950 reached a population of more than 800,000. Although the Foreland is not well endowed with mineral raw materials, Munich developed great industries making a variety of products, especially those of high value that do not require large amounts of heavy primary materials. Precision tools and machinery, optical and electrical goods, engines, chemicals, and, of course, the famous beer (brewed from the barley extensively grown in the region) are examples of the chief Munich products. Two

rather unfortunate claims to notoriety that Munich also has are
that it was the birthplace of the Nazi movement (the "beer hall
putsch") and that it was the place of signing of the Munich agreement in 1938.

Very different from the rather severe appearance of the Foreland
as a whole is that of the sunny southward-facing slopes north of
the Boden See (Lake of Constance), with their dense cover of crops
and fruit trees. The town of Constance (German: Konstanz) is a
lake port and manufacturing town occupying a "bridgehead" location on the Swiss side of the Boden See, just as the Swiss town of
Schaffhausen lies on the German side of the Rhine.

Among several Danube ports lying on the northern edge of the
Foreland, two deserve special mention. Ulm, in the west, lies at
the head of navigation on the Danube and was an important crossing point on medieval trade routes. Although the town's industries drew heavy bombings during World War II, the famous
Gothic cathedral, with one of the highest spires in Europe, was
preserved. Farther downstream is Regensburg, already mentioned
as an important river-crossing point of the ancient trade route from
Italy north to Saxony and Bohemia.

Central Mountains and Basins

Although the structure of central Germany is too complex to
permit a very detailed analysis of it in this general study, one feature is of such significance that it will be described. Reference to
A51 will reveal that Mesozoic basins (shown in vertical ruling) exist
in southeastern Britain, most of north-central France, and in south-
central Germany. Most of the sedimentary layers of these Mesozoic
basins are sandstones, limestones, and marls of the Triassic and
Jurassic periods, as described in Chapters 21 and 27. At the end
of the Mesozoic Era, these correlated strata were continuous over
a vast area of western Europe, having been deposited in a great
sea that persisted for millions of years over the area. At the time
of the tremendous upheaval that folded the Alps in the Tertiary
Period, great earth forces heaved up large masses of ancient rocks
in a focal area along the present middle Rhine valley but also in
the British Pennine Chain. This uplift or doming of the earth accelerated erosion in the highest part of the uplift, and over a very
long period of time the Triassic and Jurassic strata were eroded
away along the axis of the Rhine and over several adjacent areas.
The uplift along the upper Rhine was not supported from below

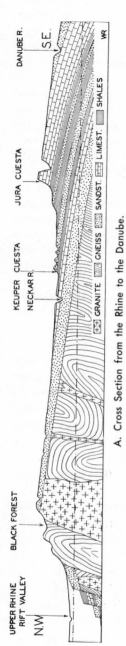

A. Cross Section from the Rhine to the Danube.

along the central axis, and a great segment of the earth's crust either did not rise or, after having risen, dropped down again several hundred feet, forming the north-northeast trending Rhine "graben" or rift valley.

Thus, at the present time, only remnants of the once-continuous strata of the Triassic and Jurassic periods are preserved in separated areas in western and central Europe. The steep slopes of their eroded edges face inward toward the centers of uplift. In England, the steep edge of the cuestas (note the Cotswold Hills escarpment in the cross section of A311) face northwesterly. The same Jurassic limestone forms the eastward-facing escarpment of the Côtes de Moselle in eastern France (A405), which in turn matches the northwestward-facing escarpment of the Swabian-Franconian Jura (note Jura Cuesta in A573).

The foregoing explanation outlines one basic factor in the relief of west-central Europe, including central Germany, but one other corollary factor should be mentioned to explain the peculiar crossing of lines of relief. This crisscross of structure is best seen around the edges of the Bohemian Plateau. Three structural lines are discernible in the relief of central Germany: the Alpine (which repeats the direction followed by the much more ancient folded system referred to as the "Variscan"), with a general northeast-southwest trend (Alps, Jura, Lower Rhine Massif, and Erzgebirge); the Hercynian, with a general northwest-southeast trend (Harz, Thuringian Forest, Sudeten, and Bohemian Forest); and the Upper Rhine System, with a north-northeast to south-southwest trend (Rhine graben, Vosges, Schwarzwald, Haardt, and Oden-Wald). Within these crisscrossing lines are occasional volcanic masses, such as the Vogelsberg, and complex masses such as the Rhön.

The characteristics of the geographical regions embraced by these physical features will be discussed roughly in order from south to north in a continuation of the descriptions already given of the Alps and the Alpine Foreland.

Upper Rhine System. *A.* General Structure. As was suggested earlier in this chapter, the broad outlines of the structure of the Upper Rhine System are traceable to a gigantic uplift during the Tertiary Period along the axis of the present upper Rhine River. Along the upper Rhine, the uplifted massif rose higher in the south than toward the north and still exists as the Schwarzwald on the east and the Vosges on the west, which mark the flanks of the great arch. Farther north, similar but less elevated flanks appear as the Oden-Wald on the east and the Haardt-Palatinate Uplands on the west. Like the collapsed keystone of an arch, the linear Rhine valley itself dropped along the axis of uplift by a series of step faults and, created the foundation for the present relatively flat-bottomed Rhine graben or rift valley.

B. Schwarzwald (Black Forest). The main mass of the Schwarz-wald is composed of ancient crystalline rocks including, especially in the south and west, granite and gneiss, although its eastern flanks are overlapped by remnants of the former Triassic sedimentary cover that are matched by correlated strata on the west flanks of the Vosges. The highest elevation is found in the granite peak of the Feldberg, 4,900 feet, in the south. Like the Vosges, the Schwarzwald was locally glaciated during the Pleistocene Ice Age.

The rugged massif was, as the name indicates, originally heavily forested with somber conifers, although some deciduous trees grew on lower slopes. Unlike many of the upland areas of central Germany that originally received the name "forest" (German: Wald), the Schwarzwald retains most of its forests, despite the fact that some slopes have been cleared for limited agriculture and pastures. Consequently, the region is sparsely populated, and economic activities are limited. The large supply of timber supports a well-developed lumbering and woodworking industry, and woodcarvings from the Schwarzwald are world famous, especially the carved cuckoo clocks. The making of watches and clocks, including the manufacturing of works for the cuckoo clocks, is a traditional industry, since it permits utilization of time in the long, cold winter. Dairying has already been mentioned as a prominent livelihood for the scattered population. A modest hydroelectric development furnishes a source of power for the small industries.

However, it is with the tourist industry that the Schwarzwald is also concerned. Thousands of visitors come from the surrounding crowded cities and industrial regions to hike through the forests, swim in the mountain lakes, or—in wintertime—ski down the

A. Valley in the Schwarzwald (Black Forest). Picturesque village combining some dairy and forestry (wood carving) with tourism (many hotels and small tourist homes). Courtesy of German Tourist Information Office.

upper slopes where trees cannot withstand the raw, windy climate.

C. Oden-Wald. Lying north of the Schwarzwald and separated from it by the Triassic lowland of the Kraichgau is the Oden-Wald, which is a smaller version of the Schwarzwald. Its lower elevation (maximum, 2,060 feet) gives it a milder climate than that of the Schwarzwald, and the forests are largely oak. The population is denser than that of the Schwarzwald, but it is still relatively sparse.

D. The Haardt-Palatinate Upland. The Haardt is the northward continuation of the Vosges, which is considered as lying south of the Gap of Saverne through which the Rhine-Marne Canal reaches Strasbourg. The Haardt, however, does not have the crystalline eastern portion displayed in the Vosges, although granite is found at a shallow depth beneath the Triassic sedimentary cover and is actually exposed in one small area west of Landau. In the Palatinate Upland north and northwest of the Haardt is a dissected plateau and hill land similar in appearance to the Haardt but underlain by different sedimentary rocks and containing extensive areas of old lava flows. The Haardt and the Palatinate Upland are separated by the structural valley of the Palatinate (or Landstuhl) Depression joining the Saar Valley and the Mainz Basin. The depression, functioning as part of the Lorraine Gateway, has been used for thousands of years as an easy route from eastern France to the Rhine plain and was especially important for the transportation of Lorraine salt eastward. The dissected uplands of this region are forested and are sparsely populated, but the valleys are intensively cultivated and support a number of settlements, among which Pirmasens, Kaiserslautern (located in the Palatinate Depression), and Zweibrücken are the most important. The western portion of the Palatinate Upland merges with the structure of the Paris Basin along the axis of the Saar River in the Saarland, an industrial region (C in A563) previously discussed at the end of Chapter 27.

E. Upper Rhine Plain. The center of all the human activities of the Upper Rhine System is the elongated Upper Rhine Plain extending in a slight curve south-southwest to north-northeast for 180 miles from the Sundgau at the Swiss frontier to the Wetterau north of Frankfurt and averaging approximately 20 miles in width. Its sides are marked by the scarps of the faults along which the block dropped to form the bottom of the graben or rift valley. The great pressure exerted by the dropping of the Rhine block forced molten lava from great depth to the surface in certain areas of structural weakness. On the Rhine plain itself is the conical lava hill of the Kaiserstuhl, west of Freiburg, reaching 1,820 feet. At the extreme northern end of the rift valley the great lava mass of the Vogelsberg, northeast of Frankfurt, is the most massive outpouring of lava from the pressure. The presence of hot springs at a great number of widely scattered points around the rift valley indicates the existence of molten rock at a relatively shallow depth.

A prominent feature of the Upper Rhine Plain is the Rhine River itself. Formerly flowing southwestward through the Belfort Gap and down the present Rhône Valley, the Rhine turned northward in late Tertiary times into its present course. Flowing on the relatively flat surface of the rift valley floor, the Rhine developed an extremely meandering course similar to that of the lower Mississippi River. Marshes were common along a wide band in the floodplain and repulsed settlement for centuries. Even at the present time few cities have grown up immediately along the river but have tended to develop on higher ground back from the floodplain. The great number of meanders, the constant shifting of the river channel, and the large number of sand bars have required the straightening of the river and its confinement to one channel for practicable navigation.

The nature of the climate in the rift valley reflects the protection afforded by the surrounding steep mountain walls. A mild winter, an early spring, and a long and rather warm summer permit the raising of crops—such as corn, tobacco, and the vine—typical of southern Europe, as was mentioned in the preceding chapter. Old river terraces, indicating higher and earlier levels of the Rhine, are in many places blanketed with loess on which have developed fertile soils.

Agricultural assets are not the only endowments of this region. During the earliest centuries of Stone Age occupation of central Europe, the valley was a principal thoroughfare; and the significance of the route has progressively increased with the development of modern civilization. Entry into the southern end of the valley may be gained through the Burgundy Gate from the southwest (Rhône-Saône corridor) or through the Rhine gap between the Jura and Schwarzwald at Basel (St. Gotthard route). A number of routes connect with the northern end of the valley: that leading through the Rhine gorge itself, and those leading northeastward through the Wetterau to Kassel or through the Fulda depression to Kassel or eastward to Saxony. In addition, two main east-west routes cross the Rhine plain in mid-course: that from the west through the Gap of Saverne to Strasbourg, where it branches north and south; and the Palatinate Depression route to Mannheim and eastward across the Triassic Depression. Finally, mainline railways parallel the Rhine on both sides of the river.

Despite the fact that the river and its valley appear to form a definite divide between the Gallic culture on the west and the Germanic culture on the east, the actual situation is that a Germanic culture developed on both sides of the rift valley as well as in the valley itself. The nature of the development in Alsace has already been discussed in the chapters on France. In spite of the Rhine's serving as the boundary between France and Germany as far north as Karlsruhe, halfway down the valley, there the boundary swings westward to include the regions of the Palatinate and the Rhineland in Germany. Consequently, the valley functions as a uniting influence, and clashing of political interests has marked the region for two thousand years.

In view of the advantages of the plain for human occupance and economic development, the crossing of trade routes, the availability of level land, and especially the function of the Rhine as a great waterway, a number of large cities have developed on the plain and at the contact of plain and mountains. Toward the south, the city of Freiburg has developed at the foot of the Schwarzwald in an indentation into the mountain wall at the northern end of the Breisgau. It is a prominent trade center for wine and Schwarzwald manufactures, a center of tourism, the seat of one of Germany's outstanding universities, and a lively manufacturing center. Toward the northern end of the Schwarzwald is the famous old spa of Baden-Baden, whose warm springs and salubrious climate have made the town one of Germany's most popular luxury watering places. Still farther north is Karlsruhe, located well out on the plain and serving as an important rail junction with a main line leading eastward to Stuttgart. Karlsruhe is a modern city, dating only from 1715, and developed originally as the capital of the Grand Duchy of Baden. The city was heavily bombed during World War II, especially because of its production of arms, but by 1950 it was again producing locomotives and rolling stock, machinery, stoves, and chemicals.

Lying at the entrance of the Neckar River into the Rhine plain at the southern edge of the Oden-Wald is the famous old university town and tourist center of Heidelberg. The site in the rather narrow valley is very picturesque and was during the Middle Ages a strategic point, since it guards the entrance to the Neckar Valley. The university, founded in 1386, is the oldest in Germany and has long attracted foreign students, including many Americans. The thirteenth-century castle, situated on a high slope overlooking the town, is a magnificent ruin with a particular fascination for tourists. From it one can look across the Neckar to the vineyard-covered southward-facing slopes of the Oden-Wald.

Northwest of Heidelberg is the twin town of Mannheim-Ludwigshafen, with the former on the east bank and the latter on the west bank of the Rhine. The combined cities, with a population of nearly 400,000, constitute one of the great industrial concentrations of Germany (F in A563). Although modern Mannheim dates only from the early seventeenth century and Ludwigshafen only from 1843, both cities developed rapidly with the growth of commerce on the Rhine and on the Neckar, since the cities are located at the confluence of these two rivers. The planned city of Mannheim is almost unique among large German cities in its regular checkerboard layout, the result of careful planning. Both cities have large river ports; Mannheim is one of the greatest Rhine ports, as is Ludwigshafen. With coal available both from the Saar and the Ruhr, both heavy and light industries have developed, producing a wide range of products. The Ludwigshafen chemical industry, one of the world's largest, was built up by the I. G. Farben combine and is of particular importance. Both cities suffered devastating bombing during World War II and will require years to rebuild.

The eastward-facing slopes of the Haardt-Palatinate Upland are clothed with the famous Rhine vineyards. The west-facing slopes of the Oden-Wald along the Bergstrasse on the opposite side of the river are, on the other hand, devoted to orchards. At the northern end of the Bergstrasse is the manufacturing city of Darmstadt, which—although it has a number of industries—is somewhat retarded because of lack of connection with the Rhine.

Opposite the confluence of the Main with the Rhine is the very ancient city of Mainz (French: Mayence). The strategic location of the site opposite the mouth of the Main and at the northern end of the Rhine plain led to its settlement by the Celts and to the utilization of the site by the Romans. During the Middle Ages "Golden Mainz" became the leader of the League of Rhenish Towns and was one of the most powerful medieval German cities. It was during this period that it became the cradle of printing through the activities of Johann Gutenberg. Mainz ranks with Karlsruhe as a Rhine port but is greatly surpassed by Mannheim-Ludwigshafen and Strasbourg.

The greatest of all the cities of the Rhine plain is Frankfurt, located on the Main at the southern end of the Wetterau depression leading northward to the Hessian basins. Such a location is one of the most favored in central Germany, since it is a focus of routes from virtually all directions. As the name indicates, the settlement originally lay at an easy crossing or ford over the Main, and the strategic location necessitated the strong fortification of the city. The development of railways and the canalization of the

Main increased the importance of the nodal position of the city, which became not only a Rhine port (via the lower Main) but an active transshipment point for goods moving up the Main and through the Ludwig Canal via Nürnberg to the Danube. During the many centuries of its existence Frankfurt developed a wide variety of functions that increased the city's importance and accelerated its growth. For centuries it was the place of election and coronation of German emperors and gradually developed into one of the leading cultural, economic, and industrial centers of Germany. Banking and publishing activities were long centered here, although leadership in banking later passed to Dresden and Berlin and in publishing to Leipzig and Berlin. Frankfurt and its peripheral satellite industrial towns (E in A563) produce a bewildering variety of products, although heavy industries are not well developed. Across the Main is Offenbach, specializing in leather goods and a wide range of machinery, including printing presses; west of Frankfurt is Höchst, former headquarters of the I. G. Farbenindustrie combine and location of many great dye and chemical plants; and east of Frankfurt is the jewelry-making center of Hanau. This great industrial region naturally became a prime target—especially because of the precision equipment factories—for American and British bombers during World War II, and destruction was staggering. Vast sections of Frankfurt, including the charming and historical Römerplatz, were sacrificed, and Hanau became almost a ghost town. Decades will be required to erase even the obvious scars of such widespread destruction.

The preceding description of the urban and industrial development of the Rhine plain has been given in some detail to emphasize the geographic significance of the distinctive tectonic feature of the Rhine graben. Here is seen a demonstration of the importance of water transportation, bringing coal from the Ruhr and Saar, and intersecting land routes. Few great sources of mineral raw materials exist locally—with the notable exception of the potash in Alsace—but numerous raw materials can easily be assembled in the region, where plains sites facilitate the spread of cities and industries. Many of the cities were especially stimulated during the seventeenth century by the immigration of Huguenots and Dutch Protestants, who brought many skills and techniques with them to their new homes.

The Jura Upland. Lying north of the Danube as far east as the Naab River is the prominent Jurassic cuesta of the Swabian-Franconian Jura (A569 and A573), which curves northward west of the Naab and extends to the upper Main River. This relatively hard limestone layer dips rather gently southeastward and disappears under the Foreland deposits, but it has a steep, erosionally ragged northwestward edge. The cuesta is appreciably higher and better developed than the correlated cuesta of the Côtes de Moselle in eastern France, and, near its southwestern end, it achieves a height of more than 3,300 feet. Its forested inner or northwestern rim is crowned here and there by ancient castles like those of Hohenzollern and Hohenstaufen. Stripped of their forest cover and subjected to a rather raw climate, the soils of the upland are generally of inferior quality and support a relatively sparse population except in a few valleys. The surface of the region tends to be rather dry because of the development of karst features in the limestone, which contains numerous caverns and underground rivers that rob the surface of its drainage. The escarpment is breached in several places so that no less than ten railway routes cross the upland. Even the Ludwig Canal was constructed through a break in the Franconian Jura southeast of Nürnberg. The Swabian Jura is separated from the Franconian Jura by an almost circular depression, the Ries, which is an old volcanic crater similar to those visible on the surface of the moon. Occasional earthquakes in the region indicate that equilibrium has not yet been established.

Triassic Depression. Northwest of the Jura cuesta is a large hilly basin, the Triassic Depression, drained principally by the Neckar and Main rivers. Here the influence of erosion on the generally soft Triassic layers, dipping eastward away from the uplifted masses along the eastern edge of the Rhine rift valley, has produced a landscape of alternating rounded divides and broad valleys. The outcrop of more resistant layers forms low escarpments, such as those of the Frankenhöhe and Steigerwald (note Keuper Cuesta in A573). In the west-central part of the region, lying between the Schwarzwald and the Oden-Wald, is the Kraichgau, an area of all-Triassic deposits in which crystalline rocks are lacking and whose loess cover supports an active agriculture. Northeast of the Oden-Wald is the Spessart, a continuation of the Oden-Wald structure but separated from it by the Main River. The Spessart supports dense forests, among which are some of the few virgin stands of oak left in Europe; they are famed for their magnificence.

Variety of relief as well as of land utilization gives charm to the landscape. From the walls of ancient cities the view widens over fields and pastures, over apple orchards and pine forests. Friendly homesteads of attractive half-timbered architecture reflect the fertility of the soil, especially where a rich loess cover exists, although soils on the sandy Keuper cuesta are infertile Podzols. In the valleys, where once the water wheel supplied power to small industries, large noisy factories represent modern industrial development.

Among a large number of modest urban developments in the Triassic basin, two cities are outstanding. In the southwest, Stuttgart (482,000) lies in a cramped location near the left bank of the Neckar, and its suburbs climb the surrounding slopes. As the capital of Württemberg, it developed into the commercial and cultural center of Swabia (Land of the Suevi—the Alamanns), extending over southwestern Germany. Gradually, the city's industrial development reached a high peak, until it produced a wide range of products from motorcars to chemicals. The specialty of Stuttgart and its satellite manufacturing centers (G in A563) is precision and electrical equipment, although other metal products, textiles, food products, and furniture are also produced. Some of the noteworthy surrounding towns are: Pforzheim on the west, Ludwigsburg and Heilbronn on the north, Esslingen and Göppingen to the southeast, and Tübingen—with its famous university—to the south on the upper Neckar. Stuttgart and most of the surrounding towns were heavily bombed in World War II because of their important industrial production.

In the eastern part of the depression is the old and charming city of Nürnberg, with a population of approximately 360,000, located along the easiest route from the Alpine passes in the south to north-central Germany. Such a strategic location permitted the city to enjoy great prosperity, especially during the sixteenth century, as a depot center on the north-south trade routes that gave such stimulus to Augsburg and Regensburg. During the same period, it was a leading southern German center of culture and manufacturing, and a number of inventions were produced by its distinguished citizens. During the 1930's, Hitler attempted to make the city a "shrine" of the Nazi party and held his gigantic and carefully staged rallies in the Nürnberg Stadium. Although its peacetime manufactured products are primarily toys, lead pencils, musical instruments, and similar items, the city produced optical products, precision machinery, and other military necessities during World War II and drew heavy bombing raids. The bombs and, later, the ground fighting reduced much of the city to a shambles and caused the loss of some of the most charming structures of the Middle Ages. East of the city is the manufacturing suburb of Fürth, and to the north is the university town of Erlangen, with some light industries.

Northeast of Nürnberg, near the confluence of the Regnitz and Main rivers is the old town of Bamberg, which shared the commercial development that stimulated the growth of Nürnberg during the late Middle Ages and Renaissance. It is a transshipment point for goods that have come up the Main from Frankfurt and that move southward through the Main-Danube Canal. Eastward and down the Main is Schweinfurt, which was a river port of some importance during the Middle Ages. It gained special notoriety during World War II when a bombing raid, although successful, on its great ball-bearing factories resulted in very high losses to the American air force. On the middle Main is the old commercial center and river port of Würtzburg, which later developed sizable industries and one of Germany's principal universities, where X-rays were discovered by Röntgen in 1895. For more than a thousand years, powerful prince-bishops of Franconia had their seat in the massive Marienburg (fortress-castle) on a hill overlooking Würtzburg, and the valley of the Main was the heart of Franconia, the center of Germany during the early Middle Ages. The chemical and machine industries drew heavy bombing raids on the city during World War II, and most of Würtzburg was destroyed.

In addition to these principal cities of the Triassic Depression, some of the towns that merit mention are: Bayreuth in the east, famed for its connections with Wagner and the great music festivals held there; Coburg in the northeast; the charming medieval town of Rothenburg, tourist center at the western foot of the Frankenhöhe; and far to the northern part of the region at the southeastern foot of the partly volcanic Rhön, the spa of Bad Kissingen, whose hot mineral springs arise from the hot lava at depth beneath the town.

Thüringer Wald (Thuringian Forest). The elongated wooded mountain range of the Thüringer Wald is a horst or uplifted block bounded by faults on both sides, and it displays the typical northwest-southeast trend of the Hercynian structure. It continues southeastward through the lower Franken-Wald and terminates at the mountain node of the Fichtel-Gebirge from which radiate the ranges around the Bohemian Basin. The complex rocks of the range yield poor soils, and the mountains remain densely forested. Settlement is sparse except in the valleys, but there a surprisingly dense population has developed in many small towns. A wide variety of home industries has existed for centuries, making use of small supplies of metals, large supplies of wood, and resources of sand and clay. An interesting specialty of the region is the making of doll heads, although musical instruments and precision instruments (such as thermometers) are produced in large quantites.

Thuringian Basin. Lying between the Thüringer Wald on the south and the Harz on the north is the Thuringian Basin, which is separated by a low upland from the Hessian Depression on the west and by the Saale River from the Saxonian Upland on the east. Somewhat like the Paris Basin, the Thuringian Basin preserves a concentric arrangement of sedimentary beds (all Triassic) with the youngest in the center. Forested sandstone escarpments, barren limestone ridges, and marl depressions under crops and pasture impart a pleasant variety and have given Thuringia a reputation for scenic charm that it fully deserves. Towns, most of which developed as local markets, have grown up in this peaceful setting as centers of science, art, and specialized industries. Salt deposits in the north and lignite in the west have caused the invasion of modern industrial life (J in A563) from Saxony and have brought a much denser population. This development, however, is still limited to outlying sections and has not greatly affected the general character of rural beauty.

Erfurt lies near the center of the basin and is surrounded by especially fertile soils on the Keuper marl, and the intensive agricultural development has given rise to very productive market gardening and horticulture in which seed production plays an outstanding role. Toward the northern edge of the basin a narrow rift valley south of the Harz has collected thick deposits of alluvium on which very fertile soils have developed, giving rise to the intensive agriculture of the Goldene Aue ("Golden Vale"). The edges of the basin are occupied by infertile soils developed on the Triassic Buntsandstein, most of which are covered by forests.

In addition to Erfurt, three other towns of the basin are noteworthy. Gotha, west of Erfurt, is an insurance and publishing center and produces light and heavy goods ranging from food products to rolling stock; and its famous Justus Perthes Geographical Institute has spread the town's name over the world through its excellent maps. Since Thuringia was included in the Soviet zone of occupation, the Perthes Institute has been devoted to production of maps for the Russians. Weimar, east of Erfurt, was the site of the meeting of the national assembly that adopted the post-World War I constitution that gave the name "Weimar Republic" to Germany of the 1920's. Jena, east of Weimar, is a famous old university town that acquired further fame as the home of the renowned Zeiss optical works, which utilized excellent sand from the Buntsandstein layers as a primary raw material.

Harz. The Harz, like the Thüringer Wald, is a horst of metamorphic and sedimentary rocks resting on a platform of granite that has also intruded the upper rocks. A great variety of mineral veins were formed during the intrusion of the granite, and for centuries the Harz produced silver, iron, copper, sulphur, lead, and arsenic. Nearly all the minerals are now exhausted except for copper, which is still produced in modest amounts. The Harz is the most northerly large mountain mass of central Europe and forms an offshoot of the Central Upland into the northern lowland. The granite summit of the Brocken, rising to 3,745 feet—the highest elevation in central Germany—was formerly a monadnock on the old Hercynian peneplain, strong evidences of which are seen in the heights. Erosion has created rugged relief, much of which supports forests, and the region attracts numerous tourists to the scenic villages along the valleys and the towns along the contact of the mountains with the surrounding fertile plain. Main lines of communication encircle the Harz, but only minor routes extend through it.

Hessian Depression. The hills and basins of the Hessian Depression lie in a confused jumble west of the Harz-Thuringian Basin and Thüringer Wald and east of the lower Rhine Massif. The region is almost coextensive with the drainage basin of the Weser River south of the northern plain, and it is sometimes referred to as the Weser Basin. As in the Triassic Depression to the south and in the Thuringian Basin to the east, most of the relief of the Hessian Depression is formed on Triassic deposits that have been greatly faulted. However, there are several scattered outpourings of lava, the most massive of which is that of the Vogelsberg, that were forced upward by the sinking of the upper Rhine valley block, as was described earlier in this chapter. The varied landscape of the hills, basins, and valleys of the region presents a picture of infinite charm: many small mountain sections covered with forest, or, if the forest is cleared, spread with meadows and devoted to stock raising; the picturesque valleys of the Weser and its branches; the scattered fertile fields on the better soils; and the numerous villages and towns along the valleys.

Economic development in terms of extensive manufactures is not great in the region, although Kassel in the Weser valley has developed large industries, both because of the influx of Huguenot refugees in the seventeenth century and because of large local supplies of lignite. Because of its industrial significance and especially because of its production of aircraft, Kassel was one of the most heavily hit cities in Germany. Göttingen is an old university town with a quaint medieval appearance that was fortunately preserved in World War II.

In the northwestern part of the region the linear folds of the Teutoburger Wald arc around the Münster Plain and are roughly paralleled by similar folds in the Wiehen-Gebirge and Weser-Gebirge on either side of the Weser Gap that forms the famous *Porta Westfalica,* where the Roman legions were turned back by Germanic tribes. Between the two ridges of the Teutoburger Wald and the Wiehen-Gebirge lies the industrial region of Bielefeld and Osnabrück. Bielefeld is the center of the Westphalian linen industry, whereas Osnabrück—which formerly specialized in linens also—has turned more to metal goods and chemicals on the basis of the small coal field and iron deposits near-by.

Lower Rhine Massif. Lying to the west of the Hessian Depression is the Lower Rhine Massif (German: Rheinisches Schiefergebirge—"Rhine Slate Mountains"), bisected by the Rhine gorge as the river turns northwestward after its sharp bend at Mainz. Most of the relief of the massif is an ideal example of the resurrected fossil Hercynian peneplain. Thus, the massif at present displays a rather uniform skyline, but the rivers rejuvenated by the uplift of the massif in late Tertiary times have dissected the former relatively level peneplain into rather rugged relief. The main structural lines follow those of the very ancient Variscan folds, trending southwest-northeast. These Variscan folds are indicated not only by the linear quartzite ridges of the Hunsrück and Taunus but also by the general courses of the rivers that join the Rhine in the region. With elevations averaging about 2,000 feet, the highland has a climate that is prevailingly raw, soils that are generally poor, and a population that is somewhat sparse and scattered on the uplands but dense in the valleys and very dense along the Rhine gorge. The twentieth century has seen the development of a large number of hydroelectric installations in the region of the Lower Rhine Massif.

West of the Rhine the massif is divided into two parts by the deeply entrenched and meandering valley of the Moselle (German: Mosel). North of the Moselle is the Eifel, which extends westward to join with the Ardennes, previously discussed in connection with Belgium and France. Moors extend over vast areas and fail even to furnish sufficient forage for the sheep that graze them in summer. The Eifel has always been a poor land and has for decades experienced a decreasing population. Several circular depressions now occupied by lakes (*Maaren*) are old volcanic craters. Lying south of the Moselle, the Hunsrück reaches an elevation of 2,675 feet in the quartzite ridge that forms the backbone of the mountains. Most of the Hunsrück remains in forest.

The Moselle Valley, with its vineyard-clad slopes, is one of the most scenic parts of Germany and is preferred by some tourists to the Rhine gorge itself. The great meanders of the river, preserved from an earlier geological age when the stream wandered over a level plain, add to the attractiveness of the valley but spoil the use of the river for navigation purposes, especially since it is subject to low-water periods in summer. If it could be made practicably navigable, the Moselle would be a great waterway for the transfer of Lorraine iron ore to the Ruhr and the return of Ruhr coal to Lorraine. A navigable Moselle would also be of value for the shipping of Saar coal, although on the Rhine the Saar coal could scarcely compete with the Ruhr product. The main city of the valley is Trier, which is believed to be the oldest city in Germany. It is the center of the active trade in Moselle wines.

East of the Rhine the Massif is divided into three parts: north of the Sieg River is the Sauerland, south of the Sieg as far as the Lahn is the Westerwald, and south of the Lahn as far as the Main is the Taunus. The Sauerland is the lowest part of the entire massif, and possesses a more gentle relief and a milder climate. Modern industries have invaded the valleys, particularly in the northwest; however, these are related to the Ruhr industrial area and will be discussed in the following chapter.

The Sieg valley was for several centuries before the rise of the Ruhr one of Germany's principal metallurgical centers. Iron ore (siderite) found in the valley and containing a high percentage of manganese as well as some lead and copper was smelted by charcoal made from the plentiful supply of timber in the area. During the nineteenth century the depletion of the forests and the increasing use of coke caused a decline in the Sieg iron and steel industries, although some ore is still produced around Siegen from depths as great as 3,500 feet. Production must, however, be subsidized.

The Westerwald—with large areas of volcanic rock—and the Taunus, separated by the Lahn River, are somewhat more attractive for human occupation than the Eifel and Hunsrück. Agriculture invades the valleys and lower slopes, although forest prevails. On the lower southern slopes of the Taunus overlooking the Rhine is the famous vineyard area of the Rheingau, producing excellent white Rhine wine. Wiesbaden, located at the contact of the plain with the Taunus, has been a favorite spa since Roman days because of its hot mineral springs; during the nineteenth century it developed appreciable industries producing machines and chemicals. Bad Homburg on the eastern slopes of the Taunus is likewise a spa but is on a much more modest scale and lacks the industries that have developed at Wiesbaden. The Westerwald gained appreciable importance as a stock raising area in conjunction with the great demands created by the dense population of the Ruhr.

The Lahn valley, somewhat like that of the Sieg, is an iron-ore-producing region, but here the ore is hematite. Although the hematite is rather rich in iron content and contains little phosphorus, its silica content is high like that of Peine near Hannover. The iron industry that formerly existed here has, like that of the Sieg valley, lost most of its importance to the Ruhr. On the middle Lahn is the small but famous optical goods center of Wetzlar, home of the well-known Leitz concern.

The uniting factor in the Lower Rhine Massif region is the Rhine gorge, whose terraces give evidence of the successive stages of the uplift that forced the river to entrench itself. The existence of former rapids, which have largely disappeared because of man's blasting out the hard rocks, indicates that the Rhine is not yet adjusted to a perfect grade in its course through the massif. The gorge is in many places so narrow that road beds and railway beds have had to be blasted out of the valley wall, and the slopes rising to the uplands are very steep. Those slopes exposed to the greatest amount of sunshine afford sites for the carefully tended and scenic vineyards that characterize much of the Rhine gorge. The famed cliffs of the Lorelei, numerous ancient castles that played important roles in the history of the Rhineland, numerous small villages of picturesque appearance, and the traditions and legends associated with the gorge make this the national valley of Germany. Passenger

A. Castle (Gutenfels) above the Rhine gorge near Caub. Note terraced vineyards. Transportation lines (roads, railroads) on narrow strip of level land along both sides of the river. Courtesy of German Tourist Information Office.

boats filled with tourists and school children sail up and down the river in the midst of long strings of barges bearing coal, lumber, cement, flour, and other heavy nonperishable products. Only at the junction of the Moselle and the Rhine is there room for a city of considerable size, and on this site has developed the city of Koblenz ("confluence").

Erzgebirge and Saxonian Upland. Marking the frontier between northwestern Czechoslovakia and Germany is the range of the Erzgebirge ("Ore Mountains"), called Krušné Hory by the Czechs. This prevailingly crystalline massif is bounded by faults on the steep Bohemian side, but it slopes relatively gently northwestward on the German side, the surface being largely a resurrected pene-

plain.   The granites and gneisses of the Erzgebirge were—as the
name of the range indicates—formerly laced with numerous veins
of metallic ores (especially silver, lead, and copper) that for many
centuries were actively exploited, making Saxony one of the richest
small states in Europe.   Down-faulting in one zone preserved
modest resources of coal.

On this gentle backslope of the massif and extending out onto
the Foreland there arose a highly developed cultural and economic
life that also benefited from trade routes that crossed the area.
A mingling of Germans and Slavs produced a vigorous biological
mixture.   Thus, for centuries and down to the present day, Saxony
has been one of the most active, highly developed, and densely
populated regions in central Europe.   Agriculture, trade, mining,
and manufacturing have contributed to a balanced economy.   As
one aspect of development began to wane, the vigorous Saxons
turned to another.   At present, the Rhine-Westphalian (especially
the Ruhr) industrial concentration surpasses Saxony in bulk production and in manpower employed, primarily on the basis of the
great coal resources, but Saxony's chief asset—despite the harmonious combination of resources—is its energetic and skilled population.   After 1945, this valuable area and its numerous and highly
varied industries came under Soviet control and formed part of
the satellite state of East Germany.   Many machines and entire
plants were removed to the Soviet Union as reparations, but apparently much was done after 1947–48 to restore many of the
factories.

The presence of the gentle slope and the attraction of mineral
wealth up the slope drew the enterprising Saxons to the ridge of
the Erzgebirge and down the steep southeastward-facing slope into
the Bohemian Basin, where they continued their active mining and
manufacturing activities and contributed enormously to the development of Bohemia and later of the Austrian Empire.   During
the 1930's, however, their emotions were played upon by their
Hitler-dominated German brothers, and the tragedy of the Sudetenland crisis was played out (see Chapter 37).   These 2.5 million
Germans have now been sent back over the mountain wall, although
some of the most highly skilled were retained by the Czechs.

The modern industrial development, the exact status of which
at mid-century was not clearly known west of the Iron Curtain,
is too varied to receive detailed description; but some broad ob-
servations must be made.   Except for Dresden, which will be discussed later, the most important center of this zone (H in A593) is

Chemnitz. On a large scale it is representative of Saxonian manufacturing, with its production of machinery, chemicals, and—above all—textiles and related products. Chemnitz is thus the Manchester of Germany, and many of the machines it produces are textile machines, just as many chemicals are dyes and bleaches. In southwestern Saxony, in the center of the Vogtland, is Plauen, also producing textiles as well as lace, embroidery, paper products, and leather goods. Between Chemnitz and Plauen is Zwickau, which lies on the small but important coal field that yields about 3 million tons annually. Iron and steel are worked in Zwickau, but many of the raw materials are normally obtained from the Ruhr.

Mention of these three manufacturing towns should not obscure the fact that a very great deal of the production of the region is carried on in many smaller towns and villages, especially in small enterprises that retain some aspects of the ancient and traditional home industries. Large factories exist, of course, but the coming of hydroelectric power permitted a continuation of home industries even in these modern days of manufacturing. Such a process is impossible in the Ruhr, where the great mills and factories work on massive equipment whose production is typically based on coal.

The greatest city of the Saxonian Upland region is Dresden, located astride the Elbe downstream from the river's exit from the fantastic Cretaceous sandstone formations of the Saxonian Switzerland. Like Chemnitz and Zwickau, Dresden was originally a Slavic settlement, established before the Slavs were pushed back by German settlement advancing eastward. The city was the capital of Saxony for centuries and as such was made a magnificent center of art, literature, and superb baroque architecture as befitted the capital of a wealthy state; thus the development of the "Florence of the Elbe" somewhat resembled that of Munich. Like Munich, Dresden was heavily hit by World War II bombings and probably suffered greater loss of its cultural buildings. The city's control of the Elbe Valley route into the Bohemian Basin has long given it great trade advantages, and the river port is a large one. Downstream from Dresden is the famous porcelain-manufacturing town of Meissen, whose near-by kaolin deposits and artistic workmen combined to produce some of the world's most prized china. Indeed, much of the so-called "Dresden china" is produced in Meissen.

The economic activities of the Saxonian Upland are closely integrated with those of the Saxonian Lowland, discussed in connection with northern Germany in the following chapter.

·36·
The Regions of Northern Germany

General Pattern of Northern Germany

"Northern Germany" is broadly interpreted to include the German portion of the great North European Plain or Central Lowlands, the Foreland zone of the Central German Uplands, and in some small areas certain structures that more strictly belong with the Hercynian system of the Central Uplands. So interpreted, northern Germany embraces areas ranging from the most densely populated (the Ruhr) to the most sparsely populated (the northwestern sandy moors) and including a great range of environments. Despite the fact that the larger portion of northern Germany is poorly developed agriculturally because of sterile soils and is hence sparsely populated, the smaller portion that is more richly endowed makes this section of very great value to Germany and—normally—to Europe. Since the significant role played by the North European Plain both in German development and in the long history of Europe has been brought out in previous chapters, this discussion concerns itself with the characteristics of the section and with the relationships between its various parts.

Except for the considerable extension of the same relief east of the Oder River, the North German Plain has no equal in central Europe. Despite the apparent general uniformity of the plain on the average map, the region is markedly different in its various parts. Moreover, the application of the term "plain" should not disguise the fact that the region possesses marked relief features, especially in the moraine heights and old glacial valleys. Although the greatest moraine heights (up to 1,100 feet) were transferred to Poland in 1945, the morainic heights of Fläming southwest of Berlin attain 700 feet.

The physiographic evolution of the surface of the plain is most directly related to the advances and retreats of the Scandinavian ice sheets during the Pleistocene Ice Age, described in Chapter 15. The connection between the Scandinavian ice sheets and the present topography of the plain is indicated by the concentric arrangement of zones roughly parallel to the Baltic coast, whose shape is itself largely the result of Pleistocene glaciation. The glacial topography toward the southern part of the plain resulted from the action of an earlier advance of the ice (Mindel), whereas that toward the northern part of the plain resulted from the action of the last ice sheet (Würm). As a consequence of the differing glacial actions and the relief along the northern edge of the central uplands, four roughly arcuate zones are recognizable in northern Germany (named from north to south): Baltic moraine zone, zone of the old glacial valleys (*Urstromtäler*), southern moraine zone, and the Foreland. A fifth zone, that of the northwestern lowlands, is found near the Dutch border. To continue the order of discussion followed in the preceding chapter, the regions of northern Germany will be described from south to north.

Foreland

The Foreland zone extends in a narrow band from west to east along the northern edge of the Central German Uplands—most of which are Hercynian massifs—from the Belgian-Dutch frontier to the upper Neisse River. Because of its transitional character between upland and plain, it is considered to include some indentations ("bays") of the true North German Plain into the upland. Thus its structure is a mixed one and varies from area to area.

One of the most significant aspects of the Foreland zone is its characteristically rich soil, developed on loess deposited during the Pleistocene by winds that had picked up the fine material from the barren ground south of the ice sheets. This zone of loessal soils, called the "Börde," extending east-southeastward along the Foreland into southern Poland—as well as far into the Ukraine—attracted early settlement during the Stone Age and Bronze Age and served as a great east-west corridor for human migrations. The reason for this function of the Börde zone is that the light soils of the loess belt carried few trees and hence attracted man at a time when forest clearing was extremely difficult and when surrounding regions were heavily forested or marshy. Later, with the development of agriculture, the soils became even more attractive because of their great fertility and easy tillability; and the Foreland zone came to be densely populated. The agricultural population is still very dense along the Börde, and other advantages reinforced the agricultural endowments so that the dense population of the zone is prominent on a population map such as A199. The zone also served as a great east-west trade route during the Middle Ages, and most of the cities in the Börde were active medieval commercial towns, and most of the larger ones were united with the Hanseatic League.

The second significant aspect of the Foreland that in modern times came to be of even greater economic significance than the loessal soils is the great wealth in minerals, especially coal, lignite, and potash. The bulk of this wealth is concentrated in two areas: the Rhine-Westphalian district in the west and the Saxonian Lowland and Harz Foreland in the east.

The Rhine-Westphalian Industrial District (A in A563). The core of the Rhine-Westphalian industrial area is the Ruhr area, the greatest single concentration of heavy industries and coal mining in Europe and one of the greatest in the world. The area has no clearly defined boundaries, but certainly the heart of it lies between the Ruhr River on the south, the Lippe on the north, the Rhine on the west, and Dortmund on the east. The entire Rhine-Westphalian district is tributary to the Ruhr, but the area described above contains most of the coal mines and the greatest concentration of heavy industry.

The great resource of the Ruhr is its coal, known reserves of which have been estimated at about 55,000 million metric tons to a depth of 3,280 feet (1,000 meters). To a depth of 6,500 feet the known and probable reserves rise to 213,600 million tons—by far the greatest coal deposit in Europe. Thus, the loss of Silesia to Poland as a result of *de facto* boundary changes after 1945—serious though it was—left Germany with its most important coal deposits. Also, the Ruhr coal contains a very high proportion of coal for making coke for use in blast furnaces, whereas only a small percentage of Silesian coal is suitable for coking.

Coal production in the Ruhr reached its peak in 1939 at 130.5 million tons and during this period averaged approximately 10 per cent of world output. Despite the great drop to 33.4 million tons in 1945, production rose steadily to approximately 120 million tons in 1951. As a result of relative ease of mining and of a high degree of mechanization, the Ruhr output per manshift (more than 1.5 metric tons) is high for Europe and is twice the French rate, although it is less than one-third that of the United States.

The significance of coal in the export economy of Germany was discussed in Chapter 34.

Crude and finished steels, along with heavy fabricated items, are the chief products of Ruhr industries. It is typical of Ruhr industries to be highly integrated, and not only do single companies —which before 1945 included some of the greatest industrial combines in the world—control the entire range of production from coal mine to final manufacturing plants, but also many installations in the Ruhr unite all functions virtually under one vast roof. Only the mining of iron is missing. The iron formerly mined in the Ruhr is exhausted, and the ore brought in from the Sieg and Lahn valleys or from the pyrite-producing area of Meggen southeast of the Ruhr furnishes only a fraction of the ore swallowed by the Ruhr blast furnaces. Therefore, the bulk of the ore used in the Ruhr is imported, chiefly from northern Sweden because of the high iron content of Kiruna ore. The amount imported from Lorraine in eastern France is appreciably smaller because of the low iron content of minette ore.

From a peak of nearly 13 million tons of crude steel in 1938— when the Ruhr alone produced more than 12 per cent of world steel and 20 per cent of European steel (including that of the Soviet Union)—production fell drastically in 1945. Immediately after World War II, the Allies imposed severe limitations on Ruhr steel production, but the urgent need for steel in Germany and the rest of western Europe, especially after 1950, caused the restrictions to be lifted; and by 1951 Ruhr production was on the level of nearly 12 million tons annually! Only six years after the Ruhr had apparently been turned into a shambles by Allied bombers, it was producing both coal and steel at a rate almost as great as that of the prewar period.

The great variety of products produced in the Ruhr includes every conceivable item of heavy equipment from steel plates to locomotives and agricultural machinery. Farther away from the coal mines are lighter metalworking and machine industries, and south of the Ruhr and west of the Rhine are great textile industries. Large amounts of varied chemical products, derived mostly from the coal tars that are by-products from the hundreds of coke ovens, are made in the heart of the Ruhr. The armaments for which the Ruhr was famous before 1945—despite the fact that the Ruhr was not predominantly an armaments center—were prohibited after

1945, but their production was resumed on a limited scale for the North Atlantic Treaty Organization after 1950.

From the Rhine eastward to Dortmund the landscape is one of a "Black Country," with an almost solidly urbanized area dominated by belching chimneys and noisy factories. In this continuously urbanized and industrialized area and the remaining tributary cities and towns in the Rhine-Westphalian industrial district live more than 7 million people. Some of Germany's largest cities have grown up here and expanded during the period 1880–1915 at rates similar to those of the phenomenal American cities during the same period. Essen, with its great Krupp works, is the largest city not only of the Ruhr but also of the entire Rhine-Westphalian district; although thousands of its inhabitants evacuated Essen after the heavy bombing raids during World War II that destroyed much of the town, its population rose to more than 600,000 after the war and surpassed that of Cologne farther south. Dortmund's population also exceeds 500,000, and other cities with populations within the range 200,000 to 300,000 include Bochum, Gelsenkirchen, and Oberhausen, all of which are coal mining and heavy industries centers. Duisburg-Hamborn, the great Rhine port for shipment of Ruhr coal, exceeds 400,000, and likewise has heavy industries.

With such a tremendous concentration of industrial power in this small area, it is no wonder that the Allies have attempted to exercise careful control over its production. Nor is it any wonder that the questions of who should control the Ruhr (the Soviet Union attempted strenuously to gain a voice in the Ruhr) and how that control should be exercised are questions of vital significance for all Europe. The Schuman Plan (discussed in Chapter 10) for integration of western European coal mining and heavy industries —a plan accepted in January, 1952, by the West German *Bundesrat* or parliament—will, if completely effected, integrate the Ruhr more into the western European economy as a whole. The Ruhr will, in fact, to an even greater extent than it has been in the past, be the heart of the new European industrial economy that will grow out of the Schuman Plan. For too long a time have the Ruhr and its powerful industrialists—many of whom backed Hitler in his bid for power—been the tail that wagged the German dog. Continued effective use of the Ruhr assets is essential, but a continuation of Ruhr political influence would be detrimental to the German good.

West of the Rhine and near the Netherlands frontier is the much smaller manufacturing region of Aachen (B in A563), which profits from a continuation of the coal deposits that extend from northern France across Belgium and southern Holland. Enormous destruction was inflicted on Aachen (French: Aix-la-Chapelle) during World War II. In the deepest indentation of the North German Plain into the Central Uplands is the ancient fortress city of Cologne (German: Köln), located on the eastern side of the extension of the plain referred to as the "Cologne Bay." In addition to its significance as a trade center and as an area rich in historical associations, the city developed thriving industries (D in A563) with its great lignite deposits and the advantage of acquiring raw materials because of its position on the Rhine waterway. Formerly the greatest city of the entire Rhine-Westphalian region, Cologne suffered such severe devastation by bombing and shelling that it lost more than a third of its population (772,000 in 1939) by 1945, but had regained enough to have nearly 600,000 by 1951. Cologne constitutes one of the most interesting cities in Europe in regard to its shape and evolution because of its growth within fortress walls against the left bank of the Rhine, and its semicircular core is a familiar pattern in maps of the city.

South of Cologne is the old university city of Bonn, which was selected as the capital of the German Federal Republic in 1949. Bonn guards the entrance to the Rhine gorge leading southward to the Upper Rhine Plain. Downstream from Cologne is Düsseldorf, formerly a Hanseatic city that developed rapidly with the growth of the Rhine-Westphalian industrial district, within which it is one of the largest and most active cities, profiting especially from its location on the Rhine. Although much of the city was wrecked in World War II bombings, its population (more than 500,000) had almost returned to its prewar level by 1951. Southeast of Düsseldorf are the two tool and hardware centers of Remscheid and Solingen, the former specializing in hand tools—especially high-quality precision and special tools—and the latter world famous for its high-grade small steel goods, especially cutlery. Thus, Remscheid and Solingen together are the Sheffield of Germany. North of Remscheid is the textile center of Wuppertal, a city formed by the amalgamation of the two towns of Elberfeld and Barmen. West of the Rhine is an extension of the industrial district where textiles are again the dominant products in such centers as München-Gladbach, Rheydt, and Krefeld. Production in all these centers not only returned to a prewar level by 1950 but also in some cases actually increased because of the migration of textile and clothing firms from Berlin and the Soviet zone: several spinning mills have settled at München-Gladbach, and some of the leading fashion designers of Berlin transferred to Krefeld.

Saxonian Lowland. The second great industrial district of the Foreland zone is that of the Saxonian Lowland centering on Leipzig in another of the "bays" indenting the Central Upland border. In certain respects this district (I in A563) is a continuation of the industrialization of the Saxonian Upland discussed in the previous chapter. The great asset of the region is in the enormous deposits of lignite around Leipzig and Halle and as far north as Bitterfeld, although the enormous potash and salt deposits also play an important role in the chemical industry. Vast expanses of the fertile, loess-covered Börde have been sacrificed to the huge open-pit lignite mines, which normally produce more than 110 million tons of lignite annually. As a result of the contiguity of the lignite and the potash and salt deposits, the region has become a great chemical-producing area, typified by the enormous Leuna works at Merseburg south of Halle.

The great center of the Saxonian Lowland both geographically and economically is Leipzig, which in 1950 was the fourth largest city in Germany. Like other towns of Saxony, Leipzig originated as a medieval trading center, but it developed especially rapidly because of its favorable location in the center of the "Leipzig Bay." Indicative of its significance are its great annual fairs, which have for centuries attracted merchants from far and wide. The cultural significance of the city is revealed by the fact that it has long been a leading publishing center; for example, the famous Baedeker guidebooks are produced in Leipzig. The famed University of Leipzig was founded in 1409 and is the principal unit in a number of educational institutions in the city. After 1945 all were under Soviet control and consequently lost much of their significance as free intellectual institutions.

Magdeburg Börde and Harz Foreland. Extending northwestward from the bay of Leipzig are the loess-blanketed Magdeburg Börde zone and, still farther west, the loess zone of the Harz Foreland. The heavily industrialized and formerly fortified city of Magdeburg has been an important commercial center since the tenth century and was one of the leading inland cities of the Hanseatic League because of its position on the Elbe where an east-west route was facilitated by the presence of an old glacial valley. Later exploitation of the great potash beds lying west of the Elbe stimulated industry, especially that of chemical production. Heavily bombed and shelled in World War II, Magdeburg suffered so severely and lost so much of its population that the capital of the provisional state of Sachsen-Anhalt in the Soviet zone was moved to Halle. The rich sugar beet area on the loess soils west of Magdeburg has given rise to a great sugar-refining industry in the city. Magdeburg's important Elbe River port continued to trade with Czechoslovakia and with cities on the Elbe within the Soviet zone of occupation, but it—like that of Dresden—suffered from lack of normal trade relations with Hamburg, which lay in Western Germany. Dessau, southeast of Magdeburg near the junction of the Mulde with the Elbe, was largely destroyed during World War II because of its large Junker aircraft factory.

The most important center on the Harz Foreland, west of Magdeburg (A569), is Braunschweig (Brunswick). It also developed as an agricultural center in the fertile rolling loess land and as a commercial city. Lying on the main east-west route that also passed through Magdeburg, Braunschweig became a Hanseatic city and preserved its medieval character until much of the city was destroyed during World War II. The city profited greatly from completion of the Mittelland Canal during the 1930's, since the waterway passes just north of the city.

One of the most interesting developments on the Harz Foreland is the industrial center of Watenstedt-Salzgitter, lying between Braunschweig and the western end of the Harz Mountains. This "youngest city of Germany" increased in population from 19,000 in 1936 to 100,000 in 1950. The basis of this great development is Germany's determination to make use of the enormous deposits (about 2,000 million metric tons) of iron ore of the Peine-Salzgitter area. These ores have long been known, but their low iron content (30 per cent) and high silica content have discouraged exploitation. The great Ruhr development rendered use of the Peine ores uneconomical, until a new process was worked out in 1936 to concentrate the Peine ores. The Hermann Göring combine built an iron and steel works in Watenstedt-Salzgitter during World War II, and the works was well on its way to being one of the largest of its kind in Europe. A branch canal was constructed to connect the city with the Mittelland Canal to the north. However, after 1945 the steel mill and eight of the twelve blast furnaces were dismantled as reparations, and the foundations were partly dynamited by the British. The immediate future of the development was in doubt at mid-century; however, there is no question that eventually a feasible arrangement can be worked out to bring coal from the Ruhr and send back concentrated ore for Ruhr furnaces. Thus, the Watenstedt-Salzgitter development is of prime importance in German economic development.

The largest city of this region is Hannover, which lies slightly north of the Harz Foreland in a fertile, loess-covered plain. Like Braunschweig and Magdeburg, it was an important interior Hanseatic city that continued its commercial importance down to the present time. During the nineteenth century an intensive industrial development created a contrast between the old medieval buildings and the new factories, which profited from modest coal deposits southwest of the city and from modest petroleum resources at Celle to the northeast. Construction of the Mittelland Canal stimulated Hannover's trade. Though bombed, Hannover did not suffer as much during World War II as other cities of the Foreland and lost little of its population of about 450,000.

Münsterland. To the east and south around the curve of the Teutoburger Wald is the "Münster Bay," third of the indentations into the Central Uplands. Lying in the center of this fertile Münster Plain is the town of Münster, an old Hanseatic city that developed primarily as an agricultural center but later developed industries using coal from the deep mines near-by. Very severely bombed during World War II and involved in bitter ground fighting in 1945, the city will require years to recover.

Southern Moraine Zone

The Southern Moraine Zone comprises old recessional moraines and accompanying ground moraine extending from northwest to southeast (A569) and deposited by the second of three or four general advances of the Scandinavian ice sheet. It is bordered on both the southwest and northeast by prominent old glacial valleys and is composed principally of the Lüneburger Heide (Lüneburg Heath) in the west and the moraine heights of Fläming east of Magdeburg. This is one of the most sparsely settled regions of Germany and possesses neither cities of significance nor any fertile agricultural areas. Heaths and moors, with some birches and pines in scattered areas, were originally the characteristic feature, although much of the waste land has been reclaimed for such crops as rye.

Zone of the Old Glacial Valleys

Although one of the best-developed old glacial valleys separates the Foreland from the Southern Moraine Zone, the channeled landscape formed by glacial meltwater is especially well developed between the Southern Moraine Zone and the Baltic Moraine Zone (A569). Called by the Germans *Urstromtäler* ("primitive stream valleys") and by the Poles *pradoliny,* these old valleys were formed during various stages of ice retreat during the Pleistocene Epoch: floods of summer meltwater pouring from the great ice mass that lay over the central part of the North European Plain were forced to follow the trough between the southward-sloping ice cap and the northward-sloping land in order to reach the sea. Since the slope of the trough was westward and northwestward, the powerful meltwater streams flowed in that general direction and escaped into the North Sea west of the Jutland Peninsula. In some areas, especially in the district around Berlin, the channels are interlaced, but in other areas they follow definite arcs that reflect perfectly the lobate form of the southern edge of the ice sheet along which the meltwater flowed.

After the retreat of the ice, short rivers flowing into the Baltic and North seas lengthened themselves by headward erosion. They thus captured the drainage of the central part of the plain and formed the present drainage pattern, which displays a peculiar zigzagging of rivers from one *Urstromtal* to the next northern one. The old channel, even where now deserted by main rivers, facilitated construction of canals such as that of the Mittelland. The depressions are utilized partly for crops of rye and potatoes, although they are chiefly left in pine forests or devoted to pasture. The richer and more easily traversable Foreland zone attracted both men and trade southward away from the marshy, forested, and poor regions of the moraine and glacial valleys, hence urban development north of the Foreland has been retarded, except along the coast. To this generalization, however, Berlin is a notable exception.

Lying in the *Urstromtal* that may be traced from the lower Elbe eastward in an arc past Warsaw, the site of Berlin was originally occupied both by Germans and Slavs because an island in the Spree facilitated crossing the river at this point. The town developed slowly until it became the seat of the Brandenburg electors and later the capital of Prussia and of all Germany. As late as the seventeenth century, its population was only 20,000, but by 1905 it had increased to more than 2 million. By the outbreak of World War II Berlin had more than 4.3 million inhabitants—a population larger than that of any other city on the European continent.

The greatest stimulus to the growth of the city came with the flowering of Germany during the days of the Empire, when the capital was adorned with hundreds of massive buildings and monuments and beautified with parks and gardens. The city acted like a magnet not only to the excess farm population of eastern Germany but also to artists and intellectuals from all Germany and from other parts of Europe. During the twentieth century Berlin expanded its economic functions and became the greatest single manufacturing city of Germany and one of the greatest in Europe. Although it specialized in scientific and precision instruments and electrical apparatus, its products covered the complete range from iron and steel to automobiles, aircraft, machinery, and tractors, and to textiles, paper, and food. With Frankfurt and Leipzig it dominated the German book publishing trade. Its university and other educational institutions ranked among the world's finest. With the evolution of the Nazi bureaucracy, Berlin became a still more powerful center, and its baroque architecture was diversified with a number of massive neoclassic Nazi buildings.

However, Berlin naturally became a prime target for Allied bombers in World War II, and during the siege of Berlin by the Red Army it suffered additional damage and destruction. The largest city ever to fall by siege, Berlin presented an appalling scene of destruction in May, 1945. Divided among all four occupational powers—although the metropolitan zone was completely surrounded by the Soviet zone of occupation—Berlin became the most intense focus of East-West antagonisms. The highly integrated character of the city was greatly disturbed by Berlin's being split into an eastern and western zone. The determination of the Allies not to be forced out by Soviet pressure—as was illustrated in the Berlin Airlift of 1948—was matched by an equal determination on the part of the West Berliners not to be intimidated by Soviet threats and tactics: an interesting example of the spirit of a frontier people.

Despite the great drop in Berlin's industrial production after 1945 because of political barriers to the active trade that the city must conduct in order to thrive, output slowly climbed from virtually zero to a level in 1950 of about 28 per cent that of 1938. The focal location of the city in the German canal network and rail net gives Berlin a sound basis for an eventual return to its former industrial greatness, but political hindrances may retard the recovery for many years. In any event, one of the most intense dramas of the mid-century world was being enacted among the ruins of a once-great city that indicates it retains many aspects of its strength, despite a loss of 1 million of its prewar population.

Baltic Moraine Zone

Within the zone of the Baltic Moraines three definite types of landscape may be distinguished. From south to north, in the order in which the landscapes were created by the retreating Scandinavian ice sheet, they are: the sandy outwash plain, the band of terminal and recessional moraines, and, next to the Baltic coast, the zone of ground moraine.

Sandy Outwash Plain. Along the southern edge of the Baltic Moraine Zone is a fringe of sand deposited as outwash materials by meltwater streams pouring off the edge of the last ice sheet. The fringe is a flat, poor area comprising part of the *Geest* of northwestern Germany. The large expanses of moor have been only partially reclaimed for fields of rye and potatoes.

Terminal and Recessional Moraines. The oscillating and retreating front of the last ice sheet deposited arcuate ridges of gravelly and stony moraines that extend across the central part of the plain from the lower Elbe eastward across northern Poland and into the Soviet Union. The greatest share of this zone lay in post-1945 Poland and is described in Chapter 43. The most southerly of these ridges marks the greatest advance of the Baltic (Würm) phase of Pleistocene glaciation and is therefore a "terminal" moraine, whereas similar ridges farther north mark stages in the retreat of the ice when the edge was stationary for long periods in a state of equilibrium. The irregularities of these moraines appear not only in a chaos of hills and undrained hollows but also in morainic tongues projecting into the sandy plain. It is within the hollows that the hundreds of lakes of northeastern Germany and northern Poland are found. The result of the disarrangement of drainage by disordered glacial deposits, such lakes are also found in the older moraine between the *Urstromtäler* farther south and in such glaciated areas as Finland and Canada. This zone is likewise sparsely settled and is lacking in notable urban development.

Around the many lakes, however, as is the case in such similar areas in the United States as Wisconsin and New England, summer cottages and summer resorts are numerous.

Ground Moraine Zone. After depositing the morainic ridges described in the preceding section, the ice sheet melted northward rather regularly and left a covering of ground moraine or glacial drift that now forms a rolling country between the last recessional moraine and the Baltic coast. This belt finds its direct continuation in the Danish islands and in Skåne in southern Sweden. The loamy soils developed on the ground moraine are much more fertile than the sandy soils farther south; therefore, agriculture along the Baltic coast is appreciably more intensive, and the density of population is somewhat higher.

Partly on the basis of the more fertile soils but also on the basis of coastal location, a number of cities have developed, all of which had their heydays during the period of Hanseatic supremacy in northern Germany and the Baltic. Some of them have continued as active seaports until the present time. Kiel is one of the main Baltic ports, profiting particularly from its position at the eastern end of the Kiel Canal, and was long Germany's chief naval base, engaging in appreciable shipbuilding. Farther to the southeast is Lübeck at the head of the Trave estuary and at the northern end of the Lübeck-Elbe Canal. Still farther east, in the German Democratic Republic, is Rostock, formerly of significance because of its position on the ferry line to Denmark through the outport of Warnemünde. However, the ferry was discontinued after 1945 by Soviet occupation authorities. Three smaller ports worthy of mention are Wismar, west of Rostock; Stralsund to the east; and Flensburg, just south of the Danish border on the Jutland Isthmus.

Northwestern Lowland

In extreme northwestern Germany is an area that is composed of marshes and sandy moors partly on glacial outwash and partly in *Urstromtäler*. The interior of the small region is the most sparsely settled part of Germany, but the estuaries of the rivers are highly developed and are densely populated.

The Marshes. Dune islands, remnants of former sand bars, form a protecting line in front of the North Sea coast of Germany. However, part of the Schleswig-Holstein coast is unprotected, and strong dikes have been built to defend the land against the furor of winter storms. Far out from the coast the tiny red sandstone rock of

Helgoland stands like a sentinel and has become a symbol of German naval interest in the North Sea. It was an important Nazi base during World War II, but the entire population was evacuated by the British after 1945. Huge demolition charges were set off to destroy the underground fortifications, and the British used the island as a bombing range until 1951. Western German authorities attempted to re-establish settlement with British permission after 1951.

The estuaries of the two chief German rivers debouching into the North Sea have become the sites for large seaports that have the special advantage of combining ocean and river traffic. It is interesting that both Bremen and Hamburg developed well up their respective estuaries in order to avoid the low-lying land near the coast and in order to utilize the more solid—but still sandy—ground of their sites. The distance from the sea has, however, encouraged the installation of outports: Cuxhaven for Hamburg, and Bremerhaven for Bremen. In the case of Bremerhaven especially, shipping tends to utilize the outport and to avoid the trip up the Weser estuary.

Hamburg's location at the outlet of the Elbe, draining a rich and highly developed hinterland, and its possession of the best harbor on the German North Sea coast have been important factors in its development into the greatest seaport of continental Europe. As mentioned in Chapter 34, Hamburg's role as a port suffered greatly after 1945, both because of very great destruction in the city and because of the disruption of manufacturing and trade in its hinterland. Nevertheless, it revived its active industrial life and restored much of its trade and shipbuilding, so that by 1950 it had regained most of the population it lost during World War II and was once again over the 1.6 million mark in population, making it the second largest city of Germany.

Although heavily hit by war destruction, Bremerhaven recovered rather well because of its use by the American occupation forces as both a freight and a passenger port. The former naval base of Wilhelmshaven on the Jade Bight was heavily bombed during World War II and was dismantled after 1945. Lying on the eastern end of the Ems-Jade Canal, it engages in shipbuilding and in making machines and precision tools. Emden, near the outlet of the Ems River and at the western end of the Ems-Jade Canal, was especially developed to become an all-German outlet for the Ruhr through the Dortmund-Ems Canal, but the arrangement was not so satisfactory as had been hoped.

The Sandy Lowland. This section of extreme northwestern Germany (A569) is a continuation of the region called the "sandy upland" in the Netherlands. The name is appropriate in Holland, but in a country like Germany, where there are so many real uplands, the name "sandy lowland" is more appropriate. Extensive moors, covered with heather and useful only as a source of turf and as grazing grounds for sheep, are still found in many areas. The Bourtanger Moor along the Dutch-German border is the core of this poor area. Reclamation by drainage and the free use of fertilizers has, however, changed a considerable part of the lowland into pasture and cropland. The only notable town in the entire region is Oldenburg, west of Bremen, which is the center for trade in livestock and agricultural produce. It is connected by canal with both the Ems and the Weser.

These three chapters have discussed Germany somewhat in detail both to show the effects of World War II and to suggest that not only has the country restored many aspects of its peacetime economic life but also that Europe needs the great factory of Germany operating at a high level in order to have many of the manufactures without which Europe could not thrive. By 1951 Western Germany had almost resumed its independent place among the democratic nations of Western Europe and was well on its way to becoming an even greater core economic area. But, as a great part of Germany lies east of the Iron Curtain, the split within the country continued to impose very great difficulties. Bonn stands opposed to eastern Berlin, and no man could see the end of the division of the country.

· 37 ·

Czechoslovakia (Československo)

A Human-Geographical Tragedy

Czechoslovakia stood out during the interwar period as a shining example of the fact that the democratic form of government could be successfully employed even in a newly constructed nation. Its famous leaders Masaryk and Beneš were regarded as champions of liberal thought. The new state, conceived in Pittsburgh in the United States during the years of World War I and officially constructed after the war, had a number of assets but also some liabilities. Among her assets was an excellent balance between a high industrial development and a productive agrarian economy. The Czechs, the core ethnic unit, were regarded as well suited to carry the burden of statehood, having been trained in the old school of Austria, where it was often said that the Poles and Czechs actually operated the government. Moreover, the new state had around the Bohemian Basin excellent "natural" boundaries—boundaries that had persisted for centuries—in the form of wooded, almost uninhabited ranges. Occupying a central location in the heart of Europe, lying astride great trade routes, and having access to such navigable rivers as the Elbe, Oder, and Danube, Czechoslovakia not only held a promise of the future but also was able to play an important role among the European nations. Most European countries looked at it with interest and often with admiration. It was an excellent case in favor of the Wilsonian principle of self-determination.

However, Czechoslovakia had quite a number of liabilities. It was forged from territory taken from Austria (slightly less than 56 per cent), Hungary (slightly less than 44 per cent), and Germany (0.23 per cent). The new state was, as the name indicates, a joint enterprise between the Czechs and Slovaks, a combination that appeared superficially to be a good one, since ethnic differences were only slight. In reality, however, despite their close relationship, the two groups had gone different ways. The Czechs, whose King-

607

dom of Bohemia during the period from the eleventh century to
the sixteenth century was itself one of the most brilliant in all
Europe, were not culturally degraded by their Austrian rulers after
the seventeenth century. The Slovaks, on the other hand, were sub-
jugated by the then less cultured Magyars in the tenth century and
were oppressed for nine centuries by the Magyar aristocrats. In
the new state after 1920, the Slovaks took the second place—or at
least felt that they were forced to do so, and this led to strained
feelings between the two groups.

A third Slavic unit, the Ruthenes or Carpatho-Ukrainians, occupied the eastern extension of Czechoslovakia. This "tail" had a
political reason: it connected Czechoslovakia with Rumania and
separated Hungary from Poland. The peasant Ruthenes themselves were more backward than the Slovaks and had little influence
in the affairs of state. Around this threefold Slavic core were arranged the minorities that made up 30 per cent of the state's population. The largest minority group was the Sudeten Germans, living chiefly inside the mountain rim of the Bohemian Plateau, which
was the main industrial area. The next largest group was the
Magyars, in southern Slovakia, who had for nearly a thousand years
been the Slovaks' masters; now they became simple citizens. It is
true that in a democratic state they could select their own representatives and voice their complaints, but they remained a minority that only grudgingly accepted the new situation. Thus the new
state began with a jigsaw puzzle of ethnographic groups.

Another liability was the attitude of Germany after Hitler came
to power. Practically all of Europe had rejoiced in the creation of
the new Czechoslovakia with its tradition of liberalism. Hitler,
however, regarded democratic Czechoslovakia as dangerous to his
plan of aggression, and he condemned it as "the Slavic dagger
pointed at the breast of Germany." The events that followed are
well known: the change of the Sudeten Germans from a mildly
protesting group into a violently antinational group; the tragedy
of Munich, where France and Britain (and, by their acquiescence,
all western nations) sacrificed the Czechs on the altar of appease-
ment; the dismemberment of Czechoslovakia and finally its total
disappearance, with only the German satellite state of Slovakia left
as a remnant. Hungary—and, to a lesser degree, Poland—came in
for the kill and took their shares. How the Czechs suffered under
German rule is also well known. The name Lidice is now a symbol for criminal terrorism.

The liberation of Czechoslovakia came during the last days of World War II. Later it became apparent that a grave mistake had been made in allowing the Russians to take the glory of liberation while American troops stood by. The reborn state, having lost its Ruthenian "tail," still tried to be democratic. President Beneš, attempting to follow his "middle course" of co-operation with both the Soviet Union and the Western Powers, found that the communists accept no middle positions. When the Czech communists could not succeed by legal means through elections, they organized a *coup d'état,* and in 1948 Czechoslovakia became a communist state. When some members of the Czech government in 1948 attempted to join the Marshall Plan, the Soviet masters withdrew the acceptance. Such indeed is the tragic story of a small state attempting to follow its democratic bent. Before other aspects of postwar Czechoslovakia are evaluated, it is necessary to examine the physical framework of the country.

Structure and Relief

Czechoslovakia consists of three sections from west to east: the Bohemian Plateau, the Moravian Depression, and the Alpine-Carpathian mountain region, each differing from the others not only in structure and relief, but also in the economic response of the people (A613 and A615).

Bohemian Plateau. The very ancient Plateau or Basin of Bohemia is one of the fundamental geological features of central Europe. During the Alpine period, as in former times of mountain building, it was the obstacle that impeded the northward advance of the waves of Alpine folding, though it did not itself escape unmarred. The old peneplain surface was uplifted in the form of a basin with a sharply defined rim, and this diamond-shaped rim has since been remodeled by erosion into the mountains that surround the western end of the country. Fault lines and uplifted blocks on the plateau itself and—in the northwest—the rift valley of the Ohře (Eger), dropped down parallel to the southeast side of the Erzgebirge, show that even the old fundamental block of Bohemia was materially affected in the Alpine upheaval. Volcanic remnants and hot springs also bear witness to these disturbances, as do similar phenomena in the Central Plateau of France.

The Bohemian Plateau lies inside a frame of wooded mountains, which include the Böhmer Wald (Czech: Český Les) on the south-

west, the Erzgebirge (Czech: Krušné Hory) on the northwest, the
Sudeten on the northeast, and the Moravian Heights (Czech: Česko-
moravská Vysočina) on the east. It is a rolling country, where fertile river basins like those of the Ohře, Berounka, Vltava, and Elbe
(Czech: Labe) are separated by forest-covered divides. The sandstone formation of central Saxony (in Germany) continues into
Bohemia along the course of the Elbe with the same sharp features
of relief that farther north have given rise to the term "Saxon Switzerland." This section, with its numerous volcanic remnants where
the Elbe River crosses the Ohře rift, presents the only young
geologic feature of the plateau. Mineral resources are numerous,
some, like the gold and silver deposits, having been famous historically. Of far more importance are the coal mines and iron ores
of the Berounka Basin and the lignite of the Ohře rift valley.

Moravian Depression. Lying east of the Moravian Heights, the
fertile Moravian Depression extends across Czechoslovakia north
and south between Vienna and Upper Silesia and is one of the
many depressions along the northern base of the Alpine mountains. The mountains, to be sure, are here broken in two by the
Danube valley as they swing from the Alps to the Carpathians.
The depression widens in southern Czechoslovakia, with the Morava, a branch of the Danube, as its chief stream. This river should
not be confused with that of the same name flowing into the
Danube below Belgrade. In northern Czechoslovakia, the Oder
River (Czech: Odra) rises near the headwaters of the Morava and
follows a low gap through the Sudeten that forms the very significant Moravian Gate near Moravská Ostrava. In this Ostrava area,
Czechoslovakia possesses a share of the Upper Silesian coal resources,
which provide as much as 75 per cent of its coal production.

Carpathian Region. Near Bratislava, east of Vienna, the Alpine
ranges cross the Danube as the Little Carpathians, which, extending northward, form an appreciable barrier between Moravia and
Slovakia. Turning eastward, they continue in the West Carpathians and form a heavily forested wall of sandstone between the
Danube and the rivers of the North European Plain. Several gaps,
however, now used by railroad lines, reduce the importance of this
wall as a "natural" boundary between Czechoslovakia and Poland.

South of the continuous range that forms the main length of
the Carpathians lies a separate knot of mountains, the High Tatra,
which forms the geographic nucleus of the Carpathians. It is composed mainly of granite and bears many marks of glaciation. The

Beskids lie on either side of the rugged Tatra. The Váh valley south of the High Tatra facilitates travel from east to west and provides an area of population concentration and agricultural production. South of the upper Váh, where the volcanic results of the sinking of the Alföld mark the inner border of the Carpathians, rise the Slovakian Ore Mountains (Czech: Slovenské Krušnohoři), a rich source of iron. Where the Váh joins the Danube, Czechoslovakia shares a part of the Little Hungarian Plain with Austria and Hungary.

Climate

The climate of Czechoslovakia is of the Central European type, becoming quite continental toward the east. It varies greatly, however, according to the physiography. The border mountains of the Bohemian Plateau are cold, with heavy rainfall, but act as a climatic barrier around the plateau itself. There the continental type of climate becomes distinct although not extreme. According to the standards of western Europe the winters are cold, averaging 30° F in January at Prague; but the summers are warm, with a July average of 67° at Prague, and there is a comparatively low rainfall of 20 inches or less.

The Moravian Depression experiences a mild winter climate and is warm in summer with a slightly higher rainfall, which at Brno amounts to 22 inches. In the Carpathians the elevation accounts for the mountain climate, and in the east there are evidences of the Eastern European type, with its cold winters and warm summers. On the Alföld and near Bratislava the July temperature often averages above 70°, and the rainfall, which is heaviest in summer, is increased to 28 inches by the nearness of the mountains.

Land Utilization

The use of the land, like the climate, is marked by transition. It changes from the rye, oats, and sugar beets of the German Lowlands, still prevailing in the Bohemian Basin, to the wheat and corn economy of the Danube basin. The soils are generally good— sometimes even excellent, especially in certain parts of the Bohemian Basin, where black soils prevail, as well as in the Moravian Depression and the Czechoslovakian portion of the Little Alföld.

Collectivization of agriculture on the Soviet model was not pushed by the communists after they seized control of the country in 1948 to the extent that it was enforced in other Soviet satellite countries. The reasons for lack of extensive collectivization in Czechoslovakia should be recalled when the agrarian situation at mid-century in the other satellite countries is studied in the following chapters. The reasons are rather simple and reflect the excellent standards of the country: there is very little land shortage, especially since the admirable agrarian reforms of the interwar years; methods of cultivation are quite good—the worst were in the Ruthenian "tail" that the Soviet Union took itself; farmers earned a generally good livelihood from their small and medium-sized holdings; and there was, consequently, no destitute peasantry and no clamor for reform. Farmers resented any attempt at collectivization. Some were organized in "co-operatives," and in some cases the organization closely approached the collective farm system. Finally, the well-developed Czech industry was well manned and did not require a flow of population from the farm to feed the manpower requirements.

Crops. A little more than 40 per cent of the land is in crops, leaving 16 per cent to meadows and pastures and 32 per cent to forests. One of the most notable features of Czechoslovakian agriculture is its well-balanced quality. Cereals do indeed occupy more than half of the cropped land, but this is a small percentage compared with the countries farther east and south. Moreover, no one cereal greatly exceeds the other, the areas devoted to rye, oats, wheat, and barley differing only slightly. Thus, there is no such great and dangerous dependence upon a single crop as in Rumania. Moreover, fodder crops are of importance, and potatoes just about rival barley. Thus, each of six different types of crops is raised on from 1.3 million to 2.1 million acres. Sugar beets are produced on an area about one third as large as that of potatoes and barley and one-fifth that of rye, but they produce so great a value per acre that they may be classed as a seventh main reliance. Czechoslovakia stands next after Germany among the countries of Europe as a producer of sugar. Of course different crops are predominant in different sections of the country (A613). Wheat and corn are raised mainly in the south; barley in upper (northern) Moravia; and sugar beets in upper (southern) Bohemia and in the Moravian lowlands.

Hops are another important industrial crop, and the relatively large areas devoted to such unusual crops as chicory and poppies, the seeds of which are raised in thousands of little plots and used on the top of bread, show how alert the farmers are to opportunities. Wine grapes grow on the border of the Danube plain; and other fruits such as apples, pears, cherries, and plums are common on the Bohemian Plateau. People from other countries are often surprised at the millions of cherry trees bordering the roads and offering their red fruit to anyone who will stand on the top of his cart and reach up to get it. Still more surprising to many foreigners is the abundance of plum trees, almost exactly one for every inhabitant. Five million currant bushes and half as many

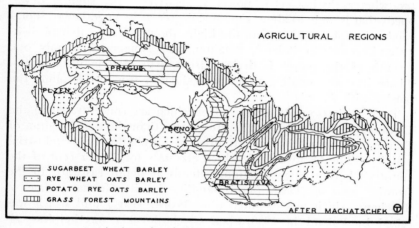

A. Agricultural Regions of Czechoslovakia.

gooseberry bushes illustrate the fact that here is a country of the western European type that raises all sorts of luxuries as well as necessities like grain.

Livestock. Stock raising, despite the presence of 3.2 million cattle and almost as many swine, is not very well developed. Dairying in particular is at a low ebb; but in Czechoslovakia the meat production is sufficient to supply the demand. The number of sheep is declining, a common experience in Europe. The imports and exports of agricultural products substantially balance one another, with importations of wheat, corn, pork, and lard, and exports of barley, malt, sugar, and hops.

Forests. In proportion to its size Czechoslovakia is one of the richest European countries in forest resources. Coniferous forests cover the mountains; and the beeches of the lower Carpathians, with the old forests of the plateau, provide a timber supply of great value; logs, sawn timber, and pulp are important exports.

Industry (A615)

Varied mineral resources, coupled with a dense population, made Czechoslovakia the industrial center of the former Austro-Hungarian Empire. One third of the population is employed in manufacturing, compared with 38 per cent in agricultural pursuits, so that in the agricultural-industrial ratio Czechoslovakia is well balanced.

Coal and lignite are the sources of industrial power in the country, whereas hydroelectric power is relatively only slightly developed—that is, only to about the same degree as in Yugoslavia. Total production of electricity is quite high: about equal to that of Switzerland, post-1945 Poland, Belgium, and Norway, but only one seventh of the power is derived from hydroelectric installations. There is a very small petroleum production from fields along the border with Austria.

Total coal resources, nearly all of which are concentrated in the Ostrava-Karvinná field (A615), are greater than those of Belgium or France—suggesting the potentialities of Czechoslovakian industrial activity. The Ostrava field, which accounts for 75 per cent of the country's hard coal production, extends at depth eastward to the frontier area of Těšín (more familiar by its German name of Teschen), which was disputed after World War I and which was seized by Poland in 1938 when Czechoslovakia was helpless, although it was returned after 1945. In 1949, all fields (shown in A615) produced 17 million tons of hard coal (about the same as the Saar production) and 26 million tons of lignite.

Total iron ore resources are, in terms of metal content, about equal to those of Spain's single deposit of Oviedo or of Sweden's Bergslagen district. Production is rather small, amounting to 500,000 tons of ore annually, and large amounts of ore must be imported (much of it from Sweden) to feed the appreciable iron and steel industry that is on the same scale as that of Italy, Poland, Luxembourg, or the Saar. Heavy industries (indicated by S in A615) are concentrated in Ostrava, Plzeň, and Prague.

A great variety of minerals is produced in modest quantities, especially in the Bohemian Basin and particularly in the Erzgebirge. Several are also found in the Slovakian Ore Mountains. The kaolin (potter's clay) deposits have supplied the main raw materials for the famous Bohemian porcelain or chinaware industry. Formerly of only moderate significance as a source of radium and as a min-

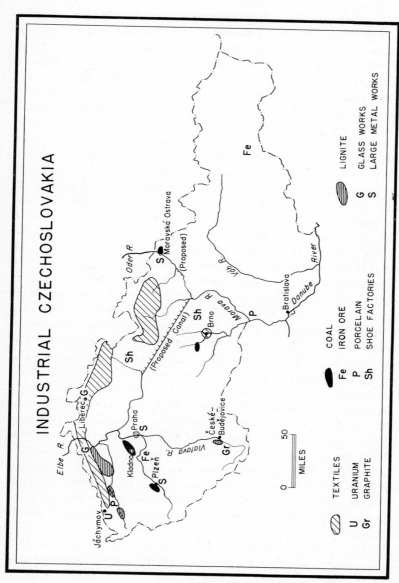

INDUSTRIAL CZECHOSLOVAKIA

TEXTILES
U URANIUM
Gr GRAPHITE

Fe COAL
Fe IRON ORE
P PORCELAIN
Sh SHOE FACTORIES

LIGNITE
G GLASS WORKS
S LARGE METAL WORKS

0   50
MILES

A. Principal Manufacturing Districts and Mineral Deposits of Czechoslovakia.

eral element in health-resort water, the uranium of Jáchymov (Joachimsthal) became of prime importance to the Soviets after 1945 and especially after 1948 as a source of material for atomic fission work. Consistent reports came out by refugees that thousands of slave laborers were working the mines under Russian direction, on both the Czech and German sides of the Erzgebirge.

Other industries run the gamut from guns to beer, and most of them are represented in the normal Czechoslovakian exports. Prague has a share of nearly all types of manufacturing, but otherwise the industries tend to be concentrated in specialized areas. Ostrava is the country's Pittsburgh, as has been indicated, and also produces a wide range of heavy machinery. The gigantic Skoda works in Plzeň, like the Krupp works in Essen and the Bofors works in Sweden, produces heavy machinery and arms. Skoda was one of the main arms suppliers for the Central Powers in World War I, for the Nazis in World War II, and for communist armies in the post-1948 period. However, it also produces a wide range of agricultural implements and machinery as well as locomotives and similar equipment. An almost continuous zone of industry extends along the foot of the Erzgebirge and Sudeten, producing machinery and textiles. Liberec is a textile center, as is Brno in Moravia. The northwestern zone of the Bohemian Basin also has a number of glassware works that produce both fine and cheap products. The mammoth Baťa shoe factory at Zlín, near Brno, is world-famed and is one of the world's largest; the Baťa family has branch shoe factories in many other countries as well as in Czechoslovakia. Other Czech leather goods are of equally high quality, especially the gloves. Beer is produced by the millions of gallons in Bohemia, but Plzeň has spread the fame of the Czech product far and wide ("Pilsner Beer"). České Budějovice (Budweis), on the upper Morava, has also built a wide reputation on its pencils, manufactured with the locally produced graphite. In addition to these great centers, there are hundreds of smaller industries such as those producing pulp and paper, sugar from sugar beets, canned goods, and similar products.

The highly developed Czechoslovakian industry, which by 1948 had recovered from the damages of World War II, is of great value among the satellite countries, since it supplies both technical goods and also exports that have long been purchased by the western countries, including the United States. However, the policy of trade restrictions imposed on the satellite countries after 1949—and on Czechoslovakia in particular after the Czech-American tension in 1951—created economic strains on Czech industrial production.

Two of the five big steel mills planned for the satellite countries were scheduled for Czechoslovakia and were widely heralded by the Czech communists. One was to be added to the industrial complex of Ostrava, and the other was to be installed in Slovakia, north of Košice, to utilize the iron ore produced from the deposits in the Slovakian Ore Mountains.

Population and Cities

With a population of about 12.5 millions and a density of 253 per square mile, Czechoslovakia ranks in the medium-sized group of European countries. The population after 1945 became much more homogeneous than it was during the interwar period. More than 2 million Germans were ejected from the rimlands of the Bohemian Basin (the "Sudetenland" of Hitler's propaganda) in order to forestall a repetition of German demands for Czech lands occupied by Germans, and the Ruthenes of the eastern "tail" were transferred with Ruthenia to the Soviet Union. The Magyars in the south are the most important remaining minority. From the viewpoint of religion the population is chiefly Roman Catholic, but the country inherited from ancient times (the Hussite Movement) a sentiment for a national church—a fact that helped the postwar communist government's attempt to break away from Rome's control. Even so, there were unmistakable signs, especially among the Slovak peasants (who are strongly attached to their village priests), that the communist persecution of church leaders was deeply resented.

Prague (Czech: Praha) stands out as the great city of the country. Some islands in the Vltava River, midway between its confluences with the Berounka and the Elbe, long ago invited settlement because the islands facilitated crossing the river here, in the same way that islands led to the original settlement of Paris and Berlin. Thus the route that passes through the geographical center of Bohemia here intersected the main road from northern Germany up the Elbe to Vienna. So the famous Hradchin castle, which still stands on the left bank of the Vltava, was built here, and Prague grew great under its protection. The region around Prague is a place of ancient battlefields reminiscent of Belgium and northern Italy, for throughout historic times it has been of great strategic importance. This is still true, for trade routes radiate in all directions from this center of the Bohemian Basin, and important manufacturing industries are centered here. An especial impulse to growth came after World War I, when Prague changed from a regional center under strong German influence to the capital of a new state and the center of the rapidly developing Czechoslovakian culture. By 1947 its population had reached 921,000.

Compared with Prague, the other cities of the Bohemian Basin are only regional centers, the industries of most of which have already been discussed. They include České Budějovici (Budweis) on the upper Vltava, Plzeň (Pilsen), Liberec, and a number of towns like Teplice and Cheb (Eger) in the industrialized sections of the Ohře rift valley southeast of the Erzgebirge. Located in western Bohemia, Marianské-Lázně (Marienbad), Karlovy Vary (the world-famous Karlsbad), the smaller Františkovy Lázně and Jáchymov owe their existence to their repute as health resort towns possessing mineral springs in the rift valley. The lignite mining center of Most also possesses a variety of industries, such as breweries, sugar refineries, and metalworking plants. Ústí nad Labem is the main river port of Bohemia.

In Moravia, on two roads connecting the Morava River with the Bohemian Plateau, two old industrial centers are located in fertile valleys. One of these, Brno (Brünn), with 273,000 inhabitants, is the second city of Czechoslovakia; and the other, Olomouc (Olmütz), much smaller than Brno, owes its importance to its location near the Moravian Gate facing Silesia and Poland. Ostrava (181,000) is the second city of Moravia and is the industrial center of the Czechoslovakian part of the Silesian mining area. Bratislava (Pressburg) is Czechoslovakia's port on the Danube, to secure which Czechoslovakian territory was extended beyond the territory actually occupied by Czechs and Slovaks in 1920. During World War II Bratislava was the capital of the puppet state of Slovakia. Across the Danube from Bratislava, at the junction of the Czech, Austrian, and Hungarian boundaries, is a small bridgehead that was enlarged at Hungary's expense by 25 square miles after World War II.

Transportation

One of the most important functions of Czechoslovakia, with its long east-west extension, is—at least under normal conditions—that of a transit land. Main routes from the North European Plain, from such cities as Berlin and Warsaw, to southern and southeastern Europe pass through the gateways of Czechoslovakia. Navigable rivers and good international rail connections give Czechoslovakia access to the rest of Europe and to many markets. The post-1948 political orientation stressed the lines to Berlin along the Elbe River and the importance of the Moravian Gate, which opens to Poland. Canals connecting the Elbe, Oder, and Danube were under construction in 1951. The Elbe especially was important, because it connects Czechoslovakia with the open ocean by way of Hamburg, where it normally has special harbor facilities. After 1948, the shift was away from the Elbe (in order to avoid contact with Western Europe) to the Oder River, which is less favorably located and is also inferior as a waterway.

The Outlook

The high level of the economic-cultural development of western Czechoslovakia is indicated by its inclusion in Europe A in A15. It showed all the attributes of a high cultural level, high agricultural yields, well-developed industries with quality products, high level of education, and a standard of life well ahead of that of her eastern neighbors. The question that arose after the country disappeared behind the Iron Curtain in 1948 was whether Czechoslovakia would retain its high traditions or whether it would be reduced to the lower level of the rest of communist Europe. For those who love the country, and there are many of them, the course of events after 1945 was tragic. The complete reorientation of trade to the demands of an eastern economy will alone have serious repercussions.

Czechoslovakia was not a country in which communism grew out of misery: it was, one might say, kidnaped, and the change could not and did not represent the will of the people. However, the Czechoslovaks have had similar misfortunes befall them before, and every time they came out of the darkness. If history repeats itself, there is hope for a better future for the state in the heart of Europe.

· 38 ·
Austria (Österreich)

The phenomenon of the "rump state" of Austria cannot be understood in the time setting either of the interwar period or of the post-1945 period without some consideration of the development and dissolution of the Austrian Empire before 1919. Much of this section is also applicable to Hungary, discussed in the following chapter.

Territorial Evolution of the Former Empire

In medieval days, when successive members of the Austrian family of Hapsburgs were heads of the Holy Roman Empire, Austria was politically, although not geographically, the central state in a political unit that embraced not only Austria but also most of Germany, northern Italy, and part of France, and even spread at times to Sicily, Spain, and the Netherlands. During the four centuries that elapsed between the peak of Hapsburg power and 1920, Austrian influence shifted more or less steadily from the west toward the east until World War I clipped it off sharply on all sides. More than a century before the Austrians reached the height of their power, Switzerland had already made itself independent. In the seventeenth century the Thirty Years' War deprived Austria of many of its western dominions. In the eighteenth century, Prussia took Silesia and diverted the interest of Bavaria from Vienna to Berlin. In the next century the newly born Italian state, with the aid of the French, drove the Austrians out of the Po Basin, leaving the Southern Tirol as a last remnant of Austria's domain south of the Alps.

In other directions, meanwhile, Austria had been expanding. As early as the sixteenth century the Hapsburgs obtained rights in Hungary and took possession of Croatia and Slavonia. Then the Austro-Hungarian Empire became firmly established. The partition of Poland added Galicia and the Kraków area to the Dual Empire. The complete expulsion of the Turks from Transylvania and the Danube Basin brought these areas under Austrian sway.

It also permitted Bosnia and Hercegovina to be annexed, and allowed the empire to play a part in the affairs of the Balkans. As a result of these developments, the Austro-Hungarian Empire finally became chiefly a Danubian state. The Bohemian Plateau, with its excellent physical boundaries, and the *glacis* or foreland of Galicia north of the Carpathians were the only parts of the empire really outside the Danube drainage system. Moreover, only the loss of Bavaria and the independence of Rumania prevented the Dual Empire from embracing the entire Danube from source to outlet.

Ethnographic Relationships

The geographical relationships of the Dual Empire can be studied from two different angles, ethnographic and economic. The ethnographic complexity of the empire was its greatest danger and at the end of World War I became the basis of the political division of the former imperial lands. Briefly, the pre-1920 pattern was as follows: a wedge of 12 million Germans and 10 million Magyars extended from west to east along the Danube, separating the two Slavic wings composed of Czechs, Slovaks, and Ruthenes in the north, and of Serbo-Croats and Slovenes in the south; 3.2 million Rumanians lived east of the Tisza River and in Transylvania; 5 million Poles inhabited Galicia, north of the Carpathians; and, finally, about 800,000 Italians inhabited the Austrian area along the Adriatic coast and in the southern valleys of the Southern Tirol.

The two politically and culturally dominant groups, Germans (Austrians) and Magyars, formed only a minority of the 50 million people in the whole empire, and the Slavic groups alone were stronger in number than the German-Hungarian nucleus around which the state was built. The division of the state into two parts, Austria and Hungary, in 1867 was a political maneuver designed to split the Slavic influence and enable the German minority in Austria and the Magyar minority in Hungary to dominate. The move failed, and the conglomeration of diverse elements was held together only by arbitrary means and threatened constantly to disintegrate into separate political units.

Protests against Austrian control by non-German peoples under Austria were relatively not exceedingly great, except in the small Italian group, backed by the slogan of *"Italia Irredenta"* or "Unredeemed Italy." Vienna was never a harsh ruler, and even the Czechs, in spite of their cry for greater freedom, prospered under Austrian domination. In the Hungarian section, however, conditions were different. Toward the southern Slavs and Rumanians, the Magyars behaved somewhat after the fashion of Asiatic conquerors. Resentment naturally developed, and Slavic ambitions continued to be fostered in the Hungarian section as well as in adjacent Serbia and Rumania. Thus, the ethnographic situation contained a great number of sore spots, which became inflamed after the death of Franz Joseph, who had done much to soften the controversies.

This brief description of the ethnographic structure of the old Dual Empire, which disappeared from the map of Europe after World War I, not only serves as an outline of the pattern of peoples in the Danube region; it also helps to explain why determination for national independence was so intense among some nationalities in the post-World War I period and what groups joined efforts for creation of new states.

Economic Relationships and Their Breakdown

Economically, the old Austro-Hungarian Empire showed a much better structure than it did ethnographically. The western part, with its highly developed manufacturing industries and intensive land utilization, contrasted sharply with the rural east, with its surplus of grain. Austria was the manufacturer and Hungary the farmer. In this respect, the empire came quite near to being an ideal self-supporting unit. The situation was improved by the fact that the entire territory of the Dual Monarchy was tied together by an intricate network of roads and railways, and by the navigable Danube, which in itself was an excellent bond of union. Moreover, the empire had a valuable, though restricted, access to the Adriatic Sea through the port of Trieste, which was another great advantage. Austro-Hungary had thus become an economic whole that could not be divided without great loss to the individual parts.

Under the organization existing prior to 1918, Vienna was one of the world's greatest capitals. Located on the Danube where the river cuts through the Alpine range and where there is easy passage both north and south and east and west, it had become a great political and cultural center with an influence far beyond the empire. Like Paris, it had won repute in the creation of objects of art and fashion, with a mingling of French and German concepts.

The shattering end to the greatness of the empire came with the defeat of Austria in World War I and the signing in 1919 of the treaty of Saint Germain-en-Laye. Disregarding the Hungarian part of the empire, Austria's area was reduced from 116,000 to 32,000 square miles and its population from 25 millions to 6.5 millions. Being thus deprived of about 70 per cent of its territory and population, remnant Austria was left without the possibility of feeding its people except by imports. It lacked most of the necessities for a sound manufacturing industry that might, as in Belgium, help to balance trade by furnishing exports. Moreover, the new Austria found itself not only without the essentials of a prosperous future, but also without the vitality to strive for one. It might be described as "the country that did not want to exist," surely a unique case in this age of nationalism. Despite a desire in the years after 1920 to join Germany, Austria was forbidden to do so by the Treaty of Saint Germain; so, with some help from the League of Nations, it was compelled to struggle on alone.

The so-called *Anschluss* movement for Austrian-German union persisted for several years, based on linguistic and other cultural affinities as well as on Austria's desire to find a source of much-needed coal and a market for manufactured products.

Austria and World War II

However, when Germany accepted Hitler's control, Austria—except for a small but vociferous Nazi party—did not follow suit and tried to live its own life in spite of German efforts to interfere. Nevertheless, in 1938, Austria—weak, confused, and isolated—saw the German army march in and force it to become a German province, while Vienna was cleared of its many Jews. As in other German-occupied areas, Austrian industries were taken over by Nazi organizations. During the war, the Allies regarded Austria as a nation to be liberated and officially promised it special treatment. Nevertheless, after the war, Austria was occupied by Allied troops in four zones of occupation (Russian, American, British, and French) with Vienna under joint control. The country has, indeed, been much better treated than Germany: it has lost no territory, it has received extensive financial aid—chiefly from the United States—and it was allowed to re-establish its own government over all the country. However, much equipment has been removed from the Russian zone, and the "Cold War" kept Austria under occupation while the occupying powers failed to agree on terms of a peace treaty. Basic in the Allied-Russian inability to agree on a peace treaty is, of course, Austria's key location in Europe. The

Western Allies believe that, without adequate guarantee of the preservation of Austrian independence from Soviet interference, they dare not withdraw their troops. Otherwise, establishment of Austria as another Soviet satellite would extend Russian domination into western Europe—indeed to the banks of the upper Rhine. Likewise, the Soviets desire to retain their hold over eastern Austria. Its location, therefore, forces Austria to suffer continued occupation as well as grave economic problems, and deprives it of the right to determine its own future.

Physiographic Diversity

The Alps. Small as it is, Austria comprises a number of geographical regions. Their large number and diversity are among the country's chief handicaps—albeit they offer certain advantages.

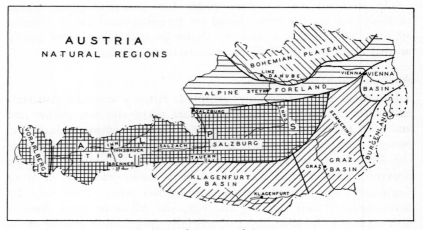

A. Natural Regions of Austria.

A624 shows that Austria includes parts of the Bohemian Plateau, the Alpine Foreland, the Alps themselves, and even a small share of the Little Hungarian Plain; Vienna in its basin is a region by itself. The Alps extend from Switzerland through Austria, but the corresponding sections of the Pre-Alps and Alpine Foreland, as described in Chapter 33, are located for the greater part outside the Austrian boundaries. In Austria, as in Switzerland, the Alps include longitudinal valleys, of which there are two in Austria. As a rule these follow the lines of contact between the limestone zones and the old mountain core of granite and other crystalline rocks. Thus the Austrian Alps show three ranges extending from east to west: the northern limestone mountains, often with high plateaus like the Dachstein (10,000 feet); the central zone with its highest elevation covered by glaciers; and the southern limestone zone, the Dolomites, extending into Italy. These three are separated by the longitudinal (east-west) depressions of the upper parts of the Inn, Salzach, and Enns valleys in the north, and of the Drava system, with the Klagenfurt Basin, in the south. Here, as in Switzerland, the present relief is probably due to the uplift and warping of an old erosion surface, after which the rivers adjusted themselves to the new conditions. Broad valleys, picturesque villages, wooded slopes, glaciated peaks, and the perpendicular walls of limestone plateaus attract thousands of visitors to the Austrian Alps, so that the care of tourists is almost as important as in Switzerland. After 1947, government tourist agencies made special efforts to encourage tourism in the country in order to obtain hard currency.

The various river valleys divide the Austrian Alps into several well-defined sections. The most western of these is the mountainous little district of Vorarlberg (A624). Lying between Bavaria on the north and the Swiss Grisons and Liechtenstein on the south and east, it is Austria's door on the Rhine. High mountains separate it from the Inn Valley farther east, and broad tributary valleys of the Rhine open westward toward Switzerland and also toward the Boden See or Lake of Constance, on the eastern end of which is the port of Bregenz. The Austrian portion of the Rhine valley contains most of the industrial life and agriculture of the region, whereas the mountains chiefly support grazing and forestry. However, increasing development of water power in the valleys of the region is stimulating industrial expansion, and Vorarlberg is one of Austria's leading regions in output of hydroelectricity. The Montafon Valley is especially significant in water power production and was developed somewhat before World War II; intensive development expanded the capacity during the war period, when power was exported to Germany, as well as after 1945. Industries of Vorarlberg produce especially fine textiles and lace, for which Dornbirn is the active center. In transportation also the region has special significance, since the Arlberg Pass is used by the railway from Paris through Basel and Zürich to Innsbruck and Vienna. The strategic value of the line is that it connects Paris and Vienna without crossing German or Italian territory. Inasmuch as most of

the people of Vorarlberg live in the Rhine valley and are separated
from the Inn Valley by high mountains, their ties with the rest of
Austria have been loose.   During the period of Austrian suffering
after World War I, they requested annexation (*Anschluss*) by Switzerland, but did not receive friendly encouragement of their plans.

A. The Gross Glockner motor road crossing the central range of the Alps in Austria.
The road was rebuilt during the Nazi period for its strategic connection between
northern Austria and the valley of the Drava River.   Courtesy of Austrian Consulate
General.

The little independent state of Liechtenstein, a historical remnant,
lies at the southwestern corner of Arlberg.   Before World War I
it was economically a part of Austria-Hungary, but now has a similar arrangement with Switzerland.   Like San Marino, Liechtenstein derives much of its income from sale of postage stamps to
collectors.

East of the Vorarlberg, a much larger Alpine region contains the
northern longitudinal valleys and the surrounding mountain ranges.
This region of the Austrian Alps may be divided into a number of
separate mountain ranges, which extend eastward from the Vorarlberg to the last spur overlooking Vienna—the Wiener Wald.   The
most important sections, from west to east, are the Ötztaler Alpen,

the Hohe Tauern (including the Gross Glockner, 12,457 feet, highest point in Austria), the Niedere Tauern, and the Hochschwab, all of which combined form the "backbone" of Austria. Human occupancy, as might be expected, is concentrated in the main valleys, where there are many prosperous villages whose inhabitants raise field crops and fruit on the valley bottoms, graze their cattle on the high meadows, and work in winter in the great mountain forests. The western part—Tirol, in the Austrian "panhandle"—has a special geographical disadvantage in that its logical outlet is northward down the Inn and Salzach valleys to the Alpine Foreland in southern Bavaria. Thus, a political cleavage inhibits economic exchange and co-operation between the mountains and the Foreland that have worked out so well in Switzerland. Similar conditions limit the development of the Salzburg area, which lies in the Austrian part of the Foreland where the boundary turns north. In both sections, Tirol and Salzburg, the tendency toward economic relationships with Germany is strongly developed. Innsbruck, a delightful old town nestled in the Inn Valley at the junction of the Arlberg railroad with the Brenner line leading into Italy, is a classical example of a city that has developed at the foot of an important mountain pass.

In the eastern part of this Alpine region, in Styria, are located large iron ore deposits centered in the famous Erzberg, lying southwest of the great bend of the Enns River. These iron reserves, which are slightly smaller than those of Luxembourg, furnish the ore for a modest iron and steel industry, although Austria's lack of coking coal retards the development of a large heavy industry.

Klagenfurt Basin. Located between the southeastward or Dinaric wing of the Alps and the central section, which continues eastward, the Klagenfurt region lies in the basin of the Drava River, which flows eastward to the Danube through Yugoslavia. The presence of a large number of Slovenes south of the Drava but still north of the mountain wall of the Karawanken encouraged Yugoslavia to demand the Klagenfurt area after World War I, but a plebiscite in 1920 indicated preference even among the Slovenes for remaining in Austria. A revival of Yugoslav claims to the region after World War II was accorded no official action. With its continental climate (cold winters and warm summers), favorable relief, and fertile soils, the basin is agriculturally productive and is densely populated, particularly around Klagenfurt itself. Its chief significance, however, is its function as a focus of railways. To the northwest a main line extends through the Tauern Tunnel to Salzburg and Munich, and to the northeast the heavily traveled route to Vienna follows the Mur-Mürz depression and crosses under the Semmering Pass through the Semmering Tunnel. Two southern rail lines continue these two roads from the north toward the south to the Italian plain and Trieste.

Graz Basin. The Mur River system of the Graz Basin also opens toward a foreign country, Yugoslavia. Relatively low elevation gives rise to a fairly warm climate and to more intensive agriculture than in any other Alpine region. The value of the basin for Austria, however, lies in its focal location in respect to the Styrian iron ores, water power, its own lignite, and the market of the plain. These make the capital, Graz, not only a rural market and university city, but also the center of industrial development in the region, with industries present also in Leoben.

Alpine Foreland. From Bavaria in the west, the Alpine Foreland (described in the chapters on Germany and Switzerland) extends south of the Danube eastward into Austria. Glacial lakes and beautiful scenery along the base of the mountains give rise to numerous summer resorts. A cover of loess makes for great fertility of soils in the hilly section with its entrenched river valleys, and widespread grain fields distinguish this Foreland as Austria's best farming region aside from the Vienna Basin. Charmingly situated at the junction of mountains and Foreland is Salzburg, the principal center of the region.

Bohemian Plateau. North of the Danube lies the southern part of the Bohemian Plateau. In places it even extends south of the river, since, instead of everywhere following the edge of the Alpine Foreland, the Danube has in some places cut its way into the plateau. The old erosion surface rises gently toward the divide between the Danube and the Elbe, which the present boundary more or less follows. Part of this upland, especially the eastern section, is of good fertility and is devoted to crops, but on the poorer parts forests prevail.

Burgenland. A small part of the Little Hungarian Plain, the so-called Burgenland, was taken from Hungary and given to Austria after World War I—the only instance of territorial gain by any of the defeated powers, although it was at the expense of another defeated power. Grapes ripen along the shores of the Neusiedler See, and grains do well except in the more sandy southern part, where forests replace crops. But the fact that the region's economic center and most important city—Sopron, formerly Ödenburg —voted in the 1921 plebiscite to remain with Hungary, although almost surrounded by Austria, deprives the region of its natural center and imposes a handicap on the Burgenland.

Vienna Basin. The rural importance of this most fertile part of Austria is entirely overshadowed by its urban importance as the seat of Vienna (Austrian: Wien), Austria's great capital. Located in the gap between the Alps and Carpathians, Vienna has been for centuries one of Europe's most important cities, often a bulwark against the east and at the same time the gate to western Europe. If ever the dream of one of the Viennese philosophers, Count Coudenhoven Kalergi, should be realized through the establishment of an economic union of all Europe, Vienna might claim that its central location makes it the most suitable place for the "Pan-European" capital. But, because it is a relic of conditions that existed before World War I, it struggled under a great handicap—comparable to the struggle that England without an empire might face. In the days before World War I Vienna used her advantageous location and her prestige as the capital of the Austro-Hungarian Empire to concentrate in herself most of the cultural and political life of the old empire as well as much of the industrial activity. After the breakup of the empire, the loss of former resources such as coal, and the assignment of territories close to the city—such as the Morava Valley—to other nations left Vienna without the necessary geographical foundation for so large an urban concentration. Nevertheless, Vienna remained one of Europe's most charming cities; its influence on science, fashion, music, and economic and social reforms went far beyond the boundaries of Austria; and industrial production remained active, with manufacturing activity extending southward along the foot of the Alps to Wiener-Neustadt. It is possible that in the long run geographical principles may prove stronger than international jealousies, and that economic co-operation among the Danube countries may not only become an asset to the entire area but will restore a measure of Vienna's former greatness as the center of a Danubian unity. It was World War II and the chaos following it that further retarded the city: aerial bombing and ground fighting destroyed much of the city physically, and occupation by troops of all the Big Four powers disrupted the flow of life during the hungry, trying days of the postwar years. Location of Vienna within the Soviet zone of occupation and unstable conditions in central Europe deprived the city of much tourist traffic. Even so, rebuilding progressed remarkably well, and the effervescent spirit of the Viennese restored some of the traditional *Gemütlichkeit*.

The Economic Balance

As a transitional zone between industrial western Europe and agrarian southeastern Europe, Austria exhibits a well-balanced relation between agriculture and manufacturing. Of the productive area—and only the high mountains are entirely unproductive—23 per cent is cropland, 38 per cent grassland, and 37 per cent forest; the rest comprises gardens and vineyards. Cropland dominates in the lowlands of the east and grassland in the mountains of the west; forests are characteristic of the mountain sections. Even before 1938, Austria supplied only 75 per cent of its own food requirements, and, after the chaos and dislocations of World War II and the postwar years, the percentage fell to a disastrous low, and only vigorous efforts by UNRRA and, after 1948, the ERP prevented mass starvation in the country. Food was, indeed, in very short supply, but actual mass dying from starvation was avoided. By 1950, self-sufficiency rose to about 68 per cent, and thousands of acres of land were being reclaimed and irrigated for food crop production. The program of reclamation is a slow and costly one, however, and plans for 1951, for example, called for improvement of only 12,500 acres. Small holdings prevail among the farms, and the agrarian reform that took place in so many parts of the old Austro-Hungarian Empire after its breakup in 1919 was unnecessary in Austria proper.

Rye with about 600,000 acres is the chief crop; but wheat and oats, each with about 500,000 acres, are nearly as important as rye. As in Germany, the potato area (430,000 acres) is very large. Grapes are of importance on some of the eastern hills and on the loess slopes around Vienna. In the mountain valleys and on the Foreland, apples are the principal fruit crop. Stock raising, which accounts for 2.2 million cattle, 1.6 million swine, and 750,000 sheep, is significant in the Alps, where dairy herds predominate, although the standard does not attain that of Switzerland.

The great woodland area, with coniferous forests (spruce and fir) on the higher sections and beeches predominating in the lower regions, is of considerable economic importance and provides the material for such industrial developments as paper mills and pulp factories. Despite serious overcutting during World War II, sawn timber, wood manufactures, and paper are exported in large quantities. However, considering the production of the land as a whole, the surplus of wood products does not offset a large deficit in grains as well as livestock. This food deficit combined with fuel shortage and need for other goods from outside countries gives Austria an unfavorable balance of trade, which has been her most serious economic problem since 1945.

Loss of the Bohemian coal deposits and other mineral wealth in 1919 greatly reduced Austria's supply of mineral raw materials, but the country's endowments in ores remains considerable and varied. The salt production of the Salzburg region is well known. Coal is now mined only in insignificant quantities, and much is imported, but a lignite production of more than 4.5 million tons and extensive use of water power partly make up for the lack of coal. Austria's petroleum production assumed much greater proportions—and significance—between 1937 and 1950, during which period the tonnage increased from 32,000 to 1.5 million. The main field, discovered in 1933, is around Zistersdorf, 30 miles northeast of Vienna near the Czech border, which means, unfortunately, that the petroleum is in Soviet hands. Much of the equipment belonged to American companies before 1938, but the Soviets claimed that the Nazis had expropriated it and that it was, therefore, German property subject to Soviet confiscation. While Austria had to pay hard currency for petroleum for its own use, the Soviets exported Austria's own petroleum to satellite countries—or even Switzerland—and pocketed the income. When or if Austria regains control over its petroleum, the use and exports of it will be a great bulwark to its economy. Metal ores are found in wide variety, but only the Styrian iron ore is of great economic importance. Austria is the chief source of iron ore in central Europe. Graphite and magnesite, both produced in Styria, are also significant: Austria produces as much magnesite as all the rest of the countries of the world combined.

Austria's iron and steel industry was expanded under German control of the country to nearly twice its 1938 capacity. The old heavy industries center of Donawitz-Leoben-Graz was expanded, and a large new plant was installed on the Danube at Linz. The total Austrian output by 1951 was at the rate of approximately 1 million tons of crude steel annually, a production about equal to that of Spain but less than half that of the Saar and about two-thirds that of Sweden.

Austria also possesses a modest but significant metals engineering industry producing precision products in such centers as Linz and Steyr as well as around Vienna. The well-developed textile industry is concentrated in two areas at opposite ends of the country: around Vienna and, as has already been mentioned, in the Vorarlberg, especially at Bregenz. Virtually all raw materials for textile manufacturing must, however, be imported. Like Paris, Vienna specializes in quality and luxury production that requires taste and skill rather than large amounts of power and raw materials. The efforts being made in Austria at mid-century to expand industry increased the level of output by 1950 to nearly 50 per cent more than in 1938. These efforts were directed toward specialization in a modest number of products that, like the Vienna manufactures, demand painstaking finishing, expert skill and workmanship, and good taste and original ideas. Austria cannot become a great mass-producer of goods. Its factories tend to be small: three fourths of all plants employ less than 100 workers. Such specialization corresponds well with the power Austria has available—hydroelectricity.

The stimulus to Austria's great hydroelectric development came after creation of a small Austria in 1920 and after the coal of Bohemia and the oil of Galicia had been lost. A good beginning was made by 1930, and, by 1938, 2,400 billion kilowatts was generated annually. By 1950 this amount had exactly doubled, giving Austria a hydroelectric output equal to that of Spain, nearly half that of Switzerland, and nearly a third that of France. The expansion of water power sites under the German-Austrian union was continued after 1950. Under construction in 1951, the great Tauern power works on the northern slopes of the Gross Glockner and near Kaprun in the Salzach Valley will be one of Europe's largest when completed. Main works long in use are the Achen See and Gerlos in the eastern Tirol, Obernberg on the Inn on the northwestern frontier, and several smaller ones in Steyr northwest of Graz.

The hydroelectric network of western Austria was systematized primarily to serve its own area in addition to serving the industries and towns of Bavaria, to which the electricity was exported. The work done by the Germans on Austrian water power plants during World War II was primarily to increase power for German industries. However, the result was that the network of western Austria was separate from that of the east. The two regions were better integrated by mid-century. Export of hydroelectricity to neighboring countries on a large scale is one of Austria's aims. But Austria also hopes that eventually it can decrease its coal imports by one half, or approximately 2.5 million tons a year.

The Outlook

In spite of the numerous serious handicaps—geographical, economic, and political—under which Austria labors, the country still has many assets: the Alps, which attract thousands of tourists in summer as well as in winter, and Vienna, which through the special character of its culture not only attracts many visitors in normal times but also continues to produce a variety of manufactures that reflect her unique cultural ability and that have always enjoyed a high reputation. The function of Austria as the merging point of many of the economic activities and cultural aspects of central Europe cannot logically be taken away. But, as is true of so many parts of Europe and of the rest of the world, the normal function can be almost disastrously corrupted: thus, whereas eastern Austria—and especially Vienna—should function as a common meeting ground for central and southeastern European cultures, it has become a zone of contention, and a barrier exists where geography encourages a merging.

The failure of the Western Powers and the Soviets to come to an agreement regarding a peace treaty for Austria is one of the most serious impediments Austria must face. The upheavals that the country experienced during the first half of the twentieth century imposed enormous difficulties on a country that, at the height of the trials, was unable to determine its own destiny: defeat in World War I, reduction to a fraction of its former size, a great depression, annexation by Nazi Germany, destruction during World War II, political and economic chaos in the postwar period, occupation by armies that had theoretically come simply to "liberate" it. Nevertheless, with great help from the Western Allies—especially the United States—Austria survived and should do well if a status resembling normalcy can return. The country may have to seek economic union with Germany—not a political union, however—in order to be economically viable. To such an arrangement there should be no great objection. Austria's commercial position—already a strong one because of the central position of Vienna in the north-south and east-west rail net—would be greatly improved with reopening of the Danube to reasonably free movement of goods from Bavaria to the Black Sea. Actual construction of adequate canals connecting the Danube with the river systems of the Rhine, Elbe, and Oder would not only be a potent stimulus to Austria but would also have a strongly beneficial effect on trade all over Europe. Such canals have long been planned and discussed, but work is yet to begin. Failure to execute bold plans like these canal projects is one example of Europe's seeming inability to realize its full potentialities. Lack of political integration is partly responsible for such failures. With the added complexity of the Iron Curtain, bold plans are even more difficult to put into operation.

· 39 ·

Hungary (Magyarorszag)

Like Austria, Hungary since 1919 has been a "rump state" in comparison with its much greater extent under the Hungarian Empire, and during the interwar years it commonly referred to itself as "dismembered Hungary." Despite some similarity between the two states in location, size, climate, and density of population, as well as in loss of most of their former territory, Hungary presents marked contrast to Austria in one essential respect: although Austria lacks an adequate geographical background for its huge capital city, Hungary comprises an excellent geographical unit. Moreover, whereas Austria between 1920 and 1938 seemed to lack also the vital energy to recover and furthermore seemed reconciled to its fate, Hungary displayed vitality and vigorously worked toward reacquisition of at least some of its former territory. After World War II, an additional contrast was introduced when Hungary became a fullfledged Soviet satellite, while Austria was occupied by the Big Four powers and only its eastern part was under Soviet influence.

It is difficult to evaluate with any degree of confidence the relations existing before World War I between the Hungarian nucleus—the Magyars—of the old Austro-Hungarian Empire and the other ethnographic groups of that country, because the evidence varies widely according to the source from which it comes. It is clear, however, that the attitude of superiority displayed by the Magyars toward their subject peoples aroused resentment. And, although several groups of peoples formerly included in Hungary were far from content after their shift following World War I to other affiliations, there was little evidence of strong desire among them to return to the old conditions. However, those Magyars—about 3 million of them—who came under foreign rule in several of the new states agitated for return to Hungarian administration. Indeed, the very fact that so many Magyars were not included in the boundaries of the new Hungary created by the Treaty of Trianon (1920) was one reason why "dismembered Hungary" clamored for boundary revisions. Another reason for special Hungarian dissatisfaction with the treaty was that the country lost almost all its natural resources and advantages except those pertaining to agriculture. In general, Hungary felt that it had been more severely dealt with than had any other defeated power.

Achievement by Nazi Germany of a dominant position in southeastern Europe in the early years of World War II gave Hungary what it thought was an opportunity to regain some of its lost territories. It joined the German camp and was, indeed, given part of Czechoslovakia and, again through German courtesy, a segment of Rumania—Transylvania. Reacquisition of Transylvania brought back the isolated Szeklers, descendants of Magyars who left the Pannonian Plain in the twelfth and thirteenth centuries to serve as frontier guards against the Tatars. Moreover, in 1941 Hungary took part in the occupation of Yugoslavia, in spite of the fact that it had signed a treaty of friendship with that country a short time before. Hungarian payment to Germany for these gains was high: Magyars fought and were killed in large numbers on the Russian front, and the country itself suffered widespread devastation when Russian armies invaded the Danube basin to force back the Germans. Budapest was defended block by block; and after the bitter fighting was over one of the most charming cities in Europe was left in ruins.

The aftermath of World War II deprived Hungary of the territory she had held temporarily and even brought a minute loss of pre-1938 territory: Czechoslovakia was awarded an increase of 25 square miles of Hungarian territory to expand the Bratislava bridgehead. Moreover, Hungary—in spite of election results to the contrary—was gradually forced to submit to communist control exercised by a small but well-organized minority that had the active support of the Soviet occupational authorities. Thus, at mid-century it lay behind the Iron Curtain. Soviet control brought many aspects of Russification, which the proud Magyar would logically resent, since he has never played the role of servant and has even long been characterized as an arrogant master. He has been a patriot above everything, with all the assets and liabilities of that characteristic. Under the well-disciplined communist surface a solid base of determined protest seemed to exist in Hungary, if the many arrests, executions, and flights by anti-communists are correctly interpreted to indicate such protest. The enduring and the changing geographic aspects of the land of Hungary, one of the mid-century Soviet satellites, are discussed in the following sections.

Structure and Relief

In general terms, Hungary occupies most of the flat floor of the great Alpine depression surrounded by the Carpathians, Alps, and Dinaric system, with numerous evidences of vulcanism along the lines of sinking. This depression was for a long time an inland sea basin, until rivers filled it with alluvium, and today only a few shallow fresh-water lakes like Balaton and Neusiedler remain as relics of the former body of water. Much of the country is so flat that the rivers meander sluggishly across the landscape, and their courses are often bordered by swamps and marshes.

One of the few elevated sections is the Bakony Forest, an extension of the Alps that connects them with the southern ranges of the Slovakian Carpathians. It divides the country into two unequal sections: the Little Hungarian Plain (Kis Alföld), shared with Austria and Czechoslovakia, in the northwest, and in the east the Great Hungarian Plain (Nagy Alföld), whose edges extend into Czechoslovakia, Soviet Union, Rumania, and Yugoslavia. Along the northern frontier of Hungary east of the Danube is the southern section of the Slovakian Carpathians, a complex system that is partly volcanic and partly limestone with karst relief. North of Gyöngös are the Matrá Mountains, reaching 3,315 feet, the highest elevation in the country. The isolated and geologically complex hill mass of the Mecsék, north of Pécs in the southwestern part of Hungary, is an "island" of older rocks rising from beneath the surrounding young alluvial deposits. The Mecsék hills are significant because of their resources of coal and other minerals.

Climate and Soils

A very important feature of Hungary is the fact that the climate is transitional. A similar transitional quality is evident in the occupations, mode of life, and character of the people. Hungary lies squarely across the economic-cultural zone called Europe B (A15), and this is one significant element in Hungarian geography. Chapter 2 indicates that marine, continental, and Mediterranean qualities are all evident in the climate. Thus in A638 the comparatively uniform rainfall from April to October at Bratislava (Pressburg) just across the border from the northwest corner of the country is evidence of marine influence from the Atlantic. So, too, is the difference between the range of temperature here and at Szeged in the southeast. Both places, to be sure, have continental temperatures (30° F in January and 70° in July at Bratislava), but Szeged is decidedly the more continental of the two. This appears from the fact that in spite of more southerly latitude its temperature is not only higher in summer but also lower in winter than that at Bratislava. Its diminished rain-

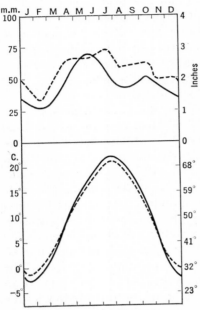

fall in winter is also a distinctively continental characteristic. And finally the decline of rainfall in summer at Szeged (not so marked at Bratislava) is evidence of typically Mediterranean influences. The total precipitation is only moderate—28 inches at Bratislava and 23 at Szeged—and the dry summers in much of the country are responsible for a kind of steppe climate with grassy vegetation rather than forests.

Most of the country has very fertile black soil, the Chernozem, like that of the grasslands of Russia. In some sections, however, the soil is unproductive, because poor drainage allows water to stand in undrained pools until it evaporates and impregnates the soil with salt. Sand dunes piled up by the winds in a dry but probably cold stage of the glacial period form a third type of soil, especially

A. Comparison of Precipitation (Top) and Temperature (Bottom) in Northwestern and Southeastern Hungary. Representative stations are Bratislava (just across border in Czechoslovakia), dashed lines, and Szeged, solid lines, in southeastern Hungary.

between the Danube and the Tisza, and north of Debrecen. Normally the dunes are covered with grass, which dies in dry seasons and allows the sand to be moved by the wind; however, afforestation has proved effective in keeping the dunes fixed. In some places, too, they are used for the production of crops such as fruits, which grow well in light soil. Between the dunes there are sometimes long, narrow, temporary ponds that dry up in summer and deposit salt.

Economy

Although Hungary lost a great part of its cropland after World War I, enough remains to enable the country to remain in the ranks of the grain-exporting countries. Of the total area, no less than 64 per cent is arable land—the highest such percentage among European countries. Cereals occupy 45 per cent of the total land area of the country, with acreage in wheat and corn about equal. Another 10 or 11 per cent is devoted to horticultural products such as vegetables and fruits, together with some industrial crops like hemp and sugar beets. Food for animals in the form of hay and pasture occupies another 26 per cent of the country. About 12 per cent, mostly in the mountains, is in forests, an area too small to supply the domestic requirements of timber. The remainder of the land is useless or is occupied by buildings and roads.

Over half a million acres of grapevines are found along the slopes of hills near Pécs in the south and around Tokaj in the northeast. Wine grapes are also produced on sand dunes, and, although they are perhaps lower in quality than the others, they are still of great value to the country. As export products, wheat and wheat flour come first in normal times, although other grains are exported in considerable quantities, along with minor amounts of sugar, beans, and wine.

Stock raising is carried on particularly with a view to the production of meat, as would normally be expected in a country where the climate approaches the dry steppe type rather than the moist marine type. Of the former grassy steppe, or Puszta, however, with its roaming herds of cattle and horses, there is not much left except in an area west of Debrecen; nevertheless, animals, and especially horses, play a significant role in the agricultural economy, as indicated by the large number of horses on farms and the innumerable horse-drawn farm wagons in the towns and cities. The exports of animal products consisted before World War II principally of cattle and swine, including lard, bacon, meat, and especially poultry.

The economic-cultural complex that the Magyars brought with them in the tenth century from their earlier home on the Russian steppes favored their adaptation to conditions on the Pannonian Plain. As nomadic herdsmen accustomed to utilization of grasslands, they found the semisteppe environment of the Alföld congenial and settled there, retaining their extensive grazing economy. It was not until the early nineteenth century that they reluctantly relinquished their pastoral life and engaged in tillage of the land. Such a cultural evolution not unnaturally led to a preference in the Magyars for large landholdings—characteristic in a grazing economy in a steppe area—and an accompanying distaste for manual labor on the farm. These attitudes were especially typical of the Magyar aristocracy, who mixed less biologically and, in some respects, even culturally with surrounding non-Magyar peoples. The proud, aristocratic Magyar was proverbial in the pre-World War I Hungarian Empire.

Thus, as a result of the system of land tenure and of the nature of the agricultural villages that developed on the plains, intensive utilization of the land was almost impossible during the nineteenth century. After World War I, however, land reforms broke up many of the large estates, although nearly a third of Hungary remained in large holdings. Two extremes of land tenure—tiny holdings and great ones—dominated Hungary's agrarian situation during the interwar period. Isolated farmhouses appeared on the open plains where lands were redistributed to small farmers, whereas elsewhere agricultural villages were the rule. The former concentration of the population in villages—some of which are compact and some of which extend for miles along a single street—reflect an old scheme of colonization intended to prevent raids by the then threatening Turkish neighbors. But the existence of such large settlements requires farmers to travel far from their homes to their fields; this consumes time for a man on foot or in a wagon, and *tanyas* or houses in the fields are occupied by some farm families in summer until after harvest.

Another great change in the Hungarian system of land tenure occurred after World War II, when nearly 6 million acres of large holdings were redistributed to 650,000 farmers in a final coup to the large Magyar estates. Agrarian Hungary is now a country of small plots, but the communist state controls the farms and disposes of the production. State farms and co-operative farms in imitation of the Soviet model have been introduced, as have machine tractor stations. In 1950 alone, the total area of state-owned agricultural farms increased from 705,900 acres to 1,075,900 acres, and the area of collective farms doubled to 1,054,300 acres. However, by 1950 only 15 per cent of Hungarian agriculture was nationalized.

The considerable industrial development of the pre-1920 Hungarian Empire was dislocated by erection of new frontiers for Hungary, and the new country devoted a great deal of effort during the interwar period to achieving better balance not only in its industrial structure but also between agriculture and industry. Some success was achieved in the effort, but much remained to be done. Therefore, after World War II, an ambitious program of industrialization was launched, and it received especial impetus when the communists came to power. All industries and transport facilities were nationalized, and high production goals were set.

For its industrialization, Hungary is not without mineral resources; however, there is little variety, and except for bauxite the reserves are small. Coal mines near Pécs and lignite beds in several localities, the most important of which is Salgotarján near the northern frontier, give Hungary part of the power for industry. Additional fuel is produced in the form of petroleum from the Lispe field. Developed after 1937, Lispe was the second (after the Rumanian fields) producing field in Europe outside the Soviet Union for a period during the 1940 decade; but production later declined to about half that of Austria and to less than that of the Netherlands. Hungary ranks with France and Yugoslavia in bauxite reserves, but the production is erratic. The small iron ore production is insufficient to supply the iron and steel industries of Miskolc at the foot of the Carpathians. One of the largest-scale projects in Hungarian industry was, in 1950–51, erection of a large iron and steel works at the little town of Dunapentele, 40 miles south of Budapest, on the Danube (Hungarian: Duna). The Dunapentele works is to be the basis of Hungary's communist-led struggle for establishment of a broad industrial basis to the country's economy. Shortage of iron ore will be the greatest difficulty, since Hungarian production is very modest (less than 100,000 tons annually); nevertheless, Hungary plans to produce as much steel annually as does Austria. In view of the lack of adequate raw materials, it is not unexpected that Hungarian industries are chiefly consumers of agricultural products: flour mills, breweries, beet sugar mills, distilleries (northeast of Debrecen), and other food and beverage industries. The textile industry (Budapest, Mohács, and in the northeast) supplies most domestic requirements, although it depends almost entirely on imported raw materials.

Population

With its present population of 9.2 millions, Hungary ranks among the smaller European states, comparable to the Netherlands and Belgium. The average density of population of about 250 per square mile is fairly high, especially for a primarily agricultural country, although the density falls quite low in the mountains and in sections of poorer soil. The population is essentially homogeneous, and the few minorities, of which the 500,000 Germans were

A. View of the partly rebuilt city of Pest from the hills of Buda across the Danube.
Courtesy of Sovfoto.

quite a problem, are now insignificant. Many of the Magyars who were left outside the 1920 frontiers gradually worked their way into the new state, and especially did they do so after 1948, when all states in the region became fellow members of the Cominform. However, many Magyars remain under alien administration. Czechoslovakia asked the United Nations to exchange its Magyars for the few Czechoslovaks then living in Hungary, and, in spite of refusal of official sanction, that procedure was undertaken. Even more difficult, because of the strained relations between Hungary and Yugoslavia, is the fate of the Magyars in northern Yugoslavia.

Budapest, which since the destruction of 1945 has regained its population of over a million, is excellently located where the Bakony Forest approaches the Danube and where the danger of floods is minimized. At the site of the city the Danube is intersected by a great east-west trade route. Thus, the city grew up as the center of the Hungarian section of the old Austro-Hungarian Empire and became by far the leading city in culture, trade, and manufacturing. It comprises the old Buda, full of historic buildings—many of them damaged in World War II—on the hills on the west side of the river, and the younger Pest expanding onto the lowland in the east. The broad Danube River, formerly laden with traffic, helped to make Budapest one of the most interesting cities of central Europe. The great damage suffered especially in 1944 was gradually being repaired in the postwar years: in 1950 the Stalin Bridge was opened. The traffic on the Danube has declined greatly because of political tension with Yugoslavia and the drop in trade with the west. The other Hungarian cities, even though they might reach a population of over 100,000, as do Szeged and Debrecen on the Tisza River, are little more than overgrown villages. Kecskemét, between the Danube and the Tisza, is a smaller place of the same type. Miskolc has already been mentioned as the center of heavy industries.

The State

Hungary is now one of the communist bastions against Yugoslavia and Western Europe. One wonders whether the Magyar leaders again have hope that, this time through Russian help, they may succeed in regaining part of the former empire, especially at the expense of Yugoslavia. Geographically quite strong in spite of small size, very compact in shape, with normally a surplus of agrarian products and enough power and minerals to favor some manufacturing, and above all with a very central Danubian location, Hungary would be a rather prosperous country in a co-operative Europe. Excluding the obvious and pervading problem common to all southeastern Europe and indeed all Europe, of Soviet expansionism and East-West antagonisms, one of Hungary's main problems is its relations with its neighbors. Czechoslovakia, Rumania, and Yugoslavia have not forgotten what Hungary did to them when they were helpless during World War II. Peace among the satellites (which, of course, do not include Yugoslavia) is preserved by the Soviet Union, but underlying tensions are still there.

Economic consequences of breakup of the Austro-Hungarian Empire still reverberate among the Danubian states. Re-establishment of some sort of Danubian federation at least on an economic basis if not a political one would be advantageous to Hungary. In such an organization, Hungary and its capital of Budapest would have a central position. Soviet efforts are, of course, somewhat directed toward a loose grouping in the region; but the dividing effects of the Iron Curtain—which severs Hungary and its neighbors from markets, raw materials, and cultural stimuli in the west—are severe hindrances to achievement of regional economic stability.

Hungary now has the Soviet Union as a neighbor on the northeast and as political and economic master in the homeland. After centuries of distrust of the Slavs and of actually serving as the dividing wedge between Slavic groups, Hungary is overwhelmed by Slavic (Russian) control. Observers cannot help wondering how Hungary likes the new role.

·40·
Yugoslavia (Jugoslavija)

After both world wars, events in Yugoslavia dramatically illustrated the significance of geographical influences and, in turn, the effects in the landscape of political and social upheavals. Among the countries of Europe, Yugoslavia is one of those that depart farthest from being genuine units both geographically and ethnographically. The lack of geographic unity is evident in the fact that the very rugged and inhospitable Karst region interposes a serious barrier between the northern plains, where most of the people live, and the coast, which would otherwise give easy access to the sea and the rest of the world. Acquisition after World War II of the port of Rijeka, the former Italian Fiume, with its good connections with the hinterland has, however, slightly improved the situation. The lack of ethnographic unity is suggested by the name of the Federal People's Republic of Yugoslavia—a combination of Slavic groups: Serbs, Croats, Slovenes, Montenegrins, and Macedonians. Even more revealing is the name originally adopted by the country when it became independent after World War I: Kingdom of the Serbs, Croats, and Slovenes. In spite of their related Slavic languages they show great cultural differences, based on their historical background and former cultural affiliations. To make the picture even more complex, there are many minorities, most of them with antinational tendencies. The Italians and Germans have now left Yugoslavia, but there are still large groups of Magyars, Albanians, Rumanians, and Bulgars who can be considered potentially dangerous to the new policy of the state.

The nucleus of Yugoslavia, as it was created after World War I, was the former Kingdom of Serbia; and the main problem pressing the new state was that of effectively uniting the nucleus with the newly obtained territories that had belonged to the Austro-Hungarian Empire and with the formerly independent little country of Montenegro. The new territories not only surpassed Serbia in size and number of inhabitants, but also, as far as the Croats and Slovenes were concerned, surpassed it culturally, since these two peoples

had been part of European culture while the rest of the peoples of
Yugoslavia had been under Turkish domination. Moreover, strong
religious differences further accentuated the human contrasts: the
Serbs are members of the Orthodox Church, whereas Croats and
Slovenes are Roman Catholic, and many of the Bosnians are Moslems. The effort made between 1920 and 1940 to bridge those differences was not successful. Moreover, the democratic form of government failed because ethnographic groups became political parties
and brought their antagonisms into the parliament. That no outward breakdown occurred was due partly to the dictatorial type of
government that developed, but also to the fact that all main groups
together faced the danger of antinational minorities and of the adverse feelings of neighboring countries that still had claims to parts
of Yugoslavia and waited for its collapse. It was a case of "united
we may stand; divided we will fall."

Nevertheless, strong discontent was partly responsible for the
rapid defeat of Yugoslavia in the spring of 1941 when Germany
struck. Temporarily, Yugoslavia, as it had been, disappeared from
the map: Slovenia was taken over by Italy and Germany; most of
Croatia became a so-called independent state; Germany, Italy, Rumania, Hungary, and Bulgaria took large sections as areas of occupation, and a small part—rump Serbia—was allowed to exist as a
kind of German satellite. But in the mountains the will for freedom became the basis for underground action that led to the defeat of local German forces; Yugoslavia liberated itself and was not
liberated by others, although the resistance forces received Allied
arms by parachute.

After 1945, the new Yugoslavia, which now includes most of former
Italian Istria, faced the very difficult task of reconstruction. There
was not only the complete ruin of most of the countryside but also
the feelings of hatred between groups that had taken different political sides, which themselves had ethnographic overtones. The
new state was again a dictatorship, this time of the communist type;
but, having learned from the past, it adopted the federal form of
government, recognizing ethnic differences and permitting the various groups a large measure of self-control. The six units of the
federation reflect the ethnographic groupings and geographic regions: Slovenia, Croatia, Bosnia and Hercegovina, Serbia, Montenegro, and Macedonia. The recognition of Macedonia as a unit
is a great step forward, because it has always been an area of conflicting sentiments. The Vojvodina district, north of Belgrade, with

its mixed population is now an autonomous province within Serbia, as is the Kosmet area in the mountain district in southeastern Serbia. Whether the new organization will work out successfully cannot be predicted after only the few years since 1945 that the reconstituted state has existed. By 1951 the arrangement seemed to work rather well, and such difficulties as existed were traceable less to the federal form of government than to the strong-arm communist control.

The geographical location of the country and the fierce love of independence of its fighting mountain peoples have influenced other significant events in Yugoslavia besides the nation's sudden decision to resist the German invasion in 1941 and its success in liberating itself in 1945. Proximity to the sphere of Russian influence brought Yugoslavia within the Soviet orbit in 1945, and for a while—despite the assistance rendered by UNRRA—the reborn state remained aggressively aloof from the United States and the "West." In a dramatic turn of events, however, Yugoslavia served notice on the Soviet Union in 1948 that it would not submit to Soviet domination any more than to that of any other country, and "Titoism" came to stand for a type of national communism. At that time, the location of Yugoslavia between East and West permitted it to turn westward for assistance in reconstruction and rehabilitation. The country thus faced westward out of sheer necessity for survival, although it retained a communist form of government that it declared was of a "purer" form than that of the Soviet Union. Nevertheless, the ring of Soviet satellites on the east made the independent stand of Yugoslavia an exceedingly dangerous one, and the loss of commercial relations with the Cominform countries was a severe blow to the Yugoslav economy.

Natural Regions

Considering that its size (98,826 square miles) is only slightly greater than that of the state of Wyoming, Yugoslavia has great diversity in its natural environment. The main Alps of central Europe end in its northwestern corner; the Dinaric Alps extend through its western part; the Balkan and Rhodope mountains of Bulgaria project into the east side; a plain lies in the northwest along the Sava, Drava, Danube, and Tisza (Slavic: Tisa) rivers; and the basins of the northward-flowing Morava and the southward-flowing Vardar form an intermediate region of chaotic and inhospitable mountains (A648).

Slovenian Alps. The northwestern corner of Yugoslavia includes
the southeastern section of the Alps. It has the same kind of relief,
climate, land utilization, and general culture as has the Alpine part
of Austria, and falls on the edge of the cultural zone called Europe
A. Forests cover the mountains and are sufficient for a small timber

A. Natural Regions of Yugoslavia. The Karst region continues northwestward into
the Istrian Peninsula, added after World War II. That portion of the Great Hungarian Plain lying in Yugoslavia is called the Vojvodina.

industry. There is more grassland than cropland, and dairying is
well developed except in the lower and more fertile basins like
those of Maribor and Ljubljana where rye, wheat, and fruits are
raised in well-protected locations. As a source of water power and
timber supply, and as an area of scenic attractions for tourists, this
mountain section is of great value to Yugoslavia. Its progressive
Slovene population of a million or more with its own Slavic tongue
has, as a result of long inclusion in the Austrian Empire, habits and
ideals much more akin to those of Austria than to those of the

Serbs, Albanians, and Macedonians to the southeast; consequently, the Slovenes resent efforts made by the Serbs of Belgrade to dominate them.

Dalmatian Coastal Zone. In Dalmatia the longitudinal limestone ranges of the Dinaric mountain system drop steeply toward the Adriatic. Along the partly drowned coast hundreds of islands represent submerged ridges of this system. The only easily habitable area consists of an extremely narrow coastal plain. The mountains rise so steeply that they allow room for only small settlements and restrict the extension of agriculture and fruit growing, which are the main occupations.

The mild Mediterranean winter climate (Dubrovnik has an average January temperature of 47° F and an annual rainfall of 60 inches), with the protection afforded by the high plateau against the cold winds or bora, especially in the autumn, has made the cultivable parts of this section a wonderful garden land. The many coastal islands, the colored limestone rocks, the subtropical vegetation merging on the lower slopes into the Mediterranean scrub or maquis, the ancient villages built along the hillsides—all these combine to make this Dalmatian Riviera a region of unusual beauty and attractiveness to tourists.

The economic value of the Dalmatian coast is limited not only by the small space available for agriculture, but also by the difficulties of communication. The obstacle to transportation interposed by the steep mountain wall and the unproductive nature of the immediate hinterland at present retard the development of such places as Split (Spalato), Dubrovnik (the old republic of Ragusa), and Kotor (Cattaro) on the beautiful Gulf of Kotor. Nevertheless, these seacoast towns of Yugoslavia with their quiet old harbors, which once shared the Adriatic prosperity of Italy when Venice was in her glory, are being increasingly promoted as tourist resorts—as well they might be—and may yet develop into active modern communities.

After World War II, the former Italian territories comprising the enclave of Zadar (Zara), the coastal islands east of the Istrian Peninsula and—what is more important—most of Istria itself were acquired by Yugoslavia. The addition of Istria and of the harbor of Fiume (now Rijeka) meant success in the long effort to bring those areas of essentially Slavic population within the confines of the Yugoslav state. The problem of Istria dates back to the period after World War I, when Italy pushed its boundaries into Slav-

occupied territory against the strong protest of the then new Yugoslavia. On the peninsula, a narrow coastal zone with Italian inhabitants is succeeded by a rather high limestone plateau—the famous Karst—with a population of Slovenes and Croats. In the
Treaty of Versailles the coast prevailed over the hinterland, but
in the treaty of 1947 the hinterland prevailed over the coast. Only

A. The Gulf of Kotor amid the mountains of what was once the state of Montenegro: terrace agriculture along the shore. An example of the ruggedness of the
Dalmatian coast.

the city of Trieste and its immediate vicinity were not transferred
to Yugoslavia in 1947 but received an autonomous status as the
Free Territory of Trieste. As friction over Istria continued between Yugoslavia and Italy, the northern zone (with Trieste) was
occupied by British and American troops and the zone to the south
was occupied by Yugoslavia (see discussion in Chapter 30).

The plateau is sparsely populated, with agricultural activity limited to the fertile red soil pockets in the limestone structure,
whereas the coast is typically Mediterranean in climate and agriculture, with vineyards and fruit gardens. The Italian population has
left that part of Istria now Yugoslav, and Slavic people have taken
over. The former Italian naval base of Pola, now called Pula, was,
after 1945, little used for the purpose for which it was developed.

Dinaric Alps and the Karst Region. From the high land north of Rijeka (formerly Fiume) to Albania in the south the country back of the Yugoslav coast consists of a lofty karst plateau—the very name was derived from this region—some sections of which exceed 8,000 feet in elevation. The successive longitudinal ridges of bare white limestone and even the valleys are mostly unproductive despite the heavy rainfall, which is as high as 180 inches, the heaviest in Europe. As is typical of karst regions, agriculture is made difficult because rain dissolves the limestone and carries it away in solution instead of permitting the formation of soil. Another trouble is that this same process of solution causes the limestone to be full of crevices and caverns into which surface water disappears and drains away very rapidly. As a result, there is little uniformly distributed or available ground water, and vast areas have no integrated surface drainage. Nevertheless, many of the *poljes,* or structural depressions often enlarged by solution, are floored with good soil and are cultivated. Even small sinkholes (called *dolines*) with a patch of soil at the bottom become sites of cultivation. On some of the slopes, too, there is grass for sheep. Therefore, the sparse population is found mainly around the poljes and where there is grass. The cold winters on the plateau offer a striking contrast to those of the neighboring Dalmatian coast. The only town of any importance, Mostar, is situated well to the south in an open valley that permits the Mediterranean climatic influences to penetrate 40 or 50 miles inland. As a barrier to both climate and transportation, the Dinaric ranges and the Karst thrust themselves upon the Yugoslavs as a challenge to their power to conquer geographic disadvantages and to open a front door through which to reach the rest of the world.

Bosnian Region. Toward the east the nature of the Karst changes. Loamy soil covers the limestone; rivers flow in valleys on the earth's surface instead of underground. Although there is less rain than farther west, grass and forests of beech, fir, and oak cover the soil; and wheat and corn as well as fruit are raised in increasing quantities. This is the heart of former Austrian Bosnia, with Sarajevo (118,000) as its center. It was in Sarajevo in 1914 that a Bosnian student of Serbian nationality killed Archduke Ferdinand, heir to the Austrian throne, and touched off World War I. The influence of the long Turkish rule appears in the great number of Moslems and the oriental appearance of most of the towns and villages. The climate is continental, with cold winters and mild summers, as indicated by data for Sarajevo, where an altitude of 2,100 feet keeps the average down to 31° F in January and 67° in July.

The Bosnian region slopes northward and shows increasing agricultural development as it reaches lower altitudes and lower relief on its approach to the plain of the Sava River. The vast wealth of its forests has been greatly depleted by long exploitation, but a great deal remains on which to base a modern timber industry. Cattle raising is carried on widely but is not of a very high standard; the same is true of swine raising.

Great Vojvodina Plain. The northern portion of Yugoslavia, except in the west, consists of the Vojvodina, the southern part of the Alföld or Great Hungarian Plain, which extends along the Danube where it is joined by the Drava, Sava, and Tisza rivers. The Bačka section between the Danube and the Tisza is occupied by a mixed population, including many Magyars; and east of the Tisza is the famous Banat, where merged ethnographic groups made the drawing of new boundaries after World War I so difficult and where national antagonisms are still strong. The origin, relief, soil, climate, and land utilization of the Vojvodina are essentially the same as those of the Hungarian portion of the plain and are discussed in the preceding chapter.

As an agricultural area the Vojvodina is of outstanding importance for Yugoslavia and, as the Yugoslav "breadbasket," has made the country one of Europe's grain exporters. Wheat and corn (maize) are the principal crops, along with grapes, tobacco (especially in the western Bačka), and even some rice. Horses and swine are raised in great numbers. The broad rivers are bordered by swamps and are connected by canals built partly for drainage, and partly to improve transportation; the monotony of the endless plain is broken only by a few sand hills.

A dense farming population of very mixed ethnic composition, including Magyars as well as Croats and Serbs, distinguishes this section from the rest of Yugoslavia. The settlements are of the same type as in Hungary, and great overgrown villages stand far apart with broad, open fields between them. The city of Subotica in the northern Bačka is the most important of these agricultural towns and has become the principal railroad junction.

The Slavonian Upland between the Sava and Drava rivers and the Croatian Upland farther southwest are not properly classified with the actual Vojvodina, but nevertheless they have slopes so gentle and so covered with fertile loess that the cultivation of wheat and corn is general. In the Croatian Upland, in contrast to the real plain, forests occur on the high sections; and walnuts, chestnuts, and plums, as well as wine grapes, give variety to the crops.

South of the Vojvodina, the northern section of Serbia—and especially the lower Morava Valley—resembles the Croatian Upland. It slopes toward the north and drops sharply to the Danube and Sava. Used mainly for grain and fruit—and in particular for wheat, corn, and plums—it was Serbia's most productive area. The former extensive oak forests, where the acorns supported herds of swine, have now mostly disappeared and have been supplanted by cropland.

Yugoslavia's two chief cities are found near the two ends of the Vojvodina with its southern fringe of low uplands. Zagreb (Agram), with a population of 291,000 and serving as the capital of Croatia, is located at the transition of the low Sava plain into the Croatian Alps. As might be expected from its far northwestern position, its cultural traditions are the most advanced in Yugoslavia, along with those of Ljubljana (Laibach), capital of Slovenia.

Belgrade (Serb: Beograd) is built on the high south bank of the Danube at the confluence of that river and the Sava. It owes much of its historic importance to its location near the northern end of the Morava Valley, up which a great trade route leads to Istanbul on the eastern branch and Thessaloníki on the southern. As the capital of the enlarged Yugoslav state, it developed rapidly between 1920 and 1940 and, along with reconstruction after World War II, received additional stimulus after 1945, having a population in 1948 of 388,246. It is the junction for the great international railroads from northern and western Europe to the Balkans, and it is also Yugoslavia's most important Danube port.

Central and Southern Highlands. The rest of Yugoslavia is a maze of highlands and mountains. East of Belgrade and the Morava River a curved link of mountains extends southward from the Transylvanian Alps to the Balkans. It is cut in two by the gorge of the Danube, where rocks and rapids at the famous Iron Gate once impeded navigation; however, this hindrance has now been removed, and locomotives on a railroad track help boats upstream. The gorge is so steep-sided and narrow that it was very difficult to build a railroad through it. In the mountains south of the Iron Gate stock raising on the rugged grasslands is the usual means of livelihood. The Timok Basin south of the Iron Gate, with its partly Bulgarian population, belongs regionally with the Walachian Plain of Rumania. There corn and wheat are again the principal crops.

A hundred miles, or less, straight south of Belgrade and just south of the Western Morava River, the landscape changes. High mountains with deeply eroded valleys cause the country to be a sparsely populated area with few activities aside from stock raising on the grassy slopes. This rough mountain country is the real home of the Serbian people, to which they have more than once retired in time of stress for protection and to regain strength. Indeed, in World War II, it was to these mountains that so many Yugoslavs retreated to escape the Germans and then, after conducting a clever and resourceful resistance to all attempts to clear them out, emerged to drive the Germans out in 1945.

Still farther south the physiography is of the Balkan type, with high mountain blocks separated by structural depressions. Two great trade routes have given this region an international importance. One is the route southward from Belgrade up the Morava River, across a low pass to Skopje, and then down the Vardar Valley to the sea at Thessaloníki in Greece. A branch of the Morava route, swinging southeastward at Niš to Sofia and the Maritsa Valley in Bulgaria, is still more important, because from the days of the Romans and Crusaders down to our own it has been the main route to Istanbul. The other route runs eastward from Shkodër (Scutari) in Albania via Prizren to join the Morava route. In ancient times this was the great land route from Rome to Byzantium, but now it has no importance and is not even followed by a railway. The mountains here in southern and central Yugoslavia are heavily forested, and the population, mostly of Albanian stock, is concentrated in the basins where agriculture is possible. Sheepherding is also widely practiced.

East of the upper Morava the high, and mostly unproductive, Rhodope massif marks the boundary toward Bulgaria. Of much greater economic value is the southward projection of Yugoslavia into what was once Macedonia. Here too the high mountains continue, often with glacial relief, but basins become more numerous and are of greater extent than those farther north. On the higher elevations, grassland with stock raising predominates; but in the basins the climate is milder, tending more to the Mediterranean type, and good crops of grains, tobacco, and fruits are raised. Of the many towns, Bitola (Monastir) and Skopje (Skoplje, Üsküb) are the most important, the latter being at the intersection of the Prizren route and the great Vardar trade route southeastward to Thessaloníki.

Chaotic relief, frequent wars, lack of roads and railroads, and bad government long combined to retard this area, but it has recently shown signs of material improvement. The Vardar Valley opens toward the south, and its vegetation is Mediterranean in character. The Serbian part of the Struma Basin farther east, with the town of Strumica, has a similar climate. The products are various, comprising wheat, rye, and tobacco, as well as grapes, figs, apricots, and the like.

All along this Macedonian section are felt strong Bulgarian influences based partly on ethnic affinity between the Bulgarians and the Macedonians, giving rise to frequent local demonstrations against the government.

Land Utilization

The bulk of Yugoslavia's agricultural production comes from her share of the Danube basin—the Vojvodina—and the side valleys of the Danube, extending into the mountain regions of Croatia, Bosnia, and Serbia. The yield of grain is, however, relatively low, and bumper crops are often followed by deficit years if the capricious summer rains fail, as they did in the crucial year of 1950. Fruit is abundant on the neighboring hills—as in much of the entire country—with plum trees a specialty. Other than in Vojvodina and adjacent uplands, agriculture is important only locally in the basins of Macedonia, the poljes of the Karst, and the few spots along the Dalmatian coast where level land is available. The mountains themselves are still forested to a large extent, and whatever agriculture is practiced is mainly of a subsistence type. Cattle, swine (still fed in some areas on the acorns of the oak forests), horses and water buffalo used for farm work, chickens enough under normal conditions to be fattened for export and to furnish eggs for export, sheep, and goats are raised on most farms in appreciable numbers. The number of cattle, for example, reached 5.2 millions in 1949, nearly a million more than in 1938, despite the great losses during World War II. Yugoslav cattle were thus twice as numerous as those in Sweden and the Netherlands and one third as numerous as those of France; however, the quality of breeding was much lower, and the percentage of fine dairy cows was very much smaller in Yugoslavia.

Postwar communist Yugoslavia made great efforts to increase agricultural production through mechanization, modernization of farm methods, and collectivism; but it was not very successful in its efforts because of the refusal by many of the farmers to submit to government control and to deliver their grain to state agents. The rebellion of the farmers against state requirements for grain deliveries forced the government in 1950 to modify the schedule of deliveries, although it can be presumed that the over-all plan will eventually be executed. In 1950 collective farms numbered 7,000, and the share of nationalized agriculture was one fourth of the arable land of the country.

Mineral Resources and Manufacturing

Yugoslavia has at least small amounts of many kinds of minerals (A657), as well as some water power, and, because some of the minerals are rather scarce in Europe, the importance of Yugoslav production is greater than the actual amounts suggest. Except for coal, Yugoslavia is one of Europe's richest countries in mineral wealth, on which it based much of its hope in the 1947–51 Five Year Plan. The rather small amount of coal is partly offset by a much larger lignite production. The oil production along the southern border of the Danube basin is small (62,000 tons in 1949), but it is still a recent development. Copper ore is a chief Yugoslav asset, the principal mines being at Bor southeast of Belgrade. Iron ore is locally important, but the total production is, for instance, only one-fourth that of Luxembourg. The main deposits are in northwestern Bosnia-Hercegovina and northeast of Sarajevo, with combined reserves exceeding those of northern Spain. There is an appreciable production of lead and zinc; and manganese, antimony, and chromium are mined in sufficient quantities to make them sizable exports. With the acquisition of Istria, Yugoslavia gained the Idria mercury deposits—some of the world's best; as for bauxite Yugoslavia mines about one-half the production of France (Europe's leading bauxite-producing country) and about the same amount that Hungary mines.

Exports of mineral products are of great significance for Yugoslavia, because there is a ready market for the minerals, and the sales provide Yugoslavia with funds to buy things she needs, such as machinery. Production of local iron ore and coal was used for a domestic steel output of 435,000 tons in 1949, and plans for expansion call for doubling this production during the 1950's. In most other respects, manufacturing is still in its infancy, although Yugoslavia possesses the raw materials for an appreciable industrialization, a fact that it recognized in the Five Year Plan that ended

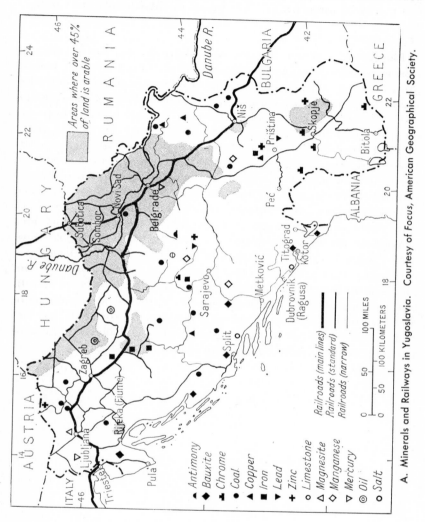

A. Minerals and Railways in Yugoslavia. Courtesy of *Focus*, American Geographical Society.

in 1951. The ambition, as shown by the plan, is to release the country from its one-sided agricultural economy and to balance farming with industry. However, shortage of coking coal and especially shortage of capital and equipment are serious obstacles to increased industrialization. Certainly expansion of manufacturing is a hopeful step in the country, although it became clear in 1948 when Yugoslavia split with the Cominform that the peasant was not to be forgotten as a key factor in the Yugoslav economy.

The Yugoslav State

The break between Moscow and Belgrade in 1948 meant the closing of most boundary traffic, except for a few (usually empty) through trains. Even the Danube, under the Russian-controlled Danube Commission, is now of little value to Yugoslavia, although traffic between Rumania and Hungary is maintained. Improvement of relations with Greece after 1948 resulted in the reopening of the railroad to Thessaloníki and the potential use of that harbor, where Yugoslavia formerly had a free zone. Connections to the west, now greatly increased in importance, are limited to the railroad to Trieste and the use of the Dalmatian harbors, of which only Rijeka has good railway connection with the interior. In spite of the constant danger of aggression by the eastern neighbors, Yugoslavia continues its efforts for improvement of its economic base. Thus, curiously enough, the communist state of Yugoslavia became by 1950 a bulwark against expansion by the Soviet Union, and was obliged to re-establish certain ties—chiefly economic—with states on its western façade that it had earlier held in contempt. Such contradictory events reflect the spirit of the Balkans: unwillingness to submit to foreign domination and determination to make the best of limited geographical possibilities.

·41·
Rumânia (Romania)

Rumania presents one of the most distressing pictures of man-land relationships among all the European countries. It is far worse than Italy, worse than Spain, and as bad as Greece. The tragic relationship is a curious one, since Rumania has many aspects that should contribute to its providing a rather comfortable milieu for its people. After an examination of the country's territorial evolution and regional framework, an analysis of the maladjustments will be made.

The Rumanian People and State

Origin of People. The Rumanians like to be regarded as descendants of the Dacians and Romans. The Dacians were the natives who lived in the Roman imperial province of Dacia, the center of which coincided with modern Walachia. With establishment of Roman control in the second century, protecting walls were built against the nomadic tribes farther north in the plain of southern Russia. One part of this Wall of Trajan extended from the Carpathians southeastward to Galaţi, where the Danube finally turns east. From there southward the broad floodplain of the Danube with its many channels and swamps afforded protection. Where the course of the river changes from eastward to northward, another section of wall, still recognizable, runs eastward to the shore of the Black Sea at Constanţa. During the 160 to 175 years of Roman control, Roman traders and merchants came to Dacia and intermarried with some of the Dacians. Latin as a regional language was widely used, and other Roman cultural influences were appreciable. When the control by the Roman Empire weakened after the middle of the third century, the walls no longer served their purpose, and the Walachian lowlands were open to invasion by the nomads. Wave after wave of invaders swept over them, often leaving an empty waste of burned villages and ruined fields. The terrified population sought refuge in the northern mountains and in Transylvania.

In later and more peaceful periods, the Romanized Dacians, who had become mountaineers, ventured again into the lowlands where life was easier than in the mountains. There they mixed with the remnants of the invaders, among whom Slavic tribes had been most numerous. The result is a biological mixture in which the traits of the Slavic language speakers are dominant, but which preserves remnants of the old Dacians with some Roman intermixture. This new mixed population, the Vlachs or Rumanians, finally occupied the lowlands of the Danube, Moldavia, and Bessarabia, as well as the mountains of Transylvania. The Rumanian language—and the very name of the country—preserve the Roman influences of 1,800 years ago. As was discussed in Chapter 12, the language has many Latin affinities, although the rural language is strongly Slavic in character, indicating that the Slav element is stronger in the peasant people. For centuries political organization was again and again prevented in this tideland of influences from the west, northeast, and southeast, and foreigners extended their power over regions inhabited by Rumanians.

Territorial Evolution. The gradual extension of Turkish power brought Constantinople under Turkish control in 1453; but, for a century before the conquest of Constantinople, the Turks had rampaged in southeastern Europe. By 1462 Walachia and Moldavia were under Turkish domination, and for the next 360 years the lands of present Rumania were under Ottoman control. Indeed, the Turks besieged Vienna twice, in 1527 and 1683, in unsuccessful attempts to conquer central Europe. It is to the exercise of control by a foreign power that did little in a constructive way for centuries that the cultural retardation of Rumania and much of the Balkan Peninsula is partly traceable. Certainly the long centuries of complete subjugation of Rumania to Turkish domination has had far-reaching consequences. Rumania, like Italy, was late in unifying: although the Turks were forced to withdraw in 1822, the principalities of Walachia and Moldavia did not unite until 1878. But, even then, Rumania was only beginning.

Much of the failure of Rumania to unite earlier resulted from the interplay between Russian and Austrian interests, and it was only when both sides were weak—after World War I—that Rumania was able to obtain its largest size (A661). Thus, after 1920, Rumania consisted of the following units: the Rumanian core land of Walachia-Moldavia; the Dobruja, obtained in 1878 from

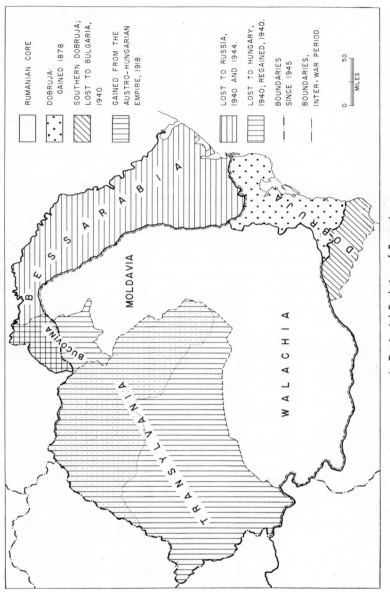

A. Territorial Evolution of Rumania.

Russia in exchange for southern Bessarabia; Bessarabia, taken from Russia in 1918 on ethnic and historical grounds; Bucovina, formerly Austrian; and Transylvania and the eastern edge of the Alföld, formerly Hungarian (compare A178, A180, and A182 while studying this section). The addition of Bessarabia, the Bucovina, and Transylvania and the eastern Banat more than doubled the country's territory to 114,000 square miles.

At this stage in its evolution it included, with one exception, all the Rumanians; however, in order to do so, it embraced many minorities who became a major source of trouble to the new, enlarged state. Among the included minorities were many Magyars in the Banat as well as in the southeastern corner of Transylvania (the Szeklers); Ukrainians, Ruthenes, and Great Russians in Bessarabia and the northern Bucovina; Germans, rather scattered but with a major concentration in southern Transylvania; Bulgars in the southern Dobruja; not to mention smaller numbers (but still in the thousands) of Jews, Turks, Gypsies, Poles, Greeks, Albanians, Armenians, and others! All together, the minority groups amounted to 28 per cent of the population of the country as a whole. In their respective sections, the main groups were sometimes as much as 75 per cent of the population—or even more. Perhaps a progressive state using a system of democratic federation might have been able to administer this ethnographic jigsaw puzzle, but Rumania certainly did not show much ability in that line.

The day of reckoning came in 1940, when Britain and France were unable to assist Rumania and it was subjected to a political squeeze by Russia, Hungary, and Bulgaria. Russia took over Bessarabia and the northern part of Bucovina; Hungary, with German co-operation, took northern Transylvania and thus reincorporated the area occupied by the Szeklers; and Bulgaria occupied the southern Dobruja. Rumania lost 20,000 square miles of territory in these seizures. Germany dominated Rumania itself, and Rumania was forced to take part in the German attack on Russia, having been promised the lost territories of Bessarabia, the Bucovina, and even a part of adjacent Russia. Rumania did, indeed, regain these lost territories for a brief period during the war, but with the defeat of Germany (and Rumania) in 1944 and arrival of the Red Army, Rumania surrendered the territories again. However, she regained northern Transylvania from Hungary, although she had to agree to Bulgaria's possession of the southern Dobruja. The peace treaty signed in Paris in 1947 officially recognized Rumania as shown within the heavy dot-dash boundary of A661. Thus Rumania in 1951 covered an area of 91,600 square miles, only 80 per cent of that of 1938, and had a population of 16 millions.

However, the dizzying ethnographic complexity has been somewhat resolved. Transfer of Bessarabia and northern Bucovina to the Soviet Union and of southern Dobruja to Bulgaria automatically reduced the number of non-Rumanians, and population transfers further reduced their number. Many Magyars and Germans still remain, however, and Yugoslav elements in the Banat were used to denounce Yugoslavia after its "Titoist" withdrawal from the Cominform in 1948.

The foregoing review of Rumania's complex territorial evolution indicates the significance of the country's location in an area in which various spheres of influence merge and conflict. Such an evolution—especially the major territorial losses and gains of the twentieth century—obviously has profound effects on the country's economic structure and viability. And, finally, it seems to indicate a certain lack of some sort of geographical cohesion in the area of Rumania.

This lack of cohesion is mainly attributable to the fact that the area occupied by a Rumanian population is divided into three definite and in some ways antagonistic geographical regions. One, Transylvania, looks westward. Another, the Walachian-Moldavian core, is self-centered and is poorly related to any other large region. Transylvania and the Walachian-Moldavian core are separated by the rugged barrier of the Carpathian and Transylvanian mountains—a barrier that is not insuperable, to be sure, but that has functioned as an effective divide. The third region is the low Dobruja Plateau near the Black Sea, a region essential to the development of Rumania, because the Black Sea coast provides the main commercial outlet of the country. Dobruja is separated from the lowlands, however, by the great Danube River and its wide, swampy floodplain; and the plateau also merges into the northern Balkan Lowland so that it has a natural connection with Bulgaria. The following section examines the Rumanian regions in greater detail.

Structure and Relief

The Mountains and the West. Physiographically there is great diversity in this country whose economic situation, as will be shown later, is so difficult. Even before it reaches Rumania the

broad band of the Czechoslovakian or Forest Carpathians narrows
down to one range—the Moldavian Carpathians (A664).   Both far-

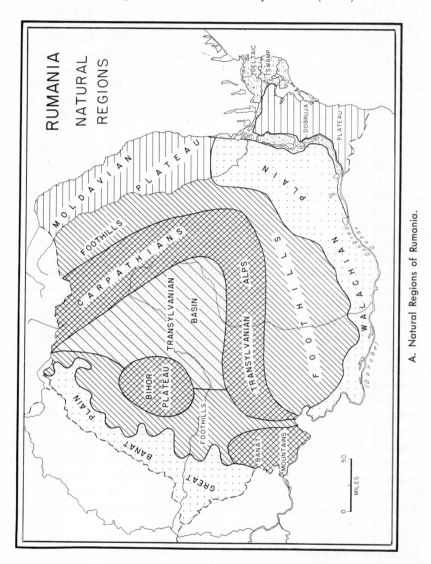

A. Natural Regions of Rumania.

ther west and in Rumania the Carpathians consist mostly of sandstone with rounded summits of low elevation that range between
3,500 and 5,500 feet, with the highest peak reaching 8,320 feet.

The barrier is, however, broken by several low passes. Beech trees, with pine forests on the higher elevations, cover a great part of the range, and the timber is brought down by aerial railways to the rivers of the Moldavian upland.

Bending toward the west in their southern or Transylvanian section, the Carpathians become of more complex structure. The existence of broad level plateaus and terraces, the fact that the river courses often break through ranges instead of avoiding them, and the presence of longitudinal depressions now occupied by rivers— all indicate a physiographic development similar to that described in Chapter 33. The uplifting and warping of a fairly level erosion surface, approaching a peneplain, were followed by stream erosion, which accounts for the present relief. The high elevation of the southern Carpathians makes it appropriate to call them the Transylvanian Alps. The elevation gave rise to glaciers during the Ice Age, and various glacial features still add to the scenic beauty. A number of routes break through the barrier: the famous Red Tower Pass (Turnul Roşu) at only 1,150 feet, through which a rail line runs southward from Sibiu; the Predeal Pass, 3,400 feet, through which a rail line runs from Oraşul Stalin (Braşov) to Ploeşti; and the Bodza Pass, 2,100 feet, through which a railroad extends from Oraşul Stalin to Bazău. These and other passes (Vulcan and Surduc) have been used throughout history for migrations and invasions and were heavily guarded in times of danger—as is evidenced by the sending of the Szeklers and Saxons (Germans) by the Magyars to act as frontier guards against invading Tatars.

At the western end of the Transylvanian Alps the mountain chain again curves, here southward and southeastward, and finally swings eastward as the Balkan range in central Bulgaria. At the curve the Danube breaks through the Kazan Gorge, whose narrowest part, the Iron Gate, is the old entrance to central Europe. The rapids here have been overcome partly by blasting away many large rocks in the river, and partly by constructing a canal around the rapids. It is here, as has been mentioned (Chapter 39), that traction locomotives assist ships upstream against the swift current. The Banat Mountains are a continuation of the Transylvanian Alps but are separated from them by a gap that the railroads use to connect the Danube basin with Walachia.

Transylvania, the rugged area of northwestern Rumania between the Transylvanian and Moldavian Carpathians, is, like the Hungarian Alföld, an old sea basin filled with river deposits. However, in contrast to the Alföld, it has been uplifted and dissected by running water so that it is now high and hilly. Although blessed with good soil and a climate better than that farther east and south, Transylvania is remote from the main currents of European life. Isolated colonies of German Lutherans, Hungarian Calvinists, and Szekler Unitarians, brought here centuries ago to protect the frontiers of Hungary, still live in their own way quite apart from their Rumanian neighbors, as do many wandering Gypsies. The complex Bihor Mountains, a part of the Carpathians exhibiting, like the main chain, signs of an old peneplain surface, enclose this basin on the west and separate it from the low plain of the Alföld, the eastern section of which belongs to Rumania. The mineral wealth of the Bihor Mountains and the forest resources of their higher parts help to make Transylvania the most prosperous part of Rumania. The climate is cooler and rainier than elsewhere, and the crops are therefore more varied and more like those of western Europe. This is the part of the country where potatoes, plums, grapes, vegetables, and forage crops are chiefly raised.

The forests of the mountainous tracts, forming 25 per cent of Rumania's area, cause timber to be an important product not only for home consumption but likewise for export. Excessive cutting for the purpose of increasing the national exports was a common practice in the interwar years, and careful methods are now essential to preclude deforestation and its disastrous consequences. Beeches, oaks, and pines are the most useful trees.

The Lowlands. Enclosed between the Carpathians and the Balkans is a depression structurally comparable with the North Italian Plain. Like that plain, it was once a gulf of the sea that has been entirely filled by river deposits. The Danube delta is still advancing into the Black Sea. In contrast to the Po Basin, these Rumanian or Walachian plains of the Lower Danube have been slightly uplifted. Hence the northern portion is now dissected into a hilly piedmont. The plain itself lies about 150 feet above sea level, and the Danube and its branches occupy broad valleys cut below the general level. The main Danube floodplain extends over a great area. Just as the middle course of the Po River has been pushed toward the southern part of the North Italian Plain by the greater supply of alluvium from the Alps in comparison with that from the Apennines, so the Danube has been pushed southward by the deposits of rivers from the Transylvanian Alps. With the Danube as the boundary between Rumania and Bulgaria, Rumania thus possesses the greater part of the lower Danubian plain. The sluggish character of the river causes it to be so impeded by its own alluvial deposits that it forms a braided channel, dividing into many interlacing branches. This network of streams combines again at Brăila but soon breaks once more into the three branches of the marshy delta, the Chilia, Sulina, and

A. The flat plain of Walachia. Courtesy of Sovfoto.

St. George (Sfântu Gheorghe). In times of flood the whole Danube floodplain forms a great lake, and the railroad between Bucharest and Constanţa has to cross it on one of the world's longest bridges.

The Dobruja, the upland area of eastern Rumania around which the Danube detours to the north, presents a pleasant and not very high mountain system in the north; but the south, most of which was transferred to Bulgaria in 1940, is a monotonous plain with steppe vegetation. On the east side of the Carpathians, the Moldavian Plateau is typically Russian in structure, climate, and land utilization. It slopes to the south, and the rivers flow in broad valleys. Near the mountains young deposits cover the underlying rocks entirely.

Now that the regional pattern of the country has been described, an examination of Rumania's problems may be made.

Wheat and Politics

The economic results of the improvement in Rumania's geographical background when surplus-grain-producing areas were added after 1920 were disappointing. In a general way this was due to the same overpopulation, low yield of crops, human inefficiency, and lack of capital that have tended to hold back all parts of Europe C. These results were also due partly to the difficulty of adjusting the newly won areas to the new political conditions; partly to the very bad state of economic affairs arising from the devastation of World War I and the great reduction in livestock; and partly also to financial difficulties and the inadequacies of the transportation system. Added to all these factors were bitter domestic political quarrels that had much to do with the astonishing lack of development.

It is a common mistake to ascribe to unfavorable political, social, educational, or religious conditions many human ills that are primarily economic. That such noneconomic factors, when unfavorable, are closely associated with all kinds of troubles is certainly true. In many cases, however, they are themselves the result as well as the cause of poor economic conditions and low standards of living. The poor economic conditions and low standards in turn are often the inevitable result of strong pressure of population. In countries like Rumania a dense population became established long ago. There, as in most places, the density of the agricultural population was based primarily on the interplay of three factors. One was the growth of population, another was the amount of production on which a family could subsist according to the prevailing standards of living, and the third was the amount of land that a family could cultivate under the very primitive methods of long ago. In recent centuries the development of better types of draft animals; the improvement in plows, scythes, mowing machines, reapers, seeders, manure spreaders, and other farm implements; and most of all the development of motor vehicles and of machinery run by power have greatly increased the amount of land and the number of animals that each farm family can take care of, and have immensely raised the possible standard of living. But, if the land available for each family is limited, it is difficult to take advantage of these improvements; and the system of agriculture and the standards of living can be improved only at a very slow rate or under drastic discipline.

A comparison of Rumania and the states of Iowa and Nebraska illustrates the point. The area of these two regions is almost the same; they lie in the same latitude; they both have large plains with excellent soil, although of course Rumania also has large mountainous areas that have no counterpart in the two American states. Climatically both regions are essentially continental even though Rumania has a seacoast, but the American states are more extreme because they are completely isolated from marine influences. In Rumania the rainfall ranges from 17 to 33 inches per year and in Iowa and Nebraska from 15 to 37. The January temperature ranges from 23° F to 31° in Rumania and from 15° to 28° in the American region, whereas that of July averages from 60° to 74° in Rumania and from 69° to 78° in Iowa and Nebraska. The chief difference is that in America there are more cyclonic storms, the rainfall during the critical summer months is more abundant and reliable, and the decline in rainfall in July and August is far less than in Rumania. In Bucharest, for example, July, August, and September each get only a little over 2 inches of rain compared with twice as much in June. Omaha, on the other hand, gets 5 inches in June, 4.5 in July, 3.5 in August, and 3 in September. In spite of the fact that Iowa and Nebraska have a decided advantage in this respect, as well as in both soil and relief, Rumania has between 4 and 5 times as many people as the American states. The respective farm populations differ still more, being 10 times as numerous in Rumania, where 72 per cent of the people are farmers, as in Nebraska and Iowa, where only half as great a percentage are supported directly by farms. Thus in Rumania about 11.5 million people earn a living from about 23 million acres of harvested land that suffers from summer droughts, whereas in Iowa and Nebraska only 1.4 million earn a living from 44 million acres where the summer rain is much less likely to fail! This comparison does not even take into account the much greater yield per acre in the two American states.

Thus, it is easy to see how the Americans have achieved a high standard of living. Undoubtedly they work harder and more intelligently than the Rumanians, but, even if their industry and intelligence were far greater than they actually are, the Americans could never have acquired the capital necessary for their present standard of living if they had been obliged to save it from the income of fields so small and crops so unreliable as those of Ru-

mania. Therefore the Rumanians are by no means to be despised
or blamed because of the difficulties under which they have labored.

This contrast between Rumania and the two American states deserves the most careful study, because it illustrates not only the
whole of Europe C, but also certain principles of widespread application. The first of these is that in most parts of the world
the density of the agricultural population in proportion to the area
actually available for cultivation is high where the production per
acre is low. This is not true when the new parts of the world are
compared with the old, but it is eminently true of Europe. Another principle is that in long-settled countries the amount of
land per family of the agricultural population declines in harmony
with the decline in the yield per acre. A third principle is that,
although methods of agriculture and the nature of the soil have
the utmost importance, the average yield of crops per acre depends
on the climate even more than upon cultivation and soil. Therefore, the magnitude of the problem Rumania faces can be appreciated. Of course, the climatic handicaps are to be considered
along with the chaotic territorial evolution of the country and the
political handicaps under which it has labored.

The Agrarian Economy

Much of the social evil in Rumania's agricultural organization
goes back to the pre-World War I period, when large landowners
held most of the land. Furthermore, the depredation made by the
Germans during World War I after Rumania decided to join the
Allies set the country's agriculture back so far that it had not fully
recovered when World War II broke out. However, during the
interwar years, even so corrupt a government as existed at that time
managed a vigorous agrarian reform, so that few great estates remained. But, as has been shown in the preceding section, the peasants had no capital with which to work; small holdings might be
totally inadequate in drought years; and village moneylenders charged
high interest.

After World War II and after communists had gained control of
the country, the agrarian situation was bad enough to discourage
even the communists. There were no large numbers of great landowners to serve as scapegoats, although there were some successful
peasants ("kulaks") that were forced into ruin. The biggest problem susceptible of remedy—greater mechanization and more effective methods—was tackled by the state along with other side issues

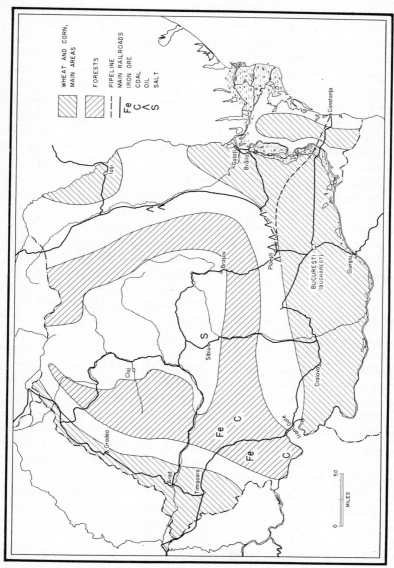

A. Economic Map of Rumania. Brasov is now called Orasul Stalin.

that, when handled to the party's satisfaction, would further communist control. As a matter of fact, co-operative farming had
begun to make promising headway in Rumania before World War
II, but this program would not suffice for the Soviet satellite. Collective farms were established, although not before 1949, reaching
the total of 1,000 in mid-1950 and embracing 1.8 million acres.
Tractors were sent to the farms from a joint Soviet-Rumanian plant
(*Sovromtractor*), but production was slow because of shortage of
raw materials, machine tools, and skilled labor. Despite the fact
that Rumania's agricultural production in 1946–47 was, in comparison with that of the 1934–38 acreage, the lowest of all European
countries, it had reached the prewar level by 1950. This probably
means that Rumania is furnishing grain to the industrialized sections of the other satellite countries, but it does not mark an improvement in the country's situation over the prewar period.

The Rumanian economy is to a very large extent a grain economy primarily of corn and wheat. Whereas the ratio between those
two was two to one during the interwar period, the shift seems to
be more and more toward corn. Both are used for export, but the
amounts vary considerably as a result of harvest fluctuation. Concentration of the grain production is on the Walachian Plain and
foothills, the plain of the Banat, and the plateaus of Moldavia and
the Dobruja. Crops such as oats, rye, and barley that replace
wheat in the drier eastern sections are only of minor significance.
The Walachian Plain in summer is one great field of grain, interrupted only by colorful patches of sunflowers from which the seeds
are used for oil. Transylvania has a more varied economy, with
oats and rye besides wheat and cotton and, locally, fruits and
vegetables. The number of cattle exceeds that of Ireland and
Spain and is almost as large as that of Yugoslavia. Rather typical
are the large numbers of sheep, which move into the mountains in
summer and descend to the plain after the harvest of the grain
crop. Forests cover the mountains, and lumber is produced on
an appreciable scale. Wine is produced in many scattered areas but
is of only local importance.

Minerals and Manufacturing

The principal mineral resource of the country is petroleum, and
Rumania is by far Europe's greatest oil producer outside the Soviet
Union. Its 1950 production (5.4 million metric tons) was nearly
four times as great as that of Austria, Rumania's nearest competi-

tor. Production reached a peak in 1936 and was declining even before the Nazis exploited the fields unmercifully during World War II and before the fields were bombed by the Americans.

The main concentration is around Ploeşti, north of Bucharest (A671), and a second field is on the east side of the Carpathians. Pipelines transport the oil from the Ploeşti field to the coast at Constanţa and to the Danube. One of the main missions of the American Fifteenth Air Force, based on the Tavoliere plain around Foggia, Italy, during 1944 and early 1945, was to destroy the Ploeşti oil complex, especially the great refinery (actually located at Câmpina) that fed the Nazi war machine. In conjunction with petroleum, mention should be made of the great natural gas deposits—largest in Europe outside Russia—of southern Transylvania, where availability of fuel has stimulated growth of small, scattered industries. In the Banat Mountains (A664) a small coal production and local supply of iron ore has led to a small steel industry, producing about 300,000 tons of steel annually at mid-century, an amount that Rumania hopes to raise to 450,000 tons. Fairly large is the salt production of southern Transylvania and other scattered localities. Manufacturing is limited to local plants and home industries, although some cities, especially Bucharest, are centers of modest production. The Rumanian home industries prove that the people are artistic and clever in their traditional handwork. The gay peasant costumes with their rich embroidery are true works of art. Only 6.5 per cent of the actively engaged population is engaged in manufacturing—indeed a very low figure, if compared with 80 per cent in agriculture.

Cities

Only Bucharest (Rumanian: Bucureşti) among Rumanian cities is a real metropolis; it, however, has 1.4 million inhabitants. Here was the life of cultured Rumania, center of the Romanic culture of which Rumania was so proud but of which, except for the language, very little is observable. However, even in Bucharest that atmosphere must have changed since the communists took over. Constanţa is the Black Sea port, and Galaţi and Brăila are the Danubian ports near the outlet. A new canal cutting through the Dobruja and providing a short cut for Danube traffic to the Black Sea was, in 1951, in full construction. Trade and the trading centers on the Danube should profit from such a canal.

All other towns are only local commercial centers. Along the edge of the Danube basin are four towns located in a north-south line, each of them marking a railroad junction: Timişoara (center for the Banat), Arad, Oradea, and Satu-Mare. The population of these towns is mixed Rumanian and Hungarian, and the Magyars always regarded their acquisition by Rumania as one of the big blows after World War I. Oraşul Stalin (called Braşov before the

A. Transylvania is also called "the land of the seven castles"; here is one of them.

communists assumed power in Rumania), Sibiu, and Cluj are the principal centers of Transylvania, with Cluj having 111,000 inhabitants to rank as the second city of Rumania. Iaşi (Jassy) is the only city of any importance on the Moldavian Plateau.

A Summary

This chapter reveals that Rumania has wealth far beyond that apparent in the level of development it has reached. The reasons for the inconsonance between potentialities and actualities—communist control notwithstanding—are to be found in many complex factors that, as this chapter has shown, have become handicaps to the country. These handicaps include: the presence of a less energetic population than that of northwestern Europe or even northern Italy; an ethnographic complexity that has led to intergroup strife and national disunity; a high birth rate, leading to constant pressure of population; corruption at all levels of authority—a tendency largely inherited from the decadent centuries of Turkish rule and continued during the leans years of the twentieth century; late unification of the country—itself chiefly traceable to Rumania's location in spheres of political-geographical influence; instability of territory; lack of sufficient, reliable rainfall and stimulating changes of weather; lack of sufficient iron ore and coal; and a location that faces Rumania eastward to a sea that is virtually a closed lake and that brings no stimulating cultural contacts or great trade, since Rumania's products are like those of her neighbors and sister-Black Sea countries.

The descent of Soviet domination and communist methods is, of course, a continuation of the same chain of misfortunes that has bound Rumania for centuries. Perhaps, despite the terror and degradation, Rumania can correct some of its maladjustments as a unit in a regional grouping. However, the cure may be much worse than the disease—as bad as the disease, indeed, is.

· 42 ·

Bulgaria

Character of Bulgaria

Two conflicting qualities, those of the warrior and the peasant, have dominated Bulgarian history. Like the region of Serbia, Bulgaria is a country of warriors who struggled through four and a half centuries of servitude to Turkey until they gained their independence in the Treaty of San Stefano in 1878. In that treaty Bulgaria was given much of the land that was contained in the Bulgarian Empire of the ninth century, when the Bulgars under Tsar Simeon ruled from the Black Sea to the Adriatic, and from the southern Carpathians to the Aegean. However, the Treaty of Berlin later in 1878 pared Bulgaria down to a fraction of the size granted it in San Stefano, and bitterness among the Bulgars has been great ever since.

Thrice their dream of the restoration of such an empire was almost realized. The first time was during the Balkan War in 1912, when the Bulgarian armies had conquered the region around the mouth of the Maritsa River, and were fighting near the walls of Constantinople. But discord between Bulgaria and its Balkan allies was followed by a war that shattered the dream, and Bulgaria lost some of its gains, although it temporarily retained the Maritsa Valley and part of the Aegean coast. The second opportunity for the dream to be realized came during World War I, when Bulgaria joined the Central Powers, helped to crush Serbia, occupied a great part of it, and reconquered the Dobruja from the Rumanians. Again it failed to find its allies in full sympathy with its aims, and it was probably in the main from dissatisfaction and disappointment that Bulgaria broke down in 1918 at the beginning of the total collapse of the Central Powers. Once more Bulgaria lost: the Dobruja remained Rumanian, the newborn Yugoslavia obtained boundary rearrangements that brought the western frontier still nearer to Sofia, and Greece shut Bulgaria off from the Aegean. The third time Bulgaria attempted to expand was during World War II, when the country permitted the German armies to use its territory for an attack on Yugoslavia and Greece and it again occupied the Aegean coast. For the third time the effort failed when Germany was defeated and only interference by Russia prevented further loss of territory. The only gain was the return to Bulgaria of the southern Dobruja, now perhaps permanently, since Rumania and Bulgaria exchanged their minorities after 1945.

After 1945, Bulgaria—under Russian pressure—accepted the communist form of government and became the Bulgarian People's Republic. The country had long felt that Russia was its main friend, because Russia helped throw back the Turks and establish an independent Bulgaria. Of course, it so happens that exertion of Russian control in Bulgaria is part of the Soviet policy of gaining access to the Mediterranean. After World War II Bulgaria became the Soviet outpost against Turkey, Greece, and—after 1948—against Yugoslavia.

Except where the country's boundaries are formed by the waters of the Danube and the Black Sea, the Bulgarians wish to push them farther back. Most of all they want an outlet on the Aegean Sea. Common Soviet control over the Balkan states, except Greece and Yugoslavia, is indeed helping to eliminate at least outward signs of some of the friction of the "Balkan problem" that has long been a great source of unrest in Europe; however, the role of Bulgaria and Yugoslavia (during the period of 1945–48 that Yugoslavia was a Soviet satellite) in the Macedonian fighting in northern Greece after World War II reveals that the old antagonisms are still present. Bulgaria still claims the northern Aegean coast.

The other side of the Bulgarian character is quite different. Quick to fight for what he considers the destiny of his homeland, the Bulgar is also a peasant, and today Bulgaria is as completely agricultural as any country in Europe. Nevertheless, the 80 per cent of the people who are peasants were, before 1945, small farmers, and most of them cultivated their own small farms created from the large estates owned by their former Turkish rulers. The Bulgarians have a high reputation in many respects. Their efforts to secure education are especially notable, and for a country less than a century out from under Turkish rule to have such a high rate of literacy (81 per cent of the males and 57 per cent of the females) is a real achievement. The Bulgar's industry, frugality, and eagerness to learn new methods of work are also notable: sometimes his thriftiness makes him stingy (the Bulgar is the "Balkan Scotsman"), and his eagerness for progress and education destroys or prevents light-hearted gaiety such as is so common in Spain, Italy, and Serbia. Before 1945 the landholdings were so small, the amount of land lying fallow was so large, and the available capital therefore so limited that it was very difficult to adopt modern methods. Wooden plows, the sowing of wheat by hand, and the reaping of it with sickles were and still are very widespread. Nevertheless, it is often said that no other Balkan country gives so strong an impression of sturdy and determined progress in spite of great discouragements.

It is clear that the character of the Bulgars is not one that submits without a struggle to a communist dictatorial type of government. Only terror and constant police supervision prevent active opposition. The communist party was well entrenched by the time V-E Day arrived, and it assumed very strong control during the rest of 1945 and during 1946. Nevertheless, vigorous opposition continued until only thousands of executions and several announced hangings of opposition leaders (some of whom were Bulgaria's finest patriots) terrorized the opposition into silence. Moreover, the Bulgars are very nationalistic, and their own plans about the Balkans do not always coincide with those of the Soviets. From the Russian point of view there is always danger of Titoism, and the frequent changes in leadership, with the customary elimination of the accused, clearly indicate that Bulgaria is far from being an abject communist tool.

Regional Characteristics

Danube Plateau. The Balkan Mountains (Bulgarian: Stara Planina—or "old mountains"), the eastward extension of the Carpathian structure, divide Bulgaria into two sections differing in relief, soil, climate, products, and type of population. North of the Balkans the North Bulgarian Platform slopes gently to the Danube and breaks off abruptly in a wall of loess and limestone about 500 feet high facing the river. This wall or cliff presents a remarkably sharp contrast to the very flat plains and broad swamps along the Rumanian side of the river. At the top of the cliff the plateau is quite flat and is covered with fertile loess, but it is broken into many small sections by deep, steep-sided valleys into which the streams have entrenched themselves.

There is a strong contrast between the valley bottoms with their narrow but level, well-watered, and fertile plains, and the uplands with their far broader stretches of soil that is also fertile but that is dry and poorly watered. The valleys are full of villages, and in them lie the small cities; the surrounding valley floors are devoted to corn and to crops like lucerne, sugar beets, vines in some sheltered spots, and vegetables like tomatoes and peppers that are very important among people whose main food is corn. From the villages in the valley the peasants climb long distances to their wheat fields on the plateau above. Although the individual fields on the

A. Natural Regions of Bulgaria.

plateau are small, the general effect is of one vast field of wheat and corn, or perhaps barley, unbroken by trees or houses, except at long intervals. The wheat is sold as a money crop and is consumed in the towns or exported; the cheaper and less easily transported maize is eaten in the villages. A similar situation prevails very widely in most of the countries of Europe, although the product eaten at home may be rye, potatoes, or even oats, rather than corn.

The contrast between the valleys and the plateau is the combined result of relief and climate. The general climate is like that of the Walachian Plain of Rumania north of the Danube. The winters are cold; and strong, disagreeable, dusty winds are common. The summers are warm, averaging above 70° F in July, and most of the rain falls in early summer. The eastern section is too dry for crops and is therefore largely devoted to sheep, but in the western section and along the mountains the rainfall is heavier. The porous character of the loess and limestone, combined with the pronounced drop in the rainfall in August and September, makes it difficult to get water at all seasons on the plateau. The

A. A typical picture of Balkan agriculture—a Bulgarian scene.

valleys, however, have plenty of springs, and they are also protected from the bitter, dusty winds of winter. Therefore, it is not strange that the people prefer to live there in spite of the long walk to the fields. Cattle are kept mainly for draft purposes, dairying is little developed, and dung is so often used for fuel that the value of the animals as a help in agriculture is much reduced.

The population of the plateau—including, of course, its valleys—is relatively dense. It produces a surplus of grain that is exported from the Danube harbors, of which Ruse is the most important, or from Stalin (Varna), main Bulgarian harbor on the Black Sea. The plateau is the old center of the Bulgarian people, where they settled on their first arrival during the time of the Hungarian invasion, and whence they advanced toward the south. Ruins, some well preserved, of the old capital may be seen at Tŭrnovo. Here again was the cradle of their movement for independence in the nineteenth century. The reacquisition of the southern Dobruja in 1940 extended this region farther to the southeast.

Balkan Mountains. The Balkan Mountains to the south of the Danube Plateau are not the great barrier that they appear to be on most maps, and low passes connect the north and south sides, the Shipka Pass (4,377 feet) being the most important. One of the branches of the Danube, the Iskŭr, cuts through the Balkan range and provides a route to the capital, Sofia. The general level of the mountain system trends downward to the Black Sea. The Tundzha Depression, resulting from a sharp down-faulting of the land, lies along its southern base, which is marked by several hot springs where thermal bathing resorts have arisen. The upper Tundzha River follows this trough-like depression for much of its east-west extent. The town of Kazanlŭk has developed as an agricultural market town, but its great specialty is the gathering of roses for making attar of roses. The towns of Kalofer and Karlovo farther west are even more actively engaged in pressing roses from the thousands of acres of bushes in this fragrant and colorful "Valley of Roses." The industry is thus reminiscent of that around Grasse in Provence in southern France. South of this depression lie the so-called Anti-Balkans (or Sredna Gora), a smaller range, which in turn separates the depression from the Maritsa Valley. A little coal, small deposits of copper, lead, and zinc, abundant forests of oak and beech, facilities for water power, and abundance of wool from the sheep of the mountains all favor the development of small home industries. Even more important, however, is the character of the people. The Bulgarians, not only here, but elsewhere, have an industrious quality and a degree of intelligence that cause home handicrafts to be more widely developed than in most parts of eastern or southern Europe. In this respect they resemble the Swiss and the Bavarians.

Maritsa Valley. The Maritsa Valley, lying between the Anti-Balkans on the north and the Rhodope on the south and containing the main Bulgarian lowland, has the climatic advantages of a protected position; the winters are less cold than those to the north, and the whole landscape exhibits a modified Mediterranean type of vegetation. Cold easterly winds in winter (the January average of Plovdiv is 33° F) prevent the growing of citrus fruits. But the many other varieties of fruits and vegetables; the vineyards; tobacco fields,

producing one of Bulgaria's main exports; rose gardens, cultivated
to supply attar of roses; extensive fields of wheat, rice, and cotton;
and even the mulberry trees and their silkworms—all contribute to
make this section of great economic value. This fruitful area has
been called "Bulgaria's California," and the farmers of the region
have earned the reputation of being some of the finest gardeners in
Europe.

Plovdiv, Bulgaria's second city (125,000) is the principal center for
the Maritsa Basin, especially now that the southern outlet to the
Aegean is blocked by Greece. Burgas, on the Black Sea, is the
main outlet for this productive region and in volume of trade surpasses Stalin (Varna).

Rhodope Mountains. The Rhodope massif, lying east of the
Mesta River along the southern Bulgarian border, is a high mountain block of alpine relief still partly covered by forests and having
a sparse population. Because of its rugged relief the Rhodope region harbors several groups of people who have often made trouble.
One is the Pomaks, or Moslem Bulgarians, who gave up Christianity and helped the Turks to persecute the Christians. They are
mainly woodcutters and charcoal burners. Another group is the
Vlachs, who are herdsmen and who are akin to the Rumanians of
Walachia (Vlach = Walachian). More troublesome than either of
these are the Macedonians in the southern and western parts of the
Rhodope region. Bulgaria often claims that the Macedonians are
actually Bulgars and has given them special autonomous rights in
contrast to the repressive treatment that they received in Serbia.
A great many Macedonian refugees have therefore settled in Bulgaria, especially in Sofia. The ardor with which the Macedonians
claim their rights and the violence that often attends their disagreements with one another as well as with other people have, nevertheless, given the Bulgarian government a difficult problem. The
Pomaks, Vlachs, and Macedonians in the shelter of the highest
Balkan mountains epitomize the confusion that has long reigned in
this whole region. The ethnographic snarl and the long-standing
desire of Bulgaria for the Aegean coast led communist-dominated
Bulgaria to encourage Macedonian dissatisfaction in chaotic postwar Greece and to join in the communist-led pressure in Greece.

The southern slope of the Rhodope falls toward the Macedonian
coastal plain with its Mediterranean climate and fertile soils; but,
in spite of Bulgarian claims, this Macedonian-Thracian coast belongs to Greece. As a harbor on the Aegean would be of the great-

est importance to Bulgaria, it desires control of at least the port of Alexandroúpolis (Dedeagach) west of the mouth of the Maritsa. Greece refuses to surrender the port, but it did offer to free a part of Thessaloníki, as it did for Yugoslavia. After 1945, however,

A. Rila Monastery in the forested Rhodope Mountains.

Greece and Bulgaria were no longer on speaking terms, especially because of the help given by Bulgaria to the Greek communists during the Greek civil war.

Western Bulgaria. The Balkan and Rhodope mountains both stem from a common massif in western Bulgaria. It comprises a complex area including the Pirin Mountains between the Struma River in the west and the Mesta on the east, the Rila Mountains north of the Pirins, and the western roots of the Balkans around

Sofia. These rugged highland areas serve as the source of four main rivers: the Maritsa, Iskŭr, Struma, and Mesta. The Rila range contains the highest peak not only of Bulgaria but of all the Balkan Peninsula, 9,593 feet, with a summit that is perennially snow-covered. Within the mountain complex of western Bulgaria are included several extensive basins, typical of those already mentioned in Chapters 32 and 40. Drained by the Iskŭr, the largest basin is that of Sofia, in which lies the capital city at an elevation of 1,830 feet. It is one of the smallest of the European capitals, having only 435,000 inhabitants. Its location is perhaps the most focal point of the Balkan Peninsula, but it is too near the present western boundary to have the most advantageous location for Bulgaria's capital. A modern city, Sofia, in addition to being the political and cultural center, is a junction point of railroads, of which the Belgrade-Constantinople line is the most important.

Land Utilization

The climatic contrast between the two sides of the Balkan Mountains is reflected in the land use. Northern Bulgaria is a region of wheat and corn, similar to Rumania except for the fact that the landscape is more rolling, rising slowly to the foothills of the Balkans. Southern Bulgaria, with its Mediterranean influence, has a more varied type of land use. Wheat still prevails, but fruits and vegetables become important and tobacco of high quality is the chief export crop. Before 1940 carloads of early strawberries and table grapes went to central Europe. Sheep are the most important type of livestock and number 9 millions; the Bulgarian yogurt, a product of sheep milk, is world famous. Two million cattle and half a million water buffalo are used as work animals in the field, and exported Bulgarian canned ham indicates the importance of swine.

Much of the arable land of Bulgaria was collectivized on the Soviet model after 1945, although resistance to the collectivization was marked. Even by 1950, however, only 11 per cent of the arable land was included in collective farms, and they produced only 20 per cent of the country's agricultural production. By 1953, Bulgarian communist plans were to reduce the share of agriculture in national production from 70 per cent to 55 per cent and to increase the share of industry from 30 per cent to 45 per cent. By the same year the share of collective farms was to amount to 60 per cent of the country's agricultural output: this was the most ambitious agrarian plan in all the satellite countries.

Manufacturing is still in its infancy. As is generally the case in the Balkans, only textile mills go beyond the scope of small local industries; Gabrovo is the chief textile city. Although the communists have announced plans for expanding Bulgarian industry, they have not indicated how they hope to achieve much of an increase.

A. Wheat harvest in the Balkans. Wheat is the chief grain crop, and on it depends the life of most of the people.

Bulgarian industry is the most limited of all the European countries, not even excepting Greece. Great percentage gains can be made by the communists—and were claimed—but the total amount will remain small.

Bulgaria and the Bulgars

As an agrarian country, Bulgaria has a solid foundation. Differences in climate result in a varied production; and as an exporter of specialty crops, such as fruits and tobacco, the country found a ready market, especially in central Europe. Bulgaria itself gives the impression of being well above the Balkan average. It is—or at least was before 1945—neat and clean; and the cities, such as Stalin (formerly Varna, the "Pearl of the Black Sea") and Sofia were rather modern in their appearance. Ancient monasteries of the Orthodox faith and such historic cities as Tŭrnovo, the old capital, were points of attraction for those interested in Slavic culture. The Bulgar himself has lost all evidence of his Asiatic descent and is typically Slavic in his songs and folklore. Minorities have gradually disappeared through exchange with the neighboring countries, although some of the exchanges were not made in the most humane way. The expulsion of 250,000 Turks, remnants of the centuries of Turkish control of the country, was made with little regard for their safety. Again the statement has to be made that what Bulgaria needs is peace and liberty for the individual.

· 43 ·

Poland (Polska)

Position of Poland and Its Territorial Evolution

One of the supreme facts in Poland's geography and history is its location near the east-west center of the North European Plain or "Central Lowland." Although the land of the Poles has for centuries been definitely framed on the south by the Sudeten-Carpathian ranges and in part on the north by the Baltic coast, its eastern and western frontiers have, for an equal number of centuries, been vague and shifting. This is largely traceable to the fact that low relief of the plain has supplied no barrier highlands or valleys to hold the Poles or to keep out neighbors on the east and west.

The Polish Core Land. Living very near the center of the area whence it is generally supposed the Slavs dispersed, the Poles have retained at least a linguistic kinship with the groups who have moved outward to become the various Slavic peoples discussed in Chapter 12 and shown in A171. Nevertheless, politically the Poles have tended to remain aloof whenever their power permitted, and they have clashed politically with their brother Slavs in Bohemia (and later, Czechoslovakia) and in Russia. The Sudeten-Carpathian ranges furnished a convenient dividing line between Poles and Czecho-Slovaks, but no such convenient line suggested a division between Poles and the eastern Slavs: Belorussians, Russians, Ukrainians, and Ruthenes.

Even more critical was the lack of an effective dividing line between the Poles and the Germans on the west. In the tenth century the Polish Slavs occupied territory as far west as the Elbe River basin, having followed behind Germanic tribes pressing westward against the Rhine frontier of the Roman Empire. But the Slavs were gradually pushed back by eastward-moving Germans during succeeding centuries until they were almost entirely east of the Oder. A small group was, however, left behind in the marshes of the Spreewald, southeast of Berlin, where the Slavic Sorbs or Wends

still live. Such conditions have caused the fringes of Polish settlement to be ragged and to be characterized by ethnographic transition areas on the east and west. For many centuries, however, the
Polish core has been the basin of the Vistula, indisputably the principal river of the Poles.

Partition of Poland. The development of states in the modern
period added political difficulties to ethnographic ones. Poland
found itself hemmed in by three great powers: Germany (Prussia)
on the west, Russia on the east, and Austria on the south. Thus
the country found itself in perpetual danger of a political "squeeze"
unless it was politically and militarily very strong. Poland's vulnerability was especially great if its neighbors acted in concert, as it
discovered in the latter part of the eighteenth century. Between
1772 and 1795, Russia, Prussia, and Austria partitioned Poland
among themselves in three stages, and Poland disappeared from the
map of Europe until after World War I. Thus, for 125 years Germans moved in from the west and Russians came in from the east.

Poland after World War I. The reconstitution of Poland by taking territories from Germany, Russia, and Austria after World War
I immediately encountered the difficult problem of locating the new
boundaries in the transitional ethnographic zones. The Treaty of
Versailles gave Poland most of the mixed zone on the west. Out of
this zone was carved the famous "Polish Corridor" giving Poland
all the Vistula and an outlet to the sea and separating East Prussia
from the main body of Germany (see A178 and A180). Danzig was
constituted a Free City under the League of Nations so that Poland
could use its port and yet not administer such a thoroughly German
city. The Allenstein-Marienwerder plebiscite held in 1920 among
the Slavic Masurians of southern East Prussia showed an overwhelming preference for continuation of German administration of the
area that they occupied. Possibly the uncertain future of a newly
re-created state offered no attraction to the Masurians.

A tentative eastern boundary was suggested in the "Curzon Line,"
which extended along the general line of the upper Bug River.
However, Poland at the time was influenced by the glory of victory
and even dreamed of partial restoration of her medieval empire,
which had extended far into the Ukraine and along the middle
Dnieper. In the confused years attending the end of World War I,
when Russia was weak and engaged in civil war, Poland pushed its
boundaries far eastward into the mixed Polish-Russian region,
using the Pripet Marshes as a defense against Russian invasion.

Along the foothills of the Carpathians, in former Austrian Galicia, Poland achieved a junction with Rumania. In the northeast, Polish territory reached Latvia along the Dvina River by means of the so-called "Vilna Corridor," which separated Lithuania from the

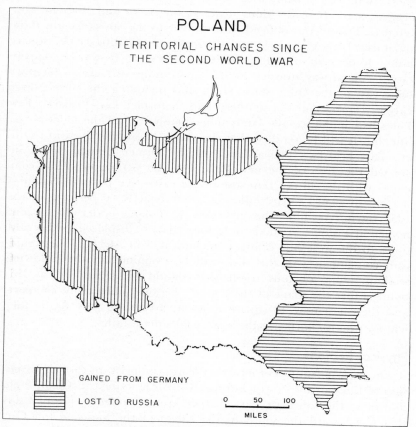

POLAND

TERRITORIAL CHANGES SINCE
THE SECOND WORLD WAR

GAINED FROM GERMANY

LOST TO RUSSIA

0   50   100

MILES

A. The Westward Displacement of Poland after World War II.

Soviet Union and placed Vilna, the traditional capital of Lithuania, in Poland. Thus, the Poland of the interwar period incurred the enmity of nearly all its neighbors.

This enmity, directed against Poland's exposed position and inflated by other factors, exhibited itself in 1939, when Germany attacked in the west, the Soviet Union marched into the east, and Poland was partitioned between the two invaders. The German-

Soviet dividing line ("Molotov-Ribbentrop Line") closely followed the old Curzon Line of 1919 except in the north. Again—for the second time in two centuries—Poland disappeared from the map.

Poland after World War II. The second disappearance was short-lived, and Poland as a state was re-created in 1945. However, as a result of decisions made at the Yalta and Potsdam conferences, Poland was obliged to surrender to the Soviet Union those territories lying east of the old Curzon Line, totaling 68,667 square miles—46 per cent of its 1938 territory. However, by way of compensation Poland was awarded 38,974 square miles of German territory lying east of the Oder-Neisse rivers and including the former Free City of Danzig and the southern half of former East Prussia. Few Poles had inhabited the lands immediately east of the Oder-Neisse line, but it will be recalled that the Slavic Masurians lived in southern East Prussia. The addition of the former German lands increased the area of the new Poland by 26 per cent, which—compared with the 46 per cent loss in the east—gave postwar Poland a net loss of 29,693 square miles or approximately 20 per cent of the 1938 territory. Thus the new state of Poland underwent a phenomenon unique in modern history: it was displaced bodily 121 miles to the west (the changes are indicated in A689). The significant consequences of this shift will be examined in the following sections. One obvious result that should be mentioned at this point is that the shape of the country became much more compact, and there are now 10 square miles of area to 1 mile of frontier length, whereas formerly there were 70 square miles.

Physical Regions

The surface features of most of Poland comprise an easterly extension of those of the North European Plain described in Chapter 36. However, the southern part includes some uplands and plateaus that rise toward the south to the ridges of the Sudeten and Carpathian mountains.

Baltic Shore. Whereas in 1938 Poland possessed 87 miles of Baltic coast, after 1945 the country had a Baltic coastline of 317 miles. Most of this Baltic coast is flat and sandy, although some moraine hills reach the sea. The shore zone is narrow along most of the coast but extends farther inland at the mouths of the Oder and Vistula rivers. Westward-flowing currents have tended to straighten the shore and have enclosed some lagoons and built long sandspits like that (Połwysep Hel) north of Gdynia and that (formerly called in German the Frische Nehrung) enclosing the Zalew Wislany (formerly the Frisches Haff). Thus the coast is, like that of the Netherlands, not especially conducive to seafaring. However, west of the mouth of the Vistula in the Gulf of Gdańsk are Poland's ports of Gdańsk (Danzig) and Gdynia, the latter having been built up after 1920 so that Poland would not have to rely on Danzig as a port. Furthermore, in extreme northwestern Poland, lying in a "bridgehead" area across the Oder is the former German port of Stettin, now called Szczecin, the natural outlet for exports—particularly coal—from Silesia. This shore zone is characterized by dunes, pastures, and thin woods.

The Baltic Zone of Lakes and Moraines. The narrow Baltic shore is succeeded on the south by a broad zone of lake-studded moraine traversed by lines of recessional moraines more or less parallel with the shore (shown as black arcs in A63). As described in Chapter 36, these moraine ridges mark various stabilized positions of the edge of the last ice sheet. Some of the recessional moraines rise to heights of slightly more than 1,100 feet, and the steeper slopes are covered with coniferous forests, although the sandy soil is often cultivated on the gentler slopes. Numerous lakes and marshes occupy the valleys between the moraine ridges. The lake region, called Pojerzierze in Polish, is divided into almost equal parts by the lower Vistula, with the Pojerzierze Pomorski to the west and extending as far south as the Noteć River, and the Pojerzierze Mazurski to the east. It was in the latter area—the Masurian Lake District—that the Russian army was soundly defeated during World War I in the Battle of Tannenberg. Although the lakes are picturesque, the region is the least populated of the five regions of Poland, since the sandy Podzols—especially along the southern and southeastern edge, where outwash sands prevail—do not encourage well-developed agriculture, and mineral wealth is lacking throughout. Urban development is restricted to relatively small, scattered towns.

Polish Lowlands. Lying south of the Baltic Lake and Moraine Zone is the largest region of the country, the Polish Lowlands, extending without interruption from the eastern to the western border. Only toward the southern part of the plain do low plateaus appear. Like the corresponding section in northern Germany, the Polish Lowlands constitute a zone of old glacial valleys (*pradoliny*—which the Germans call *Urstromtäler*) and their accompanying outwash deposits. As was explained in Chapter 36, these valleys were formed by glacial meltwater flowing along the edge of the retreating ice in the trough between the southward-sloping ice and the northward-sloping land.

As in Germany, the old glacial channels strongly influence the present drainage: the Oder, Warta, and Vistula, for most of the length of their courses, follow sections of four of the five spillway channels. The sharp bends in the courses of the rivers generally mark the entry into or departure from one of the channels. Although little of the original forest of this zone remains in central and eastern Poland, that part lying immediately east of the Neisse and of the middle Oder is dominantly in forest, and some forest stretches exist in the east. It is in the better sections of the Lowlands that several of the principal Polish cities are located, including Poznań, Łódź, and Białystok. Although most of the soils of the region are sandy Podzols, they are intensively cultivated in central Poland, and are primarily arable in the east, although pastures occupy much of the area.

Southern Uplands. In southern Poland, two main upland areas and several scattered heights interrupt the plain. In the south-center is the Małopolska Plateau, bounded on the southeast by a fault scarp overlooking the upper Vistula. In the northeastern part of the plateau, east of Kielce, is an outlier of the old Hercynian structure, the Łyso Góry, reaching an elevation of 2,000 feet and yielding small to modest amounts of iron, copper, and pyrite from its old rocks. In the southwestern part of the plateau, overlooked by cuestas of Jurassic limestone and Tertiary sandstone are the Hercynian structures of the Silesian Plateau (Wyżyna Śląska), containing one of the greatest concentrations of mineral wealth (coal, iron, lead, and zinc) in all Europe. Around the mineral wealth has developed one of Europe's main industrial regions, largely built up by the Germans before World War I, when almost all the area was in German territory, or during the interwar period, when only part of the area was left to Germany. The post-1945 Poland included the entire area, and the new country was presented with an enormous capital gain. The concentration of major cities here in Silesia (Śląsk) is the most intense in Poland.

East of the San and Vistula rivers and south of Lublin lies the Lublin Plateau, formed principally of limestone. Between it and the Małopolska Plateau to the west lies the roughly triangular San Basin, composed of alluvial materials brought down from the Carpathian slopes by northward-flowing rivers.

Toward the southern edges of these highland areas—and over the entire Lublin Plateau—as well as on the Foreland of the Sudeten and Carpathians is a rather broad and almost continuous belt of loess. The belt is a continuation of that in the Börde zone along the southern edge of the North German Plain and was deposited during the Ice Age by winds carrying loose surface materials that had been denuded of vegetation. The soil that has developed in

A. Polish dirt road in rural area near Warsaw. Courtesy of Sovfoto.

the loess belt is a rich, black soil with most characteristics of the Chernozem. The entire belt, therefore, is a rich agricultural region in which wheat is the dominant crop but sugar beets, potatoes, and rye are extensively produced.

Sudeten-Carpathian Foreland and Ranges. Lying south of the Southern Uplands and separated from them by the upper courses of the Oder, Vistula, and San rivers are the Foreland and ranges of the Sudeten and Carpathian mountains. The Foreland is principally a rolling landscape, much of which is also blanketed with loess and, like the loess areas farther north, was never densely forested. Lack of forest in the loess belt early attracted Stone Age settlers and presented an almost continuous path westward across present Germany to the English Channel. Where loess is not present much of the Foreland is in forest, although the forests become better developed higher up the slopes of the mountains immediately along the southern boundary.

The mountain frame itself is divided into two distinct parts by the Moravian Gateway through which the Oder River enters the Silesian Basin. West of the gateway lie the Sudetens, whereas to the east lie the Western Carpathians, comprising primarily the Beskids but including in a deep penetration of Poland into Slovakia the northern slopes of the High Tatra, in which is found the highest elevation in Poland, approximately 8,000 feet. The valleys and lower slopes of the southern mountains are devoted to fields of rye and potatoes, but the upper slopes are densely forested. Above the timber line are well-developed alpine meadows, giving rise to cattle raising similar to that in Alpine meadow areas in Switzerland and Austria. Because of their scenic attractions, these mountains are the most highly developed resort region of Poland and are visited by many tourists.

Climate

Like other aspects of the country, the Polish climate exhibits characteristics of a transition between west and east. Winter temperatures decrease gradually from west to east: Berlin, in Germany, has a January mean of 30° F, and Warsaw 26.4°. Summer temperatures are approximately the same over all the area, although they are slightly lower along the Baltic coast and appreciably lower in the southern mountains. Precipitation is about the same across Poland, but more of it falls as snow toward the east, and the snow remains on the ground for a longer period toward the east. Total precipitation averages between 20 and 25 inches over the lowlands, although it is slightly less in the lower Vistula basin and somewhat higher (up to 40 and 50 inches) in the southern mountains. The prevailing temperatures cause the average precipitation to be quite adequate not only for agriculture but also for forests, and the summer rainfall maximum brings moisture during the growing period. However, a slight drop in normal precipitation causes a serious drop in crop yield. Occasional extensions of extremely cold air masses from western Asia in winter are deleterious to fruit trees, which sometimes winterkill under such conditions. So far as man is concerned, winter temperatures are generally not low enough to be unfavorable to health and activity, and summer temperatures are not enervatingly high.

Agriculture

The very name of Poland means "land of fields," indicating the significance of agriculture in the original economic life of the country. The prominent part played by agriculture in the economy is still evident in the fact that 46 per cent of the economically engaged population gain a livelihood from agriculture—a decrease of 15 per cent from 1931. As has been indicated in preceding sections, the relief of the country is conducive to widespread agricultural activity, but many of the soils are either too marshy or too sandy to promote great yields of diversified crops. The loessal soils of the south are, however, excellent for agricultural purposes, whereas fertilizer must be used lavishly in central Poland if yields are to be maintained.

Although the loss of former southeastern Poland (eastern Galicia) deprived postwar Poland of valuable crop-production areas, most of the territory transferred to the Soviet Union was poor agricultural land and contained the poorest farms in pre-1938 Poland. Nevertheless, despite the gain of new territories from Germany, Poland sustained a net loss of approximately 10 per cent in arable land. However, the new territories were, under German management, characterized by a higher standard of cultivation than was typical of most of Poland. Therefore, if the new lands are properly managed, the higher yields to be expected from them should make up for the decrease in total acreage. Unfortunately, however, the new territories will require more fertilizer to maintain the high yields than did the rich loess areas of Podolia and Volhynia of the upper Dniester basin.

In tonnage of total yield, potatoes are the leading crop of Poland, although the acreage devoted to them is only half that devoted to rye. In both tonnage and acreage rye is the leading grain of Poland, and it exceeds those of wheat by three to four times. The next most important grain is oats, with the wheat crop amounting to approximately two-thirds that of oats, and the barley crop amounting to slightly more than half that of oats. The great rye crop reflects the adaptability of that grain to the sandy soils; and, in turn, rye is used to a very great extent as a bread grain. Some barley is used for bread, but oats are very little used for human food in Poland. The appreciable sugar beet production is concentrated primarily in the loessal soils of southern Poland, where warmer summers add to the advantages of that region for growth of sugar beets. Of the crops mentioned, the greatest decrease in production between prewar and postwar Poland came in that of rye, which was the main crop of that part of the lowland plain transferred to the Soviet Union. Nevertheless, Poland remains primarily a rye-potato-producing country.

During the immediate postwar years crop production was less than half that of prewar years. The reasons for the decrease have little connection with the displacement of Polish territory westward, as has already been brought out earlier in this section. The reasons have to do with factors that virtually sum up all the difficulties Poland faced after 1945: loss of population (including farm labor), lack of fertilizers, neglect during the war years, lack of tractors and horses as well as agricultural implements, lack of seed, and the large number of fields immobilized by land mines and wartime trenches. However, by 1950 Polish agriculture had made a partial recovery and had reached a level of approximately 75 per cent that of the average of the period from 1934 to 1938. Thus, Polish agriculture made the slowest recovery of all the countries of Europe, and in 1950 its level of recovery was 15 to 25 per cent lower than that of other European countries. There is nothing to prevent its eventual return to a general level equal to that of pre-1938 years.

Livestock raising, which plays a great role in the Polish economy, was also at a far lower level in 1950 than it had been before World War II. Normally, Poland raises nearly 10 million cattle, approximately twice as many as are raised in Ireland, Sweden, or Czechoslovakia, and about the same number as are raised in the United Kingdom. Along with Germany, Poland is one of the two greatest swine raising countries of Europe, and its hams have a high reputation on the world market.

Land tenure has been a serious problem in Poland since the birth of the republic after World War I. Poland of 1920 inherited a prevailing system of large estates held by the old aristocracy. From 1918 to 1938 more than 6.5 million acres of land formerly held in large estates were parceled out to create 160,000 new farms and to increase the size of some dwarf farms that had been too small to furnish a livelihood to the owners. During the same period twice as much land was involved in the consolidation, by exchange among owners, of holdings owned by one family. This consolidation increased the efficiency of agriculture to an appreciable extent, since a farmer owning scattered strips wasted many hours traveling from one strip to another to cultivate them. Therefore, by 1939 Poland was chiefly a land of small farmers who owned their own properties.

Nevertheless, an appreciable number of large landholdings still existed in Poland by 1945, and the estate was typical in the new lands received from Germany. Therefore, a vigorous program of agrarian reform was undertaken by the new communist government, and by the end of 1947 nearly 3 million acres of land formerly held in large estates were divided among more than 400,000 farm families. By 1950 Poland was even to a much greater extent than in 1939 a land of small independent farmers. The communist government moved very slowly in collectivizing farms on the Soviet model, and by 1949 less than 1 per cent of the arable land was included in 170 collective farms. On the other hand, the acquisition of approximately 39,000 square miles of nearly empty land (after the ejection of more than 6.5 million Germans) presented the state with an almost ideal opportunity to establish state farms, although many sections were surveyed for small farmers. By 1950 nearly 6 million Poles had been moved into the new territories as farmers and workers.

Mining and Manufacturing

With the transfer of the trans-Oder-Neisse territory to Poland in 1945, Poland assumed control over the entire mining and industrial basin of Silesia (shown in A698), one of the chief industrial areas of Europe. Prior to World War I, Silesia was shared by Austria and Germany (with a small area in Russia), but the boundaries as determined after World War I and partly as a result of the Upper Silesian plebiscite in 1921 gave most of the coal mines and some of the industries to Poland. Passage of the boundary through the center of the highly developed region and the separation of much of the industry from the coal created such practical difficulties that special "frontier zones" had to be created to permit workers and miners to go from home to work and back across the actual boundary line. After 1945 the area was operated as a unit by the new Poland.

The Silesian coal reserves are variously estimated to be from somewhat smaller to somewhat greater than those of the Ruhr, and they are unquestionably greater than those of the Donets Basin of the eastern Ukraine. Under German control the Silesian deposits were not thoroughly exploited because of the better location and greater value—particularly in terms of percentage of coking coal—in the Ruhr. During the interwar period the splitting of the field somewhat retarded efficient exploitation. With nearly all of the

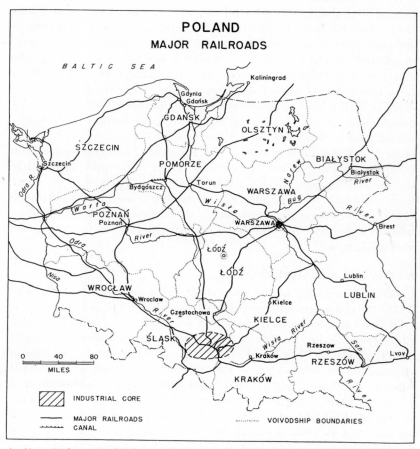

A. Main Railways and Administrative Divisions of Poland. The Upper Silesian industrial area is indicated by oblique lines.

field, except the small portion that was awarded to Czechoslovakia after World War I, under Polish control, exploitation became much more intensive after 1945, and Poland joined the ranks of the main coal-producing countries of the world, ranking fifth after the United States, Great Britain, Soviet Union, and Germany. As an exporter of coal Poland took first place in the first six years after World War

II among the countries of Europe and, except for a brief period during which the United States helped Europe overcome its coal shortage, among the countries of the world. With exports of approximately 32 million tons annually out of an annual production of about 85 million tons, Poland hoped at mid-century to boost its exports to 40 million tons out of its planned annual production of 100 million tons. Possession of the port of Szczecin at the mouth of the Oder facilitates export of coal from Silesia. To Sweden, for example, Poland sends 8 million tons of coal in exchange for iron ore for the Silesian blast furnaces.

Fortunately for Poland, the coal of the Silesian Basin is associated with significant deposits of lead, zinc, and iron ore, a combination that has led to a concentration of industries and large industrial centers in the basin. Industrial centers that were Polish even before 1938 include Katowice (156,000), with coal mines, large iron and steel works, heavy industries, and engineering and chemical works; Sosnowiec, with coal mines, blast furnaces, and textile industries; and Chorzów (formerly Królewska Huta—Königshütte before 1921), with coal mines, blast furnaces, heavy industries, coke ovens, and chemical and engineering works. Mining and industrial centers awarded to Poland in 1945 include Bytom (Beuthen), with lead and zinc mines, blast furnaces, and heavy industries; Gliwice (Gleiwitz), with large steel works; and Zabrze (Zaborze), with coal mines, coke ovens, iron and steel works, and chemical works. This impressive array of industries—all of which were nationalized by the communist government—reveals the significant role that manufacturing is playing in the new Poland.

East of the Silesian industrial concentration lies Kraków (348,-000), the third city of Poland. The ancient capital of Poland and seat of a famous old university, Kraków is as important a cultural center as Warsaw. Unlike Warsaw, it escaped serious damage in World War II, and although its art treasures were taken by the Nazis to Germany, most of them were found and returned to Kraków. Its fortress long guarded the route along the depression of the upper Vistula lying between the Carpathians and the Małopolska Plateau. The salt mines south of the city have been worked for centuries, and Kraków has become one of the chief industrial centers of Poland, producing chemicals, precision goods, textiles, and engineering products. One of the most ambitious projects of postwar Poland and of all the eastern satellite countries was undertaken outside Kraków with the erection of the new town of

Nowa Huta, developed around one of the largest integrated iron and steel works in all Europe. This single installation was planned to double the Polish output of steel and was to produce more than 2 million tons annually. Another large mill was installed at Częstochowa, 62 miles northwest of Kraków, where there are also varied industries and a monastery that attracts scores of thousands of pilgrims each year.

Down the Elbe from upper Silesia is Wrocław (formerly Breslau), the largest city taken over by the Poles after 1945. More than 600,-000 Germans were ejected from Wrocław and were supplanted by an all-Polish population—which, however, had not reached the former total by 1950. Northeast of the Silesian Basin is the mining and industrial area of Kielce near the Łyso Góry. Still farther east is Lublin at the northern edge of the Lublin Plateau.

Łódź (593,000) in central Poland developed independently of mineral resources and engages primarily in textile manufacturing, although it also has chemical and precision equipment industries. As the Manchester of Poland, it shares with Manchester crowded housing conditions and an atmosphere of bleakness. Poznań (Posen) in western Poland likewise developed its varied industries—especially those of chemical production—independently of mineral resources under German administration before it was awarded to Poland after World War I. Centuries before it was taken by the Germans, however, Poznań had been an important Polish center and shows evidences of its mixed development. Northeast of Poznań is Bydgoszcz, which, like Poznań, was transferred to Poland after World War I. Of the three ports on the Baltic—Gdańsk, Gdynia, and Szczecin—Gdańsk is the most important both as a port and as an industrial center. This once-charming old city, with its historic Hanseatic warehouses, was turned largely into rubble as a result of the severe fighting during World War II. Harbor facilities were rapidly restored after 1945, and it resumed its important function as the port at the Vistula outlet.

Unquestionably the greatest city of Poland is the capital, Warsaw (Polish: Warszawa), on the Vistula just upstream from the mouth of the Bug. Although not so centrally located in postwar Poland as it was within the pre-1938 boundaries, it is still the dominant focus of Polish life. Warsaw suffered grievously from many stages of fighting in World War II and, indeed, suffered greater destruction than any other European city; but the physical destruction was compensated by the gain of sentiment among the Poles for their heroic capital. Warsaw held out under heavy siege by the Germans in 1939 until it was starved and beaten into submission days after the rest of the country had been occupied. During the German occupation the large Jewish population (one third of the total for the city) was utterly annihilated, and the famed ghetto was turned into a heap of rubble by the fanatically anti-Jewish Nazis. But the most tragic episode in Warsaw's history occurred in the late summer and fall of 1944, when the Polish underground rose up against the Germans in anticipation of the quick arrival of the Red Army, advancing from the east. However, only when the underground had been subdued after more than two months of fighting against hopeless odds did the Russians enter the city. It was during the uprising—the "Second Battle of Warsaw"—that so much of the severe destruction took place.

Many years will be required for Warsaw to remove even the main scars of the destruction of World War II. Even six years after the war, its population (674,000) was only half that of 1938, although much had been done in the way of restoring necessary facilities and of removing the mountains of rubble. Since the capital also served as one of Poland's principal industrial centers, producing a wide variety of products, restoration of industries was one of its primary tasks. The city's advantages would suggest that it will regain its former importance: it is the country's most important railway junction, and it can utilize the Vistula for an appreciable amount of shipping. But, above all, the capital will serve as a reminder of the indestructible spirit of the Poles.

In addition to the mineral resources mentioned earlier in this section, Poland also possesses an appreciable reserve of lignite in the west-central part of the country. There are also modest reserves of petroleum in Galicia, which, however, are only a minor share of the resources that pre-1938 Poland possessed, and production in 1950 was approximately a third of the 500,000 tons produced in 1938. Some of the scattered pools were recovered in May, 1951, when an exchange of frontier territory between Poland and the Soviet Union extended Poland farther southeastward from Przemyśl.

The Outlook

Poland as it emerged from World War II faced a staggering task of reconstruction: 38 per cent of the national wealth had been destroyed; more than 6 million Polish citizens had been killed (more than half of them Jews); cities had been badly damaged—Warsaw,

Gdańsk, the Silesian cities, and many others; the new territory was depleted of its former German population and had been scorched by war; Poles moved into the new area would require some time to become accustomed to their new homes; livestock had been reduced to one third of the prewar numbers; fields lay waste; transportation was at a complete standstill; the political situation was completely unstable; members of families were scattered not only all over Poland but also all over Europe. From such a status Poland began the long road back to recovery. The role of the United Nations Relief and Rehabilitation Administration was a vital one: without UNRRA help Poland would have starved, and its recovery would have been delayed for years. By early 1947, UNRRA had furnished the equivalent of more than 475 million dollars in material aid to Poland. The scars of war were gradually erased from the Polish landscape, and by 1950 the level of industrial production was twice as high as that of prewar years, although agricultural production was still 25 per cent under that of prewar years. The explanation for the great increase in industrial production is not difficult to find: the addition of the entire German Upper Silesia area increased Poland's capacity enormously. The significance of the new territories (which are frequently referred to by the Poles as the "Regained Provinces"), not only in terms of industry and minerals but also in general terms, is shown by the fact that they contain 30 per cent of all arable land, 28 per cent of metallurgical productive capacity, 50 per cent of the textile industries, 48 per cent of the building materials, 34 per cent of the coal and coke production, and 30 per cent of the population of Poland at mid-century.

One of the most serious deterrents to Poland's continued improvement is the division of Europe by the Iron Curtain. The extent to which Poland trades with western and northwestern Europe despite the Iron Curtain is an indicator of the much greater trade in which the country would engage with a Europe blessed with a relatively free flow of commerce. Poland can offer large amounts of coal and foodstuffs (including its fine hams), as well as zinc ore and cement. And Poland must import 80 per cent of its iron ore, all of its raw cotton, nearly all of its wool, 72 per cent of its leather, and appreciable amounts of machinery. The Council for Mutual Economic Aid (the Soviet attempt at a "Marshall Plan" for the satellite countries) might help Poland overcome some of its deficiencies, but an opening of trade channels is highly desirable.

The analysis of Poland presented in this chapter reveals that, despite the loss of one fifth of its former territory, Poland possessed after 1945 a sounder geographical base than it did before 1938. Ethnographically, postwar Poland was a more uniform and unified state. Germans in the west were expelled, and various Russian groups in the east were exchanged for Polish people who were left on the eastern side of the Curzon Line after 1945. With its compact shape, its homogeneous population, its large amount of arable land, its valuable mining and associated industrial development, and its location near the heart of Europe, Poland has most of the qualities for a successful existence.

· 44 ·

The Land
of the Soviets

Difficulties in Analyzing the Geography of Russia

For a number of reasons the Soviet Union is the most difficult country in Europe to analyze geographically, and a consideration of the difficulties involved reveals significant aspects of the country. First, this vast state extends from the central meridian of Europe to the Pacific coast and is truly Eurasian in both its location and geographical character. Thus, a study of the geography of Europe must certainly give careful attention to a country that occupies most of the eastern half of the continent, and yet such a study—if restricted to Europe only—must omit consideration of by far the greater part of the Soviet Union. This is true despite the fact that the portion of the Soviet Union lying west of the Urals is alone slightly larger than all other European countries combined. Until the middle of the nineteenth century a discussion of Russia had to concern itself only with that part of the Russian Empire lying west of the Urals, since Siberia played a very minor role in the imperial economy. Today, however, central Asia and Siberia, as well as the Far Eastern regions, play a very significant role in the Soviet Union, albeit the role is still definitely subordinate to that of European Russia. In certain respects, a study of Soviet Russia that limits itself to only the European part is—as a study of the country as a whole—about as invalid as would be a study of the United States that limited itself to that part lying east of the Mississippi. The analogy is not strictly accurate, since the United States west of the Mississippi is more effectively developed than is Asiatic Russia, but as a matter of fact Soviet Asia comprises a larger portion of the Soviet Union than that part of the United States lying west of the Mississippi comprises of the United States as a whole. Therefore, in these three chapters on the Union of Soviet Socialist Republics, brief mention will be made of certain aspects of the Soviet Union as a whole, but by far the major emphasis will be on Russia in Europe.

A second difficulty in studying the geography of Russia is imposed by the country's great size. Touching the meridian of 20° East Longitude in the southeastern Baltic at its most westerly point and the meridian of 170° West Longitude at East Cape at its most easterly point, the Soviet Union thus extends through 170° of longitude, almost half the distance around the earth. However, most of this extent is at relatively high latitude and is not so great in terms of miles as might appear at first glance. Furthermore, the Union reaches from approximately 35° North Latitude (the latitude of Crete and Cyprus in the Mediterranean) to more than 80° North Latitude, appreciably farther north than North Cape in Norway. Within this vast area there are naturally tremendous differences in geographical environments. Therefore, a study such as this encounters great difficulty in reducing the geographical aspects to proportions suitable for brief examination.

The paucity of reliable information is the third and most serious difficulty in any attempt to study the geography of the Soviet Union. For three decades, almost no field work has been done in Russia by non-Soviet geographers, and the critical post-1945 period has been virtually a closed book in terms of field work in the Union by non-Russian geographers. This does not mean that the Soviet geographers themselves have not been engaged in geographical work. Indeed, geographers are key men in Soviet planning and development, and a surprising amount of their writings have reached the western world. However, such writings have been of limited value because of the small number of geographers who can utilize the Russian language. Furthermore, few statistics of any kind are released by the Soviet government. The result is that much of the information, not only about strictly geographical matters but about many others as well, that circulates has been pieced together and probably has many deficiencies. Such data as are actually furnished by the Soviet government are largely for propaganda purposes and, despite their having a certain amount of factual basis, must be handled with extreme caution. Many of the data are only half-truths or distortions because of the statistical juggling to which they have been subjected. The evidence is that they are rarely pure fabrications, but careful analysis usually reveals that they can rarely be accepted at face value. Data based on prices and wages are especially suspect, since money values in

Russia fluctuate as much as or more than those of western European countries. However that may be, interest in the Soviet Union since 1941 and especially since 1945 has stimulated an unprecedented flow of writings on the Soviet Union. Just before mid-century a number of very good geographical works on Russia appeared, and some Russian works were translated into English (see Bibliography).

A fourth difficulty is a subjective one: the way in which a student of the geography of Russia correlates one fact with another on other than a strictly concrete plane may depend to some extent on the student's economic-political philosophy. One's philosophy cannot, of course, alter the distribution of minerals and waterways, for example; but one's philosophy may well influence his belief about whether or not slave labor was used in building the Volga-Don Canal. One's philosophy cannot alter the fact that the Soviet Union is a great country in terms of area, resources, and military power; but one's philosophy may well influence his attitude concerning Soviet political maturity and territorial intentions. Likewise, one's philosophy will largely determine whether or not he believes that the growth of certain industrial areas in Russia was on the basis of radically new Soviet theories or was on the basis of long-accepted economic principles.

Finally, a view of Soviet geography is often clouded by the difficulty of separating what has been done from what is being done and, again, from what is to be done. In certain respects the Soviets are like Americans in their thinking and hoping in terms of the future, but the much greater need for development in Russia causes the Soviets frequently to speak of projects as completed when they often have only just been started. The fault is not to be entirely censured, since it indicates a recognition of a potential that is indeed great, and it indicates confidence that the dreams will actually be fulfilled. Certainly the Soviets accomplished a very great deal between 1928 and 1950, somewhat in the way that Germany exploited its potential between 1870 and 1914 or in the way that the United States has expanded in the last century. Probably the greatest difference is that the Soviet growth has been accompanied by an actual revolution and has received greater publicity, both pro and con.

Location and Area

Location. The supreme fact in Russia's geography and history is the country's interior and northerly location in the north-central part of the greatest landmass on earth. The interior location exercises profound influences on both the Russian climate and cultural-economic relationships. The effect of location on climate will be discussed in the next section. Culturally and economically, the interior location has served to isolate Russia both by sheer distance and by the nature of the peripheral zones. Consequently, Russia has not been subjected to numerous stimulating cultural contacts that have contributed to the development of either the country itself or to the breadth of thinking of the people. Only by great effort during occasional periods—of which the present time is one—have the Russians been able to lift their isolated country by the bootstraps and take advantage of new ideas and techniques, including those developed within its own borders. Thus the Russian thinking has often displayed marked provinciality and a suspicion of outsiders, and the present attitude toward foreigners is only an exaggeration of an attitude that has existed for centuries. One factor that undoubtedly contributes to such a suspicion is that the lack of great trade routes across the area has meant that any great influx of outsiders has usually been an actual invasion, such as that by the Tatars, Swedes, French, or Germans. Outsiders have indeed entered Russia peacefully—as did the Volga Germans in the eighteenth century—and the new ideas they brought invariably stimulated new developments. However, new groups were always swallowed up either by the vastness of the land or by the people, and the stimulus diminished.

Whereas the entire southern boundary of the Soviet Union is a land frontier, it is true that the northern boundary lies along the Arctic Sea coast, giving the Soviet Union one of the longest seacoasts of any country in the world. But this long Arctic coast is practically useless except at the extreme western end, where the North Atlantic Drift keeps the port of Murmansk open throughout the year. Even at Archangel, at the southern end of the White Sea, the harbor is ordinarily frozen from November to May. Farther east the ice-free period lasts for only one or two months each summer, and ships attempting to steam from Archangel and up the Yenisey to the lumber port of Igarka must adhere to close schedules. The Soviets have worked out a carefully co-ordinated system in which weather stations, icebreakers, and observation aircraft co-operate to guide freighters along the Arctic coast during the short and hazardous period of navigation. Even so, the passage of ships along the entire Arctic coast from Murmansk to Bering Strait remains a perilous undertaking in most summers.

The Pacific coast is not quite so severely handicapped. Yet even the harbor at Vladivostok—despite the fact that its latitude is about the same as that of Boston or Marseille—is kept open only with the aid of powerful icebreakers. The Sea of Okhotsk is subject to fogs and floating ice in summer, and navigation there is hazardous. Sino-Soviet agreement in 1950 on joint control of the port of Dairen (Dalny) and the naval base of Port Arthur on the Kwantung Peninsula in the northern Yellow Sea gives the Soviet Union a warm water outlet, but that outlet is into a partly enclosed sea and is far from Russia's producing and consuming centers. The same may be said of Vladivostok.

The absorption of the three former Baltic states in 1940 and acquisition of northern East Prussia in 1945 gave the Soviet Union several relatively minor ports that are ice-free at virtually all times, but these open into the Baltic, an almost enclosed sea. Leningrad harbor is iced in beyond the help of icebreakers for several months each winter, and it, too, opens into an arm of the Baltic. Thus, all Russian Baltic ports are several hundred miles from the busy sea lanes of the North Sea, and a Russian naval fleet would experience great difficulty in escaping from the Baltic against determined efforts to keep it bottled up.

The other Soviet contact with the sea is along the northern and eastern Black Sea coast. Frozen harbors do not present a great problem here, although such ports as Odessa along the northern coast are sometimes frozen in for a few weeks in winter. Even Odessa, however, is about a thousand miles from the main line of travel in the Mediterranean Sea, and again a Russian naval fleet could be restricted to the Black Sea by a strong power holding the Bosporus and the Dardanelles. Even the establishment of Soviet control over the satellite states in eastern Europe gave Russia no outlets to the open sea. Thus, in proportion to its size, the Soviet Union is astonishingly cut off from the tremendous influence of the sea in promoting cultural and economic contacts with other areas of the world.

Even on the land the Union is subjected to a frustrating isolation. Except on the west, the borders of the Soviet Union traverse thousands of miles of rugged and sparsely populated mountains or barren desert areas. Moreover, through the centuries the few people who have lived in these rugged or dry regions have themselves been culturally retarded so that contact with them has brought no greatly stimulating ideas or techniques.

It is in eastern Europe that the country has had its greatest opportunity for cultural-economic contacts. It is in this same area that the most favorable geographic environment extends into the vast Russian territory. And, as should be expected, it is in this area that Russia has had its greatest development. Until the twentieth century, Germans, Scandinavians, Austrians, Hungarians, and other European peoples entered Russia in appreciable numbers; and small numbers of influential people from such countries as France were invited to the tsar's court as architects, artists, and technicians. During the same period many Russians traveled in central and western Europe and attended schools in Switzerland, France, Germany, and England, learning of the greater development in those countries. The extension of Russia toward central Europe was—except for a few cultural centers—considered the poorest part of Europe outside the Balkans, but it was of tremendous significance to Russia. Loss of part of this territory to the "buffer states" of eastern Europe after 1920 was a great blow to the Soviet Union. However, the country turned to the general western philosophy of economic development, for assistance in the execution of which numbers of foreign technicians were imported; and increased use of modern methods of communication have tended to break down the centuries-old isolation. The adoption of western techniques and the close co-ordination between Russia and the satellite states has gone far to widen the Soviet horizon—as, indeed, did the contact of Russian soldiers with the much higher material culture of central Europe.

Nevertheless, isolation for the great mass of the Soviet peoples persists in many ways. The present Soviet government permits the people to have contact only with those aspects of the outside world that the government approves—and only in the way in which the government approves. Thus, the Soviets may have radios, but they may hear only those broadcasts that the government wants them to hear. No great streams of varied travelers or traders pass through to bring other viewpoints. Such complete control would be unthinkable in a country like Switzerland or France. Thus, the interior location of Russia has had incalculable consequences, historically, culturally, politically, and economically. Isolation has influenced human actions, and, in turn, human actions have influenced isolation.

"Geopolitical" Location. As early as 1904 the British geographer Sir Halford Mackinder viewed the interior location of Russia as possessing great hypothetical significance. Pointing to the vast area of Eurasia that lies in the drainage basins of rivers emptying into the Arctic Ocean, the interior seas, or into sandy wastes, Mackinder termed the area the "Heartland" and declared that the approximate center of the area comprised the geographical pivot of history. That point lies near the center of the present Soviet Union. Access of sea power to this vast area, Mackinder pointed out, was denied, and climate and relief made land access extremely difficult. From the Heartland have come hordes of invading Huns and Tatars who ravaged Europe. The vast rimlands around the Heartland include the African appendage of the Eurasian landmass, and the entire Eurasian-African mass constitutes what Mackinder called the "World-Island." Later, Mackinder expressed the significance of the spatial arrangements in this way:

"Who rules East Europe commands the Heartland:
Who rules the Heartland commands the World-Island:
Who rules the World-Island commands the World."

The fact that Mackinder's hypothesis is obviously debatable is illustrated by a counterhypothesis proposed by the American geopolitician Nicholas John Spykman. He declared that the foreign policy of the United States should be to prevent the same power from controlling both the Heartland of Eurasia and the rimlands. An examination of these two hypotheses is, of course, a study in itself and is beyond the scope of this volume. However, the interior location and extent of the Soviet Union obviously possess certain strategic assets, which may well be summed up in the term "political-geographical advantages" or "geopolitical advantages" if the latter is considered synonymous with the former.

Area. Some suggestion of the size of the Soviet Union was given in terms of latitudinal and longitudinal extent in the preceding section. In specific terms, this vast extent is equal to approximately 8.5 million square miles. The Soviet Union thus possesses 16 per cent or one sixth of the 50.97 million square miles of the land surface of the earth free from ice caps, or one seventh of the total land surface of the earth including Antarctica and Greenland. From the Baltic Sea to Bering Strait the Soviet Union extends for approximately 7,000 miles, and from Cape Chelyuskin to the Afghanistan frontier it reaches for nearly 3,000 miles. The Union is, then, nearly three times the size of the United States (3.02 million square miles).

Something of the significance of the interior location has already been shown. The handicaps of such great distances as exist in the Soviet Union should likewise be recognized. The difficulty of supplying the imperial army in 1904–5 during the Russo-Japanese War not only over a single-track railway but over thousands of miles of sheer distance was one important factor in Russia's defeat. The movement of goods over such great distances becomes enormously expensive, and the amount of coal burned on the Trans-Siberian Railway per ton of goods carried from end to end is very high.

An area as vast as that of Soviet Russia would have to embrace very poor country indeed not to include a large number of diverse mineral deposits. Much of the Soviet area does indeed embrace very poor country, but enough of it is well endowed to give the 8.5 million square miles of the country great mineral wealth. However, in terms of mineral wealth per square mile or per capita for the country as a whole, the Soviet Union is not especially highly endowed, as will be shown in Chapter 45.

It is easy to see how the Soviets, with such a great territorial base and with the infused pride in the Soviet system and accomplishments, should think in terms of "bigness." Like Americans, especially in the late nineteenth century and early decades of the twentieth century, the Soviets take great delight in pointing out the big things in the Soviet Union. They point out that they have the largest lake in the world (Caspian Sea), the deepest lake in the world (Lake Baikal), the longest glacier in the world (Fedchenko Glacier in the Tien Shan, 50 miles long), and the greatest deposits of several minerals (manganese and potash, for example). The Soviets also claim that they have several of the greatest man-made works in the world—such as the Kuybyshev hydroelectric dam under construction at mid-century—but such claims as these are difficult to verify. The Soviets have long "planned" to erect the tallest building in the world in their "Palace of the Soviets" in Moscow.

Climate and Real Size of the Soviet Union

The preceding section mentioned that the interior location of the Soviet Union had profound effects on the country's climate. In the case of climate, the location must be considered not only in terms of the country's interior position but also in terms of its latitude. A glance at a map will reveal that only a relatively small part of the Union lies south of the parallel of 50° North Latitude: the southern Ukraine, the Caucasus, and the desert of Turkestan. When it is remembered that no part of the United States extends as far north as 50° and that most of the most highly developed part of the United States lies between 35° and 45°, the handicap of northerly location of the Soviet Union can be appreciated—if the interior location of the Soviet Union is kept in mind. Discussions of western European countries showed that latitudes of 45° to 60° are no great handicap on the west coast of Eurasia, where the warming effect of the westerly winds blowing from the North Atlantic Drift creates abnormally high temperatures for the latitude. In the relatively large landmass of eastern Europe, on the other hand, the beneficial effects of the ocean and the westerly winds are greatly diminished. In the Asiatic extension of the Soviet Union, conditions opposite to those of northwestern Europe exist: winter temperatures are much colder for the average of the latitude rather than much warmer—as they are in western Norway, for example. The extreme winter cold of Siberia not only affects that portion of the Soviet Union but also exercises a strong influence on European Russia, since the cold air extends westward over the ineffective Urals barrier and blankets eastern Europe for weeks at a time.

The north-south trend of the January isotherms is determined both by the cold air extending westward from Asia and by the North Atlantic Drift; these lines of equal temperature in eastern Europe in A28 reveal the situation very clearly. Thus, Leningrad and Astrakhan' have approximately the same mean temperature (19° F) in January; the same is true of Moscow and Gur'yev at the northern end of the Caspian Sea (13° F). Thus, the mean temperature for January decreases regularly from west to east: at Vil'nyus 23° F, at Smolensk 18°, at Gor'kiy 11°, at Kazan' 8°, and at Molotov 3.5°. The length of duration of the snow cover increases from southwest to northeast, from 20 days per year at the mouth of the Dniester to 146 days at Moscow and to more than 220 days in the Pechora Basin west of the Northern Urals. Cloudiness and humidity are both high throughout the winter, and the average number of completely clear days for the entire year is only 39 at Leningrad and only 91 at Astrakhan'.

In summer, isotherms in European Russia extend west-southwest to east-northeast and thus lie at right angles to the winter isotherms, as is the case in Europe in general (A29). Thus, temperatures decrease not from west to east, as they do in winter, but from south to north, dropping from 77° F at Astrakhan' to 65° at Moscow and to 59° at Archangel. Thus, the summers are very warm in the southern part of European Russia but are pleasantly mild in the central part and quite cool in the north.

One of the most critical aspects of the Russian climate is the amount and variability of the precipitation. In the central and western part the total precipitation averages about 24 inches annually and is relatively reliable. The cool temperatures make this amount of precipitation adequate for agriculture and forests, as was brought out in the discussion of Poland in the preceding chapter. Toward the southeast, however, precipitation decreases steadily, and at Astrakhan' it is less than 7 inches. Most of the southern Ukraine receives 16 to 20 inches on the average, but the appreciably higher temperatures during the growing season, when most of the rain falls, make this rainfall less effective than the same amount would be farther north. More serious, however, is the fact that the rainfall is highly variable, like that of the Texas Panhandle and eastern Colorado. In more than half the years the rainfall drops well below average and in some years is as little as 10 inches. Such drought years are, of course, disastrous for crops, as was tragically illustrated in the "Dust Bowl" period in the 1930's in the United States. The critical point is that, in comparison with the United States, a far greater percentage of Soviet cropland is subject to such variability and droughts. Thus, the Soviet climate imposes four handicaps even on European Russia, the most favored part of the country: several months in winter are so cold as to thwart normal activity in most of the area; several weeks in summer are hot and dry in the southern section; variability of precipitation produces precarious agricultural conditions in most of the most important crop area; and, although the western and northern parts of the country are affected by storminess to some extent, the path of stimulating cyclones rarely crosses the core of the area, especially during the winter, when the Asiatic high pressure repels the eastward-moving storms.

The net result of the cold of the north and the dryness of the south—a pattern that is especially strong in Soviet Asia—is that much of the country is too dry or too cold for either satisfactory agriculture or effective settlement. The better conditions of the west, the increased cold of the north, and the dryness of the south combine to create a roughly triangular agricultural area with its

irregular base along the western frontier from Lake Ladoga to the
Black Sea and its apex in the Kuznetsk Basin in south-central
Siberia. Within this "Fertile Triangle" are included approximately
three fourths of the people of the Union and three fourths of the
arable land. Within it lie most of the industrial centers and, more
coincidentally than logically, most of the important mineral deposits. Thus is seen another illustration of the fact that cultural-
economic development tends to be coextensive with the area that
is most highly endowed geographically, especially in terms of climate. The interesting Soviet social experiment is thus being con-
ducted in an area that is not so highly endowed as the area of
northwestern Europe but that is achieving its best results under the
conditions most nearly approaching those of northwestern and central Europe. In this respect, the 8.5 million square miles of Soviet
area contract markedly in terms of really effective territory, since
the extent of arable land is found to be no more than that of the
United States (435 million acres), and there is evidence that it is
even less. The remaining millions of acres of tundra, forest, and
desert are not, of course, to be dismissed, since they have both economic and strategic value as well as potential significance in relation to possible future technological developments.

The Soviet State

Historical-Territorial Evolution. The growth of such a vast state
as the Soviet Union, with its complex ethnographic structure, has
naturally been a long and intricate development. Only a few of
the most significant aspects of geographical importance can be considered here.

Because of the relatively open character of the steppe joining
southern European Russia with the heart of Asia, Asiatic peoples
migrated into southern European Russia or invaded that area with
relative ease for thousands of years until about the seventeenth
century. Stone Age peoples used the steppe route as a path into the
Black Sea region, just as their contemporaries or perhaps some of
the same peoples used the loess Foreland along the northern edge
of the Central European Uplands for their movements to the English Channel. Scythians, Huns, Bulgars, Magyars, and others moved
into the Ukrainian steppe during the millennium centering on the
time of Christ. Numerous Greek colonies were established all
around the Black Sea by Greek traders passing through the Bosporus and Dardanelles. Toward the north, Finno-Ugric peoples

moved slowly through the coniferous forests from the Urals region and eventually reached the Gulf of Bothnia. Between these two groups, Slavic peoples gradually pushed eastward from a center north of the Carpathians and moved along the belt of mixed and deciduous forests into the Oka River basin.

In the ninth century, bands of Swedish Vikings (Varägians or Varangians) began pressing southeastward from the Baltic, and other Varangians under Rurik were asked to enter the lands of the Slavs to drive off the uninvited Swedes. Succeeding in their mission, Rurik and his followers united several Slavic groups and pushed down the Dnieper to establish a strong center at Kiev, whence they established trade relationships with Byzantium. The crushing invasion of the Tatars in the early thirteenth century broke Slavic power in the Ukraine, and the Tatars, after destroying lands and cities toward the south, penetrated even into the mixed forest zone to the fortified towns of Vladimir and Moscow. But these forest towns were able to maintain themselves against the Tatars, who were a steppe people unaccustomed to the forest environment. With the weakening of Tatar power, Muscovite strength was extended from its center at Moscow both northwestward and eastward down the Volga, and in the sixteenth century Ivan the Terrible was able to proclaim himself "Tsar of all the Russias." A reinvasion by Mongols took place as late as the seventeenth century, when the Kalmucks swept westward from their Asiatic homeland and even seized Moscow briefly in 1633. But the Russians were strong enough to reassert themselves almost immediately, and under such especially vigorous rulers as Peter the Great and Catherine the Great they finally extended their control to the Baltic shores and Black Sea coasts, breaking the strength of such contemporary powers as Lithuania, Poland, and Sweden.

From the seventeenth century onward, the Russians turned the tide against the peoples beyond the Urals and Caspian. Trappers and traders pushed into Siberia, utilizing the tributaries of the northward-flowing rivers to move east and west. During the nineteenth century this eastward movement became a migration, and the final outposts were conquered in Turkestan only in 1881. Thus, the conquest of the Soviet East closely paralleled in time and in character the conquest of the American West, both in Canada and in the United States.

The losses of Russian territory—most of which proved to be only temporary losses—after World War I may be seen in A180. All or parts of several of the eastern European "buffer" states were carved out of Russian territory: all of Finland (except the Åland Islands); all of the three Baltic states (Estonia, Latvia, and Lithuania), except the Memelland in southern Lithuania; much of Poland; and the Bessarabian part of Rumania. By the end of 1940 the Soviet Union had recovered—by ultimatum and, in the case of those Finnish territories that were retaken, by war—all the areas Russia lost after World War I, with the exception of most of Finland and part of Poland. The upset of territorial alignments by World War II was only temporary, and by the end of 1945 the Soviet Union had returned to its 1940 boundaries and had gained, in addition, the Pechenga (Petsamo) Corridor from Finland, northern East Prussia from Germany, the Ruthenian "tail" from Czechoslovakia, the central Asiatic territory of Tannu-Tuva (absorbed in 1944), and southern Sakhalin Island (Karafuto) and the Kuril Islands from Japan, a total gain over 1938 of approximately 270,000 square miles, an area about the size of the state of Texas.

Ethnographic and Administrative Pattern. Differences among the eastern Slavic peoples themselves and the presence of remnant peoples from the many immigrating and invading groups give European Russia—as well as Asiatic Russia—a complex ethnographic structure, partly reflected in the generalized map A171. However, outward migrations from the Moscow core area by Great Russians has tended to submerge some minority groups, and transfers of whole groups of people during World War II further simplified the pattern.

The core group of the Soviet peoples is that of the Great Russians, centering around Moscow but extending in a narrow band across Siberia to Vladivostok. They number approximately 110 millions, more than half the total population of the Soviet Union. The Ukrainians (sometimes called Little Russians) are the second largest group in the Union, numbering about 36 millions; and the Belorussians (or White Russians), the third-largest group, number about 10 millions. These three groups make up more than three fourths of the total Soviet population and 85 to 90 per cent of the population of European Russia. These are the only Soviet peoples who can properly be called "Russians," although it is preferable to call the Ukrainians by their proper name, which means "frontier people."

In northwestern European Russia are four main groups of non-Slavic peoples, including the Finno-Karelians, who number less than

500,000; the Estonians, who numbered more than a million before 1940 but many of whom have been exiled by the Soviets; the Latvians, who numbered more than 1.6 millions before several thousand of them fled Latvia during World War II and before other thousands were exiled; and the Lithuanians, who are the largest of the groups of this area, with about 2.5 millions. Most of the Germans who formerly occupied northern East Prussia fled or were expelled to post-1945 Germany. The part of European Russia that is most complex ethnographically is the Caucasus, where the three Soviet Socialist Republics of Georgia, Azerbaydzhan, and Armenia indicate that the largest groups are the Georgians, 2.3 millions; the Azerbaydzhani, 2.3 millions; and the Armenians, 2.2 millions. As is mentioned in Chapter 12, the valleys and basins of the Caucasus range are an ethnographic mosaic in which the largest groups are the Dagestans, Ossetians, and Kabardinians. In the northern Caucasus there was until World War II a Kalmuck A.S.S.R., populated by remnants of the Mongols who migrated thither in the seventeenth century. During the German invasion in World War II the Kalmucks appear to have co-operated with the Nazis, because their A.S.S.R. disappeared from the Soviet administrative map, and the Kalmucks are no longer listed as a people in the Soviet Union. The same fate befell the Crimean Tatars. The thousands of Germans who had settled in the Ukraine and in the lower Volga region were moved eastward after the Nazi invasion in 1941, and the German Volga Republic also disappeared from the map.

The entire Urals area, but especially the southern part, is also ethnographically complex, as is reflected by the presence of several A.S.S.R.'s. The largest of these groups are the Mordvinians (1.5 millions), Chuvash (1.4 millions), Bashkirs (0.9 million), Udmurts (0.6 million), and the Mari and Komi (both with less than 0.5 million).

This ethnographic complexity requires the Soviet Union to give special consideration to the many groups of people, as is indicated by the basic division of the Union into sixteen constituent republics, each of which is built around a larger ethnographic group. This same recognition is extended to the smaller groups in the A.S.S.R.'s, autonomous oblasts, and national okrugs. In following such a method, the Soviet Union has arrived at a potentially successful formula for administering numerous different peoples, and one of the most frequently sounded propaganda notes is the individual recognition accorded each people. However, despite the fact that the Soviets have long pointed out that each group was encouraged to preserve its local language and customs, all schools throughout the Union now teach Russian in addition to any existing local language. Thus, the "Russification" that had been forsworn in the 1920's is being practiced at least to some extent as it was under the tsars.

The Role of the Soviet Government. Far more than any other government in the principal states of Europe or in the world, the Soviet government plays a dominant role in the human geography of the country. Since the state has complete ownership and control over all land and producers' goods, the edicts of the government determine the details of the distribution and use of crops, factories, and even towns. Since the Communist Party is the only party permitted in Russia, and since it operates its own political machinery alongside and even above the actual governmental machinery, the effective government is actually an expression of the party. The Supreme Soviet is, it is true, composed of local representatives elected by universal suffrage, but the candidates are picked by the Communist Party and are the only candidates for which the Soviet citizen can vote. Furthermore, it is the powerful *Politburo,* an executive body of the Central Committee of the Communist Party, that informs the Supreme Soviet what policies it shall follow; the Supreme Soviet simply "rubber-stamps" the *Politburo's* decisions.

Communist dogma states that the Communist Party is the only party that is the true bearer of the rights of the workers, who are the real basis of society. Therefore, not only is there no need for opposition parties, but also opposition axiomatically becomes treasonable and can be voiced only by an obvious enemy of the people. The edicts and plans voiced by the party and "rubber-stamped" by the governmental machinery then become inviolable, and their substance cannot be criticized. Thus, a decision to establish a state farm in an area that is too dry or too cold for agriculture as it is conceived in the United States cannot be opposed. Therefore, failure of the farm to produce must be due to "sabotage" or "lax discipline."

Since 1920 every aspect of Soviet life, particularly economic and industrial activity, has been centrally planned and centrally directed. The method and results are both good and bad. Lack of planning on any scale before 1920 and lack of effort to utilize existing resources and improve techniques grievously retarded Russian cultural and economic development. It was one of the burning missions of the revolutionary government to overcome the old handicaps. Central planning and central direction on a tremendous scale drove the people into new and expanded fields of work. In three decades enormous changes had been wrought, and in many areas the landscape was completely altered. Some of these changes will be discussed in following sections. The critical point in Russia today is not whether or not certain material improvements have been made. There is absolutely no doubt that mineral production, steel production, housing, and a host of other material items have been enormously expanded. The critical point is whether the price that the Soviet people have paid on a human level was even necessary in the first place or is justified in the second place.

Imperialism by Proxy. One aspect of Soviet communism that despite its political character also has very definite geographical overtones is its alleged altruism. Communism offers itself as a philosophy unrelated to any particular state's nationalistic aspirations, yet a glance at the map will reveal that at least at the end of 1951 there was no communist state that was not either contiguous with the Soviet Union or with another state that was contiguous with the Union, with the one exception of Albania. The reason for this may, on the one hand, be laid to the normal geographical spread of an idea or technique outward from a center, or, on the other hand, it may be laid to the fact that nowhere has the communist minority been able to impose its control on a state without the backing or at least the potential backing of the Red Army or its local equivalent. The communist element in Italy, for example, has long been greater than was that of Czechoslovakia when the 1948 *coup d'état* gave the communists control.

The fact that the Soviets are obviously more interested in extending Russian power than in helping the oppressed proletariat of the world was conclusively and dramatically illustrated by the attitude that Soviet Russia and its satellites demonstrated when Yugoslavia's Tito revealed that although he intended to follow sound Marxist-Leninist doctrine—as he saw it—he had no intention of making Yugoslavia a territorial extension of the Soviet Union. Thus, despite Yugoslavia's avowed adherence to communist doctrine, the country was declared by the Cominform to be an enemy of the working people—all this not because Yugoslavia abandoned communism but because it refused to submit to Russian domination. As a result of Yugoslavia's disaffection, Albania was isolated from the rest of the communist bloc.

With this demonstration of the apparently true character of the communist movement it became apparent that the communist parties in the various countries of the world were adjuncts of the Communist Party in the Soviet Union and were, therefore, adjuncts of the Soviet government. Until the end of 1951 the latest victim of a local communist party's delivery of its country into Soviet hands was Czechoslovakia. Thus, in these seemingly strictly political connections it may be seen that there are two significant geographical aspects: there is no communist state that does not lie in the immediate peripheral area of the Soviet Union, and no local communist party has ever come to power without immediately delivering its country to Soviet control—although the single state of Yugoslavia severed its Russian connections after three years in the Russian camp. Consequently—without reference to the ideological values or dangers of communism—it would seem that world communism is a form of Russian imperialism by proxy.

Population and Pattern of Settlement

Total Population. The latest official Russian census is that of 1939, a fact that obviously makes it difficult to analyze the present demographic situation in the Soviet Union. The 1939 census gave a total population of 170.5 millions, and the territories added in 1940 brought the figure up to 193 millions. During the succeeding decade important population changes took place, but the extent of such changes can only be estimated on such bases as that of election lists, which are assembled on the basis of population. The best evidence is that the Soviet population at mid-century exceeded 200 millions, despite the very great number of war dead and an appreciable emigration. Thus, the Soviet Union as a whole has nearly three times the population of any other country of Europe.

Birth Rate and Death Rate. Like most of the other countries of Europe C, Russia has a very high birth rate. Again, figures are neither official nor exact, since the Russians have not released complete demographic statistics. However, official statistics show that in the late 1920's the birth rate varied from 40 to 43 per thousand, and the birth rate at mid-century was estimated to be roughly between 30 and 40 per thousand. Thus, the birth rate is the highest of all the Great Powers and is much higher than that of the United States. The increasing number of young people suggests that the high birth rate will continue and that by 1970 the total population of the Soviet Union will exceed 244 millions, at which time more than one out of every ten persons in the world will be a citizen of the Soviet Union. The high death rate that characterized the Soviet Union in the 1920's has been steadily decreasing through improved hygiene and medical attention, although the rate is still well above that of western Europe and appears to vary between 15 and 18 per thousand according to the section of the Soviet Union.

Density. Even the European part of the Soviet Union displays great variability in density of population from one large area to another, as do the United States and Canada. No other European country except the three Fennoscandian countries of Norway, Sweden, and Finland has such a high percentage of its territory unsuited to more than very sparse population. The tundra and taiga regions of the north, the Pripet Marsh region of the west-center, and the dry steppe and desert regions of the southeast (of European Russia) are all areas of sparse population. Central European Russia, most of the Ukraine, and the southern Urals are regions of dense population. The relatively restricted territory suitable to human settlement—principally the Fertile Triangle—and the large and growing population combine to give very high densities of population, in terms of environmental capacity, in the more favorable areas. Rural population densities range from more than 250 per square mile around Moscow and in the western Ukraine to 130 to 250 over most of the Ukraine and the broad corridor connecting the Ukraine and the Moscow region. Such densities, although high in comparison with most of the United States, do not sound startling when compared with rural densities in northern France, Belgium, or similarly favored areas of western Europe; but, when the variability of the rainfall and the length of growing season of the densely populated parts of the Soviet Union are considered, the densities become very high.

There are two other significant aspects of these densities: continued increase of the population at its present rapid rate will soon place enormous pressure on the capacity of the land to support the population; and such density also explains one reason why the Soviets are making such vigorous attempts to expand the area of effective settlement in terms of agricultural productivity. Thus, despite the enormous area of the Soviet Union and the vast expanses of territory with less than one person per square mile, Rus-

sia will in the near future actually be exerting sufficient pressure
on its resources to become "overpopulated," especially if it does
not expand its trade or if its control over its satellites is lost.

With increasing industrialization and increasing mechanization
of agriculture in the Soviet Union, the division of population between urban centers and country has undergone a rapid and startling change. From 1914 until 1926 the percentage of population
living in cities as opposed to agricultural villages and towns increased from 15 to 18 per cent, whereas from 1926 to 1939 it increased from 18 to 33 per cent. The city population has probably
increased appreciably since 1939, but no figures are available.

The Changing Russian Landscape

The dawn of the twentieth century even before the Soviets came
to power, but especially after they did so, marked the beginning
of a profound alteration in the landscape of European Russia.
The industrial revolution in Russia, which had only begun in the
latter decades of the nineteenth century, brought a fuller exploitation of resources and communications and a growing industrial
urban population. Since the Soviets seized power just as the industrial revolution reached appreciable magnitude and had as a
main point in their program a maximum economic development,
the economic-geographical alterations of the landscape in some
sections have been astonishing. The following two chapters discuss the basic geographical environments that exist in European
Russia and consider some of the broad changes that the Soviets
have made. Although such changes are great, they are actually
not so great as Soviet propaganda attempts to indicate, and probably the basic character of the Soviet people has been little altered.
The old French proverb was recently aptly applied to Russia by
a former Russian: *Plus ça change, plus c'est la même chose* (the
more it changes, the more it remains the same).

· 45 ·

Physical and
Economic Aspects
of European Russia

Structure and Relief

The Russian Platform. Except in its fringe areas, European
Russia includes a tremendous expanse of relatively level area approximately equal in size to all the rest of Europe with its great
variety of mountains, uplands, basins, rift valleys, and indentations
of the sea. Thus, the broad eastern part of Europe presents a
pronounced contrast with the western half—that is, all of non-
Russian Europe.

Underlying all of European Russia is a great thickness of very
old crystalline rocks similar to those already described in Chapter
15. This old crystalline platform has remained resistant to mountain-building forces, and has been subjected only to slight bending,
faulting, broad elevations, and depressions. During periods when
the crystalline foundation rocks were somewhat depressed, the sea
has invaded large areas, and sedimentary rocks such as limestone,
sandstone, and shale have formed in the invading seas. Under the
weight of such deposits the crystalline basement has sagged, forming great synclines in some portions.

Thus, the sedimentary cover of the basement rocks is not uniform
in thickness. Furthermore, the crystalline rocks have been pushed
upward as horsts in several places and at different geological periods. Those that exert some effect on the present relief are the
Kursk-Voronezh Horst extending northwest-southeast across the
Central Russian Upland; the Stavropol' Plateau north of the Caucasus Mountains; and the Ufa Plateau on the western flank of the
Central Urals. The crystalline rocks are found at the surface in
the northwest—an extension of the Finnish structure eastward into

the Karelo-Finnish S.S.R., and in the southwest in the Volhynian-Podolian Plateau, the watershed between the Dnieper and Dniester rivers. The trend of this plateau is indicated by the deflection of the Dnieper southeastward, although the river finally breaks through

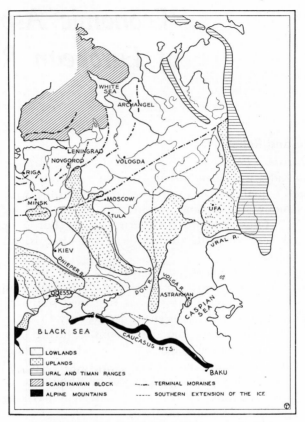

A. Physiographic Sketch Map of European Russia.

the hard rock massif and crosses it between Dnepropetrovsk and Zaporozh'ye with rapids indicating the resistance offered by the crystalline rocks. Both the Baltic Shield and the Volhynian-Podolian Plateau are important economically because of the mineral wealth they contain.

Glacial Deposits. The scouring action of the Pleistocene ice sheets described in Chapters 15 and 19 was also effective in the

Baltic Shield region of European Russia. Otherwise, the ice sheets affected the entire northwestern half of European Russia by blanketing it with glacial deposits. The great belt of terminal and recessional moraines left by the last (or Baltic stage) ice sheet as described in the chapters on Germany and Poland extend eastward from those areas and curve northeastward roughly following the Baltic Sea coast (note black arcs indicating recessional moraines in A63). The Gulf of Riga still perfectly preserves the lobate outline of the receding ice tongue that formed the indentation. The larger lakes of northwestern European Russia owe part of their formation to glacial deposits, but some are also structural depressions. Undrained hollows sometimes give rise to small lakes and sometimes form bogs, which occupy 30 to 60 per cent of large areas of northern Russia.

The southern edge of the last ice sheet crossed the present Belorussian S.S.R., and water and outwash deposits pouring into a depression between the ice edge and the Volhynian-Podolian Plateau formed an extensive area of swamp, the Pripet (or Pinsk) Marshes, now poorly draining eastward via the Pripet River. This maze of swamps is broken only by low sand dunes still largely covered with pine forests. The Pripet Marshes have played a significant role from the early centuries of settlement of eastern Europe, when they served as a refuge for the Slavs, until World War II, when they presented a formidable obstacle to the movement of motorized German and Russian armies.

As in the German and Polish plains, the last ice sheet was not the most extensive of the three or four glacial advances during the Pleistocene period. The preceding advance in eastern Europe (Riss) extended considerably farther south and reached far down the Dnieper valley as well as down the Oka-Don Lowland. Between these two extensions the Central Russian Upland prevented its southerly advance. As in the Börde belt of the Foreland north of the Central European Uplands, the area of European Russia lying south of the Pleistocene ice sheets is blanketed with thick deposits of loess on which have developed fertile soils. The loess areas are especially extensive in eastern Europe, and it is in them that so much of the fertile agricultural areas of the Ukraine are to be found. However, loessal soils also extend north of the Ukraine over part of the Central Russian Uplands.

Relief Features. On the basis of what has been said about the Russian Platform and glacial deposits, it can be seen that European

Russia embraces one of the great plains areas of the world. Nowhere does the elevation exceed 1,500 feet, and it rises above 1,000 feet in only a few scattered points. In addition to the Volhynian-Podolian Plateau already mentioned and the arcuate moraine ridges, there are the Central Russian Uplands extending southward from Moscow to join the folded Donets Ridge with its included coal beds; the Pre-Volga Heights along the west bank of the Volga; the Valdai Heights northwest of Moscow against which the last ice sheet abutted and left morainic deposits over a ridge of sedimentary rocks; the Timan Ridge, a low offshoot toward the northwest from the Northern Urals; and the Khibiny Mountains, in the center of the Kola Peninsula in the northern Baltic Shield region, reaching nearly 4,100 feet. The remainder of European Russia comprises a number of lowlands embraced by the relatively low uplands named above.

Framing the rolling lands of eastern Europe on the east, and forming the generally accepted border of Europe toward Asia is the long, north-south range of the Urals. The range was folded against the resistant crystalline platform of eastern Europe by pressure that came from the east. Therefore, the eastern side of the mountains is steeper and is geologically more complex, whereas the western slopes descending to the plain of European Russia are relatively gentle. As one climbs the western flank of the Urals on the Trans-Siberian Railway he can scarcely believe that he is crossing the famous mountain divide between Europe and Asia because the rise is such a gradual one. However, this crossing is made in the Central Urals, which are appreciably lower than the Southern or Northern Urals, where elevations of 5,000 to 5,500 feet are found. Nevertheless, the Urals do not form a significant barrier, especially to climatic influences. In this way they differ from the higher and more continuous Caucasus and Alps. The great significance of the Urals lies in their enormous mineral wealth contained in the granitic core and intrusions, which appear especially toward the east.

The rugged barrier of the Caucasus range with its alpine folds extends along a northwest to southeast axis across the Caucasian Isthmus between the Black and Caspian seas. Here are found the highest elevations not only of European Russia but of all Europe: volcanic Mount Elbrus reaches 18,481 feet, nearly 3,000 feet higher than Mont Blanc in the Alps. Glaciers are numerous amid perennially snow-capped peaks. Although there are easy routes around the two ends of the Caucasus range, there are no easy passes through the range as there are through the Alps, and no rail line crosses the Caucasus. Two old military highways go through the famous Dariel Pass (or Dariel Gorge, 7,813 feet) and the Marmison Pass (9,548 feet). The western end of the Caucasian folds dips beneath the waters of the Black Sea, but the structure reappears in the Crimean or Yaila Mountains along the southeastern coast of the Crimean Peninsula.

The relatively uniform topography of European Russia, despite the existence of a number of differences such as have already been outlined, does not lend itself to a definite delineation of physiographic regions, such as those in Germany. The sharpest regions of European Russia are, therefore, not relief regions but vegetation and soils regions. It is on the basis of vegetation and soils zones that European Russia is regionalized and discussed in the following chapter.

Rivers and Lakes

The Role of Rivers. The presence of such vast plains areas in European Russia and the existence of a relatively humid climate over much of the area, and especially over that portion in which the principal rivers have their sources, leads naturally to the development of great rivers. The role played by the Russian rivers in the historical development of the country and in the present interior transportation system can scarcely be overemphasized. It is of prime significance that each of the principal rivers is a natural "flowing highway" through forests that originally were difficult to penetrate otherwise or across steppes that were not plentifully supplied with water other than along the rivers. But it is of even greater significance that the headwaters of nearly all the great rivers of European Russia lie within a relatively limited area west of Moscow. The marshy land in and around the Valdai Heights is a common source for the Volga, Dnieper, and Western Dvina, as well as for several of their tributaries and a number of smaller rivers, such as the Lovat (flowing into Lake Ilmen) and the Velikaya (flowing into Lake Peipus). The importance of the common source area lies in the ease with which river boatmen could move from the head of one river up which they had moved to the head of another river down which they desired to go. Thus, the Varangians could travel up the Volkhov to Novgorod near Lake Ilmen, continue up the Lovat, and descend the Western Dvina to the shortest portage between it and the upper Dnieper, down which they moved to establish Kiev and to reach Constantinople across the Black Sea. Similarly, boatmen could move up the Western Dvina and cross a short portage to the upper Volga and reach the Caspian Sea.

It was to the west of the marshy source area of the rivers on a small tributary of the Oka—which is in turn a tributary of the Volga—that the Muscovite state arose both in the protection of the forest and near the strategic focus of the river headwaters. Significantly, Moscow lay neither in the unfavorable and contested concentration of portages nor on any of the main rivers that would have brought conquerors: yet it had easy access to the river network. In modern times the easy portages and relatively level terrain have facilitated construction of canals between rivers, thus enhancing the value of the natural waterways. Again, Moscow has profited by its location.

Greatest of all the rivers of European Russia is the Volga, which is to the Russians a combination of what the Rhine is to the Germans and what the Mississippi is to Americans. Wrapped in tradition and serving as a commercial life line, the Volga was at midcentury also being developed as a great source of hydroelectric power and irrigation water. Like the other larger Russian rivers, the Volga in its lower course has tended to swing toward its right (western) bank because of the right-hand force of deflection created by the earth's rotation. Thus, the right bank of the Volga is high, and the left bank, forming the bottom of the floodplain, is low and often somewhat marshy.

The Dnieper is to the Ukraine what the Volga is to the land of the Great Russians. It, too, tends to impinge on its right bank and to have a low left bank, except where it breaks through the crystalline rocks of the Volhynian-Podolian Plateau. The Don, although far less important than the Volga and even than the Dnieper, has, nevertheless, been a fairly effective factor in unifying the area between the other two rivers. The Western Dvina is the principal stream of western European Russia and has its outlet at the port of Riga in the Latvian S.S.R.

The Role of Lakes. The largest lake of European Russia is also the largest lake in the world: the salty Caspian Sea, covering an area of 169,381 square miles and with its surface 85 feet below sea level. The Caspian is actually a remnant of an arm of the ocean that formerly extended through the Black Sea across the present Caspian basin and eastward to the Aral Sea. Even after the fragmentation of this ocean extension, the Caspian extended much farther north and northwest when glacial meltwaters poured down the Volga. Complete withdrawal of the ice and increasing dryness of the climate produced a shrinkage in the Caspian and a withdrawal of the sea from its shallow former northern extension. This dry lake bottom now comprises the Caspian Depression with its salt marshes and salty soils. Despite the enclosed character of the Caspian Sea, it is of appreciable significance commercially, especially for the shipment of petroleum from the Caucasian fields to Astrakhan' and thence up the Volga. The greatest economic significance of the Caspian is, however, the rich fishing grounds in the northern part of the basin where the inflow of fresh water from the Volga creates conditions conducive to fish life. Here are the great sturgeon grounds whence comes the bulk of the caviar (fish roe) of the Soviet Union.

In northwestern European Russia is Lake Ladoga, the largest fresh-water lake in Europe, and east of it is Lake Onega, second-largest fresh-water lake in Europe. Both lakes, as well as three smaller ones to the south—Peipus, Ilmen, and Beloye—support fishing industries and have long been important in water transportation in the area.

Development and Character of Soviet Agriculture

Bases for Russian Agriculture. Some aspects of the climatic basis for Russian agriculture were given in the previous chapter, and additional details will be brought out in the following chapter. Also, the section on the Eastern Plain in Chapter 4, part of Chapter 7, and most of Chapter 6 discuss aspects of the eastern European environment pertinent to agriculture. Further discussion of these points would be mere repetition, but it is recommended that the applicable sections be referred to in connection with Soviet agriculture. This section considers some of the fundamental conditions that give Russian agriculture its distinctive character.

Agricultural Organization before 1917. As is true in the Soviet Union or in virtually any country, the agricultural system of prerevolutionary Russia reflected not only the geographical environment but also the social organization that prevailed under the tsars. In addition, the great delay in the coming of the industrial revolution to the geographically and socially isolated Russians was reflected in the agricultural practices.

Before 1917 Russia was pre-eminently an agricultural land, with more than 80 per cent of the population dependent upon farming. However, rural settlement was entirely different from that developed in the United States in both the East and the Middle West: the farm population was concentrated in scattered agricultural villages, so that the people could have better organized defense against attack, could make better use of water resources, and could satisfy the urge for gregariousness—especially during the long winters. For centuries before 1861, the farmers and their families living in the villages or *mirs* were serfs legally bound either to the state or to a nobleman. To three fourths of the population, therefore, the *mir* in which they lived was about all of the world that they knew. The *mir* council apportioned the land and was responsible for paying the taxes of the community. Not until 1861 were the serfs given their freedom from the vicious system in which they had worked for centuries—but it should be remembered that it was not until two years later that Negro slaves were freed in the United States. However, freeing of the serfs and far-reaching land reforms were not enough to solve the peasant problem in Russia.

The agricultural practices before 1917 were likewise antiquated. Tools and implements were exceedingly primitive: in 1910 there were more than twice as many wooden plows as iron plows in use in Russia. In most regions the three-field system of tillage was practiced, although such a system had long been abandoned in western Europe in favor of more intensive cultivation within a framework of scientific crop rotation and fertilization. Although scientific seed selection was known to Russian botanists, few peasants had any conception of it. Subsistence farming was the rule, and those crops that would store most easily were raised. Yields were low almost everywhere. The number of livestock was small in comparison with the number in central and western Europe, and the quality of the animals was low because of poor breeding practices. In the decade before World War I the attention given agriculture and the peasants increased appreciably, and emigration from overpopulated areas to the new lands of southern Siberia was encouraged and systematically supported. However, the steady course of improvement was interrupted by World War I and the October Revolution.

Agricultural Organization at Mid-Century. The 1920's were a decade of Soviet experimentation in many fields, and agriculture was no exception. However, with the beginning of the 1930's, and in the midst of the First Five Year Plan, the Soviets initiated a relentless assault on the independent peasants in a program of collectivizing Russian agriculture and of liquidating those farmers who had become substantial landowners and more successful farmers. These *kulaks* were made the scapegoats for many of the ills of Soviet agriculture, much as the Jews were made the scapegoats for many of Germany's ills during the Hitler period. Undoubtedly, many so-called *kulaks* achieved their success through unscrupulous practices; on the other hand, many of them were simply more capable and energetic peasants who worked harder than other peasants who had not emerged from the pre-1861 atmosphere of working only enough to keep body and soul together.

The collectivization of Soviet agriculture has taken two forms. On the one hand is the collective farm or *kolkhoz*, which basically is little different in organization from the old *mir*. The procedure of handling the land in the *kolkhoz* is, however, completely different. All the land assigned by the state to the *kolkhoz* members is operated as one great farm, and the old, inefficient system of cultivating scattered strips has been discarded. The entire farm is operated by the *kolkhoz* members as a group, and no member owns any of the land. Settlement is concentrated in a village near the center of the *kolkhoz*, much as was the case under the *mir* system. The village is frequently an appreciable improvement over the old *mir*; but, although many of the houses are adequate, the conveniences in the typical village are far behind those in the typical farm town in the American Middle West. Even by 1950, only 12 per cent of the collective farms had electricity, and most of these were in the more highly developed areas. Each family has its own house—which it theoretically owns—and is permitted to garden a small plot of land for its own benefit, whether to raise vegetables for the family or to grow whatever crops may be sold on the open market in the neighborhood. In early 1950 there were 254,000 collective farms in the Soviet Union on which were settled more than 19.2 million peasant families. The *kolkhozy* of Soviet Russia included approximately 90 per cent of the sown area in the Union and accounted for approximately 85 per cent of Soviet agricultural production. There is, of course, some variation in the size of *kolkhozy*, but in 1938 the average *kolkhoz* had 78 families working approximately 3,800 acres of land, of which about 1,200 acres were sown to crops. Each family thus cultivates about 15 acres, an acreage several times smaller than that sown per farm family in the United States—indicating the greater pressure of population on the arable land of Russia. During the course of 1950 thousands of smaller collective farms were amalgamated or consolidated with larger *kolkhozy*. The evidence at the end of 1950 was that more than 35,000 *kolkhozy* had been eliminated as separate units.

It is necessary to consider along with the *kolkhoz* the Machine Tractor Station (MTS), which is a functional unit operating the agricultural machinery used on collective farms. Each of the 8,100 Machine Tractor Stations services approximately 28 to 30 *kolkhozy* with tractors, plows, combines, and other machinery and implements. Thus, the *kolkhoz*, which is prohibited from having machinery of its own, is completely dependent upon the MTS for its planting, cultivating, and harvesting. Furthermore, the MTS serves as a check on *kolkhoz* production, since the MTS operators can determine during the harvest how much grain the *kolkhoz* produces. The greater consideration shown the MTS is indicated by the fact that 75 per cent of the stations are electrified.

The second form taken by Soviet agricultural collectivization is the state farm or *sovkhoz*, which is entirely government property— without the intermediate organizational group of *kolkhoz* members —and is operated by the state with hired labor under state-appointed managers. *Sovkhozy* are usually established in areas of marginal land where yields are low and where extensive methods of cultivation must be employed. It is through establishment of such state farms that the Soviet government has expanded the cultivated area of the Union into the drier regions and into the forest with its poorer soils. Unlike *kolkhozy*, *sovkhozy* have their own agricultural machinery and implements and are not dependent upon Machine Tractor Stations. In 1950 there were about 5,000 *sovkhozy* in the entire Soviet Union operating more than 31 million acres, somewhat less than 10 per cent of the cultivated acreage of the country. The hope is that the state farms can become more and more efficient and self-supporting until one by one they can be converted to collective farms.

The Dominance of Grains. The reorganization of Soviet agriculture as outlined above has been accompanied by appreciable changes in methods of cultivation and in crops raised. The mechanization of agriculture has been one of the principal goals of the Soviet government, and from 1928 until 1938 the number of tractors rose from 26,700 to 483,500. World War II caused not only the actual loss of large amounts of farm machinery but also a reduction in the number of tractors because of the Red Army's requisitioning of thousands of them for use as prime movers. Consequently, at mid-century the total quantity of agricultural machinery available to Soviet farms was probably not much greater than that in 1940, although the rate of production was high.

During the 1930's appreciable advances were made in increased use of fertilizers and in proper crop rotation, and such progress was continued after 1945. Although a number of new crops have been introduced, the more important changes have come in the development of crossbred seeds that permit the extension of crop areas into drier and cooler lands or give higher yields in the old producing sections.

Despite some significant alterations in the percentage of various crops in the total Soviet yield, Russian agriculture retains predominantly a grain basis. Just before World War II, 75 per cent of the cultivated area of the Union was in grains, whereas grains had occupied 90 per cent of the area in 1913. From 1913 to 1938 the percentage of the acreage in industrial crops doubled (to 8 per cent), as did the percentage of the acreage in vegetables, melons, and potatoes. The percentage of the acreage in fodder crops quadrupled during the same period. Thus, Soviet agriculture became more diversified but is still obviously largely specialized in grains.

By far the most important Soviet crop in both acreage and tonnage is wheat, occupying 105 to 110 million acres—from one third to one fourth of the total sown acreage of the Soviet Union. Rye is the second most important crop, occupying approximately half the acreage of wheat and producing approximately half as much tonnage. Oats are the next most important crop, with barley having about half as much acreage as oats. Maize, grown mainly in the southwest and in the Caucasus, occupies less than a third of the acreage of barley. The total acreage devoted to vegetables, melons, and potatoes is slightly greater than that devoted to barley alone, although much of the horticulture is carried on in irrigated districts in Soviet Central Asia.

Flax, hemp, and sunflower are the chief products among the industrial crops of European Russia. Flax and hemp are ideally suited to the cool, moist climate extending eastward from the Baltic, and the sunflower does well in the subhumid and semiarid areas of the south. Sunflower seeds are a leading source of vegetable oil for the Soviet Union. The sugar beet is raised to a sufficient extent in the Ukraine (as well as in Asiatic Russia) to supply virtually all the sugar needs of the Union. Although the greater part of the Soviet cotton crop is raised under irrigation in the Central Asiatic republics, the growing demand for cotton has stimulated attempts to produce it in the Caucasus and in the southern Ukraine. Irrigated cotton in the Caucasus has produced satisfactorily, but un-

A. Cultivation of a sunflower field on the experimental lands of a collective farm in the Soviet Union.   Courtesy of Sovfoto.

irrigated cotton in the southern Ukraine has yielded poorly. Tobacco has achieved growing importance in the Caucasus and in the southern Ukraine. Tea, grapes, and even rice are being grown on an increasing scale in the subtropical climate of the Georgian S.S.R.

In a land such as the Soviet Union, where large areas are too dry for agricultural use and where the pressure of population is great, it is only natural that irrigation should be attempted on the largest possible scale. Except for the Caucasus, most of the irrigation in European Russia has been in limited areas along the lower Volga.

Along with plans for construction of great dams along the lower Volga have gone plans for irrigating millions of acres of land on both sides of the Volga, but especially in the trans-Volga region north of the Caspian Sea. However, only construction of the dams was under way at mid-century, and little progress had been made in the irrigation.

Despite valiant Soviet efforts to suit crops more to specific environments, to introduce improved plant varieties, to utilize fertilizers to a greater extent, and to improve methods of cultivation, the yield per acre of Soviet crops in general remains low. The principal reason for the persistence of low average yields is to be found in the deficient and irregular rainfall—a geographical fact about which the Soviets can do little. In such a climate neither good soil nor fertilizer is of so much value as might be supposed. They are of great benefit only when kept moist. Denmark and Belgium show huge yields per acre not only because they use plenty of fertilizer and plow deeply, but because frequent mild rains slowly dissolve the fertilizing materials and fill the ground with plant food during the winter and early spring. Thus plenty of food is available as soon as the plants need it. Also, the relatively small numbers of livestock on the Soviet collective farms give only a small amount of organic manure. Not only have two European wars and a civil war cost the Soviet Union millions of head of livestock, but the widespread slaughter of cattle during the late 1920's, when farmers saw that collectivization was imminent, also reduced the Russian livestock population greatly. Although the Ukraine is far inferior to Belgium in climate, it is so much better than the South Ural region that it not only encourages the farmers to better methods but also gives them a surplus. Thus the Ukraine's relatively high production is due to the combined effects of climate and man.

Mineral Resources and Power (A738)

Despite Soviet claims to the contrary, most of the principal mineral deposits now known in Russia were known and at least partially exploited before 1917. In their determined effort to exploit every available resource and to increase the industrial base for the Soviet Union, the Soviets have made very intensive geological surveys to assess the country's mineral wealth. As a result, a number of new deposits have been discovered, and older deposits have been extended.

Power. A. Coal. As in most of Europe, the primary source of industrial power in Russia is coal, reserves of which for the Union as a whole are second only to those of the United States. Soviet coal production increased 700 per cent from 1913 until 1949, when —with an output of 237 million tons—Russia became the second largest coal producer in the world, although the increasing amount of lignite included in Soviet coal production figures may make the figure too high for comparative purposes. In European Russia the resources of the Donets Basin (estimated reserves: 88 billion metric tons) are the largest single deposit, although they are only half as great as the reserves of Upper Silesia in Poland, and are from one third to one half as great as those of the Ruhr. They are, nevertheless, high-quality deposits, occurring in thick, rather easily mined beds, and include a fair percentage of coking coal. In 1913 the Donets Basin produced five sixths of all the coal mined in the area now included in the Soviet Union, and the Soviets have made strong attempts to distribute the pattern of production more evenly among the various coal fields of the Union. The second largest coal area of European Russia is found in the Urals region, especially at Chelyabinsk and Kizel (northeast of Molotov)—although these deposits are of low grade and contain little coking coal. The newest Urals field, that of the Pechora Basin (centering around Vorkuta, west of the Northern Urals), appears to have good coal with an appreciable amount of coking coal. A third "coal" deposit in European Russia is found in the Moscow Basin south and southwest of the capital, but the deposits are actually lignite. Thus, the only great source of coking coal in European Russia is the Donets Basin, although the Pechora Basin is promising. With the opening of the rich Kuznetsk Basin in south-central Siberia, with probably the greatest reserves of any single deposit in the Soviet Union, and the Karaganda field in the Kazakh S.S.R., the share of the Donets Basin in Soviet coal production has been steadily decreasing.

B. Water Power. In an effort to conserve coal, to obviate the necessity for shipping large amounts of coal across country, and to utilize the hydroelectric potential of the Russian rivers, the Soviets have undertaken a vigorous program of water power development. Despite an appreciable number of announcements of projects planned and in construction, Soviet hydroelectric installations on a large scale were relatively few at mid-century. The largest and most famous hydroelectric plant is the first of the great Russian installations, the famous Dnieper dam near Zaporozh'ye, now called the

Lenin Works. With a capacity of 550,000 kilowatts, the plant was originally constructed by American engineers, but the Russians partly destroyed it when retreating in 1941; however, it was back in virtually full operation in 1950. The second greatest hydroelectric plant is at Shcherbakov (formerly Rybinsk), northeast of Moscow, where a dam has formed Eurasia's largest man-made reservoir. A third large installation on the Svir River draining from Lake Onega to Lake Ladoga has a capacity of more than 200,000 kilowatts. Several stations in the Transcaucasus have capacities of from 50,000 to 100,000 kilowatts.

All these works will be dwarfed by five great installations that were under construction at mid-century on the Volga, with one of them on the upper Kama near Molotov. This "Great Volga" scheme called for construction of a plant near Kuybyshev that will have a capacity of more than 2 million kilowatts, as well as a second dam near Syzran' (below Kuybyshev) with a capacity of 1.5 million kilowatts. The other two plants on the Volga were under construction at Gor'kiy and downstream from Shcherbakov. Other stations—especially a large one at Stalingrad that will have a capacity of 1.7 million kilowatts—in addition to these named are planned as part of the "Great Volga" scheme, with which must be considered the plans for irrigation mentioned earlier in this chapter. In 1950 generation of hydroelectric power in the Soviet Union amounted to 12,000 million kilowatt-hours, almost two and a half times as much as in 1940.

C. Peat. Less spectacular and less publicized than water power, peat was at mid-century actually the second greatest source of industrial power in the Soviet Union and furnished approximately 18 per cent of the electric power generated in the Soviet Union, as opposed to 15 per cent for water power. The peat reserves of the Soviet Union are enormous (150,000 million metric tons), and, although only 12 per cent lie in the belt from Leningrad to Gor'kiy, this belt yields 80 per cent of the total Soviet peat production of more than 34 million tons. Since the impracticability of transporting peat makes local utilization essential, several small peat-burning plants have been erected in the midst of peat bogs near Leningrad, Moscow, and Gor'kiy and have become vital factors in the electric supply of those cities.

D. Petroleum. Although the Soviet Union claims possession of 50 to 70 per cent of the world's petroleum reserves, more conservative estimates give it 12 to 15 per cent. Whatever the reserves may be, Soviet production is only one-seventh that of the United States

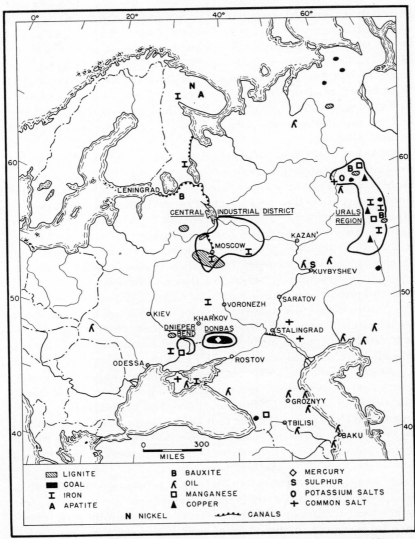

A. Principal Minerals and Industrial Regions of European Soviet Union. Names of industrial regions are underlined. Principal industrial cities outside indicated industrial regions are named. Large black dots are coal fields.

and is only about half that of Venezuela, but it is nevertheless third greatest in the world after these two countries. The rapid increase of Arabian and Iranian production suggests that unless Soviet production increases more rapidly than it has in the past the Union will drop to fifth place in world petroleum production.

The most important producing areas of the Soviet Union are in European Russia and are concentrated especially in the Caucasus. The great Baku field was one of the first pools exploited and has continued to be the primary producer. The producing zone extends westward along the northern flanks of the Caucasus through Groznyy and Maykop, which are also major producers. Soviet geologists have opened fields in the lower Emba River basin northeast of the Caspian Sea, in a large area lying between the southern Urals and the Volga River, and in the Pechora Basin in northeastern European Russia around the town of Ukhta. Most of the Soviet petroleum moves by waterway, and most of the rest by rail, although the number of pipelines is gradually increasing. The petroleum supply is also augmented by the exploitation of oil shales in several areas.

Metals. As is true of mineral resources in general, the Soviet Union is well supplied with metallic minerals, which it possesses not only in appreciable quantity but also in great variety. The greatest iron resources are found at Krivoy Rog, west of the Dnieper in the Ukraine and 200 miles west of the coal deposits of the Donets Basin. Although the Krivoy Rog reserves are, in terms of iron content, only half those of Lorraine and Kiruna, they are the third largest iron reserves known in Europe and are some of the richest ores known. On the Kerch' Peninsula in the east of the Crimea are extensive beds of oölitic ore similar to that of Lorraine. The famous "magnetic anomaly" at Kursk has long been known and has been found to be produced by a great mass of iron-bearing quartzites at a depth of 650 to 2,000 feet below the surface in the Kursk-Voronezh Horst; however, the ore of this deposit has not been greatly exploited because of the difficulty of mining it and of smelting it. The Urals region contains large deposits of iron, especially those of Mount Magnitnaya near Magnitogorsk and at Mount Blagodat farther north. However, the better Urals ores are being rapidly used up under the intensive exploitation that began in the late 1930's and extended through World War II.

A second metal that is abundant in European Russia is manganese. As was discussed in Chapter 8, the Soviet Union possesses the world's largest reserves of this vital alloy, the largest deposits of

which are found at Nikopol' on the lower Dnieper and at Chiatura
in the Georgian S.S.R. The Urals contain the largest copper deposits in European Russia, although still larger resources are exploited
in Kazakhstan. Bauxite is produced in the Urals and at Tikhvin
east of Leningrad, and aluminum is also produced from the
nepheline mined with the apatite of the Khibiny Mountains in the
Kola Peninsula. At Monchegorsk, northwest of the Khibiny Mountains, are large nickel deposits that extend into the Pechenga district. The Urals are a rich source of various alloy metals and are
a leading producing region for the rare metal, platinum.

Nonmetallic Minerals. Among many possessed by the Soviet
Union, two nonmetallic mineral deposits of European Russia are especially worthy of note. The huge apatite deposits of the Khibiny
Mountains are the world's largest and are an especially important
resource to Russia because apatite is used for the manufacture of
phosphate fertilizers. The deposits of potassium salts in the Soli-
kamsk area on the Upper Kama are one of the world's largest and
have given rise to a thriving chemical industry in the Central Urals.

Industrial Development

Growth under the Soviets. Although Russian industry before 1913
was gradually emerging from its almost medieval, home-industry
stage and in such fields as textiles and ironworking was showing considerable progress, its development in general was retarded. Russian
industrial output in 1913 represented only about 2.6 per cent of the
world total. Much of the machinery in Russian factories was imported, especially from England and Germany, and many of the
enterprises were financed entirely or in part by foreign capital. The
relatively recent coming of the industrial revolution led to the development of crowded and depressing industrial centers similar to those
that arose in Britain in the early decades of that country's industrialization.

Expansion of industry was the key goal of the Soviets upon their
assumption of control in Russia, especially in view of the fact that
much of the philosophy of Marxism was predicated on its application in an industrial society in which there was a large proletariat.
It was, indeed, strange that Marxism achieved its first real success in
a country that was overwhelmingly agricultural rather than industrial. Although the first decade of Soviet control was marked by as
much of a decline in industrial production from the prerevolutionary level during the early years as by an increase in the later years,

the initiation of the First Five Year Plan in 1928 marked the beginning of a great industrial expansion. Except for the abnormal years during World War II, the expansion has continued almost uninterruptedly. The successive Five Year Plans—the Fourth was completed in 1950—have called for and achieved increased mineral and power development as well as industrial production. It has been said that, to the Soviet officials, statistics became the new idols, replacing the familiar ikons associated with the Russian Orthodox religion under the tsarist regime.

Although it is only to be expected that the absolute output of many items would be greater during the late 1930's than during the period before 1913 (output rose in most countries during the same period), especially in view of the delayed advent of the industrial revolution in Russia, the revealing fact is that the Soviet Union made such rapid strides in improving its rank among the industrial countries of the world. Thus, whereas in 1913 the value of German industrial products was 6 times that of Russia, of British products 4.5 times as much, and of French products 2.5 times as much, by the late 1930's Soviet industrial production was at least as great as that of Germany and Britain, although it was only one fourth to one third as great as that of the United States. In terms of geographical distribution, most of pre-1930 Soviet industry was concentrated in European Russia and its fringe areas.

The great expansion of Soviet industry during the 1930's displayed a number of distinctive characteristics. First, the increase in the number and size of factories took place to some extent at the expense of home industries, which were well developed in prerevolutionary Russia, although the skill and craftsmanship were not equal to those in German home industries. Thus, the great increase in textile production, for example, as revealed in official statistics did not mean an equivalent absolute gain to Russian consumers; production of homespun materials decreased sharply during the same period.

Second, because of the lack of sufficient adequately trained technical personnel, the Soviets had to import thousands of engineers and technicians from America and western Europe to supervise the installation of many factories, mines, and electrical works. Thus, the Soviet Union was able to draw on the latest technical developments in the advanced industrialized countries. After World War II the Soviets made use of the abilities of thousands of German technicians who had either been captured in military operations or otherwise transferred to the Soviet Union. During the entire time, however, the Soviets conducted a vigorous technical training program in order to produce its own technicians; and the evidence is that the program has been as successful as could be expected.

Third, foreign machinery was imported for many of the first factories and other installations, and machine tools continued to be imported for many years. Again, however, Russia is satisfying most of its own needs in these respects. A very significant result of the late development of Soviet industry and of its entire technology is that the installations are, for the most part, equipped with the more recent machines and use the more recent technological methods. The machines and methods of Britain—or even of many American industries—are appreciably older. However, the machines and designs standardized in the Soviet Union are very often those of the 1930's: most of the tractors, for example, are of a design that passed from the American farm with the advent of the rubber-tired tractor.

Fourth, from the beginning of its rapid expansion until midcentury, Soviet industry has concentrated on the heavy phases of industry and on producers' goods. One important reason for this specialization has been that heavy industry is basic to the whole structure of manufacturing, and it must necessarily be highly developed before diversification can take place. Another important reason is that the Soviets are determined to equip themselves well with the necessary basis for military production, a determination for which they could be thankful in 1941 when they were attacked by Germany. The share of heavy industry in the total industrial output is the very high figure of more than two thirds. Thus, the production of consumers' good is still being neglected in the Soviet Union. It is logical to assume that eventually the emphasis will shift to consumers' goods once an adequate supply of producers' goods is achieved.

Fifth, in attempting to emulate American industry the Soviet Union adopted the philosophy of the large factory, especially since the large organization facilitated the "collectivization" of workers and appealed to the Soviet concept of bigness. Nearly two thirds of the Soviet workers are employed in plants with more than 1,000 employees. The danger of excessive concentration became so great that the concept of the large plant—"gigantism" or "gigantomania"—came under severe attack, and smaller, more widely distributed plants were adopted as the standard.

The severe fighting during World War II in the most highly industrialized region of the Soviet Union resulted in widespread destruction of plants that had been so laboriously developed during the 1930's. It was a cruel blow to the Soviets to see their prized achievements wrecked in a few weeks. Such heavy industrial losses partly account for the relentless removals of machinery and whole factories from Germany after 1945. Nevertheless, the general level of Soviet industrial production in 1950 was 73 per cent greater than the level of 1940; however, most of this increase was in the heavy industries segment, and the production of some consumers' goods in 1950 was at a level no higher than that of 1940.

Main Industrial Regions (A738). Although the specific character of the individual industrial regions of European Russia will be discussed in connection with the geographical regions described in the following chapter, the general distribution of principal producing regions merits brief mention at this point. Greatest of all the Russian industrial areas is the so-called "Central Industrial District" around Moscow and extending in a broad belt from Kalinin on the west to Gor'kiy on the east. The second greatest of the Soviet industrial districts is the eastern Ukraine, centering principally around the large coal deposits of the Donets Basin or "Donbas." The third greatest industrial area is the Central and Southern Urals region. A much smaller but still significant focus of manufacturing is found at Leningrad. Scattered centers of industrial production are Khar'kov, Baku, Kiev, Stalingrad, Odessa, Kazan', Kuybyshev, Tbilisi, Groznyy, and a score of cities of lesser importance. Although it lies in south-central Siberia, the Kuznetsk Basin ("Kuzbas") should be mentioned as the fourth largest industrial concentration of the Soviet Union as a whole.

Despite the great increase in production in the eastern Ukraine and in the Central Industrial District, the percentage of the total Soviet production contributed by these two areas has progressively decreased since the early 1930's. Efforts to increase the share contributed by the Urals area and by the Kuznetsk Basin—as well as by smaller centers in the Caucasus, the Soviet Central Asiatic republics, and the Far East—were greatly intensified during World War II when the entire Ukraine was enemy occupied and the Central Industrial District was seriously threatened. Not only are the Urals and the Kuzbas safer strategically as industrial bases, but expansion of their productivity affords local supplies of manufactures for the consuming areas of Soviet Asia, thus saving shipment of goods over thousands of miles of distance, and tends to siphon off excess population from European Russia.

This rationalization of industry has brought about a more even distribution of productive facilities in the Soviet Union. One reason given for the establishment of industries in such previously poorly industrialized areas as the Transcaucasus and southern Turkestan is the Soviet desire to encourage local industries in the various republics. Indeed, the percentage increases of output in such regions as the Georgian S.S.R. and especially the Central Asiatic republics are very great; however, the absolute increases are relatively small. On the other hand, the absolute increases in such old, established producing areas as the Central Industrial District and the eastern Ukraine are relatively great.

Transportation

Rail Lines. As may be seen in A159, the rail net of European Russia is an open one and is comparable with that of Rumania. The network in France and Germany is many times denser than that of Russia. By far most of the existing rail lines of European Russia were built before 1917, although the Soviets have considerably extended the rail lines of Central Asia. The most important additions west of the Urals have been the long line from Kotlas (on the Northern Dvina southeast of Archangel) to the Vorkuta coal field at the northern end of the Urals, the line paralleling the Volga along the west bank from Kazan' to Stalingrad, the Kazan'-Sverdlovsk line, and a number of shorter lines lacing together the newly developed areas of the Urals region itself. The focus of the rail lines of European Russia is Moscow, which lies in the center of a spiderweb-like pattern of rail lines, as Paris does in the French rail net.

Waterways. For hundreds of years waterways have been of prime significance in Russian transportation, and the Soviets have further increased the importance of water transportation by construction of canals and improvement of rivers for navigation. The chief water artery of European Russia is the Volga and its tributaries, the most important of which are the Oka and Kama; 11,000 miles of waterways in the Volga basin are used for navigation. Up the Volga move wheat, coal, cement, cotton, fish, and salt, and downstream move timber and heavy manufactured goods. The construction of dams along the middle and lower Volga in the "Great Volga" scheme will improve the navigability of the river as well as generate hydroelectricity and irrigate the dry lands of the lower Volga region. Nearly all the important canals of European Russia have been built to connect various regions with the Volga. Three canals are of particular significance: the Mariinsk system, connecting Leningrad with the Volga at Shcherbakov (Rybinsk), constructed under the tsarist government; the Moscow Canal, connecting the capital with the Volga and furnishing Moscow with an adequate water supply; and the Baltic-White Sea Canal, connecting Lake Onega with the White Sea. The long-dreamed-of canal between the Volga and the Don at Stalingrad was finally undertaken by the Soviets and was under construction at mid-century. The project is a very difficult one but will be a significant link between the Donbas and the Central Industrial District. Completion of the Volga-Don Canal will, as the Soviets proudly announce, make Moscow a "port of five seas"—Baltic, White, Caspian, Black, and Azov. One of the longest canals, the Manych, planned by the Soviet Union is to extend from the Caspian Sea to Rostov on the lower Don. The canal, under construction at mid-century, will follow an ancient depression formed when the Caspian overflowed to the Sea of Azov when the Caspian level was much higher than at present. Also under construction at mid-century was the Chief Turkmen Canal, extending from the eastern shore of the Caspian Depression through the Uzboy Depression to the lower Amu Darya. One great disadvantage of the Volga as a navigable waterway is the long period during which the river is frozen. At Kazan' the ice cover lasts from the end of December until the end of April, and even at Astrakhan' it persists from the middle of December until the end of March. Moreover, the spring thaw is followed by great floods that, toward the end of summer, give way to a low-water period.

Roads and Airlines. The roads of even the European portion of the Soviet Union are of limited extent and are generally poor. Nearly two thirds of the roads are natural dirt tracks used by wagons; they are muddy in spring, dusty in summer, and very rough in the winter when the ruts are frozen. However, under a snow cover, practically all the roads furnish admirable lines of communication. The Soviets have extended the length of hard-surfaced roads so as to permit greater use of trucks for carrying freight, although most of the truck hauls are for short distances. Use of highways for passenger car travel is still almost unknown. The progress of aviation in the Soviet Union is discussed in Chapter 11.

· 46 ·

The Regions
and Cities
of European Russia

It is revealing of the respective geographic environments that regions of France and Germany are delimited primarily on the basis of physiographic units such as the Paris Basin in France or the Central German Uplands in Germany, whereas regions of the Soviet Union are delimited primarily on the basis of vegetation and soil belts. Such belts develop on a broad scale, of course, only in plains areas, such as eastern Europe; appreciable relief features disturb the normal zonation of vegetation and soils, as is the case in most of central and western Europe.

Chapter 6 discusses the vegetation and soil zones of Europe and reveals that the most orderly arrangement is found in eastern Europe. A94 and A95 show how the zones of eastern Europe are related to those of Europe as a whole. A747 shows the zones of European Russia in greater detail and is the basis for the regional discussion given in this chapter. However, since the mountain regions of the Urals and Caucasus typically possess their own characters, they are discussed as separate regions. The description that follows omits repetition of facts given in Chapter 6 and concentrates on the cultural and economic aspects—especially urban development—of the regions. Some review of the vegetation and soil characteristics may be desirable at this point. It should be remembered that the boundaries between zones are not sharp and that zones of transition are usual. It should also be kept in mind in reading the discussion that certain cultural-economic developments cross vegetation boundaries.

Tundra (1)

The tundra is not extensively developed in European Russia, as may be seen in A747, but reaches its fullest extent in north-central

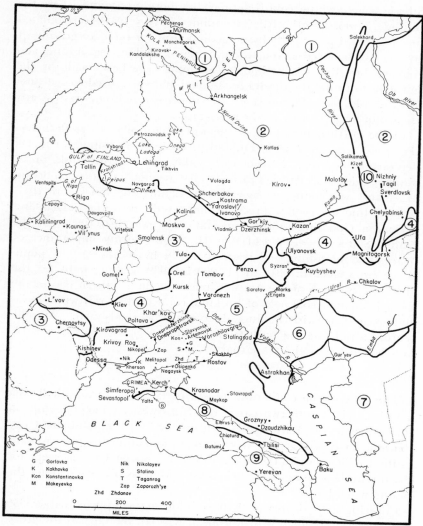

A. Regions and Cities of European Soviet Union.

1. Tundra
2. Taiga
3. Mixed Forest
4. Wooded Steppe
5. Steppe

6. Semidesert
7. Desert
8. Caucasus and Crimean Mountains
9. Transcaucasus
10. Urals

Siberia, where winter cold is appreciably more severe and where the latitude is more northerly. The tundra is very sparsely populated and is utilized principally by nomadic Lapps for reindeer grazing or by Nentsy (Samoyedes) and Komi (Zyryans) for hunting, fishing, and reindeer breeding. Experimental attempts have been made by the Russians to utilize the tundra for limited and specialized agriculture, but the cold, wet soil and short growing season militate against any chance of great success in these attempts.

In the northwestern part of the Kola Peninsula is the Pechenga (Petsamo) area, taken from Finland in 1944, where important nickel deposits are worked. Farther east is the port of Murmansk, previously mentioned as Russia's principal ice-free port on the open ocean. Murmansk was connected by rail with Leningrad even before 1917, but the line has been appreciably improved under the Soviets and became a vital link in the importation of war matériel from the United States during World War II. The growing importance of Murmansk for fishing and trade is shown by its increase in population from 3,000 in 1916 to 117,000 in 1939, making it by far the greatest city north of the Arctic Circle. At the northern end of the Urals is the new coal field of Vorkuta, connected by rail with Kotlas and from there with Leningrad, to which it sends coal. At mid-century a rail line was built from Vorkuta over the Northern Urals to Salekhard near the Ob estuary.

Taiga (2)

The zone of the coniferous forests, or taiga, of European Russia may be divided into two parts: the Northwestern Lake Region on the west, and the European North on the east. East of the Urals the zone has a still greater development, and from the Ob eastward to the Pacific occupies the full width of the Soviet Union except for the tundra belt along the Arctic coast and areas of steppe along the southern border.

Covering a total area of 1,500 million acres (approximately 350 million acres of which is in European Russia), the taiga is the greatest continuous belt of forest in the world and therefore affords the Soviet Union great timber resources. Conditions for exploitation are much poorer than those described in the chapters on Sweden and Finland, since the rivers are not so numerous, nor are they such good floatways. Nevertheless, lumbering activity is intense, with large amounts of timber floated down the Kama to the Volga and thence downstream to the steppe lands. Although the Soviet Union is one of the chief timber producers of the world, it is no longer a great timber exporter. Indeed, Russia took most of its reparations from Finland in the form of plywood and prefabricated wooden houses. After 1930 much of the timber of European Russia was devoted to papermaking, wood chemicals, and cellulose.

Although the taiga zone still largely comprises vast unbroken expanses of forest, numerous extensive areas have been cleared, especially for pasture but also for flax along the southern edge. Vigorous Soviet efforts in plant breeding have produced wheat that may be grown in the southern taiga, but the infertile Podzols must be heavily fertilized for such crops, and the seeds must be specially treated if plants are to mature during the short, cool growing season.

Northwestern Lake Region. The Northwestern Lake Region comprises chiefly the Karelo-Finnish S.S.R. but also includes adjacent parts of the R.S.F.S.R. The Karelo-Finnish S.S.R., which gained part of the territory taken from Finland in 1940, supports only a sparse population in its glaciated, lake-studded territory. The only town of importance is the capital, Petrozavodsk, on the west shore of Lake Onega, where wood products are made and modest ironworks exist.

In the center of the Kola Peninsula in the north, the great apatite-nepheline deposits of the Khibiny Mountains were subjected to intensive exploitation beginning in the 1930's, and the town of Kirovsk reached a population of 60,000 in 1939 when it was only about a decade old. The fertilizers processed from the apatite are of especial value for the infertile Podzols of northern European Russia, and the aluminum processed (at Kandalaksha) from the nepheline contributes appreciably to the Soviet supply of that metal. Northwest of Kirovsk are the nickel deposits of Monchegorsk, also intensively exploited.

The most highly developed section of the Northwestern Lake Region is found in its southern part. The focus of this development is Leningrad, which, with a population of approximately 3.5 millions, is the second largest city in the entire Soviet Union. Founded by Peter the Great in 1703, the city—successively called Petersburg, St. Petersburg, Petrograd, and Leningrad—was built from the beginning as a great capital and consequently has a majestic appearance in its core area. The tendency for Russia to become more closely associated with the rest of Europe during the eighteenth and nineteenth centuries is shown by the fact that Peter built Leningrad as his "window to Europe" and by the fact that Leningrad was the capital until 1918, when the seat of government was returned to Moscow. Lying as it does on the low delta of the Neva River draining Lake Ladoga, the city is occasionally subjected to flooding when strong westerly winds raise the level of the Gulf of Finland; and large buildings must be constructed on piles. Although the city has a number of famed cultural institutions and vies with Moscow as a Soviet cultural center, its industrial significance has also always been great and exceeded that of Moscow until the 1920's. It still rivals Moscow industrially and produces more than 10 per cent of the total Soviet manufactures. It particularly specializes in precision products, machinery, electrical goods, and chemicals, and its manpower is well known for its skill. Leningrad was the only Soviet port on the Baltic between 1920 and 1940 and has long been Russia's leading port for international trade, although the tonnage handled has been smaller in Leningrad than in such ports as Baku, with its great petroleum exports. A dredged channel leads to the naval base of Kronshtadt on Kotlin Island west of Leningrad. Leningrad suffered severely, not only through physical destruction but through human starvation, during the siege by the Nazis from 1941 until early 1943.

The expansion of Leningrad as a port encouraged the construction of the Mariinsk Canal System, the Baltic outlet of which is Leningrad itself. Through it and the Moscow Canal, Leningrad connects with the Caspian Sea and, with the completion of the Volga-Don Canal, will also connect with the Black Sea; through the Mariinsk to Lake Onega it connects with the White Sea. Rail connections are also excellent.

Leningrad is drawing increasingly on surrounding resources of raw materials and power, and it is developing an appreciable metallurgical industry on the basis of iron ore to the northwest and coal shipped hundreds of miles over the rail line from Vorkuta in the Northern Urals. Several former tsarist residences south and east of Leningrad have been turned into national museums, similar to that of Versailles in France. Northwest of Leningrad is the industrial and port town of Vyborg, formerly called Viipuri before its transfer from Finland to Russia in 1940. Separation of Vyborg from its hinterland of the Saimaa Canal robbed the city of much of its natural advantage and deprived Finland of an optimum outlet for its Saimaa System.

East of Leningrad, the Volkhov hydroelectric station was the first built by the Soviets (during the 1920's), and, although it originally supplied part of Leningrad's electricity, it now operates aluminum-producing plants utilizing bauxite from Tikhvin just to the southeast. Up the Volkhov River, near its source in Lake Ilmen, lies the historic town of Novgorod, which in 862, in the early centuries of its power, invited Rurik and his fellow Swedish Vikings to assist them in fighting other Varangians and so brought the Swedes into Russian history. From the eleventh to the fourteenth century Novgorod was a powerful and exceedingly wealthy city that became the key Hanseatic entrepôt for trade with Asia, and its population is believed to have once reached 400,000. The rise of Muscovy caused its decline, and after Leningrad was established Novgorod became a small town of little significance.

The European North. Although the remaining area of the taiga region west of the Urals covers vastly more area than the Northwestern Lake Region just described, it is not greatly developed. Increased exploitation of the timber under the Soviets and their construction of the rail line to Vorkuta to tap the coal resources there as well as the oil resources of Ukhta, midway between Kotlas and Vorkuta, stimulated increased development of the area. The Pechora River in the northeast is overshadowed by the Northern Dvina, which drains most of the European North. Kotlas is the principal center of the upper Northern Dvina basin and has developed primarily through its handling of timber and wood products; its importance naturally increased with the opening in 1942 of the rail line northeast to Vorkuta and westward to the Moscow-Archangel line. Southeast of Kotlas is the much larger and more important trading and industrial center of Kirov (formerly Vyatka), on the upper Vyatka River. It is an old center of Russian colonization but later developed as a wood-processing and leatherworking center. Vologda, northeast of the great Rybinsk Reservoir, lies toward the southern edge of the taiga and is a famous old dairy center, especially well known for its butter.

However, the principal center of the entire European North is the White Sea port of Archangel (Arkhangel'sk) located at the mouth of the Northern Dvina and at the terminus of a rail line to the Central Industrial District around Moscow. Until the eighteenth century Archangel was the only Russian seaport of significance, and it thrived especially on trade with the English, who established a trading post there in 1553. Increased development of the timber resources of the Northern Dvina basin stimulated the town's growth and led to the rise of an active sawmilling industry. In 1918–19 Archangel was a center of anti-Bolshevik intervention by British and other Allied troops. Along with Murmansk, Archangel was a great import port of war matériel during World War II, and the enormous stacks of lumber for export that normally characterized the harbor were replaced by piles of food, machines, trucks, and guns. With a population of more than 300,000, Archangel is the largest city lying at such a northerly latitude.

Mixed Forest (3)

The triangular region of the mixed forest, with its base on the western frontier of the Soviet Union and its elongated apex touching the Urals, constitutes the traditional core of Russia and comprises the northern half of the Fertile Triangle. The presence of the mixed forest vegetation reflects the relatively milder temperatures in relation to the taiga and the greater and more reliable rainfall in relation to the wooded steppe and steppe to the south. Unfortunately, the greatest area of the mixed forest in European Russia— the broad western extension (A747)—suffers from large areas of bog and marsh as well as poor, sandy soils developed on glacial deposits left by the Baltic ice sheet.

Central Industrial District. The heart of the mixed forest zone is Moscow (Moskva) and its satellite towns and cities, which also serve as the heart of European Russia and the entire Soviet Union. Although Moscow was only an obscure village while Novgorod and Kiev were great medieval cities, its very obscurity and slow growth in its mixed forest environment on the small Moskva River, a tributary of the Oka, assisted its persistence through the periods of Mongol invasions. It was, indeed, attacked several times during the twelfth to seventeenth centuries, but its location on the fringe of the territory held by the Mongols facilitated its recovery and reestablishment of its power. From it the Muscovite state expanded until finally the Great Russians established their control over all the territory now occupied by the Soviet Union as well as over areas farther west and northwest in Europe. Although Moscow was supplanted by Leningrad as the Russian capital for more than two centuries, its central position stimulated its growth, cultural significance, and economic importance during that time. The restoration of the seat of government to Moscow in 1918 and Soviet determination to equip their capital to a degree commensurate with the growing importance of the new Soviet state brought a great transformation to the city and increased its share of nearly all aspects of Soviet life. The highly centralized government of the Soviet Union produced an unusual concentration of offices and high government officials, as well as a concentration of transportation facilities, commerce, and industry, and their accompanying workers. As a result, the population doubled between 1926 and 1939 to more than 4 millions, at the same time that industrial and residential suburbs were expanding from small towns to cities of 60,000 to 80,000. Construction of the Moscow Canal during the 1930's improved the capital's transportation facilities and at the same time assured it of an adequate water supply from the upper Volga. The eleven rail lines converging on Moscow are linked by both an inner ring around the city limits and an outer ring at a distance of 20 to 50 miles.

The share of Moscow in the industrial production of the Soviet Union has increased to nearly one sixth and thus appreciably exceeds that of Leningrad. The variety of manufactures is as great as that of London or the New York City area and includes, in addition, such products as motorcars and airplanes. Moscow is also the publishing center of the Soviet Union. Although it long imported large amounts of coal from the Donbas, Moscow is making increasing use of its local lignite deposits as well as near-by peat resources, and a natural gas pipeline from the Saratov field near the Volga was completed after 1945. The Kremlin, rising from the left bank of the Moskva River, was taken over from the tsarist regime and, within its great walls, contains the nerve center of the Soviet government.

Although Moscow is the core of the Central Industrial District, there are several other cities in the area that exceed 100,000 in population and contribute a large share to the industrial output of the Soviet Union. Yaroslavl' is the oldest of the neighboring cities, having been founded in the eleventh century and rivaling Moscow until the fifteenth century. It became an important textile center with the establishment of large linen mills in the eighteenth century. With increased industrialization of Russia under the Soviets, Yaroslavl' became a center of synthetic rubber production and truck and bus manfacturing. Its population exceeded 300,000 after 1945. Southeast of Yaroslavl' is Ivanovo, the "twin city" of Yaroslavl' in terms of textile specialization. However, Ivanovo specializes in cotton textiles and has been called the Manchester of Russia. Northwest of Yaroslavl' is Shcherbakov (called Rybinsk until 1946), which developed rapidly under the Soviet regime, especially as a consequence of the damming of the Volga to form the great Rybinsk Reservoir in 1941. The Rybinsk hydroelectric station has a capacity of 330,000 kilowatts and furnishes power to much of the Central Industrial District, which is also served by other smaller hydroelectric plants on the Volga and by several large thermal stations operating on lignite and peat. Down the Volga from Yaroslavl' is Kostroma, which is also a linen textile center, as well as a major producing center for lumber and paper. South of Moscow on the southern edge of the Central Industrial District is the famous old metallurgical center of Tula, which ranks in size with Yaroslavl' and Ivanovo. Arms and various iron products have been produced in Tula since the sixteenth century on the basis of modest iron deposits and low-grade coal found in the area. "Tula wares," including cutlery, samovars, and black enamel objects inlaid with silver, have long been shipped all over the Soviet Union. Northwest of Moscow, on the upper Volga, is the old city of Kalinin (called Tver' before 1932), which, like Yaroslavl', at one time vied with Moscow for dominance of Great Russia. Lying in a great flax-producing region, Kalinin specializes in linen textiles but also produces cotton textiles, wood products, machines, and especially railroad rolling stock.

An easterly outlier of the Central Industrial District is Gor'kiy (sometimes Gorki—formerly Nizhniy Novgorod), lying at the confluence of the Oka and Volga rivers. As Nizhniy Novgorod, the city was founded as an advance fort against inroads by invaders from Asia, but later became especially famous for its great fair, which moved to Nizhniy Novgorod in 1817 from Makarev, 50 miles down the Volga. The great development of the fair, at which products from eastern Europe met those from central Asia via the great Volga waterway, indicates the significance of the location of the city for commerce. The ease of assembling raw materials at the site led to the development of Gor'kiy as the third greatest industrial city of the Soviet Union. Its automobile factories have earned for the town the nickname of the "Soviet Detroit," although Soviet automobile manufacturing is not so concentrated in Gor'kiy as the nickname might indicate. The growth of such other industries as shipbuilding, textile and machine making, aircraft manufacturing, and a great variety of additional industries increased the population from 222,000 in 1926 to more than 900,000 after 1945. Up the Oka from Gor'kiy is the industrial city of Dzerzhinsk (formerly Rastyapino), which developed almost entirely after World War I as a subsidiary of Gor'kiy and as a great chemical center using near-by deposits of phosphorites and gypsum. With a population increase from 9,000 in 1926 to 103,000 in 1939, Dzerzhinsk is a good example of the astonishing growth made by several Soviet towns during the first two Five Year Plans.

Baltic Lands. Most of the Baltic lands comprise the three former Baltic states of Estonia, Latvia, and Lithuania, which received their independence from Russia after World War I and were then reabsorbed as S.S.R.'s by the Soviet Union in 1940. Estonia surrendered two small strips of territory to the R.S.F.S.R., one east of the Narva River north of Lake Peipus and one at the southern end of the lake. Latvia also surrendered a small strip of its northeastern corner. Lithuania, on the other hand, was given back its capital of Vil'nyus along with a broad strip of territory along its eastern border. Vil'nyus had been Lithuania's traditional capital for centuries but was seized by the Poles in the fighting at the end of World War I and was not returned until the Soviets took eastern Poland in 1939. Also returned to Lithuania was the disputed "Memelland," a narrow strip of pre-1918 German territory lying north of the Neman or Memel River that was seized by Lithuania in 1923 and retaken by Germany in 1939.

The history of these Baltic lands has been an especially tragic one since they became independent in 1918. Separation of their territories from Russia, on whom they had come to depend economically, especially for exports to be shipped from their ports, created great economic difficulties during the interwar period. However, the young states were proud of their freedom and were gradually evolving economic stability when they were absorbed by the Soviet Union during the chaotic year of 1940, with no chance to defend themselves or to receive assistance from other powers. The United States has never officially recognized their transformation into Soviet constituent republics. In 1941 they were invaded by Germany, and many of their citizens were sent to Germany. The advance of the Red Army into the Baltic area in 1944–45 brought severe fighting and widespread destruction, and a number of Baltic people retreated with the Germans rather than face Soviet control again.

By 1950 the Soviet economy had become well established in the Baltic lands: agriculture had been collectivized, and all industries had been nationalized. It was reliably reported that thousands of Baltic people who were slow to accept the Soviet pattern were deported to other parts of the Soviet Union.

The Baltic region was, in former times, one of the remotest corners of Europe, where paganism existed even down to the fourteenth century. Finnish tribes, the present Estonians, occupied the north; Baltic tribes, such as the Letts or Lithuanians, and the former Prussians, occupied the south. During the thirteenth century this region became the field of expeditions by German knights and of later exploitation by German traders. Estonia and Latvia fell wholly under the influence of the Germans, but Lithuania resisted and for a time even extended its domain far south. The Baltic Germans did not keep Estonia and Latvia free from other foreigners such as the Danes, Swedes, and later the Russians; but in an economic sense the Germans remained the leaders, and the greater part of the country belonged to them as large landowners. Their influence was twofold. They brought German culture and energy and did a great deal to develop the region by furthering industries and education; but at the same time they looked upon the inhabitants as akin to slaves, and the social conditions of the peasantry were very low. Although the native population came politically under German influence, it kept its own language, and in time a strong national tendency developed, notably in the nineteenth century.

The destiny of Lithuania was different. It came under the influence of Poland and Polish land ownership. When Poland was divided it fell to Russia. There was no substantial economic improvement during the Polish and Russian occupation, and, compared with East Prussia, Lithuania was backward. From the time of the Polish influence the Roman Catholics held a leading position, although the Lutheran church prevailed generally in Latvia and Estonia.

The most important city of the Baltic lands is Riga, capital of the Latvian S.S.R., lying on the Gulf of Riga at the mouth of the Western Dvina River (called the Daugava in Latvia). Its long membership in the Hanseatic League is reflected in the style of its architecture, which the Hanseatic League and its Germanic influence fostered. With its river outlet and excellent rail connections, Riga has long been a leading Baltic port, and for the Latvians especially is an important cultural center.

Tallin (formerly Reval), capital of the Estonian S.S.R., is also a Baltic port but is not so favorably situated and does not have so large a hinterland as Riga. Like Riga, it was a Hanseatic port but later suffered from competition given by Leningrad. Vil'nyus (Russian: Vilna, Polish: Wilno) has been capital of Lithuania since 1323, except during the interwar period mentioned above. Because of its importance as a communications center, it has been subjected to repeated sieges. Its industries specialize in metal goods, electric and radio equipment, wood products, and prepared foods.

The northern half of former East Prussia was awarded to the Soviet Union at the Potsdam Conference in 1945, although it had never been Russian territory. The award gave the Soviet Union Germany's most important eastern Baltic port, the city of Königsberg, renamed Kaliningrad by the Russians. The area was called the Kaliningrad region after the main city and became the Kaliningrad Oblast after it was incorporated into the R.S.F.S.R., although it is separated from that constituent republic by the Belorussian S.S.R. and the Lithuanian S.S.R. The German population has been almost entirely evicted, and Russians have been sent in to replace the Germans. The region is primarily an agricultural one, raising especially grains but also forage grasses for dairy cattle. Horses and hogs were raised in large numbers by the pre-1945 German population. There are, however, numerous industries in the region, especially at Kaliningrad, which has shipyards, machinery works, and rolling stock factories and repair shops.

Belorussian S.S.R. Lying on the western border of the Soviet Union, the Belorussian S.S.R. is occupied by the numerically smallest of the three Russian groups—Great Russians, Ukrainians, and Belorussians (or White Russians). The westerly extension of Belorussia includes territory taken from Poland in 1939, part of which was returned at the end of World War II. The area has for centuries existed under two serious handicaps: first, it comprises hilly moraines deposited by the Baltic ice sheet, with swampy outwash sands in the south forming the Pripet Marshes—thus making Belorussia a generally poor agricultural region that is also lacking in appreciable mineral wealth; and, second, the area's location has caused it to be contested among Russians, Poles, and Lithuanians, and has placed it in the path of invading armies. As a result, Belorussia is more backward than its location in the west might indicate. The area was beginning to make some progress with the construction of railways when the heavy fighting of World War I swept back and forth across it. Soviet efforts to build up Belorussia during the interwar period received a great setback from the very severe battles that were waged there during World War II. Thus, the Belorussian S.S.R. remains a backward area economically and culturally.

In the damp, cool climate and on the soils of the moraines and outwash deposits forests thrive and still persist over large areas of Belorussia, yielding one of the area's principal resources—timber and wood products.   The very sparsely populated Pripet Marshes—the *Poles'ye* or "woodland"—are especially wooded, as the name indicates, where actual swamp does not exist.   However, vigorous efforts have been made during the twentieth century and especially since 1920 to drain large areas of the *Poles'ye* and turn them into productive agricultural lands.   Belorussia as a whole yields mainly rye, potatoes, oats, flax (especially in the north), forage grasses, summer barley, some wheat, and hemp.

As a result of World War II destruction, all the larger cities and towns lost population between 1939 and the post-1945 period, both because urban housing facilities were destroyed and because many people retreated eastward with the Red Army.   Also, large numbers of the many Jews of Belorussia were killed by the Nazis.   The largest city of the area is Minsk, the capital, which by 1948 had lost several thousand of the 239,000 inhabitants—half of whom were Jewish —it had in 1939.   The second largest city is Gomel', in the southeastern corner, which produces agricultural implements, electrical equipment, and foods.   In the northeast corner is Vitebsk, which before 1939 was even larger than Gomel', but which suffered cruelly during World War II and lost half of its population.   Lying in a productive agricultural region in which flax, truck produce, and dairying are especially important, and located at the crossing of the Western Dvina by the Smolensk-Riga railway, Vitebsk has developed major textile industries as well as factories producing optical goods, machine tools, agricultural machinery, and wood products.   Although the city of Smolensk is located east of the Belorussian S.S.R., it lies in an environment similar to that of Vitebsk and was before 1939 about the same size as Vitebsk.   However, it did not suffer so severely in World War II.   It lies at the head of navigation on the Dnieper and is an important rail junction, and its industries produce linen, textile machinery, clothing, wood products, and foods.

Wooded Steppe (4)

The transitional wooded steppe region between the mixed forest on the north and the true steppe on the south is one of the most agriculturally productive and—in terms of rural population—the most densely settled region of European Russia.   Much of the area is blanketed with loess, which in large areas has been apparently reworked by water, like the *limon* of northern France and Belgium. In the transitional climate of the region the soils have developed into Degraded Chernozems: they are primarily Chernozem in character—and are hence quite fertile—but have been somewhat leached by the greater effective precipitation relative to that farther south. Broadly speaking, the belt of the wooded steppe, extending west-southwest to east-northeast, may be divided into three parts: the Western Ukraine on the west (with which Bessarabia is included for the sake of convenience), the Central Black Earth Region in the center, and the Middle Volga Region in the east.

Western Ukraine and Bessarabia. Because of its loessal soils, over-lying the thin sedimentary cover of the crystalline rocks of the Volhynian-Podolian Horst, and its greater rainfall, this area is the most productive of European Russia and has rural population densities exceeding 250 per square mile. Sugar beets and wheat are the dominant crops, although maize is a leading crop in the Moldavian S.S.R., and truck produce is found around most of the cities. Soil erosion is a serious problem throughout much of the area because of the light texture of the soil and the concentration of rainfall in heavy spring and summer downpours. Extensive soil conservation projects have been undertaken by the Soviets in the area to preserve the high productivity of this fertile agricultural land.

The area of the Western Ukraine was appreciably increased after 1939 and again in 1945, when territory was taken from southeastern Poland (the L'vov area), eastern Czechoslovakia (Ruthenia), and northern Rumania (Northern Bucovina) and added to the Ukraine. Virtually the entire territory of the Moldavian S.S.R. is coextensive with Bessarabia, taken from Rumania in 1940. However, southern Bessarabia was given to the Ukrainian S.S.R.

The transfer of eastern Galicia to the Ukraine gave the Soviet Union most of the Galician oil fields that formerly belonged to Poland, although the territorial exchange of 1951 (see Chapter 43) returned some of the oil to Poland. Other than these modest petroleum resources and some potash around Stanislav, the area has no considerable mineral resources.

In addition to a score of towns of 30,000 to 90,000 population, there are four cities of more than 100,000, which merit at least brief mention. L'vov (Polish: Lwow, German: Lemberg) in the west was long an ethnographic melting pot with many Poles, but also a number of Jews, Ruthenes, Ukrainians, Great Russians, and other peoples. The Poles have always considered it one of their primary cultural centers and therefore were unhappy when it was transferred to Russia in 1939. Its commercial significance is shown by the fact that it is the most important railroad junction of the area, and it has large railway repair shops. Chernovtsy (Rumanian: Cernăuti, German: Czernowitz) is an old town that became the capital of the Bucovina when it was created a separate duchy in 1849. Kishinev (Rumanian: Chişinău) is the capital of the Moldavian S.S.R. and is the economic and cultural center of Bessarabia. Lying in a productive agricultural area, the city has principally agricultural interests and trade. Kirovograd lies up on the Volhynian-Podolian Plateau and is an agricultural center.

Lying on the middle Dnieper is the ancient city of Kiev (Kiyev), occupying a picturesque location on the high right bank of the river and overlooking the flat Dnieper lowlands to the east. It will be recalled that Varangians traveled down the Dnieper from Novgorod in the ninth century and established Kiev as the center of a powerful state that reached its height in the eleventh century. However, its location in an exposed position on an easily traveled river invited attacks by Mongols, and Kiev lost its leadership among medieval Russian cities and for centuries was a point of contention among Mongols, Lithuanians, Poles, and Russians. As "the Mother of Russian Cities" and the "Jerusalem of Russia," it was a great religious center until after World War I. With the establishment of the Soviet regime, Kiev assumed an even greater role as a commercial and industrial center. In addition to its beet sugar plants and other agricultural industries, it has developed large chemical, textile, and metal industries. Its population of 846,000 made Kiev the third largest city of the Soviet Union in 1939.

Central Black Earth Region. Agriculturally, the Central Black Earth Region continues the wheat-sugar beet combination that prevails in the Western Ukraine, although yields are neither so great nor so uniform. Hence, population densities are not so uniformly high, although scattered areas also exceed 250 persons per square mile. In addition to its agricultural wealth, the Central Black Earth Region possesses great potential wealth in the iron deposits of the Kursk Magnetic Anomaly, although much remains to be done before practical, large-scale exploitation of the iron-bearing quartzites is feasible. Also, the location of the area between the highly industrialized Lower Dnieper-Donbas section and the Central Industrial District has stimulated the growth of industry here. Khar'kov has been especially favored in this respect and has developed an industrial output that vies with that of Gor'kiy, and its population— despite destruction of much of the city during World War II—is approximately equal to that of Kiev and Gor'kiy. Its engineering and metals industries and especially its large tractor plant have become particularly significant. The massive Palace of Industry in Khar'kov is the nerve center of all Ukrainian industry, and the city is the most important rail junction in the Central Black Earth Region.

Near the mouth of the Voronezh River in the upper Don is Voronezh, second largest city (more than 300,000 in population) of the Central Black Earth Region. It has expanded greatly under the Soviets and not only processes many of the agricultural products of the surrounding region (sunflowers, flax, grapes, and wheat) but also manufactures agricultural machinery as well as a variety of other products ranging from aircraft and locomotives to furniture and hosiery. Other agricultural and industrial centers of the region exceeding 100,000 in population are Kursk, Tambov, Penza, and Poltava.

The Middle Volga Region. Although the Volga River itself from Kuybyshev to Saratov is the dividing line between the wooded steppe to the west and the true steppe to the east (see A747), the river and its adjacent lands from Kazan' south to Saratov will be discussed as a unit, since it is the river that supplies the unifying element in this landscape. In the agriculture of the area, the sugar beet that plays such an important role farther west largely disappears, and wheat and sunflowers cover the great open spaces. Except along the line of the limestone Pre-Volga Heights along the west bank of the river, the rainfall becomes increasingly less in relation to that of the Central Black Earth Region. The most important mineral resource is petroleum, pools of which, discovered by the Soviets, extend from the Volga to the Urals. This is the large area that the Soviets have termed their "Second Baku." Although production has been somewhat disappointing, the pools appear to promise greater yields in the future. Also present in the Pre-Volga Heights are oil shales, and near Saratov are the largest natural gas fields in the Soviet Union. Thus, in addition to serving as a transit land for goods moving up and down the Volga, the region is developing its own resources and industrial potential as well as its agricultural assets.

The greatest promise for the region lies in the two enormous hydroelectric works that at mid-century were under construction at Kuybyshev and at Perevoloki, both on the horseshoe-shaped "Samara Bend." Not only will these hydroelectric works furnish more than 2.5 million kilowatts of power, but the dams will back up Volga water for irrigation of millions of acres in the dry steppes east of the Volga as well as for large areas west of the Volga.

The anchor point on the middle Volga is Kuybyshev (formerly Samara), which not only developed rapidly under the Soviets prior to 1939 but also received a tremendous stimulus during World War II, when it became a temporary location for many government agencies during the unsuccessful Nazi attack on Moscow. Its population increased to about 600,000 in the post-1945 period, and its industrial production expanded greatly. Completion of the hydroelectric works will undoubtedly furnish Kuybyshev strong stimulus for additional growth, although a large share of the hydroelectricity is to be wired to Moscow.

Up the Volga from the Samara Bend is Ulyanovsk, the name of which was changed from Simbirsk in 1936 in honor of its most famous citizen, Lenin, whose real name was Vladimir I. Ulyanov. West of Kuybyshev is Syzran', which also expanded greatly during World War II, especially because of increased exploitation of petroleum resources in the area. Still farther up the Volga and north of the mouth of the Kama is Kazan', the capital of the Tatar A.S.S.R. It has been a Tatar stronghold for 500 years, and its original site 30 miles northeast of its present location was a Tatar stronghold for 1,000 years before that. Its strategic position on the Middle Volga prevented Muscovite use of the full length of the Volga until Kazan' was captured after a long siege by Ivan the Terrible in 1552. The Asiatic affinities of its builders are reflected in the architecture of the city, especially in its mosques. Assembling raw materials easily because of its position on the Volga and on main railways, Kazan' has developed varied industries and reached a population of approximately 500,000 after World War II.

Steppe (5)

Along a line extending northeastward from Kishinev through the northeastern Ukraine to Saratov, the wooded steppe gives way to the true steppe with its seemingly boundless, monotonous treeless expanses now primarily devoted to great wheat fields on the collective farms, which also raise maize and cotton. The decreased rainfall and higher summer temperatures make the crops of this zone more variable and lower in yield than those of the wooded steppe. In summer, hot, dry, dusty winds sweep over the unbroken expanses of the Black Sea lowlands lying between the lower Dniester and the lower Dnieper.

Of primary significance in the steppe lands of the southern Ukraine are the mining and industrial developments that have arisen in the Dnieper Bend and in the Donbas farther east. The core of this great industrial complex is the coal field of the Donets Basin or Donbas, lying south of the Donets River. The pattern of coal mining is an irregular one because of the complexity of the folded structure of the Donets Ridge, but the southwestern corner of the coal mining area is at Stalino, the northern corner is at Slavyansk, and the eastern corner is at Shakhty, in the Rostov Oblast of the R.S.F.S.R. Although the Donbas has not become a second Ruhr by any means, it has some of the same characteristics in that a number of large towns developed rapidly, and numerous large heavy industries and chemical industries have arisen in the area. One of the great advantages that the Ruhr possesses over the Donbas is its excellent system of waterways, especially the Rhine, and its general situation in the bustling area of northwestern Europe.

With a population of more than 500,000, Stalino (formerly Yuzovka, named for the Scottish industrialist, Hughes, who was instrumental in developing industry in the area during the nineteenth century) is the largest center in the Donbas. It is followed by Makeyevka (300,-000), Voroshilovgrad (200,000), Gorlovka (150,000), Konstantinovka (100,000), and a number of other towns with fewer than 100,000 inhabitants. All have iron and steel industries, coal mines, coke ovens, chemical plants using coke oven by-products, and varied related industries. In addition, mercury is mined near Gorlovka—which is also the terminus of a pipeline from the oil fields of Groznyy in the northern Caucasus, and Artemovsk and Slavyansk are producers of large amounts of salt and chemicals.

West of the Donbas is the rapidly developing industrial area of the Dnieper Bend. The original stimulus to the industrialization of the area was the high-quality iron ore of Krivoy Rog, whence ore is shipped to the coal of the Donbas and which receives coal and coke in return. Fortunately, one of the two greatest manganese deposits of the Soviet Union, and one of the world's largest, is located around Nikopol' on the Dnieper southeast of Krivoy Rog.

The Krivoy Rog-Donbas exchange was expanded not only quantitatively after the initiation of the First Five Year Plan but was diversified as a result of development of the famous Dnieper hydroelectric works (Lenin Works), opened in 1932. Although long associated with the name Dnepropetrovsk, the dam actually lies an appreciable distance down the Dnieper from Dnepropetrovsk at Zaporozh'ye.

The great supply of electric power attracted many varied industries, but special attention has been given to the making of high-quality electric steels and aluminum. The location of Dnepropetrovsk (formerly Yekaterinoslav) on the main rail line between Krivoy Rog and the Donbas permits it to receive both iron ore and coal and to produce finished steel and steel products by the usual smelting process and also by the application of electric power for special steels. Despite extensive destruction during World War II, Dnepropetrovsk had a population of more than 500,000 at mid-century. Zaporozh'ye (300,000), not quite so favorably located, has shared in some of the same development that built Dnepropetrovsk, and it has also become a large producer of aluminum. Dneprodzerzhinsk, up the Dnieper from Dnepropetrovsk, has also become an important producer of metallurgical products and chemicals.

In 1950, the Soviets announced a bold plan for development of the lower Dnieper region. A canal is to tap the Dnieper below Zaporozh'ye and divert some of its water southeastward through a canal to Nogaysk. A hydroelectric station is planned for this canal. At the site of the water power installation a second planned canal (the South Ukrainian-Northern Crimean Canal) is to run southwestward to the Crimean Peninsula, then bend eastward to reach Kerch'. At Kakhovka, on the lower Dnieper, a hydroelectric station with a capacity of 250,000 kilowatts is to be erected. Its exhaust waters are to be sent through a canal to augment the flow of the South Ukrainian-Northern Crimean Canal. The target completion date announced in 1950 is 1957.

Among a number of Black Sea ports in the southern Ukraine, the largest and most active is Odessa, the third largest city (600,000) of the Ukraine and one of the leading ports of the Soviet Union. Its location permits it to assemble a wide variety of raw materials, which it utilizes in its food processing plants, chemical plants, machine works, and other varied industries. Other ports along the northern Black Sea and Sea of Azov coasts are Nikolayev, Kherson, Melitopol, Osipenko, Zhdanov (formerly Mariupol—which also has large steel works using iron ore from Kerch' and coal from the Donbas), and Taganrog.

Rostov, lying near the mouth of the Don in Taganrog Bay of the Sea of Azov, also serves as a port, but its other commercial and industrial functions are rather more important. Rostov has been called the "Gateway to the Caucasus," and it has long served as the point of exchange of products from the Caucasus for those from farther north. Its agricultural importance has been especially great, since it is the outlet for the wheat area of the lower Don basin. The Groznyy-Gorlovka pipeline passes through Rostov and is tapped there. Two canal projects under construction at mid-century will contribute to increased expansion of Rostov's commercial and industrial functions: the Manych Canal between the lower Don and the Caspian Sea, and the Volga-Don Canal near Stalingrad. Like numerous other cities in the zone of Russo-German fighting during World War II, Rostov received extensive damage, but it maintained a population of more than 500,000.

The center for the entire lower Volga region is Stalingrad (Tsaritsyn before 1925), located on the high right bank of the Volga at the "elbow" formed by the turn of the Volga southeastward. One of the most important functions of the city has long been the transshipment of goods moving by land between the Don and Volga rivers, which make their closest approach at Stalingrad. A canal through the divide has been discussed and even planned for many years, but effective construction work began only after World War II. Completion of the canal will have far-reaching effects not only for Stalingrad but for all cities and regions related to the Volga system. The name of Stalingrad was significant in Russian military annals even before World War II because of the role the city played in the Civil War of 1917–20, when Joseph Stalin personally directed the Red Army's liberation of the city. However, in 1942 and early 1943, Stalingrad assumed a unique position among Russian cities after the desperate Nazi siege was repulsed and the vital Volga life line was kept intact. The Battle of Stalingrad was the turning point of Nazi military fortunes in World War II and left the city in ruins. However, the great steel plant and tractor works were restored, and most of the many other industries were operating again at mid-century, by which time the population had almost returned to its 1939 level of 445,000.

Well upstream from Stalingrad and on the border between the wooded steppe and steppe is the city of Saratov, which during World War II, and especially because of the natural gas of the area, expanded until it matched Stalingrad in size. On the low east bank of the Volga are the two smaller towns of Marks and Engels, formerly centers of German colonists who were shifted to Siberia with the approach of Nazi armies in 1941.

Crimean Peninsula. Although the major part—the plain lying north of the Crimean Mountains—of the Crimean Peninsula belongs to the steppe zone, the narrow coastal belt south of the mountains possesses a Mediterranean type of climate, with mild, wet winters (Yalta: 39° F in January) and warm, dry summers. Because of its similarity in climate to the Mediterranean coast of France, the southern Crimea is known as the "Russian Riviera." Sheltered from cold winds from the north by the limestone Crimean or Yaila Mountains, the southern coast is the site of numerous resorts (Yalta, Alupka,

A. Coast of the Crimean Peninsula sheltered from the cold continental air masses in winter. Courtesy of Sovfoto.

Livadiya, Alushta, and Sudak) that were the playground of the tsarist aristocracy and have since become rest resorts for Soviet workers and officials.

At the western end of the southern Crimean coast is the historical naval base of Sevastopol', famous for the sieges of 1854–56 during the Crimean War and also for those during World War II. Simferopol', north of the Crimean Mountains, is the largest city of the peninsula; primarily an agricultural center, it has a population of 143,000. Near the tip of the Kerch' Peninsula in the east is the city of Kerch', which has an iron and steel works using iron ore mined in the vicinity and coal from the Donbas. The Kerch' ore resources are very large, but because of their low iron content (35 per cent) and high phosphorus content, they have been neglected in favor of the higher-grade Krivoy Rog deposits already discussed.

Semidesert and Desert (6 and 7)

Despite the promise of the availability of large supplies of water for irrigation when the "Great Volga" scheme has been consummated, the semidesert and desert areas lying around the northern end of the Caspian Sea were at mid-century great dry expanses of exceedingly poor land. Immediately along the braided course of the Volga, irrigation has permitted the development of intensive agriculture and orcharding, but in most of this large area cattle raising supplants agriculture. Where wheat growing is attempted, the low and variable rainfall in this heart of the Russian "Famine Belt" causes the crops to be uncertain. Chestnut soils that extend into the northern rim of the region are fairly fertile, and it is on them that crop growing is mostly attempted; nevertheless, the climatic factor creates a serious problem for the state farms here. The brown and gray soils of the area north of the Caspian have developed on shifting sands or on deposits laid down when the sea extended much farther northward. In both cases, a large amount of salt is present in the soil, and a number of salt lakes are remnants of the larger Caspian. Lakes El'ton and Baskunchak are both exploited for their salt, the latter yielding nearly 25 per cent of all that produced in the Soviet Union.

That part of the semidesert and desert area lying in the western projection of the Kazakh S.S.R. is an especially poor area, receiving only 4 to 8 inches of precipitation annually. The formerly nomadic herders have gradually been settled, but the life is a meager one; and population density averages only about 3 persons per square mile. Farther east, the oil fields of the lower Emba basin have brought a new stimulus to that section, but no such mineral wealth is known in the basin of the Ural River.

The serious problem of droughts in this area and in the much more productive areas farther west has focused the attention of the Soviets on a project of shelter-belt planting in the Caspian Depression. Because hot, dry winds in summer sweep from the Central Asiatic deserts westward into the wheat lands of southern Russia, an ambitious Soviet project, announced in 1948 and planned for completion in 1965, calls for the planting of 300,000 acres to belts of oak trees that will extend for a total of 3,300 miles north and northwest of the Caspian. However, except along water courses, survival of trees in this area with less than 10 inches of rainfall seems doubtful.

By far the dominant center of the region is Astrakhan', located
on the Volga delta 55 miles from the sea. Because of its low-lying
position, it must be protected by earthen dikes against floods. It
was for centuries a Tatar stronghold and still has thousands of
Tatars among its inhabitants. However, the city was taken by Ivan
the Terrible in the sixteenth century, since it was essential to the
Russians that they control the vital mouth of the Volga. Two primary functions have led to the growth of Astrakhan': it serves as a
transshipment point for goods changing from river to sea craft or
vice versa, and it is the greatest fishing center in the Soviet Union.
Its caviar is canned and shipped all over the world, and great quantities of other fish products are also canned and distributed within
the Soviet Union.

The Caucasus (8 and 9)

As was suggested at the beginning of this chapter, the mountainous
section of the Caucasian Isthmus does not follow the systematic pattern of the vegetation zones used as a basis for the regionalization
of most of European Russia. Here relief is a powerful influence,
and variations in elevation and exposure introduce variations in the
vegetation-soil complex. The isthmus may be divided into four
parts from north to south: Ciscaucasia, the Greater Caucasus or main
Caucasus range, the Transcaucasian Depression, and the Armenian
Plateau or Lesser Caucasus.

Ciscaucasia. The steppe region described earlier extends southward into western Ciscaucasia, lying west of the Stavropol' Plateau,
and the much drier semidesert extends southwestward into eastern
Ciscaucasia. Thus a significant difference between the two sides is
already suggested. On the west is the fertile basin of the Kuban,
colonized by Russians and characterized by the end of the nineteenth
century by a well-developed and progressive agriculture specializing
in wheat. Under the Soviets, the crops have been diversified to include more maize, cotton, rice, sugar beets, and such newer crops
as soybeans. The center of the basin is Krasnodar, founded in the
eighteenth century as a settlement for Kuban Cossacks. It processes
many of the agricultural products raised in the region and also re-
fines petroleum from the oil fields around Maykop to the southeast,
from which a pipeline extends to Krasnodar.

East of the Stavropol' Plateau, agriculture is precarious, and the
dry, sandy area between the Kuma and Terek rivers is sparsely inhabited. The planned diversion of water from the lower Don

through the Manych Canal, the eastern end of which will be south of the Kuma mouth, may bring life to the area. The economically important element here is the exploitation of petroleum around Groznyy, believed to be the second most important single petroleum field in the Soviet Union. Southwest of Groznyy is Dzaudzhikau (formerly Ordzhonikidze and before that Vladikavkaz—which means "Gateway to the Caucasus"), northern terminus of the important Georgian Military Highway over the Caucasus through the Dariel Pass.

Greater Caucasus. The rugged Caucasus Mountains are said to "start in Europe and end in Asia"—indicating the significance of their function. However, it is interesting that, despite the barrier imposed by the mountains, Russian power extended over the Caucasus in the eighteenth century. The Caucasus Mountains are an extension of the alpine structure resulting from mountain-building forces of the Tertiary that formed similar rugged chains in Europe. That mountain building is still going on here is indicated by the numerous earthquakes that occur at the present time. The Caucasus Mountains are not one great, continuous chain but, rather, are composed of a crystalline backbone—largely granitic—and subsidiary masses arranged *en échelon.* The highest peaks lie north of the principal range and include the highest elevation in Europe, Mt. Elbrus. Like the French and Swiss Alps, the mountains themselves seem to be poor in mineral resources, although some metallic ores are produced. As has been mentioned previously, the Caucasus is a "graveyard of peoples," principally of groups that became isolated in the valleys and basins during periods of extensive migration.

Transcaucasian Depression. South of the Caucasus ranges is a great tectonic depression that is divided by the granitic Surami range into a smaller western part and a larger eastern part. East of this range is the basin of the Kura, which actually rises in Turkey and crosses the Surami range before entering the broad lowland in which it joins the Araks (Araxes). Well west of the Surami, the Rion rises on the southern slopes of the Caucasus and enters the flat, partly marshy lowland of Kolkhida—the Colchis of the ancient Greeks.

Two S.S.R.'s occupy the Transcaucasian Depression. On the west is the Georgian S.S.R., with its capital at Tbilisi on the Kura. The funneling effect created by the Caucasus on the north and the Pontus and Lesser Caucasus on the south causes the winds coming from the Black Sea to bring large amounts of moisture into the amphitheater-shaped basin. With precipitation of 50 to 100 inches, Georgia is

the best-watered section of the Soviet Union, and the relatively high
temperatures that exist—especially as a result of the protection afforded by the Caucasus against cold north winds—give the region a
subtropical climate.   The lush vegetation is a pronounced contrast
to that of other parts of southern Russia.   A specialized subtropical
agriculture has been developed in Georgia, with emphasis on such
crops as citrus fruits, tea, rice, tobacco, ramie, grapes, melons, and
others not traditionally associated with Russia.

The principal center of Georgia is the ancient city of Tbilisi (formerly Tiflis), which seems to have been founded in the fourth century in the vicinity of several hot mineral springs.   Its strategic location between the two parts of the Transcaucasian Depression have
caused it to be fought over through the centuries.   In modern times
this favorable location has led to its development as the agricultural
and economic center of Transcaucasia.   With its fascinating blend
of the old and the new and of many groups of people, Tbilisi added
modern industries under the Soviets.   Its textile mills are especially
important and use hydroelectric power generated on streams descending the surrounding steep slopes.   It is also worthy of note that
the second great manganese deposit—other than the one at Nikopol'—
of the Soviet Union is located at Chiatura in the very heart of the
Georgian S.S.R.   Batumi, on the Black Sea, is the terminus of a pipeline from Baku and is a principal export port and refining center.

The broad, flat Kura lowland that forms the heart of the Azerbaydzhan S.S.R. in the eastern part of the Transcaucasian Depression
presents a marked contrast to the climatic condition and vegetation
of the Rion lowland in Georgia.   This dry steppe is hot in summer
and cold in winter, and irrigation projects must be carefully executed to prevent the collection of alkali in the soil because of lack
of drainage.

The great wealth of Azerbaydzhan is overwhelmingly concentrated
in the great petroleum fields of the Apsheron Peninsula, on which
lies Baku.   The oil is found in folded structures at the point of contact between the Caucasus and the plains of the peninsula.   Petroleum was long known to exist here and was dug by hand until the
first scientifically drilled well in 1871 ushered in the modern exploitation of the field on a grand scale.   Even as late as 1950 and despite
the richness claimed by the Soviets for other petroleum-producing
areas, Baku yielded half of the oil produced by the Soviet Union.
The city itself has developed greatly under the Soviets and is one
of the five largest metropolitan centers in the Union.

Armenian Plateau. Lying south of the Transcaucasian Depression but connected with the Greater Caucasus by means of the Surami range is the Armenian Plateau. Its steep northern edge has a mountainous character and is frequently referred to as the Lesser Caucasus. The plateau averages 5,000 to 7,000 feet in elevation, but several inactive volcanoes exceed 10,000 feet. Grazing is an important element in the economy, although soils in the river valleys and moister plateaus give high yields under the long-practiced irrigation developed by the Armenian farmers. The fairly level basin of the middle Araks valley is densely populated. Plans to use the waters of Lake Sevan (or Lake Goksha) for hydroelectric development have long been announced, but little has been done to execute the project.

Capital of the Armenian S.S.R. is Yerevan, the ancient center of the Armenians that—like the Armenians themselves—has been dominated by Turks, Persians, and Russians. The Soviets have made a point of creating a model "national" capital of Yerevan and have developed a number of light industries in the city, and by the post-World War II period its population had risen to 250,000.

The Urals (10)

Above all, the great asset of the Urals region is one of the greatest concentrations of mineral wealth on earth. It is a standard saying in the Soviet Union that when a school child is asked where a certain mineral is found he can always say "the Urals" and be correct most of the time. The principal characteristic of the region's mineral wealth is not so much the quantity of any particular mineral that is found there—although great quantities of certain minerals exist in the area—but rather the bewildering variety. Of particular importance are the deposits of copper, iron, platinum, gold, potash, bauxite, magnesite, asbestos, nickel, chromium, and manganese. The large coal deposits are unfortunately of low grade, but they have nevertheless played a vital role in the economic development of the region. In addition to the important mineral deposits named above, there are smaller, but still commercially exploitable, deposits of tungsten, lead, zinc, and even precious stones, such as emeralds. This great natural wealth was known and exploited to an appreciable extent during the eighteenth century: the first Russian ironworks were established here at that time. Later, however, the region was neglected in favor of the Ukrainian coal and iron deposits. It was under the Five Year Plans and especially under the impetus of

World War II that the Urals became the third most important industrial region of the Soviet Union. The opening of the "Second Baku" on the western flank of the Urals afforded still another asset to this well-endowed area.

A detailed consideration of the industrial development of the Urals would be impossible in this brief study; however, a glance at some of the more important centers that have developed will permit an insight into the variety of the industries and the significance of the Urals in Soviet economic life. The largest city of the Urals is Sverdlovsk, which was founded by Peter the Great in 1721 and named Ekaterinburg. It has long been an important mining center and under the Soviets increased in population from 140,000 in 1926 to 600,000 after World War II. It produces not only crude steel and aluminum but also many types of machinery and electrical equipment, as well as plastics, paper, and textiles. The second largest center is Chelyabinsk, also an old town, which under the Soviets expanded from a town of 59,000 in 1926 to 500,000 after 1945. Among its varied industries the most important is the great tractor factory, producing 25 per cent of the tractors of the Soviet Union.

Located on the upper Kama on the western flank of the Urals is Molotov (formerly Perm), which manufactures dairy equipment, fertilizers, aircraft engines, electronic equipment, river boats, and wood products. Its population increased from 120,000 in 1926 to 450,000 at mid-century. Ufa, on the rail line from Kuybyshev to Chelyabinsk, is the cultural and economic center of the Bashkir A.S.S.R. and has developed particularly as a refining and supply center of the oil fields of the surrounding area. East of Molotov and lying directly in the Urals is the iron mining and steelmaking city of Nizhniy Tagil. A steel plant completed in Nizhniy Tagil during World War II is said to be one of the largest in Europe.

One of the most famous of the manufacturing centers of the Urals is Magnitogorsk, built by the Soviets on the upper Ural River in the midst of an empty steppe. From a population of zero in 1926, it had mushroomed to a population of 200,000 by the end of World War II. The basis of this phenomenal growth is the iron and steel works erected on the site to utilize the rich ores of Magnitnaya—"Magnetic Mountain," lying at the southern end of the Urals. Coal for the Magnitogorsk blast furnaces was originally brought by rail from the Kuznetsk Basin, 1,200 miles farther east; and Magnitnaya iron ore was returned to the Kuzbas for use in blast furnaces there. This widely heralded *Kombinat* was—although apparently necessary at the time—inefficient because of the long rail hauls involved. Nevertheless, the *Kombinat* led to the development of a new concentration of heavy industry at both Magnitogorsk and the Kuzbas, both of which were of vital significance during World War II. With the discovery of large amounts of coking coal at Karaganda in Kazakhstan, only half as far from Magnitogorsk, and of appreciable amounts of iron ore at Gornaya Shoriya, south of the Kuzbas, the Magnitogorsk-Kuzbas exchange diminished substantially. Nevertheless, the scale of these exchanges indicates both the determination of the Soviets to develop the eastern concentrations of heavy industry and the difficulties that they face in achieving success in their determination. Here may be seen a typical example of the nature of Soviet development at mid-century: human determination attempting to overcome geographical handicaps in order to achieve maximum realization of a great potential.

Appendix

For every European country, the following list gives the area, total population, capital city (indicated by an asterisk), cities with more than 100,000 population, and selected cities with less than 100,000. The cities are listed for each country in order of population down to 100,000. For those countries for which selected cities of less than 100,000 are given, a line of asterisks indicates the first break in the order of rank. The date given after the name of the country applies to all population figures not otherwise dated.

ALBANIA (1949)

10,629 sq. mi.
1,175,000 pop. (1948)

*Tiranë	40,000
Shkodër	30,000
Korçë	28,000

ANDORRA (1950)

191 sq. mi.
5,400 pop.

*Andorra	600

AUSTRIA (1948)

32,377 sq. mi.
7,090,000 pop. (1949)

*Vienna	1,731,557
Graz	219,974
Linz	181,532
Salzburg	105,407
Innsbruck	97,221
Klagenfurt	65,799

BELGIUM (1945)

11,783 sq. mi.
8,625,084 pop. (1949)

*Brussels (1950)	925,031
Antwerp	497,175
Liége	252,012
Ghent	219,812
Molines	61,004
Bruges	52,561
Ostend	50,569

BULGARIA (1947)

42,796 sq. mi.
7,160,000 pop. (1950)

*Sofia	434,888
Plovdiv	125,440
Stalin (Varna)	77,792
Ruse	53,420
Burgas	43,684

CZECHOSLOVAKIA (1947)

49,354 sq. mi.
12,463,000 pop. (1949)

*Prague	922,284
Brno	273,127

(CZECHOSLOVAKIA—Continued)

Ostrava	180,960
Bratislava	172,664
Plzeň	117,814

DENMARK (1945)

16,576 sq. mi.
4,230,000 pop. (1949)

*Copenhagen	1,078,892
Århus	107,393
Odense	92,436
Ålborg	60,880
Esbjerg	43,241

FINLAND (1950)

130,159 sq. mi.
4,231,279 pop.

(The name in parentheses is the Swedish form.)

*Helsinki (Helsingfors) .	399,288
Turku (Åbo)	107,148
Tampere (Tammerfors)	105,121
Pori (Björneborg) . .	45,723

FRANCE (1946)

212,659 sq. mi.
42,000,000 pop. (1951)

*Paris	4,951,000
Marseille	636,264
Lyon	460,748
Toulouse	264,411
Bordeaux	253,751
Nice	211,165
Nantes	200,265
Lille	188,871
St. Étienne	177,966
Strasbourg	175,515
Toulon	125,742
Rennes	113,781
Nancy	113,477

(FRANCE—Continued)

Reims	110,749
Clermont-Ferrand . .	108,090
Limoges	107,857
Rouen	107,739
Le Havre	106,934
Grenoble	102,161
Roubaix	100,978
Dijon	100,664
Le Mans	100,455

* * *

Nîmes	91,667
Mulhouse	87,655
Brest	74,991
Orléans	70,240
Versailles	70,141
Metz	70,105
Avignon	60,053
Calais	50,048

GERMANY (1950)

137,026 sq. mi. (excluding Saar)
65,150,932 pop. (1946)

German Federal Republic

94,634 sq. mi.
48,195,000 pop.

German Democratic Republic

42,392 sq. mi.
17,313,734 pop. (1946)

(Cities marked † are located in the German Democratic Republic, and their populations are those of the 1946 census.)

*Berlin (Ger. Dem. Rep.)	3,187,470
Hamburg	1,604,600
Munich	831,017
†Leipzig	607,655
Essen	605,125

(GERMANY—Continued)

Cologne	590,825
Frankfurt	523,923
Dortmund	500,150
Düsseldorf	498,347
Stuttgart	481,845
†Dresden	467,966
Bremen	444,196
Hannover	441,615
Duisburg	408,877
Wuppertal	362,125
Nürnberg	360,017
Gelsenkirchen	310,108
Bochum	290,406
Kiel	253,867
†Chemnitz	250,188
Mannheim	244,000
Lübeck	237,860
†Magdeburg	236,326
Braunschweig	223,263
†Halle	222,505
Wiesbaden	218,255
Oberhausen	202,343
Karlsruhe	198,014
Augsburg	184,712
†Erfurt	174,633
Krefeld	170,482
Kassel	161,322
Bielefeld	153,111
Mülheim	148,606
Solingen	147,782
Haggen	146,099
Aachen	129,967
†Zwickau	122,862
München-Gladbach	122,388
Ludwigshafen	122,329
Oldenburg	121,643
Münster	119,788
Regensburg	116,997
Heidelberg	115,750
†Rostock	114,869
Bremerhaven	113,925
†Potsdam	113,568
*Bonn (Ger. Fed. Rep.)	111,287

(GERMANY—Continued)

Herne	111,249
Freiburg	109,822
Osnabrück	108,900
Recklinghausen	104,857
Remscheid	102,929
Flensburg	102,045
Wilhelmshaven	100,926
Wattenstedt-Salzgitter	100,630

* * *

Darmstadt	93,000
Mainz	86,000
Trier	76,000
Würzburg	73,000
Ulm	69,000

GREECE (1950)

21,246 sq. mi.
7,960,000 pop.

*Athens	652,385
Piraeus	328,299
Thessaloníki (1940)	226,147

HUNGARY (1948)

35,909 sq. mi.
9,205,000 pop. (1949)

*Budapest	1,058,288
Szeged	132,688
Debrecen	119,570
Miskolc	103,698
Kecskemét	88,283

* * *

Pécs	77,529
Sopron	32,716

ICELAND (1949)

39,758 sq. mi.
141,042 pop.

*Reykjavík	54,707

IRELAND (1946)

26,602 sq. mi.
2,991,000 pop. (1949)

*Dublin   506,051
Cork   75,595
Dun Laoghaire   44,674
Limerick   42,970

ITALY (1950)

116,224 sq. mi.
46,423,000 pop.

*Rome   1,665,667
Milan   1,289,289
Naples   1,029,805
Turin   730,570
Genoa   676,071
Palermo   497,000
Florence   384,789
Bologna   346,102
Venice   321,120
Catania   294,964
Bari   271,773
Messina   228,624
Verona   198,156
Taranto   194,769
Padua   169,396
Brescia   151,847
Leghorn   147,157
Reggio di Calabria . .   142,722
Cagliari   138,242
Ferrara   137,834
Spezia   124,494
Parma   123,252
Modena   116,877
Bergamo   107,153
Reggio nell' Emilia . .   105,196

LIECHTENSTEIN (1950)

62 sq. mi.
13,571 pop.

*Vaduz   2,772

LUXEMBOURG (1948)

999 sq. mi.
295,000 pop. (1949)

*Luxembourg   61,996

MONACO (1946)

368 acres
19,242 pop.

THE NETHERLANDS (1950)

12,868 sq. mi.
10,026,773 pop.

*Amsterdam   835,834
Rotterdam   675,905
The Hague   558,849
Utrecht   193,190
Haarlem   161,980
Eindhoven   140,554
Groningen   136,556
Tilburg   120,491
Nijmegen   110,659
Enschede   106,882
Arnhem   103,317
Leiden   89,875

                *   *   *

Leeuwarden   78,659
Maastricht   77,710
Dordrecht   70,793
Delft   64,676

NORWAY (1946)

124,556 sq. mi.
3,233,000 pop. (1949)

*Oslo   418,449
Bergen   110,424
Trondheim   57,128
Stavanger   50,320

POLAND (1950)

120,359 sq. mi.
24,976,926 pop.

*Warsaw	673,959
Łódź	592,559
Kraków	347,048
Poznań	291,577
Wrocław (Breslau)	279,373
Szczecin (Stettin)	201,000
Gdańsk (Danzig)	169,675
Bydgoszcz	156,108
Katowice	156,001
Chorzów	130,901
Zabrze (Hindenburg)	128,005
Częstochowa	115,084
Gliwice (Gleiwitz)	113,517
Bytom (Beuthen)	112,336
Gdynia	111,147
Lublin	101,888

PORTUGAL

34,386 sq. mi.
8,618,000 pop. (1950)

*Lisbon (1947)	800,000
Pôrto (1940)	262,309

RUMANIA (1945)

91,671 sq. mi.
15,872,624 pop. (1948)

*Bucharest (1948)	1,041,807
Cluj	110,956
Iaşi	108,987
Timişoara	108,296
Ploeşti	105,114
Brăila	97,293
Galaţi	93,229
Oradea	92,943
Oraşul-Stalin (Braşov)	85,192
Arad	82,882
Constanţa	79,716

SAAR (1951)

991 sq. mi.
953,947 pop.

*Saarbrücken	109,852
Neunkirchen	42,106
Völklingen	39,596

SAN MARINO (1947)

38 sq. mi.
12,100 pop.

SPAIN (1950)

189,890 sq. mi.
28,626,830 pop.

*Madrid	1,511,695
Barcelona	1,285,920
Valencia	534,866
Seville	390,755
Málaga	295,757
Zaragoza	271,587
Bilbao	235,508
Murcia	220,290
Granada	174,663
Córdoba	164,415
Las Palmas (Canary Is.)	151,411
Palma de Mallorca	140,966
Vigo	139,170
Valladolid	130,475
La Coruña	129,562
Cartagena	120,208
San Sebastián	116,285
S. Cruz de Tenerife	108,657
Alicante	107,596
Santander	107,226
Gijón	107,156
Gerez de la Frontera	107,040
Oviedo	106,825
Cádiz	99,910

SWEDEN (1950)

173,390 sq. mi.
6,986,181 pop.

*Stockholm	733,615
Göteborg	349,145
Malmö	189,232
Norrköping	84,035
Hälsingborg	71,151
Örebro	65,690
Uppsala	61,539

SWITZERLAND (1950)

15,944 sq. mi.
4,696,057 pop.

Zürich	386,485
Basel	183,742
*Bern	145,740
Geneva	144,422
Lausanne	107,225
St. Gallen	67,865

TRIESTE (1949)

285 sq. mi.
383,000 pop.

*Trieste	280,000

TURKEY-IN-EUROPE (1950)

9,256 sq. mi.
1,496,612 pop. (1945)
Totals for all Turkey:
296,185 sq. mi.
20,902,628 pop.

Istanbul	1,000,092

UNION OF SOVIET SOCIALIST REPUBLICS (1939)

8,708,070 sq. mi.
201,300,000 pop. (1950)

	1946–48 estimate	1939 census
*Moscow	4,500,000	4,137,018
Leningrad	3,300,000	3,191,304
Kiev	900,000	846,293
Khar'kov	900,000	833,432
Baku	800,000	809,347
Gor'kiy	900,000	644,116
Odessa	600,000	604,223
Tbilisi	540,000	519,175
Rostov-na-Donu	500,000	510,253
Dnepropetrovsk	500,000	500,662
Stalino	500,000	462,395
Stalingrad	400,000	445,476
Sverdlovsk	600,000	425,544
Kazan'	500,000	401,665
Kuybyshev	600,000	390,267
Riga (1935)	390,000	383,699
Saratov	500,000	375,860
Voronezh	300,000	326,836
L'vov (1931)	400,000	316,177
Yaroslavl'	300,000	298,065
Zaporozh'ye	300,000	289,188
Ivanovo	300,000	285,069
Archangel	300,000	281,091
Chelyabinsk	500,000	273,127
Tula	300,000	272,403
Molotov	450,000	255,196
Astrakhan'	300,000	253,655
Ufa	300,000	245,863
Makeyevka	300,000	240,145
Minsk	231,000	238,772
Zhdanov (Mariupol')	200,000	222,427
Kalinin	300,000	216,131
Voroshilovgrad	200,000	213,007
Vil'nyus (1937)	163,000	208,000
Krasnodar	200,000	203,946
Yerevan	255,000	200,031

(USSR—Continued)

	1946–48 estimate	1939 census
Krivoy Rog .	200,000	197,621
Taganrog . .	150,000	188,808
Izhevsk . . .	200,000	175,740
Chkalov . . .	200,000	172,925
Groznyy . . .	......	172,468
Vitebsk . . .	80,000	167,424
Nikolayev . .	200,000	167,108
Nizhniy Tagil	250,000	159,864
Penza	250,000	157,145
Smolensk . .	150,000	156,677
Shakhty . . .	......	155,081
Dneprodzerzhinsk	......	147,829
Magnitogorsk	200,000	145,900
Gomel' . . .	120,000	144,169
Kirov	250,000	143,181
Simferopol' .	......	142,678
Shcherbakov (Rybinsk) .	150,000	139,011
Tallin (1934) .	190,000	137,792
Poltava . . .	......	130,305
Dzaudzhikau .	......	127,172
Tambov . . .	150,000	121,285
Kostroma . .	150,000	121,205
Kursk	......	119,972
Murmansk .	150,000	117,054
Kishinev (1930) . .	110,000	114,896
Sevastopol' .	......	111,946
Orel	......	110,567
Gorlovka . .	......	108,693
Kaunas (1938)	......	108,200
Kerch' . . .	......	104,471
Dzerzhinsk . .	......	103,415
Ul'yanovsk .	200,000	102,106
Kirovograd .	......	100,331
Mogilev . . .	80,000	99,440
Orekhovo-Zuyevo	......	99,329
Zlatoust . . .	150,000	99,272
Kirovabad . .	110,000	98,743
Kherson . . .	......	97,186
Ryazan' . . .	......	95,358

(USSR—Continued)

	1946–48 estimate	1939 census
Novorossiysk .	......	95,280
Vologda . . .	......	95,194
Zhitomir . .	......	95,090
Konstantinovka	......	95,087
* * *		
Syzran' . . .	150,000	77,679
Melitopol' . .	......	75,735
Batumi . . .	......	70,807
Maykop . . .	......	67,302
Nikopol' . .	......	57,841

UNITED KINGDOM (1951)

94,279 sq. mi.
49,919,000 pop. (1950)

England

50,874 sq. mi.
40,809,000 pop. (1950)

*London	8,417,377
Birmingham	1,118,720
Liverpool	803,610
Manchester	704,640
Sheffield	515,240
Leeds	509,970
Bristol	442,850
Nottingham	307,550
Hull	302,550
Newcastle	295,020
Bradford	294,290
Leicester	287,790
Stoke-on-Trent	276,140
Coventry	257,040
Croydon	251,770
Portsmouth	240,070
Plymouth	209,100

Appendix

(UNITED KINGDOM—Continued)

Ealing	188,940
Ilford	186,210
Willesden	181,720
Southampton . . .	181,060
Sunderland	178,400
Salford	177,760
West Ham	173,350
Bolton	168,530
Wolverhampton . . .	162,420
Brighton	157,830
Southend-on-Sea . . .	152,230
Blackpool	149,470
Middlesbrough . . .	145,800
Derby	143,610
Birkenhead	143,270
Stockport	142,100
Bournemouth . . .	139,480
Huddersfield . . .	129,700
Tottenham	129,240
Walthamstow . . .	122,870
East Ham	121,860
Preston	120,380
Norwich	119,760
Oldham	119,670
Reading	115,890
Gateshead	115,630
Walsall	114,690
St. Helens	112,650
Blackburn	111,420
Luton	110,380
South Shields . . .	109,460
Oxford	108,420
York	107,760
Newport	107,450
Leyton	106,120
Northampton . . .	105,670
Ipswich	104,240
Wallasey	102,560

Scotland

30,411 sq. mi.
5,148,000 pop. (1950)

Glasgow	1,087,300
*Edinburgh	488,000
Aberdeen	187,200
Dundee	178,200

Wales

7,466 sq. mi.
2,591,000 pop. (1949)

Cardiff	245,020
Swansea	161,560
Rhondda	112,390

Northern Ireland

5,238 sq. mi.
1,371,000 pop. (1950)

*Belfast (1948)	455,000

VATICAN CITY (1947)

108.7 acres
940 pop.

YUGOSLAVIA (1948)

95,576 sq. mi.
15,772,098 pop.

*Belgrade	389,114
Zagreb	290,667
Ljubljana	120,944
Sarajevo	118,806
Subotica	112,530
Skopje	91,491
Novi Sad	77,713

Bibliography

The following list of books and articles, selected from among the thousands in print, is intended only to suggest some of the more recent and useful additional readings on the geographical aspects and the countries of Europe. Some especially helpful foreign materials are listed separately. Teachers and students—as well as general readers—should make constant use of the statistical publications given.

BIBLIOGRAPHICAL AIDS

For further bibliographical investigation, the standard general bibliographical aids available in any good library should be supplemented by three guides that are of especially great value in connection with geography and the geography of Europe:

Bibliographie géographique internationale (annual), published in Paris but containing articles in several common languages, including English; it is particularly useful for references on European geography.

Current Geographical Publications (10 times a year), published in New York by the American Geographical Society; it is the best aid in keeping abreast of the latest geographical publications.

Wright, John K., and Elizabeth T. Platt, *Aids to Geographical Research* (2nd ed.; American Geographical Society Research Series No. 22). New York, Columbia University Press, 1947. This excellent publication will guide the researcher into every conceivable avenue of approach to materials. It lists, in addition to bibliographies of topics and regions, outstanding serials (journals) in all languages as well as outstanding national atlases.

For an exhaustive list of geographical serials, see:

Harris, Chauncy D., and Jerome D. Fellmann, *A Union List of Geographical Serials* (2nd ed.; University of Chicago Department of Geography Research Paper No. 10). Chicago, 1950.

GENERAL STATISTICS

The marvelously comprehensive statistical publications of the United Nations that have been initiated in recent years make available data that formerly were very difficult or impossible to find. Specialized statistical publications (such as those on trade) are listed under the respective topics below, but for general purposes the most useful are:

United Nations *Statistical Yearbook.*

Monthly Bulletin of Statistics.

Economic Bulletin for Europe (published quarterly by the United Nations Economic Commission for Europe; it includes, in addition to statistics, numerous articles of interest).

Economic Survey of Europe (it is very helpful for each of the years 1947 through 1950 and will, presumably, continue to be an annual publication).

Statesman's Year-Book (published annually since 1863); it is an old, reliable publication that is a mine of information.

Foreign Commerce Yearbook (compiled by the United States Department of Commerce; it contains much more than trade statistics).

SUGGESTED READINGS

Chapter 1: Europe as a Continent

Blanchard, Raoul, and Raymond E. Crist, *A Geography of Europe.* New York, Henry Holt and Company, 1935.

Bogardus, James F., *Europe: A Geographical Survey.* New York, Harper and Brothers, 1934.

East, William Gordon, *An Historical Geography of Europe* (3rd ed. rev.). London, Methuen and Company, Ltd., 1948.

Fischer, Eric, *The Passing of the European Age.* Cambridge, Harvard University Press, 1948.

Gottmann, Jean, *A Geography of Europe.* New York, Henry Holt and Company, 1950.

Hubbard, George D., *The Geography of Europe.* New York, Appleton-Century-Crofts, 1952.

Jefferson, Mark, *Man in Europe.* Ypsilanti (Michigan), The Author, 1924.

Pearcy, G. Etzel, Russell H. Fifield, and Associates, *World Political Geography.* New York, Thomas Y. Crowell Company, 1948.

Shackleton, Margaret Reid, *Europe: A Regional Geography* (4th ed.). London and New York, Longmans, Green and Company, 1950.

Stamp, L. Dudley, *Europe and the Mediterranean: A Regional Geography.* New York, Longmans, Green and Company, 1931.

Chapter 2: Climate

Brooks, C. E. P., *Climate, A Handbook.* London, Ernest Benn, Ltd., 1929.

Kendrew, W. G., *The Climates of the Continents.* Oxford, University Press, 1927.

Markham, Sydney F., *Climate and the Energy of Nations* (2nd ed.). New York, Oxford University Press, 1947.

Chapters 3, 4, and 5: Regional Description

Lobeck, A. K., *Physiographic Diagram of Europe.* New York, The Geographical Press (Columbia University), 1923.

Wright, William B., *The Quaternary Ice Age.* London, Macmillan and Company, 1934.

Chapter 6: Soils and Vegetation

Glinka, R. D., *The Great Soil Groups of the World and Their Development.* Ann Arbor (Michigan), Edwards Brothers, 1927.

Hardy, Marcel E., *The Geography of Plants.* Oxford, University Press, 1925.

Newbigin, Marion I., *Plant and Animal Geography* (2nd ed.). New York, E. P. Dutton and Company, 1949.

Robinson, G. W., *Soils: Their Origin, Constitution, and Classification* (3rd ed.). New York, John Wiley and Sons, 1949.

Stremme, H., *General Map of the Soils of Europe, 1927,* translated by W. G. Ogg. Edinburgh, Oliver and Boyd, 1929.

Chapter 7: Use of the Land and the Ocean

Grass, Norman S. C., *A History of Agriculture in Europe and America.* New York, F. S. Crofts, 1925.

"Long-Term Trends in European Agriculture." *Economic Bulletin for Europe* (United Nations Economic Commission for Europe), III, 2 (2nd Quarter, 1951), 19–48.

Morgan, Ora S., *Agricultural Systems of Middle Europe, A Symposium.* New York, The Macmillan Company, 1933.

United Nations Food and Agriculture Organization, *Yearbook of Fisheries Statistics.*

———, *Yearbook of Food and Agriculture Statistics* (Vol. I: Production).

———, *Yearbook of Forest Products Statistics.*

United States Department of Agriculture, *Agricultural Geography of Europe and the Near East* (Miscellaneous Publication No. 665). Washington, United States Government Printing Office, 1948.

———, *A Graphic Summary of World Agriculture* (Miscellaneous Publication No. 705). Washington, United States Government Printing Office, 1949.

Chapter 8: Power and Minerals; and Chapter 9: Manufacturing

Bateman, Alan M., *Economic Mineral Deposits* (2nd ed.). New York, John Wiley and Sons, 1950.

"Changes in the Relationship between European Production and Trade." *Economic Bulletin for Europe* (United Nations Economic Commission for Europe), II, 1 (1st Quarter, 1950), 17–37.

"The Coal and Steel Industries of Western Europe." *Economic Bulletin for Europe* (United Nations Economic Commission for Europe), II, 2 (2nd Quarter, 1950), 16–51.

"Coal Production and Trade in Europe since the War." *Economic Bulletin for Europe* (United Nations Economic Commission for Europe), I, 3 (3rd Quarter, 1949), 13–23.

Day, Clive, *Economic Development in Europe*. New York, The Macmillan Company, 1942.

Dietz, F. C., *The Industrial Revolution*. New York, Henry Holt and Company, 1927.

McFarlane, John, and C. F. W. R. Gullick, *Economic Geography* (5th ed.). London, Sir Isaac Pitman and Sons, 1949.

Mutton, Alice F. A., "Hydro-Electric Power in Western Europe." *Geographical Journal*, CXVII, Part 3 (September, 1951), 328–42.

United Nations Department of Economic Affairs, *World Iron Ore Resources and Their Utilization*. Lake Success, 1950.

United States Department of State, *Energy Resources of the World*. Washington, United States Government Printing Office, 1949.

Chapter 10: Trade; and Chapter 11: Transportation

Berglund, A., *Ocean Transportation*. New York, Longmans, Green and Company, 1931.

Jefferson, Mark, "The Civilizing Rails." *Economic Geography*, IV, 3 (July, 1928), 217–231.

McPherson, Logan G., *Transportation in Europe*. New York, Henry Holt and Company, 1910.

"Recent Developments in Trade between Eastern and Western Europe." *Economic Bulletin for Europe* (United Nations Economic Commission for Europe), III, 2 (2nd Quarter, 1951), 49–66.

Rimington, Critchell, *Merchant Fleets*. New York, Dodd, Mead and Company, 1944.

United Nations Department of Economic Affairs, *Yearbook of International Trade Statistics*. (First appeared for the year 1950.)

United Nations Food and Agriculture Organization, *Yearbook of Food and Agriculture Statistics* (Vol. II: Trade and Commerce).

Van Cleef, Eugene, *Trade Centers and Trade Routes*. New York, Appleton-Century, 1937.

Van Zandt, J. Parker, *The Geography of World Air Transport*. Washington, The Brookings Institution, 1944.

Chapter 12: Peoples and Political Units

Bowman, Isaiah, *The New World: Problems in Political Geography* (4th ed.). Yonkers (New York), World Book Company, 1928.

Burns, Cecil Delisle, *The First Europe; a Study of the Establishment of*

Medieval Christendom, A.D. 400–800. London, George Allen and Unwin, Ltd., 1947.

Chadwick, Hector Munro, *The Nationalities of Europe and the Growth of National Ideologies.* New York, The Macmillan Company, 1946.

Coon, Carlton S., *The Races of Europe.* New York, The Macmillan Company, 1939.

Cornish, Vaughan, *Borderlands of Language in Europe and Their Relation to the Historic Frontier of Christendom.* London, Sifton, 1936.

Dominian, Leon, *The Frontiers of Language and Nationality in Europe.* New York, Henry Holt and Company, 1917.

Fitzgerald, Walter, *The New Europe.* New York, Harper and Brothers, 1946.

Janowsky, Oscar J., *Nationalities and National Minorities.* New York, The Macmillan Company, 1945.

Morant, Geoffrey M., *The Races of Central Europe.* London, Allen, 1939.

Pounds, Norman J. G., *An Historical and Political Geography of Europe.* London, George G. Harrap and Company, Ltd., 1947.

Chapter 13: Population: Problems and Distribution

Ahlmann, Hans W:son, "The Geographic Study of Settlements." *Geographical Review,* XVIII, 1 (January, 1928), 93–128.

Brunhes, Jean, *Human Geography.* Chicago, Rand McNally and Company, 1921.

De la Blache, Vidal, *Principles of Human Geography.* New York, Henry Holt and Company, 1926.

Kirk, Dudley, *Europe's Population in the Interwar Years.* Geneva, League of Nations, 1946.

Notestein, Frank W., and others, *The Future Population of Europe and the Soviet Union.* Geneva, League of Nations, 1944.

"Population Changes in Europe, 1938–1947." *Economic Bulletin for Europe* (United Nations Economic Commission for Europe), I, 1 (1st Quarter, 1949), 11–21.

United Nations *Demographic Yearbook.*

Chapter 14: The March of Civilization

Keyserling, Count Hermann, *Europe.* New York, Harcourt, Brace and Company, 1928.

Spengler, Oswald, *The Decline of the West.* New York, Alfred A. Knopf, 1926.

Thorndike, Lynn, *A Short History of Civilization.* New York, F. S. Crofts, 1926.

Toynbee, Arnold J., *A Study of History* (Abridgment of Vols. I–VI by D. C. Somervell). New York, Oxford University Press, 1947.

Chapter 15: Fennoscandia as a Unit

Ahlmann, Hans W:son, *Glaciological Research on the North Atlantic Coasts* (Royal Geographical Society Research Series No. 1). London, 1948.

Gathorne-Hardy, G. M., and others, *The Scandinavian States and Finland: A Political and Economic Survey.* London, Royal Institute of International Affairs, 1951.

The Northern Countries in World Economy: Denmark, Finland, Iceland, Norway, Sweden (2nd rev. ed.; Delegations for the Promotion of Economic Co-operation between the Northern Countries). ?, Finland, Otava Printing Office, 1939.

Seidenfaden, Erik, "Scandinavia Charts a Course." *Foreign Affairs*, XXVI, 4 (July, 1948), 653–664.

Woods, Ethel G., *The Baltic Region; A Study in Physical and Human Geography.* London, Methuen and Company, Ltd., 1932.

Chapter 16: Denmark and Iceland

Gedde, Knud, *This Is Denmark.* Copenhagen, Jul. Gjellerups Forlag, 1948.

Nielsen, Niels, *Atlas over Danmark.* København, H. Hagerup, 1949. (Text in English and Danish; additional volume of description in English.)

Stefansson, Vilhjalmur, *Iceland, the First American Republic.* New York, Doubleday, Doran and Company, 1939.

Thorsteinson, T., *Iceland: A Handbook.* Reykjavík, Prentsmidjan Gutenberg, 1930.

Chapter 17: Norway

Fischer, Karl, *Norway To-Day.* Oslo, Sverre Mortensen Forlag, 1933.

Hölaas, Odd, *The World of the Norseman.* London, Bond, 1949.

Lund, Diderich H., "The Revival of Northern Norway." *Geographical Journal*, CIX, 4–6 (April-June, 1947), 185–197.

Mortensen, Sverre, and A. Skøien, *The Norway Yearbook, 1950.* Oslo, Johan Grundt Tanum, 1950.

Norway Travel Association, *Norway.* Oslo, Grøndahl and Son, 1948.

Nuttonson, M. Y., *Ecological Crop Geography of Norway and Its Agroclimatic Analogues in North America* (International Agro-Climatological Series, Study No. 12). Washington, American Institute of Crop Ecology, 1950.

Sund, Tore, and Axel Sømme, *Norway in Maps* (in three parts: A, Text Volume; B, Sketch Maps and Photographs; and C, Box of Maps). Bergen, A. S. John Griegs Boktrykkeri, 1947.

Svalbard: A Norwegian Outpost. Bergen, J. W. Eides Forlag, 1950.

Chapter 18: Sweden

Andersson, Ingvar, and others, *Introduction to Sweden,* translated by Nils G. Sahlin (2nd ed. rev.). Stockholm, Swedish Institute, 1950.

Carlson, Lucile, "The Mining District of Kiruna Stad, Sweden." *Scientific Monthly*, LXXIV, 2 (February, 1952), 76–83.

Eldh, Arvid, *Facts about Sweden 1949–50*. Stockholm, Swedish Institute, 1949.

Hille, Edric A., *Swedish Life and Landscapes*. London, P. Eleh, 1947.

Löwengren, Gunnar, *Swedish Iron and Steel: A Historical Survey*, translated by Nils G. Sahlin. Stockholm, Svenska Handelsbanken, 1948.

Lundquist, Gösta, *Sweden, Past and Present*. Stockholm, Swedish Tourist Traffic Association, 1948.

Nuttonson, M. Y., *Agricultural Climatology of Sweden and Its Agroclimatic Analogues in North America* (International Agro-Climatological Series, Study No. 11). Washington, American Institute of Crop Ecology, 1950.

Chapter 19: Finland

Atlas of Finland, 1925. Helsinki, The Geographical Society of Finland, 1925–28. (In Finnish, Swedish, and English. Separate volume of English text, Helsinki, 1929.)

Scott, A. MacCallum, *Suomi, the Land of the Finns*. London, Thornton Butterworth, Ltd., 1925.

Sletholt, Erik, "Finland Today." *International Journal*, VI, 2 (Spring, 1951), 118–126.

Toivola, Vrho (ed.), *The Finland Year Book, 1947*. Helsinki, Mercatorin Kerjapaino Ja Kustannus, 1947.

Van Cleef, Eugene, *Finland, the Republic Farthest North*. Columbus, Ohio State University Press, 1929.

Chapters 20, 21, and 22: Great Britain

Demangeon, Albert, *The British Isles* (2nd ed.). London, Wm. Heinemann, Ltd., 1949.

Finlay, Ian, *Scotland*. London, Oxford University Press, 1945.

Kimble, George H. T., "Great Britain." *Focus* (American Geographical Society), II, 7 (March, 1952).

Mackinder, Halford J., *Britain and the British Seas*. Oxford, University Press, 1922.

Meikle, Henry W. (ed.), *Scotland: A Description of Scotland and Scottish Life*. London, Thomas Nelson and Sons, 1947.

Mogey, J. M., *Rural Life in Northern Ireland*. Oxford, University Press, 1947.

Ogrizek, Doré (ed.), *Great Britain: England, Scotland and Wales* (The World in Color Series). New York, McGraw-Hill Book Company, 1949.

Owen, Sir David John, *The Origin and Development of the Ports of the United Kingdom*. London, Allmann and Sons, 1945.

Smith, Wilfred, *An Economic Geography of Great Britain*. New York, E. P. Dutton and Company, 1949.

Stamp, L. Dudley, *Britain's Structure and Scenery* (2nd ed.). London, William Collins Sons and Company, 1947.

——, *The Face of Britain.* London, Longmans, Green and Company, 1940.

——, *The Land of Britain: Its Use and Misuse.* New York, Longmans, Green and Company, 1948.

——, and S. H. Beaver, *British Isles, a Geographic and Economic Survey* (3rd ed.). New York, Longmans, Green and Company, 1947.

Chapter 23: Ireland

Fletcher, George (ed.), *Ireland and the Provinces of Ireland* (5 vols.). Cambridge, University Press, 1922.

Freeman, Thomas W., *Ireland, Its Physical, Historical, Social and Economic Geography.* New York, E. P. Dutton and Company, 1950.

Stamp, L. Dudley, *An Agricultural Atlas of Ireland.* London, G. Gill and Sons, Ltd., 1931.

Chapter 24: The Netherlands

Bowen, Marjorie, *Holland.* Garden City, Doubleday, Doran and Company, 1929.

Ogrizek, Doré (ed.), *The Netherlands* (The World in Color Series). New York, McGraw-Hill Book Company, 1951.

Tesch, P., "Physiographic Regions of the Netherlands." *Geographical Review,* XIII, 4 (October, 1923), 507–517.

Veen, Joh. van, *Dredge, Drain, Reclaim; the Art of a Nation.* The Hague, Martinus Nijhoff, 1948.

Chapter 25: Belgium and Luxembourg

Alexander, Lewis M., "Economic Problems in the Benelux Union." *Economic Geography,* XXVI, 1 (January, 1950), 29–36.

Ogrizek, Doré (ed.), *Belgium and Luxembourg* (The World in Color Series). New York, McGraw-Hill Book Company, 1950.

Chapters 26 and 27: France (and the Saar)

Martonne, Emmanuel de, *Geographical Regions of France,* translated by H. C. Brentnall. London, Wm. Heinemann, Ltd., 1933.

Ogrizek, Doré (ed.), *France, Paris and the Provinces* (The World in Color Series). New York, McGraw-Hill Book Company, 1948.

——, *The Paris We Love* (The World in Color Series). New York, McGraw-Hill Book Company, 1950.

Ormsby, Hilda, *France: A Regional and Economic Geography* (2nd ed.). New York, E. P. Dutton and Company, 1950.

Cowan, Laing Gray, *France and the Saar, 1680–1948.* New York, Columbia University Press, 1950.

Held, Colbert C., "The New Saarland." *Geographical Review,* XLI, 4 (October, 1951), 590–605.

Russell, Frank M., *The Saar, Battleground and Pawn.* Stanford (California), Stanford University Press, 1951.

General Works on Southern Europe

Cary, Max, *Geographical Background of Greek and Roman History.* New York, Oxford University Press, 1949.

East, William Gordon, *Mediterranean Problems* (2nd ed.). London, Thomas Nelson and Sons, 1943.

Lyde, L. W., *Peninsular Europe.* London, Longmans, Green and Company, 1931.

Newbigin, M. I., *Mediterranean Lands.* New York, Alfred A. Knopf, 1924.

———, *Southern Europe* (3rd ed., revised by R. J. Harrison Church). London, Methuen and Company, Ltd., 1949.

Semple, Ellen C., *The Geography of the Mediterranean Region.* New York, Henry Holt and Company, 1931.

Chapter 28: Spain and Portugal

Barnes, Wilfrid J., *Portugal: Gateway to Greatness.* London, E. Stanford, 1950.

Dobby, E. H. G., "Galicia: A Little-Known Corner of Spain." *Geographical Review,* XXVI, 4 (October, 1936), 555–580.

Ericsson, Emily, "Little Land (Portugal)." *Scientific Monthly,* LXXI, 1 (July, 1950), 15–23.

Fairman, Churton, "Village Life in Old Castile." *Geographical Magazine,* XXII, 11 (March, 1950), 437–445.

Houston, J. M., "Irrigation as a Solution to Agrarian Problems in Modern Spain." *Geographical Journal,* CXVI, 1–3 (September, 1950), 55–63.

"Mineral Resources of Spain." *Foreign Minerals Survey* (United States Department of the Interior, Bureau of Mines), II, 1 (May, 1945).

Chapters 29 and 30: Italy (and Trieste)

Almagià, Roberto, "The Repopulation of the Roman Campagna." *Geographical Review,* XIX, 4 (October, 1929), 529–555.

Banca Nazionale del Lavoro Quarterly Review (in English).

Grindrod, Muriel, *The New Italy: Transition from War to Peace.* London, Royal Institute of International Affairs, 1947.

Ivella, Vittorio, "Favorable Omens in Italy." *Foreign Affairs,* XXVI, 4 (July, 1948), 701–708.

Longobardi, Cesare, *Land-Reclamation in Italy.* London, P. S. King and Son, 1936.

"Mineral and Metal Production of Italy." *Foreign Minerals Survey* (United

States Department of the Interior, Bureau of Mines), I, 1 (November, 1943).

Ogrizek, Doré (ed.), *Italy* (The World in Color Series). New York, McGraw-Hill Book Company, 1950.

"Progress in Italian Land Reform." *The World Today,* VIII, 3 (March, 1952), 104–111.

Sforza, Carlo, *Italy and the Italians.* New York, E. P. Dutton and Company, 1949.

Wiskemann, Elizabeth, *Italy.* London, Oxford University Press, 1947.

Albrecht-Carrie, Rene, "The Northeastern Frontier of Italy." *Journal of Central European Affairs,* V, 3 (October, 1945), 229–242.

Moodie, A. E., *The Italo-Yugoslav Boundary, a Study in Political Geography.* London, G. Philip and Sons, Ltd., 1945.

Trieste Handbook 1950 (rev. ed.). Trieste, Allied Military Government, British-United States Zone, Free Territory of Trieste, 1950.

Chapter 31: Albania and Turkey-in-Europe

"Mineral Resources of Albania." *Foreign Minerals Survey* (United States Department of the Interior, Bureau of Mines), I, 3 (January, 1944).

Nowack, Ernest, "A Contribution to the Geography of Albania." *Geographical Review,* XI, 4 (October, 1921), 503–540.

Stotz, Carl L., "Coastal Lands of the Sea of Marmara." *Journal of Geography,* XXXII, 8 (November, 1933), 305–315.

Swire, Joseph, *King Zog's Albania.* London, R. Hale, 1937.

Chapter 32: Greece

Anastassiades, Phoebus A., "General Features of the Soils of Greece." *Soil Science,* LXVII, 5 (May, 1949), 347–362.

Forest Map of Greece (Legend in Greek and English). Athens, Ministry of Agriculture, 1947.

"Mineral Resources of Greece." *Foreign Minerals Survey* (United States Department of the Interior, Bureau of Mines), I, 5 (March, 1944).

Smothers, Frank, and others, *Report on the Greeks.* New York, Twentieth Century Fund, 1948.

United Nations Food and Agriculture Organization, *Report of the FAO Mission for Greece.* Washington, 1947.

Chapter 33: Switzerland

Egli, Emil, *Swiss Life and Landscapes.* London, P. Elek, 1949.

Ogrizek, Doré, and J. G. Rufenacht, *Switzerland* (The World in Color Series). New York, McGraw-Hill Book Company, 1949.

Switzerland and Her Industries. Lausanne, Swiss Office for the Development of Trade, 1948.

Walker, J. Hubert, *The Population of Switzerland.* New York, Columbia University Press, 1952.

Chapters 34, 35, and 36: Germany

Dickinson, Robert E., *The Regions of Germany.* London, Kegan, Paul, Trench, Trubner, and Company, 1945.

Eisen, Edna E., "The Structure of Rhine Traffic." *Economic Geography,* X, 3 (July, 1934), 254–267.

Koranyi, Karl, and Myrtle Brickman, "The Ruhr Area: Its Structure and Economic Importance." Washington, United States Office of International Trade, 1950.

Niehaus, Heinrich, "Agricultural Conditions and Regions in Germany." *Geographical Review,* XXIII, 1 (January, 1933), 23–47.

"The West German Coal and Steel Industries since the War." *The World Today,* VIII, 3 (March, 1952), 111–123.

Chapter 37: Czechoslovakia

Czechoslovakia in Maps and Statistics. London, "Czechoslovak," 1945.

Moscheles, Julie, "Natural Regions of Czechoslovakia." *Geographical Review,* XIV, 4 (October, 1924), 561–575.

Steers, J. A. (Mrs.), "The Middle People: Resettlement in Czechoslovakia." *Geographical Journal,* CXII, 1–3 (July-September, 1948), 28–42.

Chapter 38: Austria

Buschbeck, E. H., *Austria.* London, Oxford University Press, 1949.

Hoffman, George W., "The Survival of an Independent Austria." *Geographical Review,* XLI, 4 (October, 1951), 606–621.

Marboe, Ernst, *The Book of Austria,* translated by G. E. R. Gedye. Vienna, Österreichische Staatsdruckerei, 1948.

" 'Slovene Carinthia'; the Austro-Yugoslav Frontier Question." *The World Today,* III, 9 (September, 1947), 389–397.

Straus, F. S., "Austrian Agriculture." *Foreign Agriculture,* XI, 5–6 (April-May, 1947), 50–64.

General Works on Eastern Europe

Margold, Stella K., "Economic Life in Russia's Orbit." *Harvard Business Review,* XXVIII, 5 (September, 1950), 65–78; XXVIII, 6 (November, 1950), 86–113.

Rouček, Joseph S., *Central Eastern Europe.* New York, Prentice-Hall, 1946.

—— (ed.), "Moscow's European Satellites." *Annals of the Academy of Political and Social Science,* CCLXXI (September, 1950), 1–184.

Wanklyn, Harriet Grace, *Eastern Marchlands of Europe.* New York, The Macmillan Company, 1942.

Chapter 39: Hungary

Kemény, György, *Economic Planning in Hungary, 1947–9.* London, Royal Institute of International Affairs, 1952.

"Mineral Resources of Hungary." *Foreign Minerals Survey* (United States Department of the Interior, Bureau of Mines), II, 2 (May, 1945).

Chapter 40: Yugoslavia

Kerner, Robert J. (ed.), *Yugoslavia.* Berkeley, University of California Press, 1949.

"Mineral Resources of Yugoslavia." *Foreign Minerals Survey* (United States Department of the Interior, Bureau of Mines), I, 6 (June, 1944).

St. John, Robert, *The Silent People Speak.* Garden City, Doubleday and Company, 1948.

"Yugoslavia." *Focus* (American Geographical Society), I, 6 (March, 1951).

Chapter 41: Rumania

Fleure, H. J., and R. A. Pelham (eds.), *Eastern Carpathian Studies: Rumania.* London, Le Play House Press, 1936.

Hielscher, K., *Rumania: Landscape, Buildings, National Life.* Leipzig, F. A. Brockhaus, 1933.

"Mineral Resources of Rumania." *Foreign Minerals Survey* (United States Department of the Interior, Bureau of Mines), I, 10 (December, 1944).

Rouček, Joseph S., "Economic Geography of Rumania." *Economic Geography,* VII, 4 (October, 1931), 390–400.

Chapter 42: Bulgaria

Donkas, Kimon A., "Bulgaria's Mode of Transport." *Economic Geography,* XIX, 4 (October, 1943), 337–346.

"Mineral Resources of Bulgaria." *Foreign Minerals Survey* (United States Department of the Interior, Bureau of Mines), I, 9 (September, 1944).

Monroe, Will S., *Bulgaria and Her People.* Boston, L. C. Page and Company, 1914.

Chapter 43: Poland

Kondracki, Jerzy, *Mały Atlas Polski (Little Atlas of Poland).* Warszawa, Head Office of Survey with Co-operation of the Polish Geographical Society, 1947. (Text in Polish, French, Russian, and English.)

Leszczycki, Stanisław, "The Geographical Bases of Contemporary Poland." *Journal of Central European Affairs,* VII, 4 (January, 1948), 357–373.

Pronin, Dimitri T., "Land Reform in Poland: 1920–1945." *Land Economics,* XXV, 2 (May, 1949), 133–145.

Rouček, Joseph S., "Geopolitics of Poland." *American Journal of Economics and Sociology,* VII, 4 (July, 1948), 421–427.

United Nations Food and Agriculture Organization, *Report of the FAO Mission to Poland.* Washington, 1948.

Van Cleef, Eugene, "Danzig and Gdynia." *Geographical Review,* XXIII, 1 (January, 1933), 101–107.

Wilder, Jan Antoni, *The Polish Regained Provinces: A Survey of a Year's Achievement.* London, W. Hodge, 1948.

Yearbook of Poland. Warsaw, Central Statistical Office, 1949.

Chapters 44, 45, and 46: Union of Soviet Socialist Republics

Balzak, S. S., V. F. Vasyutin, and Ya. G. Feigen, *Economic Geography of the USSR* (American edition edited by Chauncy D. Harris, translated by Robert M. Hankin and Olga Adler Titelbaum). New York, The Macmillan Company, 1949.

Berg, L. S., *Natural Regions of the USSR* (American edition edited by John A. Morrison, translated by Olga Adler Titelbaum). New York, The Macmillan Company, 1950.

Cressey, George B., *The Basis of Soviet Strength.* New York, McGraw-Hill Book Company, 1945.

Gray, G. D. B., *Soviet Land: The Country, Its People, and Their Work.* London, Adam and Charles Black, Ltd., 1947.

Gregory, James S., and D. W. Shave, *The USSR: A Geographical Survey.* New York, John Wiley and Sons, 1944.

Jorré, Georges, *The Soviet Union: The Land and Its People,* translated by E. D. Laborde. New York, Longmans, Green and Company, 1950.

Mandel, William M., *A Guide to the Soviet Union.* New York, Dial Press, 1946.

Manning, Clarence A., *Twentieth-Century Ukraine.* New York, Bookman Associates, 1951.

Mikhailov, Nikolai M., *Soviet Russia.* New York, Sheridan House, 1948.

Mirov, N. T., *Geography of Russia.* New York, John Wiley and Sons, 1951.

Olkhousky, Victor, *Russian Trade and Industry, Geography, History, Economy, Sociology.* New York, Pitman Publ. Corp., 1944.

Schwartz, Harry, *Russia's Soviet Economy.* New York, Prentice-Hall, 1950.

Shabad, Theodore, *Geography of the USSR: A Regional Survey.* New York, Columbia University Press, 1951.

Simmons, Ernest J. (ed.), *USSR: A Concise Handbook.* Ithaca, Cornell University Press, 1947.

Thiel, Eric, "The Power Industry in the Soviet Union." *Economic Geography,* XXVII, 2 (April, 1951), 107–122.

FOREIGN BIBLIOGRAPHY

By far the most comprehensive and useful material available on the regional geography of Europe is included in the pertinent parts of the 23 volumes of the *Géographie Universelle,* edited by Vidal de la Blache and Lucien Gallois and published by Librairie Armand Colin in Paris in French between 1926 and 1948. It is not only well written, but its maps and half-tones are also excellent and are useful to anyone who has the barest knowledge of French. The bibliographies are comprehensive and include primarily French sources.

Also useful is the German series, *Handbuch der Geographischen Wissenschaft,* edited by Fritz Klute and published in 10 volumes between 1930 and 1938 by the Akademische Verlagsgesellschaft Athenaion, Wildpark-Potsdam.

Europe in General

Alt, E., *Klimakunde von Mittel und Süd Europa* (Köppen Handbuch). Berlin, Borntraeger, 1932.

Berkeland, B., *Klimakunde von Nordwest Europa* (Köppen Handbuch). Berlin, Borntraeger, 1932.

Brunhes, Jean, *La géographie humaine* (2nd ed.). Paris, Presses Universitaires de France, 1947.

Bubnoff, Serge von, *Geologie von Europa.* Berlin, Borntraeger, 1926.

Geographie Europas ohne Deutschland (E. von Seydlitz'sche Geographie, Hundertjahr-Ausgabe). Breslau, Ferdinand Hirt, 1931.

Hettner, Alfred, *Europa.* Leipzig, Teubner, 1925.

Köppen, Wladimer P., *Die Klimate der Erde.* Berlin, de Gruyter, 1923.

Philippson, Alfred, *Europa: Europa ausser Deutschland* (Dritte Auflage). Leipzig, Bibliographisches Institut, 1928.

Staub, R., *Der Bau der Alpen.* Bern, Franke, 1924.

Steinmetz, S. R., *Die Nationaliten in Europa.* Berlin, Reimer, 1927.

Western and Northwestern Europe

Ahlmann, Hans W:son, *Norge: Natur och Näringsliv.* Stockholm, Kooperativa förbundets bokförlag, 1943.

——, and others (eds.), *Sverige Nu: AVC:s Atlas över Sverige's folk, land och näringar.* Stockholm, Carlsons Bokförlags AB, 1949.

Atlas de France. Paris, Éditions géographiques de France, 1945.

Braun, Gustav, *Die Nordischen Staaten.* Breslau, Ferdinand Hirt, 1924.

Chabot, Georges, "Problèmes de l'économie scandinave." *Annales de Géographie,* LV, 300 (October-December, 1946), 259–281.

De Geer, Gerard, *Sveriges Naturrihedomar.* Stockholm, A. Bonniers förlag, 1946.

Essen, Jac van, *Mein Holland.* Amsterdam, Volk und Reich Verlag, 1944.

Granger, Ernest, *La France.* Paris, Fayard, 1932.

Gredner, W., *Landschaft und Wirtschaft in Schweden.* Breslau, Ferdinand Hirt, 1926.

Martonne, Emmanuel de, *Les régions géographiques de la France.* Paris, Flammarion, 1921.

Tuckermann, Walther, *Länderkunde der Niederlande und Belgien.* Leipzig, Deuticke, 1931.

Verschueren, Joseph, *Atlas van België; zes en dertig natuurkundige, economische en staatkundige kaarten.* Antwerpen, Uitgeversmij. n.v. Standaard-boekhandel, 1945.

Southern Europe

Birot, Pierre, *Le Portugal; étude de géographie régionale.* Paris, Armand Colin, 1950.

Bourcart, J., *L'Albanie et les Albaniens.* Paris, Bissack, 1921.

Clough, R. T., *Cenni geografici sull' Italia.* New York, Columbia University Press, 1940.

Echeverría, L. Martín, *Geografía de España* (3 vols.). Barcelona, 1928.

Greim, Georg, *Italien.* Breslau, Ferdinand Hirt, 1926.

Lautensach, Hermann, *Portugal auf Grund eigener Reisen und der Literatur,* in two parts: *Das Land als Ganzes* and *Die Portugiesischen Landschaften. Petermann's Mitteilungen, Ergänzunsheft,* 1932 and 1937, respectively.

Luckwald, Erich von, *Albanien, Land zwischen Gestern und Morgen.* München, F. Bruckmann, 1942.

Peyret, J. Corts, *Geografía e Historia de Andorra.* Barcelona, 1945.

Philippson, Alfred, *Das Mittelmeergebiet* (4th ed.). Leipzig, Teubner, 1922.

Ribeiro, Orlando, *Livretsguide* (4 vols.). Lisbon, 1949.

Central Europe

Atlas de la République tchèco-slovaque. Prague, 1937.

Braun, Gustav, *Deutschland.* Berlin, Borntraeger, 1926.

Früh, Jacob, *Geographie der Schweiz* (3 vols.). St. Gallen, Fehr, 1930–1945.

Hassinger, Hugo, *Die Tschechoslowakei.* Wien, Rikola, 1925.

Hiltbrunner, H., *Das Fürstentum Liechtenstein.* Zürich, 1945.

Krause, Kurt, and Rudolf Reinhard (eds.), *Deutschland* (E. von Seydlitz'sche Geographie, Hundertjahr-Ausgabe). Breslau, Ferdinand Hirt, 1925.

Krebs, Norbert (ed.), *Landeskunde von Deutschland* (3 vols.). Leipzig and Berlin, Teubner, 1931–1935.

Machatschek, Fritz, *Länderkunde von Mitteleuropa.* Leipzig, Deuticke, 1925.

Martonne, Emmanuel de, *Europe Centrale* (2 vols.). Paris, Armand Colin, 1934.

Eastern and Southeastern Europe

Cvijic, Jovan, *La péninsule balkanique.* Paris, Armand Colin, 1928.

Gellert, Johannes Fürchtegott, *Die politisch-geographische Entwicklung und Struktur Bulgariens.* Berlin-Grunewald, K. Vowinckel, 1933.

Haucke, Kurt, *Bulgarien.* Bayreuth, Gauverlag Bayreuth, 1942.

Hettner, Alfred, *Russland.* Leipzig, Teubner, 1925.

Leimbach, Werner, *Die Sowjetunion: Natur, Volk und Wirtschaft.* Stuttgart, Franckh'sche Verlagshandlung, 1950.

März, Josef, *Jugoslawien, Probleme aus Raum, Volk und Wirtschaft.* Berlin, Deut. Verlag für Politik und Wirtschaft, 1938.

Rungaldier, Randolph, *Natur- und Kulturlandschaft zwischen Donau und Theiss.* Wien, Deuticke, 1943.

Tuckermann, Walther, *Osteuropa.* Breslau, Ferdinand Hirt, 1922.

Index